Math for Business Analysis

MATH 110 at San Francisco State University

2nd Special Edition

Stefan Waner I Steven R. Costenoble

CENGAGE
Learning

Australia • Brazil • Japan • Korea • Mexico • Singapore • Spain • United Kingdom • United States

CENGAGE
Learning™

Math for Business Analysis: MATH 110 at San Francisco State University, 2nd Special Edition

Stefan Waner I Steven R. Costenoble

Executive Editor:
Maureen Staudt
Michael Stranz

Senior Project Development Manager:
Linda de Stefano

Marketing Specialist:
Sara Mercurio
Lindsay Shapiro

Production/Manufacturing Manager:
Donna M. Brown

PreMedia Supervisor:
Joel Brennecke

Rights & Permissions Specialist:
Todd Osborne

Cover Image:
Getty Images*

For product information and technology assistance, contact us at
Cengage Learning Customer & Sales Support, 1-800-354-9706

For permission to use material from this text or product, submit all requests online at **cengage.com/permissions**
Further permissions questions can be emailed to
permissionrequest@cengage.com

ISBN-13: 978-1-111-07195-0

ISBN-10: 1-111-07195-0

Cengage Learning
5191 Natorp Boulevard
Mason, Ohio 45040
USA

Cengage Learning is a leading provider of customized learning solutions with office locations around the globe, including Singapore, the United Kingdom, Australia, Mexico, Brazil, and Japan. Locate your local office at: **international.cengage.com/region**

Cengage Learning products are represented in Canada by Nelson Education, Ltd.

For your lifelong learning solutions, visit **www.cengage.com/custom**

Visit our corporate website at **www.cengage.com**

Printed in the United States of America
1 2 3 4 5 6 7 12 11 10 09 08

ENHANCED
WEBASSIGN

The Start Smart Guide
for Students

CENGAGE
Learning™

Australia • Brazil • Japan • Korea • Mexico • Singapore • Spain • United Kingdom • United States

CENGAGE
Learning™

Enhanced WebAssign: The Start Smart Guide for Students

Acquisitions Editor: Gary Whalen

Copyeditor: Deborah Todd

Editorial Assistant: Lynh Pham

Cover Design: Fabio Fernandes

WebAssign © 2003–2007 by
Advanced Instructional Systems, Inc.

All rights reserved

WebAssign
Centennial Campus
730 Varsity Drive
Raleigh, NC 27606
Web: http://webassign.net
Tel: (800) 955-8275 or (919) 829-8181
Fax: (919) 829-1516
E-mail: info@webassign.net

WebAssign® is a registered service
mark of North Carolina State
University under license to Advanced
Instructional Systems, Inc.

Enhanced WebAssign™ is a trade-
mark of Advanced Instructional
Systems and Cengage Learning.

> For product information and technology
> assistance, contact us at **Cengage Learning Customer
> & Sales Support, 1-800-354-9706**
> For permission to use material from this text
> or product, submit all requests online at
> **www.cengage.com/permissions**
> Further permissions questions can be emailed to
> **permissionrequest@cengage.com**

ISBN-13: 978-0-495-38479-3

ISBN-10: 0-495-38479-8

Cengage Learning is a leading provider of customized
learning solutions with office locations around the globe,
including Singapore, the United Kingdom, Australia,
Mexico, Brazil, and Japan. Locate your local office at:
www.cengage.com/global

Cengage Learning products are represented in Canada
by Nelson Education, Ltd.

To learn more about Cengage Learning, visit
www.cengage.com

Purchase any of our products at your local college store
or at our preferred online store **www.ichapters.com**

Printed in the United States of America
6 7 8 9 10 11 10 09 08

CONTENTS

WebAssign works with any recent browser and computer. Some assignments may require plugins like Java, Flash, Shockwave, or Adobe Reader.

For technical support go to http://webassign.net/student.html or email support@webassign.net.

GETTING STARTED

Welcome to Enhanced WebAssign, the integrated, online learning system that gives you 24/7 access to your math, physics, astronomy, chemistry, biology, and statistics assignments.

Now, you can do homework, take quizzes and exams, and receive your scores and graded assignments from any computer with an Internet connection and web browser, any time of the day or night.

Note: As a live, web-based program, Enhanced WebAssign is updated regularly with new features and improvements. Please refer to WebAssign's online Help for the most current information.

Technical Startup Tips

Before you start, please note the following important points:

○ Most standard web connections should work with WebAssign. We recommend using Firefox 1.0 or later, or Internet Explorer 5.5 or later. *We do not recommend the AOL browser.*

○ You can use a 56 KBPS modem, broadband, or school network connection.

○ Your browser needs to have both JavaScript and Java enabled.

○ *You cannot skip the login page.* WebAssign must know it is you before delivering your assignments.

Note: If you'd like to bookmark WebAssign on your computer, we recommend that you bookmark **https://www.webassign.net/login.html** or the appropriate address for your school.

Login to WebAssign

In order to access WebAssign your instructor will provide you with login information or a Class Key. Login information will consist of a username, institution code, and an initial password. The Class Key will allow you to self-register and create your own login. You will need to remember the username and initial password you set after self-registering.

Please note that Class Keys are not the same as access codes. See pages 8–9 for instructions on registering your access code number. You will need to login first before you are able to register an access code.

➢ **To get started**

1. If you are using a shared computer, completely exit any browsers that are already open.

2. Open a new web browser and go to https://www.webassign.net/login.html, or the web address provided by your instructor.

   If your instructor has provided you with a **Username, Institution** (school code), and **Password,** continue with step 3. If you have been provided with a **Class Key** (usually your institution name and a series of numbers), then skip to step 5.

3. Enter your **Username, Institution** (school code), and **Password** *provided by your instructor.*

   ### Institution

   If you do not know your **Institution,** you can search for it by clicking **(what's this?)** above the **Institution** entry box.

   In the **What's My Institution Code** pop-up window, enter your school name and click **go!**. The **Institution Search Results** table will give you choices of the School Names that most closely match your entry, and the **Institution Code** that you should enter in the **Institution** entry box on the **WebAssign Login** screen.

   ### Password

   If you have forgotten or do not know your **Password,** click **(Reset Password)** above the **Password** entry box, and follow the directions on the **WebAssign New Password Request** screen. You will need to submit your username, institution code, and the email address on file in your WebAssign account. If you are unsure of your username or listed email address, please check with your instructor. WebAssign cannot reset your username or password.

4. Click **Log In**.

5. If your instructor gave you a **Class Key,** you will use it to create your account. Click the **I have a Class Key** button. You will need to use this key only once when you register.

6. Enter the Class Key code in the field provided and click **Submit**. If your Class Key is recognized, you will be given fields for creating your username and password and for entering basic student information.

7. Enter a username in the field provided and then click **Check Availability** to determine whether or not your username is already in use. If it is, an available alternate username will be suggested. Remember your username because you will use it every time you login to WebAssign.

8. Enter and then re-enter a password. Remember your password because you will use it every time you login to WebAssign.

9. Under **Student Information** enter your first and last name, email address, and student ID.

10. Click **Create My Account**.

11. If you see confirmation of your account creation, you will now be able to login to WebAssign. Click **Log in now**.

Note: Before starting WebAssign on a shared computer, always exit any browsers and restart your browser application. *If you simply close the browser window or open a new window, login information contained in an encrypted key may not be yours.*

Logout

When you are finished with your work, click the **Logout** link in the upper right corner of your Home page, and *exit the browser completely* to avoid the possibility of someone else accessing your work.

YOUR ENHANCED WEBASSIGN HOME PAGE

Your personalized Home page is your hub for referencing and managing all of your Enhanced WebAssign assignments.

Using Access Codes

Some classes require an **access code** for admission. Please remember:

○ An **access code** is *not* the same as a Class Key or a login password.

○ An **access code** is good for *one class only* unless the textbook includes a two-term **access code**.

○ An **access code** is an alphanumeric code that is *usually* packaged with your textbook. It can begin with 2 or 3 letters, followed by an alphanumeric code, or it can have a longer prefix such as **BCEnhanced-S** followed by four sets of four characters.

○ If your textbook did not include an **access code**, you can buy one at your bookstore, or from your personalized Home page by clicking the **Purchase an access code online** button.

➤ To enter an Access Code

1. Under **WebAssign Notices**, select the proper prefix from the **Choose your access code prefix** pull-down menu.

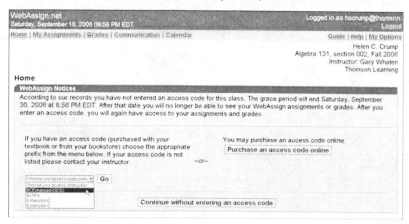

WebAssign notices

2. Click **Go**.

3. In the entry boxes, type in your access code *exactly* as it appears on your card. (When you purchase online, the access code is entered automatically.)

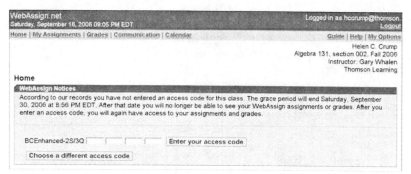

Access code entry

4. Click **Enter your access code.**

If you have chosen the wrong prefix from the previous screen, you can click the **Choose a different access code** button to try again.

If your **access code** is a valid unused code, you will receive a message that you have successfully entered the code for the class. Click the **Home** or **My Assignments** button to proceed.

Customizing Your Home Page

Your instructor has initial control over what you see on your Home page to make sure that you have all of the information you need. Your instructor might also set controls so that you can further personalize this page by moving or hiding certain modules.

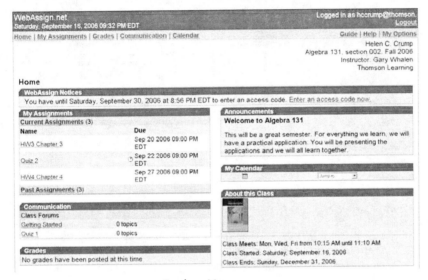

Student Home page

If your instructor has allowed you to personalize your Home page, each module will have markings like this:

Calendar module

To move a module

On the module's heading line, click an up, down, or sideways arrow (indicated by white triangles) until the module is where you'd like it placed on the page.

To minimize a module

On the module's heading line, click the underscore.

To hide a module

On the module's heading line, click the x.

Changing Your Password

For your personal security, it's a good idea to change the initial password provided by your instructor.

➤ To change your password

1. Click the **My Options** link in the upper right of your Home page.

2. In the **My Options** pop-up window, under the **Personal Info** tab:

   Enter your *new* password in the **Change Password** entry box next to **(enter new password)**, then

   Reenter your new password *exactly* the same in the entry box next to **(reenter for confirmation)**.

3. Enter your *current* password in the entry box under **If you made any changes above, enter your current password here and then click save:**, located at the bottom of the pop-up window.

4. Click the **Save** button in the bottom right corner of the pop-up window.

   If the change was successful, you will see the message **Your password has been changed**.

Note: Passwords are case-sensitive. This means that if you capitalize any of the letters, you must remember to capitalize them the same way each time you sign in to Enhanced WebAssign.

Changing Your Email Address

If your instructor provided you with an email address, you can easily change it to your own personal email address any time.

➤ To change your email address

1. Click the **My Options** link in the upper right of your Home page.

---

2. In the **My Options** pop-up window, under the **Personal Info** tab, enter your *valid* email address in the **Email Address** box.

3. Enter your current password in the entry box under **If you made any changes above enter your current password here and then click save:**, located at the bottom of the pop-up screen.

4. Click the **Save** button in the bottom right corner of the pop-up window.

A confirmation email will be sent to your new email address.

Once you receive the confirmation email, you must click the link in the email to successfully complete and activate this change.

WORKING WITH ASSIGNMENTS

The courses that have been set up for you by your instructor(s) appear on your Enhanced WebAssign personalized Home page. If you have more than one course, simply select the course you want to work with from the pull-down menu.

Assignment Summary

There are two ways to get a quick summary of your assignments. On the Home page:

○ Click the **My Assignments** link in the upper left *menu bar, or*

○ Click the **Current Assignments** link in the **My Assignments** *module* on the Home page.

Accessing an Assignment

Once your assignments are displayed on your Home page, simply click the name of the assignment you'd like to begin.

○ If you have previously submitted an assignment, you will see your most recent responses, if your instructor allows this feature.

○ If you have already submitted the assignment, there will usually be a link to **Review All Submissions** on the page, if your instructor has allowed it.

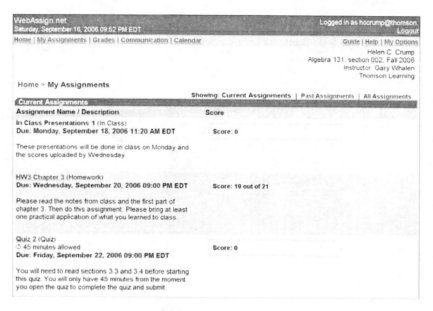

Assignment summary

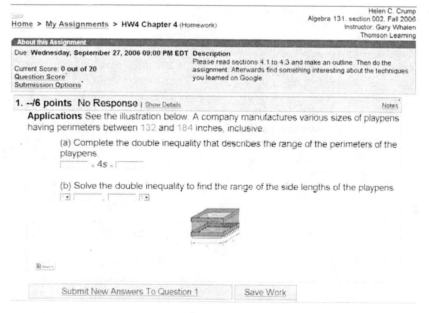

Math assignment

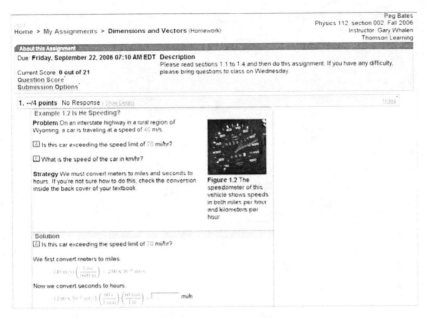

Physics assignment

Using the Assignment Page

When you click on an assignment name, your assignment will load. Within the **About this Assignment** page are links to valuable information about your assignment's score, submission options, and saving your work in progress. Within each question, there might also be "enhanced" action links to useful tutorial material such as book content, videos, animations, active figures, simulations, and practice problems. The links available may vary from one assignment to another.

Actions

Click a button or link to take one of the following actions:

Current Score

This gives you a quick look at your current score versus the maximum possible score.

Question Score

This gives you a pop-up window showing your score for each question.

Submission Options

This gives you a pop-up window explaining how you can submit the assignment and whether it can be submitted by question part, by whole question, or by the whole assignment.

Submissions Made

This shows you the number of submissions you've made. This information is only displayed on assignments that require submission of the entire assignment.

Notes

This feature gives you a pop-up window with a text box in which you can enter and save notes or show your work with a particular question.

Submit New Answers To Question

Use this button when you're ready to submit your answer for the question. This feature allows you to answer just the parts you want scored. If you leave any part of a question unanswered, the submission *will not* be recorded for that part.

Submit Whole Question

Use this button to submit your answer(s) for the entire question. If you leave any part of a question unanswered, the submission *will* be recorded as if the entire question has been answered, and graded as such.

Save Work

This button allows you to save the work you've done so far on a particular question, but does not submit that question for grading.

View Saved Work

Located in the question's header line, this allows you to view work that you previously saved for that question.

Show Details

Located in the question's header line, this link shows your score on each part of the question, how many points each part of the question is worth, and how many submissions are allowed for each part if you can submit each part separately.

Submit All New Answers

This submits all of your new answers for all of the questions in the assignment.

Save All Work

This allows you to save all the work you've done on all of the questions in the assignment, but does not submit your work for grading.

Ask Your Teacher

This feature allows you to send a question about the assignment to your instructor.

Extension Request

This allows you to submit a request to your instructor for an extension of time on an assignment.

Home

This link takes you to your personalized Home page.

My Assignments

This link takes you to your assignments page.

Open Math Palette

This opens a tool to use in writing answers that require math notation.

Read it

This links to question-specific textbook material in PDF form.

Practice Another Version

This provides you with an alternate version of the assigned problem. Within the pop-up window you will be able to answer the practice problem and have that answer checked. You will also be able to practice additional versions of your assigned problem.

Practice it

This links to a practice problem or set of practice problems in a pop-up window. No grade is recorded on the work you do on practice problems.

See it

This links to a tutorial video.

Hint

This links to a pop-up window with helpful hints in case you get stuck on a question.

Hint: Active Figure

This links to an animated simulation to help you better understand the concepts being covered.

Note: Your instructor has the ability to turn on/off many of the options listed above.

ANSWERING QUESTIONS

Enhanced WebAssign uses a variety of question types that you're probably already familiar with using, such as multiple choice, true/false, free response, etc.

Always be sure to pay close attention to any instructions within the question regarding how you are supposed to submit your answers.

Numerical Questions

There are a few key points to keep in mind when working on numerical questions:

- Numbers can be entered in both scientific notation and numerical expressions, such as fractions.

- WebAssign uses the standard scientific notation "E" or "e" for "times 10 raised to the power." (Note: both uppercase E and lowercase e are acceptable in WebAssign.) For example, 1e3 is the scientific notation for 1000.

- Numerical answers may *not* contain commas (,) or equal signs (=).

- Numerical answers may only contain:

  - Numbers

  - E or e for scientific notation

  - Mathematical operators +, -, *, /

- Numerical answers within 1% of the actual answer are counted as correct, unless your instructor chooses a different tolerance. This is to account for rounding errors in calculations. In general, enter three significant figures for numerical answers.

➤ **Example: Numerical Question**

Let's suppose you're presented a question to which your answer is the fraction "one over sixty-four." Following are examples of Correct and Incorrect answer formats:

Correct Answers

Any of these formats would be correct:

1/64

0.015625

0.0156

.0156

1.5625E-2

Incorrect Answers

These formats would be graded as incorrect:

O.015625	The first character is the letter "O"
0. 015625	There is an improper space in the answer
1.5625 E-2	There is an improper space using E notation
l/64	The first character is lowercase letter "L"
5,400	There is a comma in the answer
1234.5=1230	There is an equal sign in the answer

Numerical Questions with Units

Some Enhanced WebAssign questions require a number and a unit, and this is generally, although not always, indicated in the instructions in the question.

You will know that a unit is expected when there is no unit after the answer box.

When you are expected to enter units and do not, you will get an error message telling you that units are required.

Note: Whether omission of the unit counts as a submission depends on the submission options chosen by the instructor.

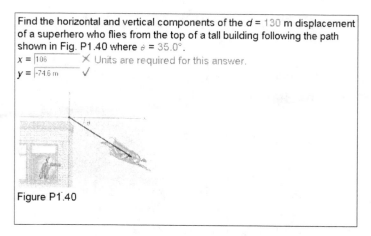

Find the horizontal and vertical components of the $d = 130$ m displacement of a superhero who flies from the top of a tall building following the path shown in Fig. P1.40 where $\theta = 35.0°$.

$x = $ [106] ✗ Units are required for this answer.

$y = $ [-74.6 m] ✓

Figure P1.40

Numerical with units

The easiest units to use in this question are m, but the answer converted to yd would also be scored correct.

Numerical Questions with Significant Figures

Some numerical questions require a specific number of significant figures (sig figs) in your answer. If a question checks sig figs, you will see a sig fig icon next to the answer box.

If you enter the correct value with the wrong number of sig figs, you will not receive credit, but you will receive a hint that your number does not have the correct number of sig figs. The sig fig icon [4.0✓] is also a link to the rules used for sig figs in WebAssign.

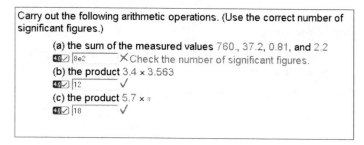

Carry out the following arithmetic operations. (Use the correct number of significant figures.)

(a) the sum of the measured values 760., 37.2, 0.81, and 2.2
[4.0✓] [8e2]　✗ Check the number of significant figures.

(b) the product 3.4×3.563
[4.0✓] [12]　✓

(c) the product $5.7 \times \pi$
[4.0✓] [18]　✓

Check for significant figures

Math Notation: Using the Math Palette

In many math questions, Enhanced WebAssign gives you an answer
box with a **Math Palette** button. The **Math Palette** provides easy input
of math answers, even the more complicated ones.

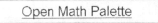

Math Palette button

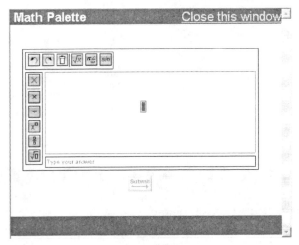

Math Palette tool

Top Symbols

The **Math Palette** has a toolbar of symbols on top that, when
selected, give you a drop-down menu with more symbols from
which to choose.

Side Symbols

The buttons on the side are single input buttons for frequently
used operations.

The yellow buttons are editing buttons:

Arrow keys are for undo and redo

Trashcan is to clear your input and start over
with an empty field

The red "x" is used as a short cut for the answer
"no solution."

After using the **Math Palette** to write your answer, click the **Submit** button. Your answer will appear in the appropriate boxed area with the question. Your answer will be graded once you actually submit your answers for grading.

Let $f(x) = 8x + 2$ and $g(x) = x^2 - 5x - 9$. Find the value below.

$g(r)$

$x^2 - 5r - 9$ ✓

After using Math Palette

Math Notation: Using the Keyboard

If you use your keyboard to enter math notation (calculator notation), *you must use the exact variables specified in the questions.*

The order is not important, as long as it is mathematically correct.

➤ Example: Math Notation Using Keyboard

In the example below, the keyboard is used to enter the answer in the answer field.

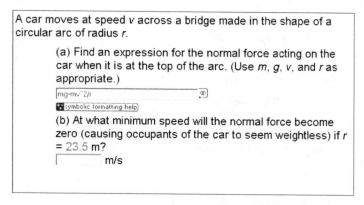

A car moves at speed v across a bridge made in the shape of a circular arc of radius r.

(a) Find an expression for the normal force acting on the car when it is at the top of the arc. (Use m, g, v, and r as appropriate.)

mg-mv^2/r

symbolic formatting help

(b) At what minimum speed will the normal force become zero (causing occupants of the car to seem weightless) if r = 23.5 m?

_____ m/s

Symbolic question

Expression Preview

Clicking the eye button 👁 allows you to preview the expression you've entered in calculator notation.

Use this preview feature to help determine if you have properly placed your parentheses.

Symbolic Formatting Help

If you're unsure about how to symbolically enter your answer properly, use the **symbolic formatting help** button to display allowed notation.

Allowed notation for symbolic formatting

+ for addition	x+1
- for subtraction	x-1, or −x
* or nothing for multiplication	4*x, or 4x
/ for division	x/4
** or ^ for exponential	x**3, or x^3
( ) where necessary to group terms	4/(x+1), or 3(x+1)
abs( ) to take the absolute value of a variable or expression	abs(-5) = 5
sin, cos, tan, sec, csc, cot, asin, acos, atan functions (angle x expressed in radians)	sin(2x)
sqrt( ) for square root of an expression	sqrt(x/5)
x^ (1/n) for the nth root of a number	x^ (1/3), or (x-3)^ (1/5)
pi for 3.14159…	2 pi x
e for scientific notation	1e3 = 1000
ln( ) for natural log	ln(x)
exp( ) for "e to the power of"	exp(x) = e^x

USING THE GRAPHPAD

Introduction

The Enhanced WebAssign GraphPad lets you graph one or more mathematical elements directly on a set of coordinate axes. Your graph is then scored automatically when you submit the assignment for grading.

The GraphPad currently supports points, rays, segments, lines, circles, and parabolas. Inequalities can also be indicated by filling one or more areas.

GraphPad Interface Overview

The middle of GraphPad is the drawing area. It contains labeled coordinate axes, which may have different axis scales and extents depending on the nature of the question you are working on.

On the left side of GraphPad is the list of Tools that lets you create graph objects and select objects to edit.

The bottom of the GraphPad is the Object Properties toolbar, which becomes active when you have a graph element selected. This toolbar shows you all the details about the selected graph object and also lets you edit properties of that.

On the right side of GraphPad is the list of Actions that lets you create fills and delete objects from your graph.

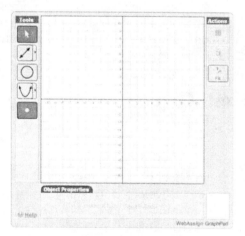

Drawing Graph Objects

To draw a line, first click on the line button in the Tools area. The line button will highlight to blue, and then you can place two points (which are on that line) by clicking twice within the drawing area. Don't worry if you don't place the line exactly where you want it initially; you can move these points around before submitting for grading. The arrows on the end of the line indicate that the line goes off to infinity on both ends.

To draw a ray or a segment, first click the small arrow on the right side of the line button to open the selection of line-type tools. Choose ray or segment, and then place it by clicking twice within the drawing area. For rays, the first point is the endpoint of the ray. The arrow on the other end of the ray indicates that it goes off to infinity on that end.

Circles, points, and parabolas can be drawn in the same manner. Circles are drawn by placing a point at the center first, then a point on the radius of the circle. Parabolas are drawn by placing the vertex first, then a point on the parabola. Parabolas can be horizontal or vertical. Points are even easier—just click the point button and then click where you want the point to appear.

Selecting Graph Objects

To edit a graph object you have drawn, that object must be "selected" as the active object. (When you first draw an object, it is created in the selected state.) When a graph element is "selected", the color of the line changes and two "handles" are visible. The handles are the two square points you clicked to create the object. To select an object, click on the object's line. To deselect the object, click on the object's line, a blank area on the drawing area, or a drawing tool.

Not Selected

Selected

The Start Smart Guide for Students

Moving and Editing Graph Objects

Once an object is selected, you can modify it by using your mouse or the keyboard. As you move it, you'll notice that you cannot move the handles off the drawing area.

To move an object with the mouse, click and drag the object's line. Or click and drag one of the handles to move just that handle.

On the keyboard, the arrow keys also move the selected object around by one unit.

As you move the object or handle you'll see that the Object Properties toolbar changes to remain up to date.

You can also use the coordinate boxes in the Object Properties toolbar to edit the coordinates of the handles directly. Use this method to enter decimal or fractional coordinates.

Using Fractions or Decimals as Coordinates

To draw an object with handle coordinates that are fractions or decimals, you must use the Object Properties toolbar. Draw the desired object anywhere on the drawing area, then use the coordinate boxes in the Object Properties toolbar to change the endpoint(s) to the desired value. To enter a fraction just type "3/4", for example.

Note: The points and lines you draw must be exactly correct when you submit for grading. This means you should not round any of your values—if you want a point at 11/3, you should enter 11/3 in the coordinate box rather than 3.667. Also, mixed fractions are not acceptable entries. This means that 3 2/3 is an incorrect entry.

Endpoints—Closed or Open?

If the selected object is a segment or ray, the Endpoint controls in the Object Properties toolbar can be clicked to toggle the endpoint from closed to open.

As a shortcut, you can also toggle an endpoint by clicking on the endpoint when the ray or segment is in the unselected state.

Graph Objects—Solid or Dashed?

For any selected object other than a point, the Solid/Dash buttons in the Object Properties toolbar can be used to make the object solid or dashed. To change graph objects to solid or dashed (for inequalities, for example), select the object and click the Solid or Dash button.

Specifying a Region with a Fill for Inequalities

To graph an inequality, you must specify a region on the graph. To do this, first draw the line(s), circle(s), or other object(s) that will define the region you want to represent your answer. Be sure to specify the objects as either solid or dashed, according to the inequality you are graphing! Then choose the fill button in the Actions area, and click inside the region that you want filled.

If you decide you wanted the fill in a different area, you can use the fill tool again to undo and then redo the fill in a different location. Choose the fill tool, click the filled region that you want to unfill, and then click the region that you do want to fill.

Erasing One Graph Object

To erase a single graph object, first select that element in the drawing area, then click the Delete icon in the Actions area or press the Delete key on your keyboard.

Erasing Everything on Your Graph

The Clear All button in the Actions area will erase all of your graph objects. (If the drawing area is already empty, the Clear All button is disabled.)

Example: Graphing Question

Let's suppose you're asked to graph the inequality $y > 5x + \frac{1}{5}$, and you want to use the points $\left(0, \frac{1}{5}\right)$ and $\left(1, 5\frac{1}{5}\right)$. You would first place any line on the drawing area.

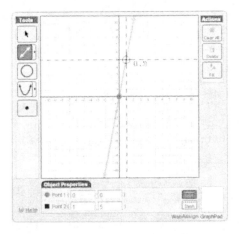

Then, adjust the points using the Object Properties Boxes.

Next, you would define the line as dashed since the inequality does not include the values on the line.

Finally, you would select the Fill Tool and click on the desired region to complete the graph.

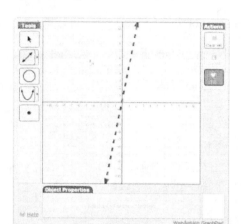

ADDITIONAL FEATURES

Calendar

The Calendar link presents you with a calendar showing all of your assignments on their due dates. You can also click on any date and enter your own personal events.

Communication

The Communication link gives you access to **Private Messages** and course **Forums**, if your instructor has enabled these features.

Forums

The **Forums** are for discussions with all the members of your class. Your instructor can create forums, and you can create topics within a forum or contribute to a current topic.

Private Messages

Private Messages are for communication between you and your instructor. If your instructor has enabled private messages, click the **New Message** link to send your instructor a message.

GRADES

The **Grades** link at the top of all your WebAssign pages gives you access to the raw scores and grades that your instructor posts. This page may also include statistics on the whole class, and a histogram of scores for each category of assignment and each individual assignment. It may have your individual average for each category of assignment, as well as the score on each of your assignments.

Your instructor will let you know what Scores and Grades will be posted in your course.

If your instructor has enabled all of the options, your display will be similar to the one below.

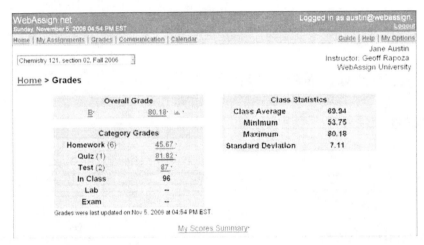

Grades

Overall Grade

This score is calculated from the various categories of assignments, for example, **Homework, Test**, **In Class**, **Quiz**, **Lab**, and **Exam**. Your instructor may have different categories.

Category Grades

The **Category Grades** give the contribution to your overall grade from each of the categories. If you click a grade that is a link, you will get a pop-up window explaining how the number was calculated.

Class Statistics

Class Statistics shows the averages, minimum scores, maximum scores, and standard deviation of the class at large.

My Scores Summary

This link presents a pop-up window with a summary of your raw scores and the class statistics on each assignment, if your teacher has posted these.

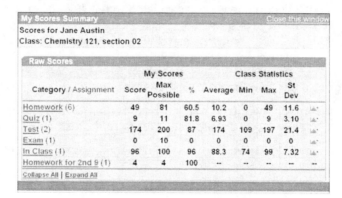

My Scores summary

TECHNICAL TIPS

Enhanced WebAssign relies on web browsers and other related technology that can lead to occasional technical issues. The following technical tips can help you avoid some common problems.

Cookies

Allow your browser to accept cookies.

WebAssign will work if you set your browser to not accept cookies; however, if an encrypted cookie is not saved to your

---

**For technical support go to http://webassign.net/student.html
or email support@webassign.net.**

---

computer during your session, you may be asked to login again more frequently. Once you logout and exit your browser, the cookie is deleted.

Login and Credit

If you see an assignment that does not have your name at the top, you have not logged in properly.

You will not receive credit for any work you do on an assignment if your name is not associated with it. If you find yourself in the midst of this situation, make notes of your solution(s) and start over. Be aware that any randomized values in the questions will probably change.

Logout When You Finish Your Session

If someone wants to use your computer for WebAssign, logout and exit the browser before relinquishing control.

Otherwise, the work you have just completed may be written over by the next user.

Server

Although it is very rare, the WebAssign server may occasionally be unavailable.

If the WebAssign server is unavailable, instructors will provide instructions for submitting your assignments—possibly including new due dates. The policy for handling server problems will vary from instructor to instructor.

Use the Latest Browser Software

Use the latest version of Firefox, Mozilla, Netscape, or Internet Explorer browsers.

Older versions of browsers may not be supported by WebAssign.

For technical support go to http://webassign.net/student.html or email support@webassign.net.

CONTENTS

O Precalculus Review

Web Site
www.AppliedCalc.org

- At the Web site you will find section-by-section interactive tutorials for further study and practice.

DreamPictures/Taxi/Getty Images

Introduction

In this appendix we review some topics from algebra that you need to know to get the most out of this book. This appendix can be used either as a refresher course or as a reference.

There is one crucial fact you must always keep in mind: The letters used in algebraic expressions stand for numbers. All the rules of algebra are just facts about the arithmetic of numbers. If you are not sure whether some algebraic manipulation you are about to do is legitimate, try it first with numbers. If it doesn't work with numbers, it doesn't work.

0.1 Real Numbers

The **real numbers** are the numbers that can be written in decimal notation, including those that require an infinite decimal expansion. The set of real numbers includes all integers, positive and negative; all fractions; and the irrational numbers, those with decimal expansions that never repeat. Examples of irrational numbers are

$$\sqrt{2} = 1.414213562373\ldots$$

and

$$\pi = 3.141592653589\ldots$$

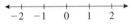

Figure 1

It is very useful to picture the real numbers as points on a line. As shown in Figure 1, larger numbers appear to the right, in the sense that if $a < b$ then the point corresponding to b is to the right of the one corresponding to a.

Intervals

Some subsets of the set of real numbers, called **intervals**, show up quite often and so we have a compact notation for them.

Interval Notation

Here is a list of types of intervals along with examples.

	Interval	Description	Picture	Example
Closed	$[a, b]$	Set of numbers x with $a \le x \le b$	a b (includes end points)	$[0, 10]$
Open	(a, b)	Set of numbers x with $a < x < b$	a b (excludes end points)	$(-1, 5)$
Half-Open	$(a, b]$	Set of numbers x with $a < x \le b$	a b	$(-3, 1]$
	$[a, b)$	Set of numbers x with $a \le x < b$	a b	$[0, 5)$

Infinite	$[a, +\infty)$	Set of numbers x with $a \le x$		$[10, +\infty)$
	$(a, +\infty)$	Set of numbers x with $a < x$		$(-3, +\infty)$
	$(-\infty, b]$	Set of numbers x with $x \le b$		$(-\infty, -3]$
	$(-\infty, b)$	Set of numbers x with $x < b$		$(-\infty, 10)$
	$(-\infty, +\infty)$	Set of all real numbers		$(-\infty, +\infty)$

Operations

There are five important operations on real numbers: addition, subtraction, multiplication, division, and exponentiation. "Exponentiation" means raising a real number to a power; for instance, $3^2 = 3 \cdot 3 = 9$; $2^3 = 2 \cdot 2 \cdot 2 = 8$.

A note on technology: Most graphing calculators and spreadsheets use an asterisk * for multiplication and a caret sign ^ for exponentiation. Thus, for instance, 3×5 is entered as $3*5$, $3x$ as $3*x$, and 3^2 as $3\char94 2$.

When we write an expression involving two or more operations, like

$$2 \cdot 3 + 4$$

or

$$\frac{2 \cdot 3^2 - 5}{4 - (-1)}$$

we need to agree on the order in which to do the operations. Does $2 \cdot 3 + 4$ mean $(2 \cdot 3) + 4 = 10$ or $2 \cdot (3 + 4) = 14$? We all agree to use the following rules for the order in which we do the operations.

Standard Order of Operations

Parentheses and Fraction Bars   First, calculate the values of all expressions inside parentheses or brackets, working from the innermost parentheses out, before using them in other operations. In a fraction, calculate the numerator and denominator separately before doing the division.

Quick Examples

1. $6(2 + [3 - 5] - 4) = 6(2 + (-2) - 4) = 6(-4) = -24$
2. $\dfrac{(4 - 2)}{3(-2 + 1)} = \dfrac{2}{3(-1)} = \dfrac{2}{-3} = -\dfrac{2}{3}$
3. $3/(2 + 4) = \dfrac{3}{2 + 4} = \dfrac{3}{6} = \dfrac{1}{2}$
4. $(x + 4x)/(y + 3y) = 5x/(4y)$

Exponents   Next, perform exponentiation.

Quick Examples

1. $2 + 4^2 = 2 + 16 = 18$ ⎫
2. $(2 + 4)^2 = 6^2 = 36$ ⎬   Note the difference.

3. $2\left(\dfrac{3}{4-5}\right)^2 = 2\left(\dfrac{3}{-1}\right)^2 = 2(-3)^2 = 2 \times 9 = 18$

4. $2(1 + 1/10)^2 = 2(1.1)^2 = 2 \times 1.21 = 2.42$

Multiplication and Division   Next, do all multiplications and divisions, from left to right.

Quick Examples

1. $2(3 - 5)/4 \cdot 2 = 2(-2)/4 \cdot 2$ Parentheses first

   $\qquad\qquad\quad = -4/4 \cdot 2$ Left-most product

   $\qquad\qquad\quad = -1 \cdot 2 = -2$ Multiplications and divisions, left to right

2. $2(1 + 1/10)^2 \times 2/10 = 2(1.1)^2 \times 2/10$ Parentheses first

   $\qquad\qquad\qquad\quad = 2 \times 1.21 \times 2/10$ Exponent

   $\qquad\qquad\qquad\quad = 4.84/10 = 0.484$ Multiplications and divisions, left to right

3. $4\dfrac{2(4-2)}{3(-2 \cdot 5)} = 4\dfrac{2(2)}{3(-10)} = 4\dfrac{4}{-30} = \dfrac{16}{-30} = -\dfrac{8}{15}$

Addition and Subtraction   Last, do all additions and subtractions, from left to right.

Quick Examples

1. $2(3 - 5)^2 + 6 - 1 = 2(-2)^2 + 6 - 1 = 2(4) + 6 - 1 = 8 + 6 - 1 = 13$

2. $\left(\dfrac{1}{2}\right)^2 - (-1)^2 + 4 = \dfrac{1}{4} - 1 + 4 = -\dfrac{3}{4} + 4 = \dfrac{13}{4}$

3. $3/2 + 4 = 1.5 + 4 = 5.5$ ⎫
4. $3/(2 + 4) = 3/6 = 1/2 = 0.5$ ⎬   Note the difference.

5. $4/2^2 + (4/2)^2 = 4/2^2 + 2^2 = 4/4 + 4 = 1 + 4 = 5$

▣ Entering Formulas

Any good calculator or spreadsheet will respect the standard order of operations. However, we must be careful with division and exponentiation and use parentheses as necessary. The following table gives some examples of simple mathematical expressions and their equivalents in the functional format used in most graphing calculators, spreadsheets, and computer programs.

Mathematical Expression	Formula	Comments
$\dfrac{2}{3-x}$	`2/(3-x)`	Note the use of parentheses instead of the fraction bar. If we omit the parentheses, we get the expression shown next.
$\dfrac{2}{3}-x$	`2/3-x`	The calculator follows the usual order of operations.
$\dfrac{2}{3\times5}$	`2/(3*5)`	Putting the denominator in parentheses ensures that the multiplication is carried out first. The asterisk is usually used for multiplication in graphing calculators and computers.
$\dfrac{2}{x}\times5$	`(2/x)*5`	Putting the fraction in parentheses ensures that it is calculated first. Some calculators will interpret $2/3*5$ as $\dfrac{2}{3\times5}$, but $2/3(5)$ as $\dfrac{2}{3}\times5$.
$\dfrac{2-3}{4+5}$	`(2-3)/(4+5)`	Note once again the use of parentheses in place of the fraction bar.
2^3	`2^3`	The caret $^\wedge$ is commonly used to denote exponentiation.
2^{3-x}	`2^(3-x)`	Be careful to use parentheses to tell the calculator where the exponent ends. Enclose the *entire exponent* in parentheses.
2^3-x	`2^3-x`	Without parentheses, the calculator will follow the usual order of operations: exponentiation and then subtraction.
3×2^{-4}	`3*2^(-4)`	On some calculators, the negation key is separate from the minus key.
$2^{-4\times3}\times5$	`2^(-4*3)*5`	Note once again how parentheses enclose the entire exponent.
$100\left(1+\dfrac{0.05}{12}\right)^{60}$	`100*(1+0.05/12)^60`	This is a typical calculation for compound interest.
$PV\left(1+\dfrac{r}{m}\right)^{mt}$	`PV*(1+r/m)^(m*t)`	This is the compound interest formula. *PV* is understood to be a single number (present value) and not the product of P and V (or else we would have used `P*V`).
$\dfrac{2^{3-2}\times5}{y-x}$	`2^(3-2)*5/(y-x)` or `(2^(3-2)*5)/(y-x)`	Notice again the use of parentheses to hold the denominator together. We could also have enclosed the numerator in parentheses, although this is optional. (Why?)
$\dfrac{2^y+1}{2-4^{3x}}$	`(2^y+1)/(2-4^(3*x))`	Here, it is necessary to enclose both the numerator and the denominator in parentheses.
$2^y+\dfrac{1}{2}-4^{3x}$	`2^y+1/2-4^(3*x)`	This is the effect of leaving out the parentheses around the numerator and denominator in the previous expression.

Accuracy and Rounding

When we use a calculator or computer, the results of our calculations are often given to far more decimal places than are useful. For example, suppose we are told that a square has an area of 2.0 square feet and we are asked how long its sides are. Each side is the square root of the area, which the calculator tells us is

$$\sqrt{2} \approx 1.414213562$$

However, the measurement of 2.0 square feet is probably accurate to only two digits, so our estimate of the lengths of the sides can be no more accurate than that. Therefore, we round the answer to two digits:

Length of one side $\approx$ 1.4 feet

The digits that follow 1.4 are meaningless. The following guide makes these ideas more precise.

Significant Digits, Decimal Places, and Rounding

The number of **significant digits** in a decimal representation of a number is the number of digits that are not leading zeros after the decimal point (as in .0005) or trailing zeros before the decimal point (as in 5,400,000). We say that a value is **accurate to n significant digits** if only the first n significant digits are meaningful.

When to Round

After doing a computation in which all the quantities are accurate to no more than n significant digits, round the final result to n significant digits.

Quick Examples

1. 0.00067 has two significant digits.   The 000 before 67 are leading zeros.

2. 0.000670 has three significant digits.   The 0 after 67 is significant.

3. 5,400,000 has two or more significant digits.   We can't say how many of the zeros are trailing.*

4. 5,400,001 has 7 significant digits.   The string of zeros is not trailing.

5. Rounding 63,918 to three significant digits gives 63,900.

6. Rounding 63,958 to three significant digits gives 64,000.

7. $\pi = 3.141592653...$ $\frac{22}{7} = 3.142857142...$ Therefore, $\frac{22}{7}$ is an approximation of π that is accurate to only three significant digits (3.14).

8. $4.02(1 + 0.02)^{1.4} \approx 4.13$ We rounded to three significant digits.

*If we obtained 5,400,000 by rounding 5,401,011, then it has three significant digits because the zero after the 4 is significant. On the other hand, if we obtained it by rounding 5,411,234, then it has only two significant digits. The use of scientific notation avoids this ambiguity: 5.40×10^6 (or 5.40 E6 on a calculator or computer) is accurate to three digits and 5.4×10^6 is accurate to two.

One more point, though: If, in a long calculation, you round the intermediate results, your final answer may be even less accurate than you think. As a general rule,

When calculating, don't round intermediate results. Rather, use the most accurate results obtainable or have your calculator or computer store them for you.

When you are done with the calculation, *then* round your answer to the appropriate number of digits of accuracy.

0.1 EXERCISES

Calculate each expression in Exercises 1–24, giving the answer as a whole number or a fraction in lowest terms.

1. $2(4 + (-1))(2 \cdot -4)$

2. $3 + ([4 - 2] \cdot 9)$

3. `20/(3*4)-1`

4. `2-(3*4)/10`

5. $\dfrac{3 + ([3 + (-5)])}{3 - 2 \times 2}$

6. $\dfrac{12 - (1 - 4)}{2(5 - 1) \cdot 2 - 1}$

7. `(2-5*(-1))/1-2*(-1)`

8. `2-5*(-1)/(1-2*(-1))`

9. $2 \cdot (-1)^2 / 2$

10. $2 + 4 \cdot 3^2$

11. $2 \cdot 4^2 + 1$

12. $1 - 3 \cdot (-2)^2 \times 2$

13. `3^2+2^2+1`

14. `2^(2^2-2)`

15. $\dfrac{3 - 2(-3)^2}{-6(4 - 1)^2}$

16. $\dfrac{1 - 2(1 - 4)^2}{2(5 - 1)^2 \cdot 2}$

17. `10*(1+1/10)^3`

18. `121/(1+1/10)^2`

19. $3\left(\dfrac{-2 \cdot 3^2}{-(4 - 1)^2}\right)$

20. $-\left(\dfrac{8(1 - 4)^2}{-9(5 - 1)^2}\right)$

21. $3\left(1 - \left(-\dfrac{1}{2}\right)^2\right)^2 + 1$

22. $3\left(\dfrac{1}{9} - \left(\dfrac{2}{3}\right)^2\right)^2 + 1$

23. `(1/2)^2-1/2^2`

24. `2/(1^2)-(2/1)^2`

Convert each expression in Exercises 25–50 into its technology formula equivalent as in the table in the text.

25. $3 \times (2 - 5)$

26. $4 + \dfrac{5}{9}$

27. $\dfrac{3}{2 - 5}$

28. $\dfrac{4 - 1}{3}$

29. $\dfrac{3 - 1}{8 + 6}$

30. $3 + \dfrac{3}{2 - 9}$

31. $3 - \dfrac{4 + 7}{8}$

32. $\dfrac{4 \times 2}{\left(\frac{2}{3}\right)}$

33. $\dfrac{2}{3 + x} - xy^2$

34. $3 + \dfrac{3 + x}{xy}$

35. $3.1x^3 - 4x^{-2} - \dfrac{60}{x^2 - 1}$

36. $2.1x^{-3} - x^{-1} + \dfrac{x^2 - 3}{2}$

37. $\dfrac{\left(\frac{2}{3}\right)}{5}$

38. $\dfrac{2}{\left(\frac{3}{5}\right)}$

39. $3^{4-5} \times 6$

40. $\dfrac{2}{3 + 5^{7-9}}$

41. $3\left(1 + \dfrac{4}{100}\right)^{-3}$

42. $3\left(\dfrac{1 + 4}{100}\right)^{-3}$

43. $3^{2x-1} + 4^x - 1$

44. $2^{x^2} - (2^{2x})^2$

45. $2^{2x^2 - x + 1}$

46. $2^{2x^2 - x} + 1$

47. $\dfrac{4e^{-2x}}{2 - 3e^{-2x}}$

48. $\dfrac{e^{2x} + e^{-2x}}{e^{2x} - e^{-2x}}$

49. $3\left(1 - \left(-\dfrac{1}{2}\right)^2\right)^2 + 1$

50. $3\left(\dfrac{1}{9} - \left(\dfrac{2}{3}\right)^2\right)^2 + 1$

0.2 Exponents and Radicals

In Section 1 we discussed exponentiation, or "raising to a power"; for example, $2^3 = 2 \cdot 2 \cdot 2$. In this section we discuss the algebra of exponentials more fully. First, we look at *integer* exponents: cases in which the powers are positive or negative whole numbers.

Integer Exponents

Positive Integer Exponents

If a is any real number and n is any positive integer, then by a^n we mean the quantity $a \cdot a \cdot \cdots \cdot a$ (n times); thus, $a^1 = a$, $a^2 = a \cdot a$, $a^5 = a \cdot a \cdot a \cdot a \cdot a$. In the expression a^n the number n is called the **exponent**, and the number a is called the **base**.

Quick Examples

$$3^2 = 9 \qquad 2^3 = 8$$
$$0^{34} = 0 \qquad (-1)^5 = -1$$
$$10^3 = 1{,}000 \qquad 10^5 = 100{,}000$$

Negative Integer Exponents

If a is any real number *other than zero* and n is any positive integer, then we define

$$a^{-n} = \frac{1}{a^n} = \frac{1}{a \cdot a \cdot \cdots \cdot a} \quad (n \text{ times})$$

Quick Examples

$$2^{-3} = \frac{1}{2^3} = \frac{1}{8} \qquad\qquad 1^{-27} = \frac{1}{1^{27}} = 1$$
$$x^{-1} = \frac{1}{x^1} = \frac{1}{x} \qquad\qquad (-3)^{-2} = \frac{1}{(-3)^2} = \frac{1}{9}$$
$$y^7 y^{-2} = y^7 \frac{1}{y^2} = y^5 \qquad 0^{-2} \text{ is not defined}$$

Zero Exponent

If a is any real number other than zero, then we define

$$a^0 = 1$$

Quick Examples

$$3^0 = 1 \qquad\qquad 1{,}000{,}000^0 = 1$$
$$0^0 \text{ is not defined}$$

When combining exponential expressions, we use the following identities.

Exponent Identity	**Quick Examples**
1. $a^m a^n = a^{m+n}$	$2^3 2^2 = 2^{3+2} = 2^5 = 32$
	$x^3 x^{-4} = x^{3-4} = x^{-1} = \dfrac{1}{x}$
	$\dfrac{x^3}{x^{-2}} = x^3 \dfrac{1}{x^{-2}} = x^3 x^2 = x^5$
2. $\dfrac{a^m}{a^n} = a^{m-n}$ if $a \neq 0$	$\dfrac{4^3}{4^2} = 4^{3-2} = 4^1 = 4$
	$\dfrac{x^3}{x^{-2}} = x^{3-(-2)} = x^5$
	$\dfrac{3^2}{3^4} = 3^{2-4} = 3^{-2} = \dfrac{1}{9}$
3. $(a^n)^m = a^{nm}$	$(3^2)^2 = 3^4 = 81$
	$(2^x)^2 = 2^{2x}$
4. $(ab)^n = a^n b^n$	$(4 \cdot 2)^2 = 4^2 2^2 = 64$
	$(-2y)^4 = (-2)^4 y^4 = 16y^4$
5. $\left(\dfrac{a}{b}\right)^n = \dfrac{a^n}{b^n}$ if $b \neq 0$	$\left(\dfrac{4}{3}\right)^2 = \dfrac{4^2}{3^2} = \dfrac{16}{9}$
	$\left(\dfrac{x}{-y}\right)^3 = \dfrac{x^3}{(-y)^3} = -\dfrac{x^3}{y^3}$

Caution

- In the first two identities, the bases of the expressions must be the same. For example, the first gives $3^2 3^4 = 3^6$, but does *not* apply to $3^2 4^2$.

- People sometimes invent their own identities, such as $a^m + a^n = a^{m+n}$, which is wrong! (Try it with $a = m = n = 1$.) If you wind up with something like $2^3 + 2^4$, you are stuck with it; there are no identities around to simplify it further. (You can factor out 2^3, but whether or not that is a simplification depends on what you are going to do with the expression next.)

EXAMPLE 1 Combining the Identities

$$\frac{(x^2)^3}{x^3} = \frac{x^6}{x^3} \qquad \text{By (3)}$$
$$= x^{6-3} \qquad \text{By (2)}$$
$$= x^3$$

$$\frac{(x^4 y)^3}{y} = \frac{(x^4)^3 y^3}{y} \qquad \text{By (4)}$$
$$= \frac{x^{12} y^3}{y} \qquad \text{By (3)}$$
$$= x^{12} y^{3-1} \qquad \text{By (2)}$$
$$= x^{12} y^2$$

EXAMPLE 2 Eliminating Negative Exponents

Simplify the following and express the answer using no negative exponents.

a. $\dfrac{x^4 y^{-3}}{x^5 y^2}$ **b.** $\left(\dfrac{x^{-1}}{x^2 y} \right)^5$

Solution

a. $\dfrac{x^4 y^{-3}}{x^5 y^2} = x^{4-5} y^{-3-2} = x^{-1} y^{-5} = \dfrac{1}{x y^5}$

b. $\left(\dfrac{x^{-1}}{x^2 y} \right)^5 = \dfrac{(x^{-1})^5}{(x^2 y)^5} = \dfrac{x^{-5}}{x^{10} y^5} = \dfrac{1}{x^{15} y^5}$

Radicals

If a is any non-negative real number, then its **square root** is the non-negative number whose square is a. For example, the square root of 16 is 4, because $4^2 = 16$. We write the square root of n as $\sqrt{n}$. (Roots are also referred to as **radicals**.) It is important to remember that $\sqrt{n}$ is never negative. Thus, for instance, $\sqrt{9}$ is 3, and not -3, even though $(-3)^2 = 9$. If we want to speak of the "negative square root" of 9, we write it as $-\sqrt{9} = -3$. If we want to write both square roots at once, we write $\pm\sqrt{9} = \pm 3$.

The **cube root** of a real number a is the number whose cube is a. The cube root of a is written as $\sqrt[3]{a}$ so that, for example, $\sqrt[3]{8} = 2$ (because $2^3 = 8$). Note that we can take the cube root of any number, positive, negative, or zero. For instance, the cube root of -8 is $\sqrt[3]{-8} = -2$ because $(-2)^3 = -8$. Unlike square roots, the cube root of a number may be negative. In fact, the cube root of a always has the same sign as a.

Higher roots are defined similarly. The **fourth root** of the *non-negative* number a is defined as the non-negative number whose fourth power is a, and written $\sqrt[4]{a}$. The **fifth root** of any number a is the number whose fifth power is a, and so on.

Note We cannot take an even-numbered root of a negative number, but we can take an odd-numbered root of any number. Even roots are always positive, whereas odd roots have the same sign as the number we start with. ∎

EXAMPLE 3 *n*th Roots

$$\sqrt{4} = 2 \qquad \text{Because } 2^2 = 4$$

$$\sqrt{16} = 4 \qquad \text{Because } 4^2 = 16$$

$$\sqrt{1} = 1 \qquad \text{Because } 1^2 = 1$$

$$\text{If } x \geq 0, \text{ then } \sqrt{x^2} = x \qquad \text{Because } x^2 = x^2$$

$$\sqrt{2} \approx 1.414213562 \qquad \sqrt{2} \text{ is not a whole number.}$$

$$\sqrt{1+1} = \sqrt{2} \approx 1.414213562 \qquad \text{First add, then take the square root.*}$$

$$\sqrt{9+16} = \sqrt{25} = 5 \qquad \text{Contrast with } \sqrt{9} + \sqrt{16} = 3 + 4 = 7.$$

---

*In general, $\sqrt{a+b}$ means the square root of the *quantity* $(a+b)$. The radical sign acts as a pair of parentheses or a fraction bar, telling us to evaluate what is inside before taking the root. (See the Caution on next page.)

$$\frac{1}{\sqrt{2}} = \frac{\sqrt{2}}{2}$$

Multiply top and bottom by $\sqrt{2}$.

$$\sqrt[3]{27} = 3$$

Because $3^3 = 27$

$$\sqrt[3]{-64} = -4$$

Because $(-4)^3 = -64$

$$\sqrt[4]{16} = 2$$

Because $2^4 = 16$

$\sqrt[4]{-16}$ is not defined

Even-numbered root of a negative number

$\sqrt[5]{-1} = -1$, since $(-1)^5 = -1$

Odd-numbered root of a negative number

$\sqrt[n]{-1} = -1$ if n is any odd number

Q : *In the example we saw that $\sqrt{x^2} = x$ if x is non-negative. What happens if x is negative?*

A : If x is negative, then x^2 is positive, and so $\sqrt{x^2}$ is still defined as the non-negative number whose square is x^2. This number must be $|x|$, the **absolute value of x**, which is the non-negative number with the same size as x. For instance, $|-3| = 3$, while $|3| = 3$, and $|0| = 0$. It follows that

$$\sqrt{x^2} = |x|$$

for every real number x, positive or negative. For instance,

$$\sqrt{(-3)^2} = \sqrt{9} = 3 = |-3|$$

and $\sqrt{3^2} = \sqrt{9} = 3 = |3|$.

In general, we find that

$$\sqrt[n]{x^n} = x \text{ if } n \text{ is odd, and } \sqrt[n]{x^n} = |x| \text{ if } n \text{ is even.}$$

We use the following identities to evaluate radicals of products and quotients.

Radicals of Products and Quotients

If a and b are any real numbers (non-negative in the case of even-numbered roots), then

$$\sqrt[n]{ab} = \sqrt[n]{a}\,\sqrt[n]{b}$$

Radical of a product = Product of radicals

$$\sqrt[n]{\frac{a}{b}} = \frac{\sqrt[n]{a}}{\sqrt[n]{b}} \quad \text{if } b \neq 0$$

Radical of a quotient = Quotient of radicals

Notes

• The first rule is similar to the rule $(a \cdot b)^2 = a^2 b^2$ for the square of a product, and the second rule is similar to the rule $\left(\dfrac{a}{b}\right)^2 = \dfrac{a^2}{b^2}$ for the square of a quotient.

• *Caution* There is no corresponding identity for addition:

$$\sqrt{a+b} \text{ is } not \text{ equal to } \sqrt{a} + \sqrt{b}$$

(Consider $a = b = 1$, for example.) Equating these expressions is a common error, so be careful! ∎

Quick Examples

1. $\sqrt{9\cdot 4}=\sqrt{9}\sqrt{4}=3\times 2=6$ Alternatively, $\sqrt{9\cdot 4}=\sqrt{36}=6$

2. $\sqrt{\dfrac{9}{4}}=\dfrac{\sqrt{9}}{\sqrt{4}}=\dfrac{3}{2}$

3. $\dfrac{\sqrt{2}}{\sqrt{5}}=\dfrac{\sqrt{2}\sqrt{5}}{\sqrt{5}\sqrt{5}}=\dfrac{\sqrt{10}}{5}$

4. $\sqrt{4(3+13)}=\sqrt{4(16)}=\sqrt{4}\sqrt{16}=2\times 4=8$

5. $\sqrt[3]{-216}=\sqrt[3]{(-27)8}=\sqrt[3]{-27}\sqrt[3]{8}=(-3)2=-6$

6. $\sqrt{x^3}=\sqrt{x^2\cdot x}=\sqrt{x^2}\sqrt{x}=x\sqrt{x}$ if $x\ge 0$

7. $\sqrt{\dfrac{x^2+y^2}{z^2}}=\dfrac{\sqrt{x^2+y^2}}{\sqrt{z^2}}=\dfrac{\sqrt{x^2+y^2}}{|z|}$ We can't simplify the numerator any further.

Rational Exponents

We already know what we mean by expressions such as x^4 and a^{-6}. The next step is to make sense of *rational* exponents: exponents of the form p/q with p and q integers as in $a^{1/2}$ and $3^{-2/3}$.

Q: *What should we mean by* $a^{1/2}$?

A: The overriding concern here is that all the exponent identities should remain true. In this case the identity to look at is the one that says that $(a^m)^n=a^{mn}$. This identity tells us that

$$(a^{1/2})^2=a^1=a.$$

That is, $a^{1/2}$, when squared, gives us a. But that must mean that $a^{1/2}$ is the *square root* of a, or

$$a^{1/2}=\sqrt{a}.$$

A similar argument tells us that, if q is any positive whole number, then

$$a^{1/q}=\sqrt[q]{a},\text{ the }q\text{th root of }a.$$

Notice that if a is negative, this makes sense only for q odd. To avoid this problem, we usually stick to positive a.

Q: *If p and q are integers (q positive), what should we mean by* $a^{p/q}$?

A: By the exponent identities, $a^{p/q}$ should equal both $(a^p)^{1/q}$ and $(a^{1/q})^p$. The first is the qth root of a^p, and the second is the pth power of $a^{1/q}$, which gives us the following.

Conversion Between Rational Exponents and Radicals

If a is any non-negative number, then

$$a^{p/q} = \sqrt[q]{a^p} = \left(\sqrt[q]{a}\right)^p.$$

⟍ Using exponents   ⟍ Using radicals

In particular,

$$a^{1/q} = \sqrt[q]{a}, \text{ the } q\text{th root of } a.$$

Notes

• If a is negative, all of this makes sense only if q is odd.
• All of the exponent identities continue to work when we allow rational exponents p/q. In other words, we are free to use all the exponent identities even though the exponents are not integers. ■

Quick Examples

1. $4^{3/2} = (\sqrt{4})^3 = 2^3 = 8$

2. $8^{2/3} = (\sqrt[3]{8})^2 = 2^2 = 4$

3. $9^{-3/2} = \dfrac{1}{9^{3/2}} = \dfrac{1}{(\sqrt{9})^3} = \dfrac{1}{3^3} = \dfrac{1}{27}$

4. $\dfrac{\sqrt{3}}{\sqrt[3]{3}} = \dfrac{3^{1/2}}{3^{1/3}} = 3^{1/2 - 1/3} = 3^{1/6} = \sqrt[6]{3}$

5. $2^2 2^{7/2} = 2^2 2^{3 + 1/2} = 2^2 2^3 2^{1/2} = 2^5 2^{1/2} = 2^5 \sqrt{2}$

EXAMPLE 4 Simplifying Algebraic Expressions

Simplify the following.

a. $\dfrac{(x^3)^{5/3}}{x^3}$

b. $\sqrt[4]{a^6}$

c. $\dfrac{(xy)^{-3} y^{-3/2}}{x^{-2}\sqrt{y}}$

Solution

a. $\dfrac{(x^3)^{5/3}}{x^3} = \dfrac{x^5}{x^3} = x^2$

b. $\sqrt[4]{a^6} = a^{6/4} = a^{3/2} = a \cdot a^{1/2} = a\sqrt{a}$

c. $\dfrac{(xy)^{-3} y^{-3/2}}{x^{-2}\sqrt{y}} = \dfrac{x^{-3} y^{-3} y^{-3/2}}{x^{-2} y^{1/2}} = \dfrac{1}{x^{-2+3} y^{1/2 + 3 + 3/2}} = \dfrac{1}{xy^5}$

Converting Between Rational, Radical, and Exponent Form

In calculus we must often convert algebraic expressions involving powers of x, such as $\dfrac{3}{2x^2}$, into expressions in which x does not appear in the denominator, such as $\dfrac{3}{2} x^{-2}$. Also, we must often convert expressions with radicals, such as $\dfrac{1}{\sqrt{1+x^2}}$, into expressions with no radicals and all powers in the numerator, such as $(1 + x^2)^{-1/2}$. In these cases, we are converting from **rational form** or **radical form** to **exponent form**.

Rational Form

An expression is in **rational form** if it is written with positive exponents only.

Quick Examples

1. $\dfrac{2}{3x^2}$ is in rational form.

2. $\dfrac{2x^{-1}}{3}$ is not in rational form because the exponent of x is negative.

3. $\dfrac{x}{6} + \dfrac{6}{x}$ is in rational form.

Radical Form

An expression is in **radical form** if it is written with integer powers and roots only.

Quick Examples

1. $\dfrac{2}{5\sqrt[3]{x}} + \dfrac{2}{x}$ is in radical form.

2. $\dfrac{2x^{-1/3}}{5} + 2x^{-1}$ is not in radical form because $x^{-1/3}$ appears.

3. $\dfrac{1}{\sqrt{1+x^2}}$ is in radical form, but $(1 + x^2)^{-1/2}$ is not.

Exponent Form

An expression is in **exponent form** if there are no radicals and all powers of unknowns occur in the numerator. We write such expressions as sums or differences of terms of the form

$$\text{Constant} \times (\text{Expression with } x)^p \qquad \text{As in } \frac{1}{3}x^{-3/2}$$

Quick Examples

1. $\dfrac{2}{3}x^4 - 3x^{-1/3}$ is in exponent form.

2. $\dfrac{x}{6} + \dfrac{6}{x}$ is not in exponent form because the second expression has x in the denominator.

3. $\sqrt[3]{x}$ is not in exponent form because it has a radical.

4. $(1 + x^2)^{-1/2}$ is in exponent form, but $\dfrac{1}{\sqrt{1+x^2}}$ is not.

EXAMPLE 5 **Converting from One Form to Another**

Convert the following to rational form:

a. $\dfrac{1}{2}x^{-2} + \dfrac{4}{3}x^{-5}$

b. $\dfrac{2}{\sqrt{x}} - \dfrac{2}{x^{-4}}$

Convert the following to radical form:

c. $\dfrac{1}{2}x^{-1/2} + \dfrac{4}{3}x^{-5/4}$

d. $\dfrac{(3+x)^{-1/3}}{5}$

Convert the following to exponent form:

e. $\dfrac{3}{4x^2} - \dfrac{x}{6} + \dfrac{6}{x} + \dfrac{4}{3\sqrt{x}}$

f. $\dfrac{2}{(x+1)^2} - \dfrac{3}{4\sqrt[5]{2x-1}}$

Solution For (a) and (b), we eliminate negative exponents as we did in Example 2:

a. $\dfrac{1}{2}x^{-2} + \dfrac{4}{3}x^{-5} = \dfrac{1}{2} \cdot \dfrac{1}{x^2} + \dfrac{4}{3} \cdot \dfrac{1}{x^5} = \dfrac{1}{2x^2} + \dfrac{4}{3x^5}$

b. $\dfrac{2}{\sqrt{x}} - \dfrac{2}{x^{-4}} = \dfrac{2}{\sqrt{x}} - 2x^4$

For (c) and (d), we rewrite all terms with fractional exponents as radicals:

c. $\dfrac{1}{2}x^{-1/2} + \dfrac{4}{3}x^{-5/4} = \dfrac{1}{2} \cdot \dfrac{1}{x^{1/2}} + \dfrac{4}{3} \cdot \dfrac{1}{x^{5/4}}$

$\qquad = \dfrac{1}{2} \cdot \dfrac{1}{\sqrt{x}} + \dfrac{4}{3} \cdot \dfrac{1}{\sqrt[4]{x^5}} = \dfrac{1}{2\sqrt{x}} + \dfrac{4}{3\sqrt[4]{x^5}}$

d. $\dfrac{(3+x)^{-1/3}}{5} = \dfrac{1}{5(3+x)^{1/3}} = \dfrac{1}{5\sqrt[3]{3+x}}$

For (e) and (f), we eliminate any radicals and move all expressions involving x to the numerator:

e. $\dfrac{3}{4x^2} - \dfrac{x}{6} + \dfrac{6}{x} + \dfrac{4}{3\sqrt{x}} = \dfrac{3}{4}x^{-2} - \dfrac{1}{6}x + 6x^{-1} + \dfrac{4}{3x^{1/2}}$

$\qquad = \dfrac{3}{4}x^{-2} - \dfrac{1}{6}x + 6x^{-1} + \dfrac{4}{3}x^{-1/2}$

f. $\dfrac{2}{(x+1)^2} - \dfrac{3}{4\sqrt[5]{2x-1}} = 2(x+1)^{-2} - \dfrac{3}{4(2x-1)^{1/5}}$

$\qquad = 2(x+1)^{-2} - \dfrac{3}{4}(2x-1)^{-1/5}$

Solving Equations with Exponents

EXAMPLE 6 **Solving Equations**

Solve the following equations:

a. $x^3 + 8 = 0$ **b.** $x^2 - \dfrac{1}{2} = 0$ **c.** $x^{3/2} - 64 = 0$

Solution

a. Subtracting 8 from both sides gives $x^3 = -8$. Taking the cube root of both sides gives $x = -2$.

b. Adding $\frac{1}{2}$ to both sides gives $x^2 = \frac{1}{2}$. Thus, $x = \pm\sqrt{\frac{1}{2}} = \pm\frac{1}{\sqrt{2}}$.

c. Adding 64 to both sides gives $x^{3/2} = 64$. Taking the reciprocal (2/3) power of both sides gives

$$(x^{3/2})^{2/3} = 64^{2/3}$$
$$x^1 = \left(\sqrt[3]{64}\right)^2 = 4^2 = 16$$

so $x = 16$.

0.2 EXERCISES

Evaluate the expressions in Exercises 1–16.

1. 3^3 **2.** $(-2)^3$ **3.** $-(2 \cdot 3)^2$ **4.** $(4 \cdot 2)^2$

5. $\left(\dfrac{-2}{3}\right)^2$ **6.** $\left(\dfrac{3}{2}\right)^3$ **7.** $(-2)^{-3}$ **8.** -2^{-3}

9. $\left(\dfrac{1}{4}\right)^{-2}$ **10.** $\left(\dfrac{-2}{3}\right)^{-2}$ **11.** $2 \cdot 3^0$ **12.** $3 \cdot (-2)^0$

13. $2^3 \, 2^2$ **14.** $3^2 3$ **15.** $2^2 2^{-1} 2^4 2^{-4}$ **16.** $5^2 5^{-3} 5^2 5^{-2}$

Simplify each expression in Exercises 17–30, expressing your answer in rational form.

17. $x^3 x^2$ **18.** $x^4 x^{-1}$ **19.** $-x^2 x^{-3} y$ **20.** $-xy^{-1}x^{-1}$

21. $\dfrac{x^3}{x^4}$ **22.** $\dfrac{y^5}{y^3}$ **23.** $\dfrac{x^2 y^2}{x^{-1} y}$ **24.** $\dfrac{x^{-1} y}{x^2 y^2}$

25. $\dfrac{(xy^{-1}z^3)^2}{x^2 yz^2}$ **26.** $\dfrac{x^2 yz^2}{(xyz^{-1})^{-1}}$ **27.** $\left(\dfrac{xy^{-2}z}{x^{-1}z}\right)^3$

28. $\left(\dfrac{x^2 y^{-1}z^0}{xyz}\right)^2$ **29.** $\left(\dfrac{x^{-1}y^{-2}z^2}{xy}\right)^{-2}$ **30.** $\left(\dfrac{xy^{-2}}{x^2 y^{-1}z}\right)^{-3}$

Convert the expressions in Exercises 31–36 to rational form.

31. $3x^{-4}$ **32.** $\dfrac{1}{2}x^{-4}$ **33.** $\dfrac{3}{4}x^{-2/3}$

34. $\dfrac{4}{5}y^{-3/4}$ **35.** $1 - \dfrac{0.3}{x^{-2}} - \dfrac{6}{5}x^{-1}$ **36.** $\dfrac{1}{3x^{-4}} + \dfrac{0.1x^{-2}}{3}$

Evaluate the expressions in Exercises 37–56, rounding your answer to four significant digits where necessary.

37. $\sqrt{4}$ **38.** $\sqrt{5}$ **39.** $\sqrt{\dfrac{1}{4}}$

40. $\sqrt{\dfrac{1}{9}}$ **41.** $\sqrt{\dfrac{16}{9}}$ **42.** $\sqrt{\dfrac{9}{4}}$

43. $\dfrac{\sqrt{4}}{5}$ **44.** $\dfrac{6}{\sqrt{25}}$ **45.** $\sqrt{9} + \sqrt{16}$

46. $\sqrt{25} - \sqrt{16}$ **47.** $\sqrt{9+16}$ **48.** $\sqrt{25-16}$

49. $\sqrt[3]{8-27}$ **50.** $\sqrt[4]{81-16}$ **51.** $\sqrt[3]{27/8}$

52. $\sqrt[3]{8 \times 64}$ **53.** $\sqrt{(-2)^2}$ **54.** $\sqrt{(-1)^2}$

55. $\sqrt{\dfrac{1}{4}(1+15)}$ **56.** $\sqrt{\dfrac{1}{9}(3+33)}$

Simplify the expressions in Exercises 57–64, given that x, y, z, a, b, and c are positive real numbers.

57. $\sqrt{a^2 b^2}$ **58.** $\sqrt{\dfrac{a^2}{b^2}}$ **59.** $\sqrt{(x+9)^2}$

60. $(\sqrt{x+9})^2$ **61.** $\sqrt[3]{x^3(a^3+b^3)}$ **62.** $\sqrt[4]{\dfrac{x^4}{a^4 b^4}}$

63. $\sqrt{\dfrac{4xy^3}{x^2 y}}$ **64.** $\sqrt{\dfrac{4(x^2+y^2)}{c^2}}$

Convert the expressions in Exercises 65–84 to exponent form.

65. $\sqrt{3}$ **66.** $\sqrt{8}$ **67.** $\sqrt{x^3}$

68. $\sqrt[3]{x^2}$ **69.** $\sqrt[3]{xy^2}$ **70.** $\sqrt{x^2 y}$

71. $\dfrac{x^2}{\sqrt{x}}$ **72.** $\dfrac{x}{\sqrt{x}}$ **73.** $\dfrac{3}{5x^2}$

74. $\dfrac{2}{5x^{-3}}$ **75.** $\dfrac{3x^{-1.2}}{2} - \dfrac{1}{3x^{2.1}}$ **76.** $\dfrac{2}{3x^{-1.2}} - \dfrac{x^{2.1}}{3}$

77. $\dfrac{2x}{3} - \dfrac{x^{0.1}}{2} + \dfrac{4}{3x^{1.1}}$ **78.** $\dfrac{4x^2}{3} + \dfrac{x^{3/2}}{6} - \dfrac{2}{3x^2}$

79. $\dfrac{3\sqrt{x}}{4} - \dfrac{5}{3\sqrt{x}} + \dfrac{4}{3x\sqrt{x}}$ **80.** $\dfrac{3}{5\sqrt{x}} - \dfrac{5\sqrt{x}}{8} + \dfrac{7}{2\sqrt[3]{x}}$

81. $\dfrac{3\sqrt[5]{x^2}}{4} - \dfrac{7}{2\sqrt{x^3}}$ **82.** $\dfrac{1}{8x\sqrt{x}} - \dfrac{2}{3\sqrt[5]{x^3}}$

83. $\dfrac{1}{(x^2+1)^3} - \dfrac{3}{4\sqrt[3]{(x^2+1)}}$ **84.** $\dfrac{2}{3(x^2+1)^{-3}} - \dfrac{3\sqrt[3]{(x^2+1)^7}}{4}$

Convert the expressions in Exercises 85–96 to radical form.

85. $2^{2/3}$ **86.** $3^{4/5}$ **87.** $x^{4/3}$ **88.** $y^{7/4}$

89. $(x^{1/2}y^{1/3})^{1/5}$ **90.** $x^{-1/3}y^{3/2}$ **91.** $-\dfrac{3}{2}x^{-1/4}$ **92.** $\dfrac{4}{5}x^{3/2}$

93. $0.2x^{-2/3} + \dfrac{3}{7x^{-1/2}}$

94. $\dfrac{3.1}{x^{-4/3}} - \dfrac{11}{7}x^{-1/7}$

95. $\dfrac{3}{4(1-x)^{5/2}}$

96. $\dfrac{9}{4(1-x)^{-7/3}}$

Simplify the expressions in Exercises 97–106.

97. $4^{-1/2}4^{7/2}$

98. $2^{1/a}/2^{2/a}$

99. $3^{2/3}3^{-1/6}$

100. $2^{1/3}2^{-1}2^{2/3}2^{-1/3}$

101. $\dfrac{x^{3/2}}{x^{5/2}}$

102. $\dfrac{y^{5/4}}{y^{3/4}}$

103. $\dfrac{x^{1/2}y^2}{x^{-1/2}y}$

104. $\dfrac{x^{-1/2}y}{x^2y^{3/2}}$

105. $\left(\dfrac{x}{y}\right)^{1/3}\left(\dfrac{y}{x}\right)^{2/3}$

106. $\left(\dfrac{x}{y}\right)^{-1/3}\left(\dfrac{y}{x}\right)^{1/3}$

Solve each equation in Exercises 107–120 for x, rounding your answer to four significant digits where necessary.

107. $x^2 - 16 = 0$

108. $x^2 - 1 = 0$

109. $x^2 - \dfrac{4}{9} = 0$

110. $x^2 - \dfrac{1}{10} = 0$

111. $x^2 - (1 + 2x)^2 = 0$

112. $x^2 - (2 - 3x)^2 = 0$

113. $x^5 + 32 = 0$

114. $x^4 - 81 = 0$

115. $x^{1/2} - 4 = 0$

116. $x^{1/3} - 2 = 0$

117. $1 - \dfrac{1}{x^2} = 0$

118. $\dfrac{2}{x^3} - \dfrac{6}{x^4} = 0$

119. $(x - 4)^{-1/3} = 2$

120. $(x - 4)^{2/3} + 1 = 5$

0.3 Multiplying and Factoring Algebraic Expressions

Multiplying Algebraic Expressions

Distributive Law

The **distributive law** for real numbers states that

$$a(b \pm c) = ab \pm ac$$
$$(a \pm b)c = ac \pm bc$$

for any real numbers a, b, and c.

Quick Examples

1. $2(x - 3)$ is *not* equal to $2x - 3$ but is equal to $2x - 2(3) = 2x - 6$.
2. $x(x + 1) = x^2 + x$
3. $2x(3x - 4) = 6x^2 - 8x$
4. $(x - 4)x^2 = x^3 - 4x^2$
5. $(x + 2)(x + 3) = (x + 2)x + (x + 2)3$
   $$= (x^2 + 2x) + (3x + 6) = x^2 + 5x + 6$$
6. $(x + 2)(x - 3) = (x + 2)x - (x + 2)3$
   $$= (x^2 + 2x) - (3x + 6) = x^2 - x - 6$$

There is a quicker way of expanding expressions like the last two, called the "FOIL" method (First, Outer, Inner, Last). Consider, for instance, the expression $(x + 1)(x - 2)$. The FOIL method says: Take the product of the first terms: $x \cdot x = x^2$, the product of the outer terms: $x \cdot (-2) = -2x$, the product of the inner terms: $1 \cdot x = x$, and the product of the last terms: $1 \cdot (-2) = -2$, and then add them all up, getting $x^2 - 2x + x - 2 = x^2 - x - 2$.

EXAMPLE 1 FOIL

a. $(x - 2)(2x + 5) = 2x^2 + 5x - 4x - 10 = 2x^2 + x - 10$

$$\uparrow \qquad \uparrow \qquad \uparrow \qquad \uparrow$$
$$\text{First} \quad \text{Outer} \quad \text{Inner} \quad \text{Last}$$

b. $(x^2 + 1)(x - 4) = x^3 - 4x^2 + x - 4$

c. $(a - b)(a + b) = a^2 + ab - ab - b^2 = a^2 - b^2$

d. $(a + b)^2 = (a + b)(a + b) = a^2 + ab + ab + b^2 = a^2 + 2ab + b^2$

e. $(a - b)^2 = (a - b)(a - b) = a^2 - ab - ab + b^2 = a^2 - 2ab + b^2$

The last three are particularly important and are worth memorizing.

Special Formulas

$$(a - b)(a + b) = a^2 - b^2 \qquad \text{Difference of two squares}$$
$$(a + b)^2 = a^2 + 2ab + b^2 \qquad \text{Square of a sum}$$
$$(a - b)^2 = a^2 - 2ab + b^2 \qquad \text{Square of a difference}$$

Quick Examples

1. $(2 - x)(2 + x) = 4 - x^2$

2. $(1 + a)(1 - a) = 1 - a^2$

3. $(x + 3)^2 = x^2 + 6x + 9$

4. $(4 - x)^2 = 16 - 8x + x^2$

Here are some longer examples that require the distributive law.

EXAMPLE 2 Multiplying Algebraic Expressions

a. $(x + 1)(x^2 + 3x - 4) = (x + 1)x^2 + (x + 1)3x - (x + 1)4$

$$= (x^3 + x^2) + (3x^2 + 3x) - (4x + 4)$$
$$= x^3 + 4x^2 - x - 4$$

b. $\left(x^2 - \dfrac{1}{x} + 1\right)(2x + 5) = \left(x^2 - \dfrac{1}{x} + 1\right)2x + \left(x^2 - \dfrac{1}{x} + 1\right)5$

$$= (2x^3 - 2 + 2x) + \left(5x^2 - \dfrac{5}{x} + 5\right)$$
$$= 2x^3 + 5x^2 + 2x + 3 - \dfrac{5}{x}$$

c. $(x - y)(x - y)(x - y) = (x^2 - 2xy + y^2)(x - y)$

$$= (x^2 - 2xy + y^2)x - (x^2 - 2xy + y^2)y$$
$$= (x^3 - 2x^2y + xy^2) - (x^2y - 2xy^2 + y^3)$$
$$= x^3 - 3x^2y + 3xy^2 - y^3$$

Factoring Algebraic Expressions

We can think of factoring as applying the distributive law in reverse—for example,

$$2x^2 + x = x(2x + 1),$$

which can be checked by using the distributive law. Factoring is an art that you will learn with experience and the help of a few useful techniques.

Factoring Using a Common Factor

To use this technique, locate a **common factor**—a term that occurs as a factor in each of the expressions being added or subtracted (for example, x is a common factor in $2x^2 + x$, because it is a factor of both $2x^2$ and x). Once you have located a common factor, "factor it out" by applying the distributive law.

Quick Examples

1. $2x^3 - x^2 + x$ has x as a common factor, so
$$2x^3 - x^2 + x = x(2x^2 - x + 1)$$

2. $2x^2 + 4x$ has $2x$ as a common factor, so
$$2x^2 + 4x = 2x(x + 2)$$

3. $2x^2y + xy^2 - x^2y^2$ has xy as a common factor, so
$$2x^2y + xy^2 - x^2y^2 = xy(2x + y - xy)$$

4. $(x^2 + 1)(x + 2) - (x^2 + 1)(x + 3)$ has $x^2 + 1$ as a common factor, so
$$(x^2 + 1)(x + 2) - (x^2 + 1)(x + 3) = (x^2 + 1)[(x + 2) - (x + 3)]$$
$$= (x^2 + 1)(x + 2 - x - 3)$$
$$= (x^2 + 1)(-1) = -(x^2 + 1)$$

5. $12x(x^2 - 1)^5(x^3 + 1)^6 + 18x^2(x^2 - 1)^6(x^3 + 1)^5$ has $6x(x^2 - 1)^5(x^3 + 1)^5$ as a common factor, so
$$12x(x^2 - 1)^5(x^3 + 1)^6 + 18x^2(x^2 - 1)^6(x^3 + 1)^5$$
$$= 6x(x^2 - 1)^5(x^3 + 1)^5[2(x^3 + 1) + 3x(x^2 - 1)]$$
$$= 6x(x^2 - 1)^5(x^3 + 1)^5(2x^3 + 2 + 3x^3 - 3x)$$
$$= 6x(x^2 - 1)^5(x^3 + 1)^5(5x^3 - 3x + 2)$$

We would also like to be able to reverse calculations such as $(x + 2)(2x - 5) = 2x^2 - x - 10$. That is, starting with the expression $2x^2 - x - 10$, we would like to **factor** it to get the expression $(x + 2)(2x - 5)$. An expression of the form $ax^2 + bx + c$, where a, b, and c are real numbers, is called a **quadratic** expression in x. Thus, given a quadratic expression $ax^2 + bx + c$, we would like to write it in the form $(dx + e)(fx + g)$ for some real numbers d, e, f, and g. There are some quadratics, such as $x^2 + x + 1$, that cannot be factored in this form at all. Here, we consider only quadratics that do factor, and in such a way that the numbers d, e, f, and g are integers (whole numbers; other cases are discussed in Section 5). The usual technique of factoring such quadratics is a "trial and error" approach.

Factoring Quadratics by Trial and Error

To factor the quadratic $ax^2 + bx + c$, factor ax^2 as $(a_1x)(a_2x)$ (with a_1 positive) and c as c_1c_2, and then check whether or not $ax^2 + bx + c = (a_1x \pm c_1)(a_2x \pm c_2)$. If not, try other factorizations of ax^2 and c.

Quick Examples

1. To factor $x^2 - 6x + 5$, first factor x^2 as $(x)(x)$, and 5 as $(5)(1)$:

$(x + 5)(x + 1) = x^2 + 6x + 5$.   No good

$(x - 5)(x - 1) = x^2 - 6x + 5$.   Desired factorization

2. To factor $x^2 - 4x - 12$, first factor x^2 as $(x)(x)$, and -12 as $(1)(-12)$, $(2)(-6)$, or $(3)(-4)$. Trying them one by one gives

$(x + 1)(x - 12) = x^2 - 11x - 12$.   No good

$(x - 1)(x + 12) = x^2 + 11x - 12$.   No good

$(x + 2)(x - 6) = x^2 - 4x - 12$.   Desired factorization

3. To factor $4x^2 - 25$, we can follow the above procedure, or recognize $4x^2 - 25$ as the difference of two squares:

$$4x^2 - 25 = (2x)^2 - 5^2 = (2x - 5)(2x + 5).$$

Note: Not all quadratic expressions factor. In Section 5 we look at a test that tells us whether or not a given quadratic factors.

Here are examples requiring either a little more work or a little more thought.

EXAMPLE 3 Factoring Quadratics

Factor the following: **a.** $4x^2 - 5x - 6$ **b.** $x^4 - 5x^2 + 6$

Solution

a. Possible factorizations of $4x^2$ are $(2x)(2x)$ or $(x)(4x)$. Possible factorizations of -6 are $(1)(-6), (2)(-3)$. We now systematically try out all the possibilities until we come up with the correct one.

$(2x)(2x)$ and $(1)(-6)$: $(2x + 1)(2x - 6) = 4x^2 - 10x - 6$ No good

$(2x)(2x)$ and $(2)(-3)$: $(2x + 2)(2x - 3) = 4x^2 - 2x - 6$ No good

$(x)(4x)$ and $(1)(-6)$: $(x + 1)(4x - 6) = 4x^2 - 2x - 6$ No good

$(x)(4x)$ and $(2)(-3)$: $(x + 2)(4x - 3) = 4x^2 + 5x - 6$ Almost!

Change signs: $(x - 2)(4x + 3) = 4x^2 - 5x - 6$ Correct

b. The expression $x^4 - 5x^2 + 6$ is not a quadratic, you say? Correct. It's a quartic (a fourth degree expression). However, it looks rather like a quadratic. In fact, it is quadratic *in* x^2, meaning that it is

$$(x^2)^2 - 5(x^2) + 6 = y^2 - 5y + 6$$

where $y = x^2$. The quadratic $y^2 - 5y + 6$ factors as

$$y^2 - 5y + 6 = (y - 3)(y - 2)$$

so

$$x^4 - 5x^2 + 6 = (x^2 - 3)(x^2 - 2)$$

This is a sometimes useful technique.

Our last example is here to remind you why we should want to factor polynomials in the first place. We shall return to this in Section 5.

EXAMPLE 4 Solving a Quadratic Equation by Factoring

Solve the equation $3x^2 + 4x - 4 = 0$.

Solution We first factor the left-hand side to get

$$(3x - 2)(x + 2) = 0.$$

Thus, the product of the two quantities $(3x - 2)$ and $(x + 2)$ is zero. Now, if a product of two numbers is zero, one of the two must be zero. In other words, either $3x - 2 = 0$, giving $x = \frac{2}{3}$, or $x + 2 = 0$, giving $x = -2$. Thus, there are two solutions: $x = \frac{2}{3}$ and $x = -2$.

0.3 EXERCISES

Expand each expression in Exercises 1–22.

1. $x(4x + 6)$

2. $(4y - 2)y$

3. $(2x - y)y$

4. $x(3x + y)$

5. $(x + 1)(x - 3)$

6. $(y + 3)(y + 4)$

7. $(2y + 3)(y + 5)$

8. $(2x - 2)(3x - 4)$

9. $(2x - 3)^2$

10. $(3x + 1)^2$

11. $\left(x + \dfrac{1}{x}\right)^2$

12. $\left(y - \dfrac{1}{y}\right)^2$

13. $(2x - 3)(2x + 3)$

14. $(4 + 2x)(4 - 2x)$

15. $\left(y - \dfrac{1}{y}\right)\left(y + \dfrac{1}{y}\right)$

16. $(x - x^2)(x + x^2)$

17. $(x^2 + x - 1)(2x + 4)$

18. $(3x + 1)(2x^2 - x + 1)$

19. $(x^2 - 2x + 1)^2$

20. $(x + y - xy)^2$

21. $(y^3 + 2y^2 + y)(y^2 + 2y - 1)$

22. $(x^3 - 2x^2 + 4)(3x^2 - x + 2)$

In Exercises 23–30, factor each expression and simplify as much as possible.

23. $(x + 1)(x + 2) + (x + 1)(x + 3)$

24. $(x + 1)(x + 2)^2 + (x + 1)^2(x + 2)$

25. $(x^2 + 1)^5(x + 3)^4 + (x^2 + 1)^6(x + 3)^3$

26. $10x(x^2 + 1)^4(x^3 + 1)^5 + 15x^2(x^2 + 1)^5(x^3 + 1)^4$

27. $(x^3 + 1)\sqrt{x + 1} - (x^3 + 1)^2\sqrt{x + 1}$

28. $(x^2 + 1)\sqrt{x + 1} - \sqrt{(x + 1)^3}$

29. $\sqrt{(x + 1)^3} + \sqrt{(x + 1)^5}$

30. $(x^2 + 1)\sqrt[3]{(x + 1)^4} - \sqrt[3]{(x + 1)^7}$

In Exercises 31–48, (a) factor the given expression; (b) set the expression equal to zero and solve for the unknown (x in the odd-numbered exercises and y in the even-numbered exercises).

31. $2x + 3x^2$

32. $y^2 - 4y$

33. $6x^3 - 2x^2$

34. $3y^3 - 9y^2$

35. $x^2 - 8x + 7$

36. $y^2 + 6y + 8$

37. $x^2 + x - 12$

38. $y^2 + y - 6$

39. $2x^2 - 3x - 2$

40. $3y^2 - 8y - 3$

41. $6x^2 + 13x + 6$

42. $6y^2 + 17y + 12$

43. $12x^2 + x - 6$

44. $20y^2 + 7y - 3$

45. $x^2 + 4xy + 4y^2$

46. $4y^2 - 4xy + x^2$

47. $x^4 - 5x^2 + 4$

48. $y^4 + 2y^2 - 3$

0.4 Rational Expressions

Rational Expression

A **rational expression** is an algebraic expression of the form $\dfrac{P}{Q}$, where P and Q are simpler expressions (usually polynomials) and the denominator Q is not zero.

Quick Examples

1. $\dfrac{x^2 - 3x}{x}$ $P = x^2 - 3x, \ Q = x$

2. $\dfrac{x + \frac{1}{x} + 1}{2x^2 y + 1}$ $P = x + \dfrac{1}{x} + 1, \ Q = 2x^2 y + 1$

3. $3xy - x^2$ $P = 3xy - x^2, \ Q = 1$

Algebra of Rational Expressions

We manipulate rational expressions in the same way that we manipulate fractions, using the following rules:

Algebraic Rule	**Quick Example**
Product: $\dfrac{P}{Q} \cdot \dfrac{R}{S} = \dfrac{PR}{QS}$	$\dfrac{x+1}{x} \cdot \dfrac{x-1}{2x+1} = \dfrac{(x+1)(x-1)}{x(2x+1)} = \dfrac{x^2-1}{2x^2+x}$
Sum: $\dfrac{P}{Q} + \dfrac{R}{S} = \dfrac{PS + RQ}{QS}$	$\dfrac{2x-1}{3x+2} + \dfrac{1}{x} = \dfrac{(2x-1)x + 1(3x+2)}{x(3x+2)}$ $= \dfrac{2x^2 + 2x + 2}{3x^2 + 2x}$
Difference: $\dfrac{P}{Q} - \dfrac{R}{S} = \dfrac{PS - RQ}{QS}$	$\dfrac{x}{3x+2} - \dfrac{x-4}{x} = \dfrac{x^2 - (x-4)(3x+2)}{x(3x+2)}$ $= \dfrac{-2x^2 + 10x + 8}{3x^2 + 2x}$
Reciprocal: $\dfrac{1}{\left(\frac{P}{Q}\right)} = \dfrac{Q}{P}$	$\dfrac{1}{\left(\frac{2xy}{3x-1}\right)} = \dfrac{3x-1}{2xy}$
Quotient: $\dfrac{\left(\frac{P}{Q}\right)}{\left(\frac{R}{S}\right)} = \dfrac{P}{Q} \cdot \dfrac{S}{R} = \dfrac{PS}{QR}$	$\dfrac{\left(\frac{x}{x-1}\right)}{\left(\frac{y-1}{y}\right)} = \dfrac{xy}{(x-1)(y-1)} = \dfrac{xy}{xy - x - y + 1}$
Cancellation: $\dfrac{P\cancel{R}}{Q\cancel{R}} = \dfrac{P}{Q}$	$\dfrac{(x-1)(xy+4)}{(x^2y-8)(x-1)} = \dfrac{xy+4}{x^2y-8}$

Caution Cancellation of summands is *invalid*. For instance,

$$\frac{\cancel{x} + (2xy^2 - y)}{\cancel{x} + 4y} = \frac{(2xy^2 - y)}{4y} \qquad \text{✗ \textbf{WRONG!}} \qquad \text{Do } not \text{ cancel a summand.}$$

$$\frac{\cancel{x}(2xy^2 - y)}{4\cancel{x}y} = \frac{(2xy^2 - y)}{4y} \qquad \text{✔ \textbf{CORRECT}} \qquad \text{Do cancel a factor.}$$

Here are some examples that require several algebraic operations.

EXAMPLE 1 Simplifying Rational Expressions

a. $\dfrac{\left(\frac{1}{x+y} - \frac{1}{x}\right)}{y} = \dfrac{\left(\frac{x - (x+y)}{x(x+y)}\right)}{y} = \dfrac{\left(\frac{-y}{x(x+y)}\right)}{y} = \dfrac{-y}{xy(x+y)} = -\dfrac{1}{x(x+y)}$

b. $\dfrac{(x+1)(x+2)^2 - (x+1)^2(x+2)}{(x+2)^4} = \dfrac{(x+1)(x+2)[(x+2) - (x+1)]}{(x+2)^4}$

$$= \dfrac{(x+1)(x+2)(x+2-x-1)}{(x+2)^4} = \dfrac{(x+1)(x+2)}{(x+2)^4} = \dfrac{x+1}{(x+2)^3}$$

c. $\dfrac{2x\sqrt{x+1} - \frac{x^2}{\sqrt{x+1}}}{x+1} = \dfrac{\left(\frac{2x\left(\sqrt{x+1}\right)^2 - x^2}{\sqrt{x+1}}\right)}{x+1} = \dfrac{2x(x+1) - x^2}{(x+1)\sqrt{x+1}}$

$$= \dfrac{2x^2 + 2x - x^2}{(x+1)\sqrt{x+1}} = \dfrac{x^2 + 2x}{\sqrt{(x+1)^3}} = \dfrac{x(x+2)}{\sqrt{(x+1)^3}}$$

0.4 EXERCISES

Rewrite each expression in Exercises 1–16 as a single rational expression, simplified as much as possible.

1. $\dfrac{x-4}{x+1} \cdot \dfrac{2x+1}{x-1}$

2. $\dfrac{2x-3}{x-2} \cdot \dfrac{x+3}{x+1}$

3. $\dfrac{x-4}{x+1} + \dfrac{2x+1}{x-1}$

4. $\dfrac{2x-3}{x-2} + \dfrac{x+3}{x+1}$

5. $\dfrac{x^2}{x+1} - \dfrac{x-1}{x+1}$

6. $\dfrac{x^2-1}{x-2} - \dfrac{1}{x-1}$

7. $\dfrac{1}{\left(\frac{x}{x-1}\right)} + x - 1$

8. $\dfrac{2}{\left(\frac{x-2}{x^2}\right)} - \dfrac{1}{x-2}$

9. $\dfrac{1}{x}\left[\dfrac{x-3}{xy} + \dfrac{1}{y}\right]$

10. $\dfrac{y^2}{x}\left[\dfrac{2x-3}{y} + \dfrac{x}{y}\right]$

11. $\dfrac{(x+1)^2(x+2)^3 - (x+1)^3(x+2)^2}{(x+2)^6}$

12. $\dfrac{6x(x^2+1)^2(x^3+2)^3 - 9x^2(x^2+1)^3(x^3+2)^2}{(x^3+2)^6}$

13. $\dfrac{(x^2-1)\sqrt{x^2+1} - \frac{x^4}{\sqrt{x^2+1}}}{x^2+1}$

14. $\dfrac{x\sqrt{x^3-1} - \frac{3x^4}{\sqrt{x^3-1}}}{x^3-1}$

15. $\dfrac{\frac{1}{(x+y)^2} - \frac{1}{x^2}}{y}$

16. $\dfrac{\frac{1}{(x+y)^3} - \frac{1}{x^3}}{y}$

0.5 Solving Polynomial Equations

Polynomial Equation

A **polynomial equation** in one unknown is an equation that can be written in the form

$$ax^n + bx^{n-1} + \cdots + rx + s = 0$$

where $a, b, \ldots, r$, and s are constants.

We call the largest exponent of x appearing in a nonzero term of a polynomial the **degree** of that polynomial.

Quick Examples

1. $3x + 1 = 0$ has degree 1 because the largest power of x that occurs is $x = x^1$. Degree 1 equations are called **linear** equations.
2. $x^2 - x - 1 = 0$ has degree 2 because the largest power of x that occurs is x^2. Degree 2 equations are also called **quadratic equations**, or just **quadratics**.
3. $x^3 = 2x^2 + 1$ is a degree 3 polynomial (or **cubic**) in disguise. It can be rewritten as $x^3 - 2x^2 - 1 = 0$, which is in the standard form for a degree 3 equation.
4. $x^4 - x = 0$ has degree 4. It is called a **quartic**.

Now comes the question: How do we solve these equations for x? This question was asked by mathematicians as early as 1600 BC. Let's look at these equations one degree at a time.

Solution of Linear Equations

By definition, a linear equation can be written in the form

$$ax + b = 0. \qquad \text{\small a and b are fixed numbers with $a \neq 0$.}$$

Solving this is a nice mental exercise: Subtract b from both sides and then divide by a, getting $x = -b/a$. Don't bother memorizing this formula; just go ahead and solve linear equations as they arise. If you feel you need practice, see the exercises at the end of the section.

Solution of Quadratic Equations

By definition, a quadratic equation has the form

$$ax^2 + bx + c = 0. \qquad \text{\small a, b, and c are fixed numbers and $a \neq 0$.[1]}$$

---

[1] What happens if $a = 0$?

The solutions of this equation are also called the **roots** of $ax^2 + bx + c$. We're assuming that you saw quadratic equations somewhere in high school but may be a little hazy about the details of their solution. There are two ways of solving these equations—one works sometimes, and the other works every time.

Solving Quadratic Equations by Factoring (works sometimes)

If we can factor* a quadratic equation $ax^2 + bx + c = 0$, we can solve the equation by setting each factor equal to zero.

Quick Examples

1. $x^2 + 7x + 10 = 0$
   $(x + 5)(x + 2) = 0$ Factor the left-hand side.
   $x + 5 = 0$ or $x + 2 = 0$ If a product is zero, one or both factors is zero.
   Solutions: $x = -5$ and $x = -2$
2. $2x^2 - 5x - 12 = 0$
   $(2x + 3)(x - 4) = 0$ Factor the left-hand side.
   $2x + 3 = 0$ or $x - 4 = 0$
   Solutions: $x = -3/2$ and $x = 4$

---

*See the section on factoring for a review of how to factor quadratics.

Test for Factoring

The quadratic $ax^2 + bx + c$, with a, b, and c being integers (whole numbers), factors into an expression of the form $(rx + s)(tx + u)$ with r, s, t, and u integers precisely when the quantity $b^2 - 4ac$ is a perfect square. (That is, it is the square of an integer.) If this happens, we say that the quadratic **factors over the integers**.

Quick Examples

1. $x^2 + x + 1$ has $a = 1$, $b = 1$, and $c = 1$, so $b^2 - 4ac = -3$, which is not a perfect square. Therefore, this quadratic does not factor over the integers.
2. $2x^2 - 5x - 12$ has $a = 2$, $b = -5$, and $c = -12$, so $b^2 - 4ac = 121$. Because $121 = 11^2$, this quadratic does factor over the integers. (We factored it above.)

Solving Quadratic Equations with the Quadratic Formula (works every time)

The solutions of the general quadratic $ax^2 + bx + c = 0$ ($a \neq 0$) are given by

$$x = \frac{-b \pm \sqrt{b^2 - 4ac}}{2a}.$$

We call the quantity $\Delta = b^2 - 4ac$ the **discriminant** of the quadratic (Δ is the Greek letter delta), and we have the following general rules:

- If Δ is positive, there are two distinct real solutions.
- If Δ is zero, there is only one real solution: $x = -\dfrac{b}{2a}$. (Why?)
- If Δ is negative, there are no real solutions.

Quick Examples

1. $2x^2 - 5x - 12 = 0$ has $a = 2$, $b = -5$, and $c = -12$.

$$x = \frac{-b \pm \sqrt{b^2 - 4ac}}{2a} = \frac{5 \pm \sqrt{25 + 96}}{4} = \frac{5 \pm \sqrt{121}}{4} = \frac{5 \pm 11}{4}$$

$$= \frac{16}{4} \text{ or } -\frac{6}{4} = 4 \text{ or } -3/2 \qquad \text{Δ is positive in this example.}$$

2. $4x^2 = 12x - 9$ can be rewritten as $4x^2 - 12x + 9 = 0$, which has $a = 4$, $b = -12$, and $c = 9$.

$$x = \frac{-b \pm \sqrt{b^2 - 4ac}}{2a} = \frac{12 \pm \sqrt{144 - 144}}{8} = \frac{12 \pm 0}{8} = \frac{12}{8} = \frac{3}{2}$$

Δ is zero in this example.

3. $x^2 + 2x - 1 = 0$ has $a = 1$, $b = 2$, and $c = -1$.

$$x = \frac{-b \pm \sqrt{b^2 - 4ac}}{2a} = \frac{-2 \pm \sqrt{8}}{2} = \frac{-2 \pm 2\sqrt{2}}{2} = -1 \pm \sqrt{2}$$

The two solutions are $x = -1 + \sqrt{2} = 0.414\ldots$ and $x = -1 - \sqrt{2} = -2.414\ldots$ $\qquad$ Δ is positive in this example.

4. $x^2 + x + 1 = 0$ has $a = 1$, $b = 1$, and $c = 1$. Because $\Delta = -3$ is negative, there are no real solutions. $\qquad$ Δ is negative in this example.

Q: *This is all very useful, but where does the quadratic formula come from?*

A: To see where it comes from, we will solve a general quadratic equation using "brute force." Start with the general quadratic equation.

$$ax^2 + bx + c = 0.$$

First, divide out the nonzero number a to get

$$x^2 + \frac{bx}{a} + \frac{c}{a} = 0.$$

Now we **complete the square**: Add and subtract the quantity $\dfrac{b^2}{4a^2}$ to get

$$x^2 + \frac{bx}{a} + \frac{b^2}{4a^2} - \frac{b^2}{4a^2} + \frac{c}{a} = 0.$$

We do this to get the first three terms to factor as a perfect square:

$$\left(x + \frac{b}{2a}\right)^2 - \frac{b^2}{4a^2} + \frac{c}{a} = 0.$$

(Check this by multiplying out.) Adding $\dfrac{b^2}{4a^2} - \dfrac{c}{a}$ to both sides gives:

$$\left(x + \frac{b}{2a}\right)^2 = \frac{b^2}{4a^2} - \frac{c}{a} = \frac{b^2 - 4ac}{4a^2}.$$

Taking square roots gives

$$x + \frac{b}{2a} = \frac{\pm\sqrt{b^2 - 4ac}}{2a}.$$

Finally, adding $-\dfrac{b}{2a}$ to both sides yields the result:

$$x = -\frac{b}{2a} + \frac{\pm\sqrt{b^2 - 4ac}}{2a}$$

or

$$x = \frac{-b \pm \sqrt{b^2 - 4ac}}{2a}.$$

Solution of Cubic Equations

By definition, a cubic equation can be written in the form

$$ax^3 + bx^2 + cx + d = 0. \qquad \text{a, b, c, and d are fixed numbers and $a \neq 0$.}$$

Now we get into something of a bind. Although there is a perfectly respectable formula for the solutions, it is very complicated and involves the use of complex numbers rather heavily.[2] So we discuss instead a much simpler method that *sometimes* works nicely. Here is the method in a nutshell.

Solving Cubics by Finding One Factor

Start with a given cubic equation $ax^3 + bx^2 + cx + d = 0$.

Step 1 By trial and error, find one solution $x = s$. If a, b, c, and d are integers, the only possible *rational* solutions* are those of the form $s = \pm(\text{factor of } d)/(\text{factor of } a)$.

Step 2 It will now be possible to factor the cubic as

$$ax^3 + bx^2 + cx + d = (x - s)(ax^2 + ex + f) = 0$$

To find $ax^2 + ex + f$, divide the cubic by $x - s$, using long division.[†]

Step 3 The factored equation says that either $x - s = 0$ or $ax^2 + ex + f = 0$. We already know that s is a solution, and now we see that the other solutions are the roots of the quadratic. Note that this quadratic may or may not have any real solutions, as usual.

---

* There may be *irrational* solutions, however; for example, $x^3 - 2 = 0$ has the single solution $x = \sqrt[3]{2}$.

† Alternatively, use "synthetic division," a shortcut that would take us too far afield to describe.

---

[2] It was when this formula was discovered in the 16th century that complex numbers were first taken seriously. Although we would like to show you the formula, it is too large to fit in this footnote.

Quick Example

To solve the cubic $x^3 - x^2 + x - 1 = 0$, we first find a single solution. Here, $a = 1$ and $d = -1$. Because the only factors of ± 1 are ± 1, the only possible rational solutions are $x = \pm 1$. By substitution, we see that $x = 1$ is a solution. Thus, $(x - 1)$ is a factor. Dividing by $(x - 1)$ yields the quotient $(x^2 + 1)$. Thus,

$$x^3 - x^2 + x - 1 = (x - 1)(x^2 + 1) = 0$$

so that either $x - 1 = 0$ or $x^2 + 1 = 0$.

Because the discriminant of the quadratic $x^2 + 1$ is negative, we don't get any real solutions from $x^2 + 1 = 0$, so the only real solution is $x = 1$.

Possible Outcomes When Solving a Cubic Equation

If you consider all the cases, there are three possible outcomes when solving a cubic equation:

1. One real solution (as in the Quick Example above)
2. Two real solutions (try, for example, $x^3 + x^2 - x - 1 = 0$)
3. Three real solutions (see the next example)

EXAMPLE 1 Solving a Cubic

Solve the cubic $2x^3 - 3x^2 - 17x + 30 = 0$.

Solution   First we look for a single solution. Here, $a = 2$ and $d = 30$. The factors of a are ± 1 and ± 2, and the factors of d are ± 1, ± 2, ± 3, ± 5, ± 6, ± 10, ± 15, and ± 30. This gives us a large number of possible ratios: ± 1, ± 2, ± 3, ± 5, ± 6, ± 10, ± 15, ± 30, $\pm 1/2$, $\pm 3/2$, $\pm 5/2$, $\pm 15/2$. Undaunted, we first try $x = 1$ and $x = -1$, getting nowhere. So we move on to $x = 2$, and we hit the jackpot, because substituting $x = 2$ gives $16 - 12 - 34 + 30 = 0$. Thus, $(x - 2)$ is a factor. Dividing yields the quotient $2x^2 + x - 15$. Here is the calculation:

$$
\begin{array}{r}
2x^2 + x - 15 \\
x - 2 \,\overline{\smash{\big)}\, 2x^3 - 3x^2 - 17x + 30} \\
\underline{2x^3 - 4x^2} \\
x^2 - 17x \\
\underline{x^2 - 2x} \\
-15x + 30 \\
\underline{-15x + 30} \\
0.
\end{array}
$$

Thus,

$$2x^3 - 3x^2 - 17x + 30 = (x - 2)(2x^2 + x - 15) = 0.$$

Setting the factors equal to zero gives either $x - 2 = 0$ or $2x^2 + x - 15 = 0$. We could solve the quadratic using the quadratic formula, but, luckily, we notice that it factors as

$$2x^2 + x - 15 = (x + 3)(2x - 5).$$

Thus, the solutions are $x = 2$, $x = -3$ and $x = 5/2$.

Solution of Higher-Order Polynomial Equations

Logically speaking, our next step should be a discussion of quartics, then quintics (fifth degree equations), and so on forever. Well, we've got to stop somewhere, and cubics may be as good a place as any. On the other hand, since we've gotten so far, we ought to at least tell you what is known about higher order polynomials.

Quartics Just as in the case of cubics, there is a formula to find the solutions of quartics.[3]

Quintics and Beyond All good things must come to an end, we're afraid. It turns out that there is no "quintic formula." In other words, there is no single algebraic formula or collection of algebraic formulas that gives the solutions to all quintics. This question was settled by the Norwegian mathematician Niels Henrik Abel in 1824 after almost 300 years of controversy about this question. (In fact, several notable mathematicians had previously claimed to have devised formulas for solving the quintic, but these were all shot down by other mathematicians—this being one of the favorite pastimes of practitioners of our art.) The same negative answer applies to polynomial equations of degree 6 and higher. It's not that these equations don't have solutions; it's just that they can't be found using algebraic formulas.[4] However, there are certain special classes of polynomial equations that can be solved with algebraic methods. The way of identifying such equations was discovered around 1829 by the French mathematician Évariste Galois.[5]

---

[3] See, for example, *First Course in the Theory of Equations* by L. E. Dickson (New York: Wiley, 1922), or *Modern Algebra* by B. L. van der Waerden (New York: Frederick Ungar, 1953).

[4] What we mean by an "algebraic formula" is a formula in the coefficients using the operations of addition, subtraction, multiplication, division, and the taking of radicals. Mathematicians call the use of such formulas in solving polynomial equations "solution by radicals." If you were a math major, you would eventually go on to study this under the heading of Galois theory.

[5] Both Abel (1802–1829) and Galois (1811–1832) died young. Abel died of tuberculosis at the age of 26, while Galois was killed in a duel at the age of 20.

0.5 EXERCISES

Solve the equations in Exercises 1–12 for x (mentally, if possible).

1. $x + 1 = 0$

2. $x - 3 = 1$

3. $-x + 5 = 0$

4. $2x + 4 = 1$

5. $4x - 5 = 8$

6. $\frac{3}{4}x + 1 = 0$

7. $7x + 55 = 98$

8. $3x + 1 = x$

9. $x + 1 = 2x + 2$

10. $x + 1 = 3x + 1$

11. $ax + b = c$　$(a \neq 0)$

12. $x - 1 = cx + d$　$(c \neq 1)$

By any method, determine all possible real solutions of each equation in Exercises 13–30. Check your answers by substitution.

13. $2x^2 + 7x - 4 = 0$

14. $x^2 + x + 1 = 0$

15. $x^2 - x + 1 = 0$

16. $2x^2 - 4x + 3 = 0$

17. $2x^2 - 5 = 0$

18. $3x^2 - 1 = 0$

19. $-x^2 - 2x - 1 = 0$

20. $2x^2 - x - 3 = 0$

21. $\frac{1}{2}x^2 - x - \frac{3}{2} = 0$

22. $-\frac{1}{2}x^2 - \frac{1}{2}x + 1 = 0$

23. $x^2 - x = 1$

24. $16x^2 = -24x - 9$

25. $x = 2 - \frac{1}{x}$

26. $x + 4 = \frac{1}{x - 2}$

27. $x^4 - 10x^2 + 9 = 0$

28. $x^4 - 2x^2 + 1 = 0$

29. $x^4 + x^2 - 1 = 0$

30. $x^3 + 2x^2 + x = 0$

33. $x^3 + 4x^2 + 4x + 3 = 0$

34. $y^3 + 64 = 0$

35. $x^3 - 1 = 0$

36. $x^3 - 27 = 0$

37. $y^3 + 3y^2 + 3y + 2 = 0$

38. $y^3 - 2y^2 - 2y - 3 = 0$

39. $x^3 - x^2 - 5x + 5 = 0$

40. $x^3 - x^2 - 3x + 3 = 0$

41. $2x^6 - x^4 - 2x^2 + 1 = 0$

42. $3x^6 - x^4 - 12x^2 + 4 = 0$

43. $(x^2 + 3x + 2)(x^2 - 5x + 6) = 0$

44. $(x^2 - 4x + 4)^2(x^2 + 6x + 5)^3 = 0$

Find all possible real solutions of each equation in Exercises 31–44.

31. $x^3 + 6x^2 + 11x + 6 = 0$

32. $x^3 - 6x^2 + 12x - 8 = 0$

0.6 Solving Miscellaneous Equations

Equations often arise in calculus that are not polynomial equations of low degree. Many of these complicated-looking equations can be solved easily if you remember the following, which we used in the previous section:

Solving an Equation of the Form $P \cdot Q = 0$

If a product is equal to 0, then at least one of the factors must be 0. That is, if $P \cdot Q = 0$, then either $P = 0$ or $Q = 0$.

Quick Examples

1. $x^5 - 4x^3 = 0$

$x^3(x^2 - 4) = 0$ Factor the left-hand side.

Either $x^3 = 0$ or $x^2 - 4 = 0$ Either $P = 0$ or $Q = 0$.

$x = 0, 2$ or -2.   Solve the individual equations.

2. $(x^2 - 1)(x + 2) + (x^2 - 1)(x + 4) = 0$

$(x^2 - 1)[(x + 2) + (x + 4)] = 0$ Factor the left-hand side.

$(x^2 - 1)(2x + 6) = 0$

Either $x^2 - 1 = 0$ or $2x + 6 = 0$ Either $P = 0$ or $Q = 0$.

$x = -3, -1$, or 1.   Solve the individual equations.

EXAMPLE 1 Solving by Factoring

Solve $12x(x^2 - 4)^5(x^2 + 2)^6 + 12x(x^2 - 4)^6(x^2 + 2)^5 = 0$.

Solution

Again, we start by factoring the left-hand side:

$$12x(x^2 - 4)^5(x^2 + 2)^6 + 12x(x^2 - 4)^6(x^2 + 2)^5$$
$$= 12x(x^2 - 4)^5(x^2 + 2)^5[(x^2 + 2) + (x^2 - 4)]$$
$$= 12x(x^2 - 4)^5(x^2 + 2)^5(2x^2 - 2)$$
$$= 24x(x^2 - 4)^5(x^2 + 2)^5(x^2 - 1).$$

Setting this equal to 0, we get:

$$24x(x^2 - 4)^5(x^2 + 2)^5(x^2 - 1) = 0,$$

which means that at least one of the factors of this product must be zero. Now it certainly cannot be the 24, but it could be the x: $x = 0$ is one solution. It could also be that

$$(x^2 - 4)^5 = 0$$

or

$$x^2 - 4 = 0,$$

which has solutions $x = \pm 2$. Could it be that $(x^2 + 2)^5 = 0$? If so, then $x^2 + 2 = 0$, but this is impossible because $x^2 + 2 \geq 2$, no matter what x is. Finally, it could be that $x^2 - 1 = 0$, which has solutions $x = \pm 1$. This gives us five solutions to the original equation:

$$x = -2, -1, 0, 1, \text{ or } 2.$$

EXAMPLE 2 Solving by Factoring

Solve $(x^2 - 1)(x^2 - 4) = 10$.

Solution Watch out! You may be tempted to say that $x^2 - 1 = 10$ or $x^2 - 4 = 10$, but this does not follow. If two numbers multiply to give you 10, what must they be? There are lots of possibilities: 2 and 5, 1 and 10, $-500,000$ and -0.00002 are just a few. The fact that the left-hand side is factored is nearly useless to us if we want to solve this equation. What we will have to do is multiply out, bring the 10 over to the left, and hope that we can factor what we get. Here goes:

$$x^4 - 5x^2 + 4 = 10$$
$$x^4 - 5x^2 - 6 = 0$$
$$(x^2 - 6)(x^2 + 1) = 0$$

(Here we used a sometimes useful trick that we mentioned in Section 3: We treated x^2 like x and x^4 like x^2, so factoring $x^4 - 5x^2 - 6$ is essentially the same as factoring $x^2 - 5x - 6$.) *Now* we are allowed to say that one of the factors must be 0: $x^2 - 6 = 0$ has solutions $x = \pm\sqrt{6} = \pm 2.449\ldots$ and $x^2 + 1 = 0$ has no real solutions. Therefore, we get exactly two solutions, $x = \pm\sqrt{6} = \pm 2.449\ldots$.

To solve equations involving rational expressions, the following rule is very useful.

Solving an Equation of the Form *P/Q* = 0

If $\dfrac{P}{Q} = 0$, then $P = 0$.

How else could a fraction equal 0? If that is not convincing, multiply both sides by Q (which cannot be 0 if the quotient is defined).

Quick Example

$$\frac{(x+1)(x+2)^2 - (x+1)^2(x+2)}{(x+2)^4} = 0$$

$(x+1)(x+2)^2 - (x+1)^2(x+2) = 0$ If $\frac{P}{Q} = 0$, then $P = 0$.

$(x+1)(x+2)[(x+2) - (x+1)] = 0$ Factor.

$(x+1)(x+2)(1) = 0$

Either $x + 1 = 0$ or $x + 2 = 0$,

$x = -1$ or $x = -2$

$x = -1$ $x = -2$ does not make sense in the original equation: it makes the denominator 0. So it is not a solution and $x = -1$ is the only solution.

EXAMPLE 3 Solving a Rational Equation

Solve $1 - \dfrac{1}{x^2} = 0$.

Solution Write 1 as $\frac{1}{1}$, so that we now have a difference of two rational expressions:

$$\frac{1}{1} - \frac{1}{x^2} = 0.$$

To combine these we can put both over a common denominator of x^2, which gives

$$\frac{x^2 - 1}{x^2} = 0.$$

Now we can set the numerator, $x^2 - 1$, equal to zero. Thus,

$$x^2 - 1 = 0$$

so

$$(x-1)(x+1) = 0,$$

giving $x = \pm 1$.

➡ **Before we go on...** This equation could also have been solved by writing

$$1 = \frac{1}{x^2}$$

and then multiplying both sides by x^2. ∎

EXAMPLE 4 **Another Rational Equation**

Solve $\dfrac{2x - 1}{x} + \dfrac{3}{x - 2} = 0$.

Solution We *could* first perform the addition on the left and then set the top equal to 0, but here is another approach. Subtracting the second expression from both sides gives

$$\frac{2x - 1}{x} = \frac{-3}{x - 2}$$

Cross-multiplying [multiplying both sides by both denominators—that is, by $x(x - 2)$] now gives

$$(2x - 1)(x - 2) = -3x$$

so

$$2x^2 - 5x + 2 = -3x.$$

Adding $3x$ to both sides gives the quadratic equation

$$2x^2 - 2x + 1 = 0.$$

The discriminant is $(-2)^2 - 4 \cdot 2 \cdot 1 = -4 < 0$, so we conclude that there is no real solution.

➡ **Before we go on...** Notice that when we said that $(2x - 1)(x - 2) = -3x$, we were *not* allowed to conclude that $2x - 1 = -3x$ or $x - 2 = -3x$. ∎

EXAMPLE 5 **A Rational Equation with Radicals**

Solve $\dfrac{\left(2x\sqrt{x + 1} - \frac{x^2}{\sqrt{x+1}}\right)}{x + 1} = 0$.

Solution Setting the top equal to 0 gives

$$2x\sqrt{x + 1} - \frac{x^2}{\sqrt{x + 1}} = 0.$$

This still involves fractions. To get rid of the fractions, we could put everything over a common denominator ($\sqrt{x + 1}$) and then set the top equal to 0, or we could multiply the whole equation by that common denominator in the first place to clear fractions. If we do the second, we get

$$2x(x + 1) - x^2 = 0$$
$$2x^2 + 2x - x^2 = 0$$
$$x^2 + 2x = 0.$$

Factoring,

$$x(x + 2) = 0$$

so either $x = 0$ or $x + 2 = 0$, giving us $x = 0$ or $x = -2$. Again, one of these is not really a solution. The problem is that $x = -2$ cannot be substituted into $\sqrt{x + 1}$, because we would then have to take the square root of -1, and we are not allowing ourselves to do that. Therefore, $x = 0$ is the only solution.

0.6 EXERCISES

Solve the following equations:

1. $x^4 - 3x^3 = 0$

2. $x^6 - 9x^4 = 0$

3. $x^4 - 4x^2 = -4$

4. $x^4 - x^2 = 6$

5. $(x + 1)(x + 2) + (x + 1)(x + 3) = 0$

6. $(x + 1)(x + 2)^2 + (x + 1)^2(x + 2) = 0$

7. $(x^2 + 1)^5(x + 3)^4 + (x^2 + 1)^6(x + 3)^3 = 0$

8. $10x(x^2 + 1)^4(x^3 + 1)^5 - 10x^2(x^2 + 1)^5(x^3 + 1)^4 = 0$

9. $(x^3 + 1)\sqrt{x + 1} - (x^3 + 1)^2\sqrt{x + 1} = 0$

10. $(x^2 + 1)\sqrt{x + 1} - \sqrt{(x + 1)^3} = 0$

11. $\sqrt{(x + 1)^3} + \sqrt{(x + 1)^5} = 0$

12. $(x^2 + 1)\sqrt[3]{(x + 1)^4} - \sqrt[3]{(x + 1)^7} = 0$

13. $(x + 1)^2(2x + 3) - (x + 1)(2x + 3)^2 = 0$

14. $(x^2 - 1)^2(x + 2)^3 - (x^2 - 1)^3(x + 2)^2 = 0$

15. $\dfrac{(x + 1)^2(x + 2)^3 - (x + 1)^3(x + 2)^2}{(x + 2)^6} = 0$

16. $\dfrac{6x(x^2 + 1)^2(x^2 + 2)^4 - 8x(x^2 + 1)^3(x^2 + 2)^3}{(x^2 + 2)^8} = 0$

17. $\dfrac{2(x^2 - 1)\sqrt{x^2 + 1} - \dfrac{x^4}{\sqrt{x^2+1}}}{x^2 + 1} = 0$

18. $\dfrac{4x\sqrt{x^3 - 1} - \dfrac{3x^4}{\sqrt{x^3-1}}}{x^3 - 1} = 0$

19. $x - \dfrac{1}{x} = 0$

20. $1 - \dfrac{4}{x^2} = 0$

21. $\dfrac{1}{x} - \dfrac{9}{x^3} = 0$

22. $\dfrac{1}{x^2} - \dfrac{1}{x + 1} = 0$

23. $\dfrac{x - 4}{x + 1} - \dfrac{x}{x - 1} = 0$

24. $\dfrac{2x - 3}{x - 1} - \dfrac{2x + 3}{x + 1} = 0$

25. $\dfrac{x + 4}{x + 1} + \dfrac{x + 4}{3x} = 0$

26. $\dfrac{2x - 3}{x} - \dfrac{2x - 3}{x + 1} = 0$

0.7 The Coordinate Plane

Q: *Just what is the xy-plane?*

A: The *xy*-plane is an infinite flat surface with two perpendicular lines, usually labeled the **x-axis** and **y-axis**. These axes are calibrated as shown in Figure 2. (Notice also how the plane is divided into four **quadrants**.)

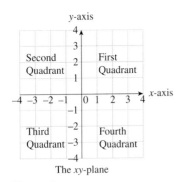

The *xy*-plane

Figure 2

Thus, the *xy*-plane is nothing more than a very large—in fact, infinitely large—flat surface. The purpose of the axes is to allow us to locate specific positions, or **points**, on the plane, with the use of **coordinates**. (If Captain Picard wants to have himself beamed to a specific location, he must supply its coordinates, or he's in trouble.)

Q: *So how do we use coordinates to locate points?*

A: The rule is simple. Each point in the plane has two coordinates, an **x-coordinate** and a **y-coordinate**. These can be determined in two ways:

1. The *x*-coordinate measures a point's distance to the right or left of the *y*-axis. It is positive if the point is to the right of the axis, negative if it is to the left of the axis, and 0 if it is on the axis. The *y*-coordinate measures a point's distance above or below the *x*-axis. It is positive if the point is above the axis, negative if it is below the axis, and 0 if it is on the axis. Briefly, the *x*-coordinate tells us the *horizontal* position (distance left or right), and the *y*-coordinate tells us the *vertical* position (height).

2. Given a point P, we get its x-coordinate by drawing a vertical line from P and seeing where it intersects the x-axis. Similarly, we get the y-coordinate by extending a horizontal line from P and seeing where it intersects the y-axis.

This way of assigning coordinates to points in the plane is often called the system of **Cartesian** coordinates, in honor of the mathematician and philosopher René Descartes (1596–1650), who was the first to use them extensively.

Here are a few examples to help you review coordinates.

EXAMPLE 1 **Coordinates of Points**

a. Find the coordinates of the indicated points. (See Figure 3. The grid lines are placed at intervals of one unit.)

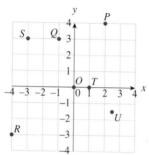

Figure 3

b. Locate the following points in the xy-plane.

$$A(2, 3), B(-4, 2), C(3, -2.5), D(0, -3), E(3.5, 0), F(-2.5, -1.5)$$

Solution

a. Taking them in alphabetical order, we start with the origin O. This point has height zero and is also zero units to the right of the y-axis, so its coordinates are $(0, 0)$. Turning to P, dropping a vertical line gives $x = 2$ and extending a horizontal line gives $y = 4$. Thus, P has coordinates $(2, 4)$. For practice, determine the coordinates of the remaining points, and check your work against the list that follows:

$$Q(-1, 3), R(-4, -3), S(-3, 3), T(1, 0), U(2.5, -1.5)$$

b. In order to locate the given points, we start at the origin $(0, 0)$, and proceed as follows. (See Figure 4.)

To locate A, we move 2 units to the right and 3 up, as shown.

To locate B, we move -4 units to the right (that is, 4 to the *left*) and 2 up, as shown.

To locate C, we move 3 units right and 2.5 down.

We locate the remaining points in a similar way.

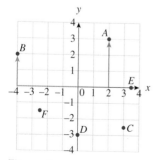

Figure 4

The Graph of an Equation

One of the more surprising developments of mathematics was the realization that equations, which are algebraic objects, can be represented by graphs, which are geometric objects. The kinds of equations that we have in mind are equations in x and y, such as

$$y = 4x - 1, \quad 2x^2 - y = 0, \quad y = 3x^2 + 1, \quad y = \sqrt{x - 1}.$$

The **graph** of an equation in the two variables x and y consists of all points (x, y) in the plane whose coordinates are solutions of the equation.

EXAMPLE 2 Graph of an Equation

Obtain the graph of the equation $y - x^2 = 0$.

Solution We can solve the equation for y to obtain $y = x^2$. Solutions can then be obtained by choosing values for x and then computing y by squaring the value of x, as shown in the following table:

x	-3	-2	-1	0	1	2	3
$y = x^2$	9	4	1	0	1	4	9

Plotting these points (x, y) gives the following picture (left side of Figure 5), suggesting the graph on the right in Figure 5.

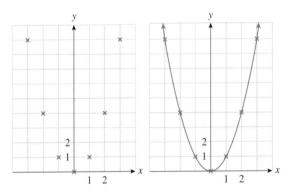

Figure 5

Distance

The distance between two points in the xy-plane can be expressed as a function of their coordinates, as follows:

Distance Formula

The distance between the points $P(x_1, y_1)$ and $Q(x_2, y_2)$ is

$$d = \sqrt{(x_2 - x_1)^2 + (y_2 - y_1)^2} = \sqrt{(\Delta x)^2 + (\Delta y)^2}.$$

Derivation

The distance d is shown in the figure below.

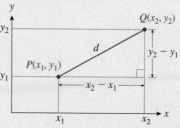

By the Pythagorean theorem applied to the right triangle shown, we get

$$d^2 = (x_2 - x_1)^2 + (y_2 - y_1)^2.$$

Taking square roots (d is a distance, so we take the positive square root), we get the distance formula. Notice that if we switch x_1 with x_2 or y_1 with y_2, we get the same result.

Quick Examples

1. The distance between the points $(3, -2)$ and $(-1, 1)$ is

$$d = \sqrt{(-1-3)^2 + (1+2)^2} = \sqrt{25} = 5.$$

2. The distance from (x, y) to the origin $(0, 0)$ is

$$d = \sqrt{(x-0)^2 + (y-0)^2} = \sqrt{x^2 + y^2}. \qquad \text{Distance to the origin}$$

The set of all points (x, y) whose distance from the origin $(0, 0)$ is a fixed quantity r is a circle centered at the origin with radius r. From the second Quick Example, we get the following equation for the circle centered at the origin with radius r:

$$\sqrt{x^2 + y^2} = r. \qquad \text{Distance from the origin} = r.$$

Squaring both sides gives the following equation:

Equation of the Circle of Radius r Centered at the Origin

$$x^2 + y^2 = r^2$$

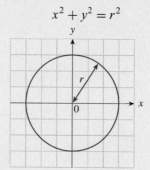

Quick Examples

1. The circle of radius 1 centered at the origin has equation $x^2 + y^2 = 1$.

2. The circle of radius 2 centered at the origin has equation $x^2 + y^2 = 4$.

0.7 EXERCISES

1. Referring to the following figure, determine the coordinates of the indicated points as accurately as you can.

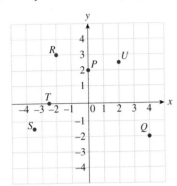

2. Referring to the following figure, determine the coordinates of the indicated points as accurately as you can.

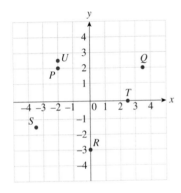

3. Graph the following points.

$P(4, 4)$, $Q(4, -4)$, $R(3, 0)$, $S(4, 0.5)$, $T(0.5, 2.5)$, $U(-2, 0)$, $V(-4, 4)$

4. Graph the following points.

$P(4, -2)$, $Q(2, -4)$, $R(1, -3)$, $S(-4, 2)$, $T(2, -1)$, $U(-2, 0)$, $V(-4, -4)$

Sketch the graphs of the equations in Exercises 5–12.

5. $x + y = 1$ 6. $y - x = -1$

7. $2y - x^2 = 1$ 8. $2y + \sqrt{x} = 1$

9. $xy = 4$ 10. $x^2 y = -1$

11. $xy = x^2 + 1$ 12. $xy = 2x^3 + 1$

In Exercises 13–16, find the distance between the given pairs of points.

13. $(1, -1)$ and $(2, -2)$ 14. $(1, 0)$ and $(6, 1)$

15. $(a, 0)$ and $(0, b)$ 16. (a, a) and (b, b)

17. Find the value of k such that $(1, k)$ is equidistant from $(0, 0)$ and $(2, 1)$.

18. Find the value of k such that (k, k) is equidistant from $(-1, 0)$ and $(0, 2)$.

19. Describe the set of points (x, y) such that $x^2 + y^2 = 9$.

20. Describe the set of points (x, y) such that $x^2 + y^2 = 0$.

1

Functions and Linear Models

Case Study Modeling Spending on Internet Advertising

You are the new director of *Impact Advertising Inc.'s* Internet division, which has enjoyed a steady 0.25% of the Internet advertising market. You have drawn up an ambitious proposal to expand your division in light of your anticipation that Internet advertising will continue to skyrocket. The VP in charge of Financial Affairs feels that current projections (based on a linear model) do not warrant the level of expansion you propose. **How can you persuade the VP that those projections do not fit the data convincingly?**

Jeff Titcomb/Photographer's Choice / Getty Images

Introduction

To analyze recent trends in spending on Internet advertising and to make reasonable projections, we need a mathematical model of this spending. Where do we start? To apply mathematics to real-world situations like this, we need a good understanding of basic mathematical concepts. Perhaps the most fundamental of these concepts is that of a function: a relationship that shows how one quantity depends on another. Functions may be described numerically and, often, algebraically. They can also be described graphically—a viewpoint that is extremely useful.

The simplest functions—the ones with the simplest formulas and the simplest graphs—are linear functions. Because of their simplicity, they are also among the most useful functions and can often be used to model real-world situations, at least over short periods of time. In discussing linear functions, we will meet the concepts of slope and rate of change, which are the starting point of the mathematics of change.

In the last section of this chapter, we discuss *simple linear regression*: construction of linear functions that best fit given collections of data. Regression is used extensively in applied mathematics, statistics, and quantitative methods in business. The inclusion of regression utilities in computer spreadsheets like Excel® makes this powerful mathematical tool readily available for anyone to use.

algebra Review

For this chapter, you should be familiar with real numbers and intervals. To review this material, see **Chapter 0.**

1.1 Functions from the Numerical and Algebraic Viewpoints

The following table gives the approximate number of Facebook users at various times since its establishment early in 2004.[1]

Year t (Since start of 2004)	0	0.5	1	1.5	2	2.5	3	3.5	4	4.5
Facebook Members n (Millions)	0	0.5	1	2	5.5	7	12	30	58	80

Let's write $n(0)$ for the number of members (in millions) at time $t = 0$, $n(0.5)$ for the number at time $t = 0.5$, and so on. (We read $n(0)$ as "n of 0.") Thus, $n(0) = 0$, $n(0.5) = 0.5, n(1) = 1, n(1.5) = 2, \ldots, n(4.5) = 80$. In general, we write $n(t)$ for the number of members (in millions) at time t. We call n a **function** of the variable t, meaning that for each value of t between 0 and 4.5, n gives us a single corresponding number $n(t)$ (the number of members at that time).

In general, we think of a function as a way of producing new objects from old ones. The functions we deal with in this text produce new numbers from old numbers. The numbers we have in mind are the *real* numbers, including not only positive and negative integers and fractions but also numbers like $\sqrt{2}$ or π. (See Appendix A for more on real numbers.) For this reason, the functions we use are called **real-valued functions of a real variable**. For example, the function n takes the year since the start of 2004 as input and returns the number of Facebook members as output (Figure 1).

Year
t

n

$n(t)$
Members

Figure 1

---

[1] Sources: www.facebook.com, www.insidehighered.com (Some data are interpolated.)

The variable t is called the **independent** variable, while n is called the **dependent variable** as its value depends on t. A function may be specified in several different ways. Here, we have specified the function n **numerically** by giving the values of the function for a number of values of the independent variable, as in the preceding table.

Q: *For which values of t does it make sense to ask for n(t)? In other words, for which years t is the function n defined?*

A: Because $n(t)$ refers to the number of members from the start of 2004 to the middle of 2008, $n(t)$ is defined when t is any number between 0 and 4.5, that is, when $0 \leq t \leq 4.5$. Using interval notation (see Chapter 0), we can say that $n(t)$ is defined when t is in the interval [0, 4.5].

The set of values of the independent variable for which a function is defined is called its **domain** and is a necessary part of the definition of the function. Notice that the preceding table gives the value of $n(t)$ at only some of the infinitely many possible values in the domain [0, 4.5]. The domain of a function is not always specified explicitly; if no domain is specified for the function f, we take the domain to be the largest set of numbers x for which $f(x)$ makes sense. This "largest possible domain" is sometimes called the **natural domain**.

The previous Facebook data can also be represented on a graph by plotting the given pairs of numbers $(t, n(t))$ in the xy-plane. (See Figure 2.) We have connected successive points by line segments. In general, the **graph** of a function f consists of all points $(x, f(x))$ in the plane with x in the domain of f.

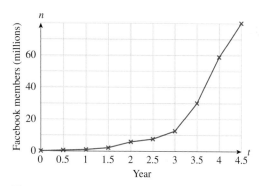

Figure 2

* **NOTE** In a graphically defined function, we can never know the y coordinates of points exactly; no matter how accurately a graph is drawn, we can obtain only *approximate* values of the coordinates of points. That is why we have been using the word *estimate* rather than *calculate* and why we say "$n(3) \approx 12$" rather than "$n(3) = 12$."

In Figure 2 we specified the function n **graphically** by using a graph to display its values. Suppose now that we had only the graph without the table of data. We could use the graph to find approximate values of n. For instance, to find $n(3)$ from the graph, we do the following:

1. Find the desired value of t at the bottom of the graph ($t = 3$ in this case).

2. Estimate the height (n-coordinate) of the corresponding point on the graph (around 12 in this case).

Thus, $n(3) \approx 12$ million members.*

In some cases we may be able to use an algebraic formula to calculate the function, and we say that the function is specified **algebraically**. These are not the only ways in which a function can be specified; for instance, it could also be specified **verbally**, as in "Let $n(t)$ be the number of Facebook members, in millions, t years since the start of 2004."* Notice that any function can be represented graphically by plotting the points $(x, f(x))$ for a number of values of x in its domain.

Here is a summary of the terms we have just introduced.

✳ **NOTE** Specifying a function verbally in this way is useful for understanding what the function is doing, but it gives no numerical information.

Functions

A **real-valued function f of a real-valued variable x** assigns to each real number x in a specified set of numbers, called the **domain** of f, a unique real number $f(x)$, read "f of x." The variable x is called the **independent variable**, and f is called the **dependent variable**. A function is usually specified **numerically** using a table of values, **graphically** using a graph, or **algebraically** using a formula. The **graph of a function** consists of all points $(x, f(x))$ in the plane with x in the domain of f.

Quick Examples

1. **A function specified numerically:** Take $f(t)$ to be the amount of freon (in tons) produced in developing countries in year t since 2000, represented by the following table:

t (Year Since 2000)	$f(t)$ (Tons of Freon 22)
0	100
2	140
4	200
6	270
8	400
10	590

Source: *New York Times*, February 23, 2007, p. C1.

The domain of f is [0, 10], the independent variable is t, the number of years since 2000, and the dependent variable is f, the number of tons of freon produced in a year in developing countries. Some values of f are:

$f(0) = 100$ 100 tons of freon were produced in developing countries in 2000.

$f(6) = 270$ 270 tons of freon were produced in developing countries in 2006.

$f(10) = 590$ 590 tons of freon were produced in developing countries in 2010.

Graph of f: Plotting the pairs $(t, f(t))$ gives the following graph:

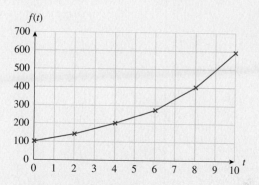

2. **A function specified graphically:** Take $p(t)$ to be the home price index as a percentage change from 2003 in year t, represented by the following graph:

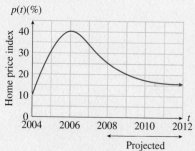

S&P/Case-Shiller Home Price Index. Source: Standard & Poors/Bloomberg Financial Markets/*New York Times*, September 29, 2007, p. C3. Projection is the authors'.*

The domain of p is [2004, 2012], the independent variable is the the year t, and the dependent variable is the percentage p above the 2003 value. Some values of p are:

$p(2004) \approx 10$ In 2004 the index was about 10% above the 2003 value.

$p(2006) \approx 40$ In 2006 the index was about 40% above the 2003 value.

$p(2009) \approx 20$ In 2009 the index was about 20% above the 2003 value.

3. **A function specified algebraically:** Let $f(x) = \frac{1}{x}$. The function f is specified algebraically. The independent variable is x and the dependent variable is f. The natural domain of f consists of all real numbers except zero because $f(x)$ makes sense for all values of x other than $x = 0$. Some specific values of f are

$$f(2) = \frac{1}{2} \qquad f(3) = \frac{1}{3} \qquad f(-1) = \frac{1}{-1} = -1$$

$f(0)$ is not defined because 0 is not in the domain of f.

✳ NOTE *added in July 2009:* Our projection turned out to be wrong: The index fell further than we anticipated and wound up negative! This error illustrates the pitfalls of *extrapolation*—a point we will discuss after Example 1.

4. The graph of a function: Let $f(x) = x^2$, with domain the set of all real numbers. To draw the graph of f, first choose some convenient values of x in the domain and compute the corresponding y-coordinates $f(x)$:

x	-3	-2	-1	0	1	2	3
$f(x) = x^2$	9	4	1	0	1	4	9

Plotting these points $(x, f(x))$ gives the picture on the left, suggesting the graph on the right.*

* NOTE If you plot more points, you will find that they lie on a smooth curve as shown. That is why we did not use line segments to connect the points.

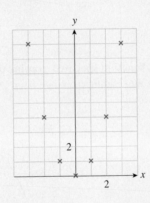

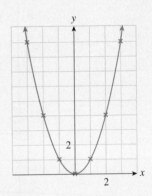

(This particular curve happens to be called a **parabola**, and its lowest point, at the origin, is called its **vertex**.)

EXAMPLE 1 iPod Sales

The number of iPods sold by Apple Inc. each year from 2004 through 2007 can be approximated by

$$f(x) = -x^2 + 20x + 3 \text{ million iPods} \qquad (0 \le x \le 3)$$

where x is the number of years since 2004.*

a. What is the domain of f? Compute $f(0)$, $f(1)$, $f(2)$, and $f(3)$. What do these answers tell you about iPod sales? Is $f(-1)$ defined?

b. Compute $f(a)$, $f(-b)$, and $f(a + h)$ assuming that the quantities a, $-b$, and $a + h$ are in the domain of f.

c. Sketch the graph of f. Does the shape of the curve suggest that iPod sales were accelerating or decelerating?

Solution

a. The domain of f is the set of numbers x with $0 \le x \le 3$—that is, the interval $[0, 3]$. If we substitute 0 for x in the formula for $f(x)$, we get

$$f(0) = -(0)^2 + 20(0) + 3 = 3 \qquad \text{In 2004 approximately 3 million iPods were sold.}$$

* Source for data: Apple quarterly earnings reports at www.apple.com/investor/.

Bartomeu Amengual/Index Stock Imagery / PhotoLibrary

so $f(0) = 3$. Similarly,

$$f(1) = -(1)^2 + 20(1) + 3 = 22 \qquad \text{In 2005 approximately 22 million iPods were sold.}$$
$$f(2) = -(2)^2 + 20(2) + 3 = 39 \qquad \text{In 2006 approximately 39 million iPods were sold.}$$
$$f(2) = -(3)^2 + 20(3) + 3 = 54 \qquad \text{In 2007 approximately 54 million iPods were sold.}$$

Because -1 is not in the domain of f, $f(-1)$ is not defined.

b. To find $f(a)$ we substitute a for x in the formula for $f(x)$ to get

$$f(a) = -a^2 + 20a + 3. \qquad \text{Substitute } a \text{ for } x.$$

Similarly,

$$f(-b) = -(-b)^2 + 20(-b) + 3 \qquad \text{Substitute } -b \text{ for } x.$$
$$= -b^2 - 20b + 3 \qquad (-b)^2 = b^2$$
$$f(a + h) = -(a + h)^2 + 20(a + h) + 3 \qquad \text{Substitute } (a + h) \text{ for } x.$$
$$= -(a^2 + 2ah + h^2) + 20a + 20h + 3 \qquad \text{Expand.}$$
$$= -a^2 - 2ah - h^2 + 20a + 20h + 3$$

Note how we placed parentheses around the quantities at which we evaluated the function. If we omitted any of these parentheses, we would likely get errors.

$$f(-b) = -(-b)^2 + 20(-b) + 3 \checkmark \qquad \text{NOT } -{-b^2} + 20(-b) + 3 \times$$
$$f(a + h) = -(a + h)^2 + 20(a + h) + 3 \checkmark \qquad \text{NOT } -a + h^2 + 20a + h + 3 \times$$

c. To draw the graph of f, we plot points of the form $(x, f(x))$ for several values of x in the domain of f. Let us use the values we computed in part (a):

x	0	1	2	3
$f(x) = -x^2 + 20x + 3$	3	22	39	54

Graphing these points gives the graph shown in Figure 3(a), suggesting the curve shown in Figure 3(b).

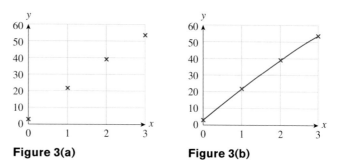

Figure 3(a)   **Figure 3(b)**

The graph is becoming less steep as we move from left to right, suggesting that iPod sales were decelerating slightly. (This concept will be made more precise in Chapter 4.)

---

using Technology

See the Technology Guide at the end of the chapter for detailed instructions on how to obtain the table of values and graph in Example 1 using a TI-83/84 Plus or Excel. Here is an outline:

TI-83/84 Plus
Table of values:
Y_1=-X^2+20X+3
2ND TABLE.
Graph: WINDOW;
Xmin = 0, Xmax = 3
ZOOM 0.
[More details on page 110.]

Excel
Table of values: Headings x and $f(x)$ in A1–B1; t-values 0, 1, 2, 3 in A2–A5.
=-1*A2^2+20*A2+3
in B2; copy down through B5.
Graph: Highlight A1 through B5 and insert a Scatter chart.
[More details on page 116.]

Web Site
www.AppliedCalc.org
Go to the Function Evaluator and Grapher under Online Utilities and enter
-x^2+20x+3
for y_1. To obtain a table of values, enter the x-values 0, 1, 2, 3 in the Evaluator box and press "Evaluate."
Graph: Set Xmin = 0 and Xmax = 3, and press "Plot Graphs."

➡ **Before we go on...** The following table compares the value of f in Example 1 with the actual sales figures:

Year x	0	1	2	3
$f(x) = -x^2 + 20x + 3$	3	22	39	54
Actual iPod Sales (millions)	4	22	39	52

The actual figures are stated here only for integer values of x; for instance, $x = 2$ gives the sales for the year ending December 2006. But what were, for instance, the sales for the year ending June 2007 ($x = 2.5$)? This is where our formula comes in handy: We can use the formula for f to **interpolate**; that is, to find sales at values of x between those that are stated:

$$f(2.5) = -(2.5)^2 + 20(2.5) + 3 = 46.75 \approx 47 \text{ million iPods}$$

We can also use the formula to **extrapolate**; that is, to predict sales at values of x *outside* the domain—say, for $x = 3.5$ (the year ending June 2008):

$$f(3.5) = -(3.5)^2 + 20(3.5) + 3 = 60.75 \approx 61 \text{ million iPods}$$

As a general rule, extrapolation is far less reliable than interpolation: Predicting the future from current data is difficult, especially given the vagaries of the marketplace.

We call the algebraic function f an **algebraic model** of iPod sales because it uses an algebraic formula to model—or mathematically represent (approximately)—the annual sales. The particular kind of algebraic model we used is called a **quadratic model**. (See the end of this section for the names of some commonly used models.) ■

Note Equation and Function Notation
Instead of using *function notation*

$$f(x) = -x^2 + 20x + 3 \qquad \text{Function notation}$$

we could use *equation notation*

$$y = -x^2 + 20x + 3 \qquad \text{Equation notation}$$

(the choice of the letter y is a convention) and we say that "y is a function of x." When we write a function in this form, the variable x is the independent variable and y is the dependent variable.

We could also write the above function as $f = -x^2 + 20x + 3$, in which case the dependent variable would be f. ■

Look again at the graph of the number of Facebook users in Figure 2. From year 0 through year 3, the membership appears to curve gently upward, but then increases quite dramatically from year 3 to year 4. This behavior can be modeled by using two different functions: one for the interval [0, 3] and another for the interval [3, 4]. (See Figure 4.)

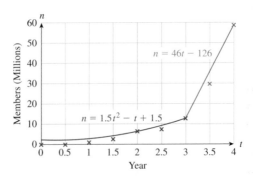

Figure 4

A function specified by two or more different formulas like this is called a **piecewise-defined function**.

using Technology

See the Technology Guide at the end of the chapter for detailed instructions on how to obtain the values and graph of n in Example 2 using a TI-83/84 Plus or Excel. Here is an outline:

TI-83/84 Plus
Table of values:
Y₁=(X ≤ 3)(1.5X²−X+1.5) +(X>3)(46X−126)
2ND TABLE .
Graph: WINDOW ; Xmin = 0, Xmax = 5; ZOOM 0 .
[More details on page 110.]

Excel
Table of values: Headings t and $n(t)$ in A1 and B1; t-values 0, 0.5, 1, 1.5, . . . , 5 in A2–A12.
=(A2<=3)*(1.5*A2^2− A2+1.5)+(A2>3)*(46* A2−126)
in B2; copy down through B12.
Graph: Highlight A1–B10; insert Scatter chart. [More details on page 117.]

Web Site
www.AppliedCalc.org
Go to the Function Evaluator and Grapher under Online Utilities, and enter
(x<=3)(1.5x^2−x+1.5) +(x>3)(46x−126)
for y_1. To obtain a table of values, enter the x-values 0, 0.5, 1, 1.5, . . . , 5 in the Evaluator box, and press "Evaluate."
Graph: Set Xmin = 0 and Xmax = 5, and press "Plot Graphs."

EXAMPLE 2 **A Piecewise-Defined Function: Facebook Membership**

The number $n(t)$ of Facebook members can be approximated by the following function of time t in years ($t = 0$ represents January 2004):*

$$n(t) = \begin{cases} 1.5t^2 - t + 1.5 & \text{if } 0 \le t \le 3 \\ 46t - 126 & \text{if } 3 < t \le 5 \end{cases} \quad \text{million members}$$

(Its graph is shown in Figure 4.) What was the approximate membership of Facebook in January 2005, January 2007, and June 2008? Sketch the graph of n by plotting several points.

Solution We evaluate the given function at the corresponding values of t:

Jan. 2005 ($t = 1$): $n(1) = 1.5(1)^2 - 1 + 1.5 = 2$ Use the first formula because $0 \le t \le 3$.

Jan. 2007 ($t = 3$): $n(3) = 1.5(3)^2 - 3 + 1.5 = 12$ Use the first formula because $0 \le t \le 3$.

June 2008 ($t = 4.5$): $n(4.5) = 46(4.5) - 126 = 81$ Use the second formula because $3 < t \le 5$.

Thus, the number of Facebook members was approximately 2 million in January 2005, 12 million in January 2007, and 81 million in June 2008.

To sketch the graph of n, we use a table of values of $n(t)$ (some of which we have already calculated above), plot the points, and connect them to sketch the graph:

t	0	1	2	3	3.5	4	4.5	5
$n(t)$	1.5	2	5.5	12	35	58	81	104

First formula   Second formula

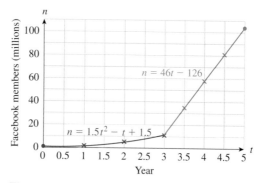

Figure 5

The graph (Figure 5) has the following features:

1. The first formula (the curve) is used for $0 \le t \le 3$.

2. The second formula (ascending line) is used for $3 < t \le 5$.

___
* Source for data: www.facebook.com/press.php.

3. The domain is $[0, 5]$, so the graph is cut off at $t = 0$ and $t = 5$.

4. The solid dots at the ends indicate the endpoints of the domain.

using Technology

See the Technology Guide at the end of the chapter for detailed instructions on how to obtain the values and graph of *f* in Example 3 using a TI-83/84 Plus or Excel. Here is an outline:

TI-83/84 Plus

Y₁=(X<-1)*(-1)+
(-1≤X)*(X≤1)*X+
(1<X)*(X²-1)
Table of values: 2ND TABLE.
Graph: WINDOW; Xmin = -4,
Xmax = 2; ZOOM 0.
[More details on page 111.]

Excel

Headings *x* and *f(x)* in A1 and B1; *x*-values -4, -3.9, . . . , 2 in A2–A62.
=(A2<-1)*(-1)+
(-1<=A2)*(A2<=1)*A2
+(1<A2)*(A2^2-1)
in B2; copy down through B62.
Graph: Highlight A1–B62; insert Scatter chart. [More details on page 117.]

Web Site

www.AppliedCalc.org
Go to the Function Evaluator and Grapher under Online Utilities and enter
=(x<-1)*(-1)+(-1<=x)*
(x<=1)*x+(1<x)*(x^2-1)
for y₁. To obtain a table of values, enter the *x*-values 0, 0.5, 1, 1.5, . . . , 3 in the Evaluator box and press "Evaluate."
Graph: Set Xmin = -4 and Xmax = 2, and press "Plot Graphs."

EXAMPLE 3 More Complicated Piecewise-Defined Functions

Let f be the function specified by

$$f(x) = \begin{cases} -1 & \text{if } -4 \le x < -1 \\ x & \text{if } -1 \le x \le 1 \\ x^2 - 1 & \text{if } 1 < x \le 2 \end{cases}.$$

a. What is the domain of f? Find $f(-2)$, $f(-1)$, $f(0)$, $f(1)$, and $f(2)$.

b. Sketch the graph of f.

Solution

a. The domain of f is $[-4, 2]$, because $f(x)$ is specified only when $-4 \le x \le 2$.

$f(-2) = -1$	We used the first formula because $-4 \le x < -1$.
$f(-1) = -1$	We used the second formula because $-1 \le x \le 1$.
$f(0) = 0$	We used the second formula because $-1 \le x \le 1$.
$f(1) = 1$	We used the second formula because $-1 \le x \le 1$.
$f(2) = 2^2 - 1 = 3$	We used the third formula because $1 < x \le 2$.

b. To sketch the graph by hand, we first sketch the three graphs $y = -1$, $y = x$, and $y = x^2 - 1$, and then use the appropriate portion of each (Figure 6).

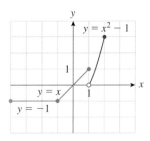

Figure 6

Note that solid dots indicate points on the graph, whereas the open dots indicate points *not* on the graph. For example, when $x = 1$, the inequalities in the formula tell us that we are to use the middle formula (x) rather than the bottom one $(x^2 - 1)$. Thus, $f(1) = 1$, not 0, so we place a solid dot at $(1, 1)$ and an open dot at $(1, 0)$.

Vertical Line Test

Every point in the graph of a function has the form $(x, f(x))$ for some x in the domain of f. Because f assigns a *single* value $f(x)$ to each value of x in the domain, it follows that, in the graph of f, there should be only one y corresponding to any such value of x—namely, $y = f(x)$. In other words, *the graph of a function cannot contain two or more points with the same x-coordinate—that is, two or more points on the same vertical line.* On the other hand, a vertical line at a value of x not in the domain will not contain any points in the graph. This gives us the following rule.

Vertical-Line Test

For a graph to be the graph of a function, every vertical line must intersect the graph in *at most* one point.

Quick Examples

As illustrated below, only graph B passes the vertical line test, so only graph B is the graph of a function.

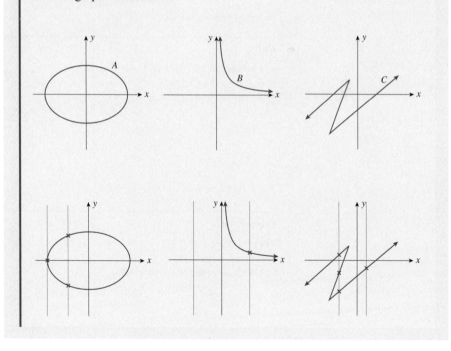

Table 1 lists some common types of functions that are often used to model real world situations.

Table 1 A Compendium of Functions and Their Graphs

Type of Function	*Examples*
Linear $f(x) = mx + b$ m, b constant Graphs of linear functions are straight lines. The quantity m is the **slope** of the line; the quantity b is the **y-intercept** of the line. [See Section 1.3.] Technology formulas:	$y = x$ $y = -2x + 2$ X -2*x+2
Quadratic $f(x) = ax^2 + bx + c$ a, b, c constant $(a \neq 0)$ Graphs of quadratic functions are called **parabolas**. [See Section 2.1.] Technology formulas:	$y = x^2$ $y = -2x^2 + 2x + 4$ x^2 -2*x^2+2*x+4
Cubic $f(x) = ax^3 + bx^2 + cx + d$ a, b, c, d constant $(a \neq 0)$ Technology formulas:	$y = x^3$ $y = -x^3 + 3x^2 + 1$ x^3 -x^3+3*x^2+1
Polynomial $f(x) = ax^n + bx^{n-1} + \ldots + rx + s$ $a, b, \ldots, r, s$ constant (includes all of the above functions) Technology formula:	All the above, and $f(x) = x^6 - 2x^5 - 2x^4 + 4x^2$ x^6-2x^5-2x^4+4x^2

Table 1 (*Continued*)

Type of Function	Examples
Exponential $f(x) = Ab^x$ A, b constant $(b > 0 \text{ and } b \neq 1)$ The y-coordinate is multiplied by b every time x increases by 1.	$y = 2^x$ $y = 4(0.5)^x$
	y is doubled every time x increases by 1. *y is halved every time x increases by 1.*
Technology formulas:	$2\texttt{^}x$ $4\texttt{*}0.5\texttt{^}x$
Rational $f(x) = \dfrac{P(x)}{Q(x)};$ $P(x)$ and $Q(x)$ polynomials The graph of $y = 1/x$ is a **hyperbola**. The domain excludes zero because $1/0$ is not defined.	$y = \dfrac{1}{x}$ $y = \dfrac{x}{x - 1}$
Technology formulas:	$1/x$ $x/(x\texttt{-}1)$
Absolute value For x positive or zero, the graph of $y = |x|$ is the same as that of $y = x$. For x negative or zero, it is the same as that of $y = -x$.	$y = |x|$ $y = |2x + 2|$
Technology formulas:	$\texttt{abs(x)}$ $\texttt{abs(2*x+2)}$
Square Root The domain of $y = \sqrt{x}$ must be restricted to the nonnegative numbers, because the square root of a negative number is not real. Its graph is the top half of a horizontally oriented parabola.	$y = \sqrt{x}$ $y = \sqrt{4x - 2}$
Technology formulas:	$\texttt{x\texttt{^}0.5}$ or $\sqrt{}\texttt{(x)}$ $\texttt{(4*x-2)\texttt{^}0.5}$ or $\sqrt{}\texttt{(4*x-2)}$

Go to the Web site and follow the path

Online Text

→ New Functions from Old: Scaled and Shifted Functions

where you will find complete online interactive text, examples, and exercises on scaling and translating the graph of a function by changing the formula.

Functions and models other than linear ones are called **nonlinear**.

1.1 EXERCISES

 more advanced   ◆ challenging
 indicates exercises that should be solved using technology

In Exercises 1–4, evaluate or estimate each expression based on the following table. HINT [See Quick Example 1 on page 42.]

x	−3	−2	−1	0	1	2	3
$f(x)$	1	2	4	2	1	0.5	0.25

1. a. $f(0)$ **b.** $f(2)$ **2. a.** $f(-1)$ **b.** $f(1)$
3. a. $f(2) - f(-2)$ **b.** $f(-1)f(-2)$ **c.** $-2f(-1)$
4. a. $f(1) - f(-1)$ **b.** $f(1)f(-2)$ **c.** $3f(-2)$

In Exercises 5–8, use the graph of the function f to find approximations of the given values. HINT [See Example 1.]

5. ◆

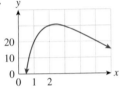

a. $f(1)$ **b.** $f(2)$
c. $f(3)$ **d.** $f(5)$
e. $f(3) - f(2)$

6.

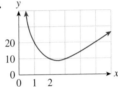

a. $f(1)$ **b.** $f(2)$
c. $f(3)$ **d.** $f(5)$
e. $f(3) - f(2)$

7.

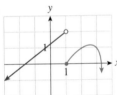

a. $f(-3)$ **b.** $f(0)$
c. $f(1)$ **d.** $f(2)$
e. $\dfrac{f(3) - f(2)}{3 - 2}$

8.

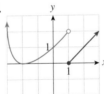

a. $f(-2)$ **b.** $f(0)$
c. $f(1)$ **d.** $f(3)$
e. $\dfrac{f(3) - f(1)}{3 - 1}$

In Exercises 9–12, say whether or not $f(x)$ is defined for the given values of x. If it is defined, give its value. HINT [See Quick Example 3 page 43.]

9. $f(x) = x - \dfrac{1}{x^2}$, with domain $(0, +\infty)$
  a. $x = 4$ **b.** $x = 0$ **c.** $x = -1$

10. $f(x) = \dfrac{2}{x} - x^2$, with domain $[2, +\infty)$
  a. $x = 4$ **b.** $x = 0$ **c.** $x = 1$

11. $f(x) = \sqrt{x + 10}$, with domain $[-10, 0)$
  a. $x = 0$ **b.** $x = 9$ **c.** $x = -10$

12. $f(x) = \sqrt{9 - x^2}$, with domain $(-3, 3)$
  a. $x = 0$ **b.** $x = 3$ **c.** $x = -3$

13. Given $f(x) = 4x - 3$, find **a.** $f(-1)$ **b.** $f(0)$
  c. $f(1)$ **d.** $f(y)$ **e.** $f(a + b)$ HINT [See Example 1.]

14. Given $f(x) = -3x + 4$, find **a.** $f(-1)$ **b.** $f(0)$
  c. $f(1)$ **d.** $f(y)$ **e.** $f(a + b)$

15. Given $f(x) = x^2 + 2x + 3$, find **a.** $f(0)$ **b.** $f(1)$
  c. $f(-1)$ **d.** $f(-3)$ **e.** $f(a)$ **f.** $f(x + h)$
  HINT [See Example 1.]

16. Given $g(x) = 2x^2 - x + 1$, find **a.** $g(0)$ **b.** $g(-1)$
  c. $g(r)$ **d.** $g(x + h)$

17. Given $g(s) = s^2 + \dfrac{1}{s}$, find **a.** $g(1)$ **b.** $g(-1)$
  c. $g(4)$ **d.** $g(x)$ **e.** $g(s + h)$ **f.** $g(s + h) - g(s)$

18. Given $h(r) = \dfrac{1}{r + 4}$, find **a.** $h(0)$ **b.** $h(-3)$
  c. $h(-5)$ **d.** $h(x^2)$ **e.** $h(x^2 + 1)$ **f.** $h(x^2) + 1$

In Exercises 19–24, graph the given functions. Give the technology formula and use technology to check your graph. We suggest that you become familiar with these graphs in addition to those in Table 2. HINT [See Quick Example 4 on page 44.]

19. $f(x) = -x^3$ (domain $(-\infty, +\infty)$)
20. $f(x) = x^3$ (domain $[0, +\infty)$)
21. $f(x) = x^4$ (domain $(-\infty, +\infty)$)
22. $f(x) = \sqrt[3]{x}$ (domain $(-\infty, +\infty)$)
23. $f(x) = \dfrac{1}{x^2}$ $(x \neq 0)$ **24.** $f(x) = x + \dfrac{1}{x}$ $(x \neq 0)$

In Exercises 25 and 26, match the functions to the graphs. Using technology to draw the graphs is suggested, but not required.

25. **a.** $f(x) = x$ $(-1 \leq x \leq 1)$
  b. $f(x) = -x$ $(-1 \leq x \leq 1)$
  c. $f(x) = \sqrt{x}$ $(0 < x < 4)$
  d. $f(x) = x + \dfrac{1}{x} - 2$ $(0 < x < 4)$
  e. $f(x) = |x|$ $(-1 \leq x \leq 1)$
  f. $f(x) = x - 1$ $(-1 \leq x \leq 1)$

(I)

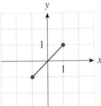

(II)

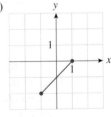

(III)

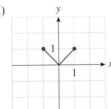

(IV)

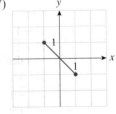

(V)

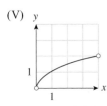

(VI)

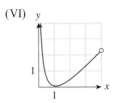

26. ▣ **a.** $f(x) = -x + 4$ $(0 < x \le 4)$

b. $f(x) = 2 - |x|$ $(-2 < x \le 2)$

c. $f(x) = \sqrt{x + 2}$ $(-2 < x \le 2)$

d. $f(x) = -x^2 + 2$ $(-2 < x \le 2)$

e. $f(x) = \dfrac{1}{x} - 1$ $(0 < x \le 4)$

f. $f(x) = x^2 - 1$ $(-2 < x \le 2)$

(I)

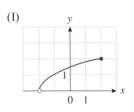

(II)

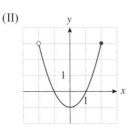

(III)

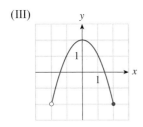

(IV)

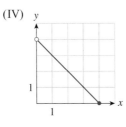

(V)

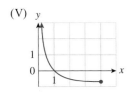

(VI)

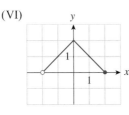

▣ *In Exercises 27–30, first give the technology formula for the given function and then use technology to evaluate the function for the given values of x (when defined there).*

27. ▣ $f(x) = 0.1x^2 - 4x + 5$; $x = 0, 1, \ldots, 10$

28. ▣ $g(x) = 0.4x^2 - 6x - 0.1$; $x = -5, -4, \ldots, 4, 5$

29. ▣ $h(x) = \dfrac{x^2 - 1}{x^2 + 1}$; $x = 0.5, 1.5, 2.5, \ldots, 10.5$ (Round all answers to four decimal places.)

30. ▣ $r(x) = \dfrac{2x^2 + 1}{2x^2 - 1}$; $x = -1, 0, 1, \ldots, 9$ (Round all answers to four decimal places.)

In Exercises 31–36, sketch the graph of the given function, evaluate the given expressions, and then use technology to duplicate the graphs. Give the technology formula. HINT [See Example 2.]

31. $f(x) = \begin{cases} x & \text{if } -4 \le x < 0 \\ 2 & \text{if } 0 \le x \le 4 \end{cases}$

  a. $f(-1)$ **b.** $f(0)$ **c.** $f(1)$

32. $f(x) = \begin{cases} -1 & \text{if } -4 \le x \le 0 \\ x & \text{if } 0 < x \le 4 \end{cases}$

  a. $f(-1)$ **b.** $f(0)$ **c.** $f(1)$

33. $f(x) = \begin{cases} x^2 & \text{if } -2 < x \le 0 \\ 1/x & \text{if } 0 < x \le 4 \end{cases}$

  a. $f(-1)$ **b.** $f(0)$ **c.** $f(1)$

34. $f(x) = \begin{cases} -x^2 & \text{if } -2 < x \le 0 \\ \sqrt{x} & \text{if } 0 < x < 4 \end{cases}$

  a. $f(-1)$ **b.** $f(0)$ **c.** $f(1)$

35. $f(x) = \begin{cases} x & \text{if } -1 < x \le 0 \\ x + 1 & \text{if } 0 < x \le 2 \\ x & \text{if } 2 < x \le 4 \end{cases}$

  a. $f(0)$ **b.** $f(1)$ **c.** $f(2)$ **d.** $f(3)$ HINT [See Example 3.]

36. $f(x) = \begin{cases} -x & \text{if } -1 < x \le 0 \\ x - 2 & \text{if } 0 \le x \le 2 \\ -x & \text{if } 2 < x \le 4 \end{cases}$

  a. $f(0)$ **b.** $f(1)$ **c.** $f(2)$ **d.** $f(3)$

*In Exercises 37–40, find and simplify **(a)** $f(x + h) - f(x)$*

(b) $\dfrac{f(x + h) - f(x)}{h}$

37. ▼ $f(x) = x^2$ **38.** ▼ $f(x) = 3x - 1$

39. ▼ $f(x) = 2 - x^2$ **40.** ▼ $f(x) = x^2 + x$

APPLICATIONS

41. *Oil Imports from Mexico* The following table shows U.S. oil imports from Mexico, for 2001–2006 ($t = 1$ represents 2001):[2]

t (year since 2000)	1	2	3	4	5	6
I (million gallons/day)	1.35	1.5	1.55	1.6	1.5	1.5

  a. Find $I(3)$, $I(5)$, and $I(6)$. Interpret your answers.

  b. What is the domain of I?

  c. Represent I graphically, and use your graph to estimate $I(4.5)$. Interpret your answer. HINT [See Quick Example 1 on page 42.]

[2] Figures are approximate. Source: Energy Information Administration: Pemex/*New York Times*, March 9, 2007, p. C4.

42. Oil Production in Mexico The following table shows oil production by **Pemex**, Mexico's national oil company, for 2001–2006 ($t = 1$ represents 2001):[3]

t (year since 2000)	1	2	3	4	5	6
P (million gallons/day)	3.1	3.2	3.4	3.4	3.4	3.3

a. Find $P(3)$, $P(4)$, and $P(6)$. Interpret your answers.
b. What is the domain of P?
c. Represent P graphically, and use your graph to estimate $P(1.5)$. Interpret your answer.

Housing Starts *Exercises 43–46 refer to the following graph, which shows the number f(t) of housing starts in the U.S. each year from 2000 through 2007 (t = 0 represents 2000, and f(t) is the number of housing starts in year t in thousands of units).*[4]

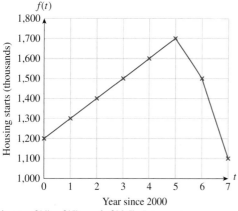

43. Estimate $f(4)$, $f(5)$, and $f(6.5)$. Interpret your answers.
44. Estimate $f(3)$, $f(6)$, and $f(5.5)$. Interpret your answers.
45. Which has the larger magnitude: $f(5) - f(0)$ or $f(7) - f(5)$? Interpret the answer.
46. Which has the larger magnitude: $f(7) - f(6)$ or $f(5) - f(0)$? Interpret the answer.
47. **Trade with China** The value of U.S. trade with China from 1994 through 2004 can be approximated by
$$C(t) = 3t^2 - 7t + 50 \text{ billion dollars}$$
(t is time in years since 1994).[5]
a. Find an appropriate domain of C. Is $t \geq 0$ an appropriate domain? Why or why not?
b. Compute $C(10)$. What does the answer say about trade with China?

48. Scientific Research The number of research articles in *Physical Review* that were written by researchers in the United States from 1983 through 2003 can be approximated by
$$A(t) = -0.01\,t^2 + 0.24t + 3.4 \text{ hundred articles}$$
(t is time in years since 1983).[6]
a. Find an appropriate domain of A. Is $t \leq 20$ an appropriate domain? Why or why not?
b. Compute $A(10)$. What does the answer say about the number of research articles?

49. Satellite Radio Losses The following graph shows the approximate annual loss $L(t)$ of **Sirius Satellite Radio** for the perod 2001–2006 ($t = 1$ represents the start of 2001).[7]

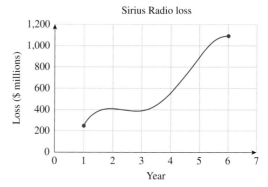

a. What is the domain of L?
b. Estimate $L(2)$, $L(5)$, and $L(6)$. Interpret your answers.
c. At approximately which value of t is $L(t)$ increasing most rapidly? Interpret the result.

50. Satellite Radio Losses The following graph shows the approximate annual loss $L(t)$ of **XM Satellite Radio** for the period 2001–2006 ($t = 1$ represents the start of 2001).

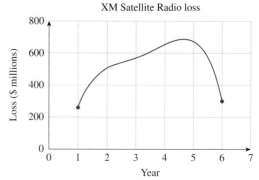

a. What is the domain of L?
b. Estimate $L(2)$, $L(3.5)$, and $L(6)$. Interpret your answers.
c. At approximately which value of t is $L(t)$ increasing most rapidly? Interpret the result.

[3] Figures are approximate. Source: Energy Information Administration: Pemex/*New York Times*, March 9, 2007, p. C4.

[4] Figures are rounded. Source: www.census.gov (2007).

[5] Based on a regression by the authors. Source for data: U.S. Census Bureau/*New York Times*, September 23, 2004, p. C1.

[6] Based on a regression by the authors. Source for data: The American Physical Society/*New York Times*, May 3, 2003, p. A1.

[7] Source: Bloomberg Financial Markets, Sirius Satellite Radio/*New York Times*, February 20, 2008, p. C2.

51. *Processor Speeds* The processor speed, in megahertz, of Intel processors could be approximated by the following function of time t in years since the start of 1995:[8]

$$P(t) = \begin{cases} 75t + 200 & \text{if } 0 \leq t \leq 4 \\ 600t - 1900 & \text{if } 4 < t \leq 9 \end{cases}$$

a. Evaluate $P(0)$, $P(4)$, and $P(5)$ and interpret the results.
b. Sketch the graph of P and use your graph to estimate when processor speeds first reached 2.0 gigahertz (1 gigahertz = 1,000 megahertz).
c. ⊞ Use technology to generate a table of values for $P(t)$ with $t = 0, 1, \ldots, 9$.

52. *Leading Economic Indicators* The value of the Conference Board Index of 10 economic indicators in the United States could be approximated by the following function of time t in months since the end of December 2002:[9]

$$E(t) = \begin{cases} 0.4t + 110 & \text{if } 6 \leq t \leq 15 \\ -0.2t + 119 & \text{if } 15 < t \leq 20 \end{cases}$$

a. Estimate $E(10)$, $E(15)$, and $E(20)$ and interpret the results.
b. Sketch the graph of E and use your graph to estimate when the index first reached 115.
c. ⊞ Use technology to generate a table of values for $E(t)$ with $t = 6, 7, \ldots, 20$.

53. ▼ *Income Taxes* The U.S. Federal income tax is a function of taxable income. Write T for the tax owed on a taxable income of I dollars. For tax year 2007, the function T for a single taxpayer was specified as follows:

If your taxable income was			of the amount
Over—	**But not over—**	**Your tax is**	**over—**
$0	7,825	.... 10%	$0
7,825	31,850	**$782.50 + 15%**	$7,825
31,850	77,100	**4,386.25 + 25%**	$31,850
77,100	160,850	**15,698.75 + 28%**	$77,100
160,850	349,700	**39,148.75 + 33%**	$160,850
349,700	....	**101,469.25 + 35%**	$349,700

What was the tax owed by a single taxpayer on a taxable income of $26,000? On a taxable income of $65,000?

54. ▼ *Income Taxes* The income tax function T in Exercise 53 can also be written in the following form:

$$T(I) = \begin{cases} 0.10I & \text{if } 0 < I \leq 7,825 \\ 782.50 + 0.15(I - 7,825) & \text{if } 7,825 < I \leq 31,850 \\ 4,386.25 + 0.25(I - 31,850) & \text{if } 31,850 < I \leq 77,100 \\ 15,698.75 + 0.28(I - 77,100) & \text{if } 77,100 < I \leq 160,850 \\ 39,148.75 + 0.33(I - 160,850) & \text{if } 160,850 < I \leq 349,700 \\ 101,469.25 + 0.35(I - 349,700) & \text{if } I > 349,700 \end{cases}$$

What was the tax owed by a single taxpayer on a taxable income of $25,000? On a taxable income of $125,000?

55. ⊞ ▼ *Acquisition of Language* The percentage $p(t)$ of children who can speak in at least single words by the age of t months can be approximated by the equation[10]

$$p(t) = 100\left(1 - \frac{12{,}200}{t^{4.48}}\right) \quad (t \geq 8.5)$$

a. Give a technology formula for p.
b. Graph p for $8.5 \leq t \leq 20$ and $0 \leq p \leq 100$.
c. Create a table of values of p for $t = 9, 10, \ldots, 20$ (rounding answers to one decimal place).
d. What percentage of children can speak in at least single words by the age of 12 months?
e. By what age are 90% or more children speaking in at least single words?

56. ⊞ ▼ *Acquisition of Language* The percentage $p(t)$ of children who can speak in sentences of five or more words by the age of t months can be approximated by the equation[11]

$$p(t) = 100\left(1 - \frac{5.27 \times 10^{17}}{t^{12}}\right) \quad (t \geq 30)$$

a. Give a technology formula for p.
b. Graph p for $30 \leq t \leq 45$ and $0 \leq p \leq 100$.
c. Create a table of values of p for $t = 30, 31, \ldots, 40$ (rounding answers to one decimal place).
d. What percentage of children can speak in sentences of five or more words by the age of 36 months?
e. By what age are 75% or more children speaking in sentences of five or more words?

COMMUNICATION AND REASONING EXERCISES

57. If the market price m of gold varies with time t, then the independent variable is ____ and the dependent variable is ____.

58. Complete the following sentence: If weekly profit P is specified as a function of selling price s, then the independent variable is ____ and the dependent variable is ____.

59. Complete the following: The function notation for the equation $y = 4x^2 - 2$ is ____.

---

[8] Source: Sandpile.org/*New York Times*, May 17, 2004, p. C1.
[9] Source: The Conference Board/*New York Times*, November 19, 2004, p. C7.

[10] The model is the authors' and is based on data presented in the article *The Emergence of Intelligence* by William H. Calvin, *Scientific American*, October, 1994, pp. 101–107.
[11] Ibid.

60. Complete the following: The equation notation for $C(t) = -0.34t^2 + 0.1t$ is ____.

61. True or false? Every graphically specified function can also be specified numerically. Explain.

62. True or false? Every algebraically specified function can also be specified graphically. Explain.

63. True or false? Every numerically specified function with domain [0, 10] can also be specified algebraically. Explain.

64. True or false? Every graphically specified function can also be specified algebraically. Explain.

65. ▼ True or false? Every function can be specified numerically.

66. ▼ Which supplies more information about a situation: a numerical model or an algebraic model?

67. ▼ Why is the following assertion false? "If $f(x) = x^2 - 1$, then $f(x + h) = x^2 + h - 1$."

68. ▼ Why is the following assertion false? "If $f(2) = 2$ and $f(4) = 4$, then $f(3) = 3$."

69. How do the graphs of two functions differ if they are specified by the same formula but have different domains?

70. How do the graphs of two functions $f(x)$ and $g(x)$ differ if $g(x) = f(x) + 10$? (Try an example.)

71. ▼ How do the graphs of two functions $f(x)$ and $g(x)$ differ if $g(x) = f(x - 5)$? (Try an example.)

72. ▼ How do the graphs of two functions $f(x)$ and $g(x)$ differ if $g(x) = f(-x)$? (Try an example.)

1.2 Functions and Models

The functions we used in Examples 1 and 2 in Section 1.1 are **mathematical models** of real-life situations, because they model, or represent, situations in mathematical terms.

Mathematical Modeling

To mathematically model a situation means to represent it in mathematical terms. The particular representation used is called a **mathematical model** of the situation. Mathematical models do not always represent a situation perfectly or completely. Some (like Example 1 of Section 1.1) represent a situation only approximately, whereas others represent only some aspects of the situation.

Quick Examples

Situation	Model
1. The temperature is now 10°F and increasing by 20° per hour.	$T(t) = 10 + 20t$ (t = time in hours, T = temperature)
2. I invest $1,000 at 5% interest compounded quarterly. Find the value of the investment after t years.	$A(t) = 1,000 \left(1 + \dfrac{0.05}{4}\right)^{4t}$ This is the compound interest formula we will study in Example 6.
3. I am fencing a rectangular area whose perimeter is 100 ft. Find the area as a function of the width x.	Take y to be the length, so the perimeter is $100 = x + y + x + y = 2(x + y)$ so $x + y = 50$. Thus the length is $y = 50 - x$. Area $A = xy = x(50 - x)$.
4. iPod sales	The function $f(x) = -x^2 + 20x + 3$ in Example 1 of Section 1.1 is an **algebraic model** of iPod sales.

5. Facebook membership

The function

$$n(t) = \begin{cases} 1.5t^2 - t + 1.5 & \text{if } 0 \le t \le 3 \\ 46t - 126 & \text{if } 3 < t \le 4 \end{cases}$$

in Example 2 of Section 1.1 is a **piecewise algebraic model** of Facebook membership.

Analytical and Curve-Fitting Models

Quick Examples 1–3 are **analytical models**, obtained by analyzing the situation being modeled, whereas Quick Examples 4 and 5 are **curve-fitting models**, obtained by finding mathematical formulas that approximate observed data.

Cost, Revenue, and Profit Models

EXAMPLE 1 Modeling Cost: Cost Function

As of October 2007, Yellow Cab Chicago's rates were $1.90 on entering the cab plus $1.60 for each mile.*

a. Find the cost C of an x-mile trip.

b. Use your answer to calculate the cost of a 40-mile trip.

c. What is the cost of the second mile? What is the cost of the tenth mile?

d. Graph C as a function of x.

Solution

a. We are being asked to find how the cost C depends on the length x of the trip, or to find C as a function of x. Here is the cost in a few cases:

Cost of a 1-mile trip: $C = 1.60(1) + 1.90 = 3.50$ 1 mile @ $1.60 per mile plus $1.90

Cost of a 2-mile trip: $C = 1.60(2) + 1.90 = 5.10$ 2 miles @ $1.60 per mile plus $1.90

Cost of a 3-mile trip: $C = 1.60(3) + 1.90 = 6.70$ 3 miles @ $1.60 per mile plus $1.90

Do you see the pattern? The cost of an x-mile trip is given by the linear function

$$C(x) = 1.60x + 1.90.$$

Notice that the cost function is a sum of two terms: the **variable cost** $1.60x$, which depends on x, and the **fixed cost** 1.90, which is independent of x:

Cost = Variable Cost + Fixed Cost.

The quantity 1.60 by itself is the incremental cost per mile; you might recognize it as the *slope* of the given linear function. In this context we call 1.60 the **marginal cost**. You might recognize the fixed cost 1.90 as the *C-intercept* of the given linear function.

---

* According to their Web site at www.yellowcabchicago.com/.

b. We can use the formula for the cost function to calculate the cost of a 40-mile trip as

$$C(40) = 1.60(40) + 1.90 = \$65.90.$$

c. To calculate the cost of the second mile, we *could* proceed as follows:

Find the cost of a 1-mile trip: $C(1) = 1.60(1) + 1.90 = \$3.50$.

Find the cost of a 2-mile trip: $C(2) = 1.60(2) + 1.90 = \$5.10$.

Therefore, the cost of the second mile is $\$5.10 - \$3.50 = \$1.60$.

But notice that this is just the marginal cost. In fact, the marginal cost is the cost of each additional mile, so we could have done this more simply:

Cost of second mile = Cost of tenth mile = Marginal cost = $\$1.60$

d. Figure 7 shows the graph of the cost function, which we can interpret as a *cost vs. miles* graph. The fixed cost is the starting height on the left, while the marginal cost is the slope of the line: It rises 1.60 units per unit of x. (See Section 1.3 for a discussion of properties of straight lines.)

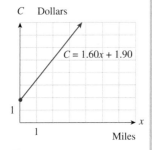

C Dollars

$C = 1.60x + 1.90$

Miles

Figure 7

➡ **Before we go on...** The cost function in Example 1 is an example of an *analytical model:* We derived the form of the cost function from a knowledge of the cost per mile and the fixed cost.

As we discussed on page 46 in Section 1.1, we can use equation notation to specify a function. In equation notation, the function C in Example 1 is

$$C = 1.60x + 1.90. \qquad \text{Equation notation}$$

The independent variable is x and the dependent variable is C. Function notation and equation notation, using the same letter for the function name and the dependent variable, are often used interchangeably. It is important to be able to switch back and forth between function notation and equation notation easily. ■

Here is a summary of some terms we used in Example 1, along with an introduction to some new terms:

Cost, Revenue, and Profit Functions

A **cost function** specifies the cost C as a function of the number of items x. Thus, $C(x)$ is the cost of x items, and has the form

Cost = Variable cost + Fixed cost

where the variable cost is a function of x and the fixed cost is a constant. A cost function of the form

$$C(x) = mx + b$$

is called a **linear cost function**; the variable cost is mx and the fixed cost is b. The slope m, the **marginal cost**, measures the incremental cost per item.

The **revenue** resulting from one or more business transactions is the total payment received, sometimes called the gross proceeds. If $R(x)$ is the revenue from selling x items at a price of m each, then R is the linear function $R(x) = mx$ and the selling price m can also be called the **marginal revenue**.

The **profit**, on the other hand, is the *net* proceeds, or what remains of the revenue when costs are subtracted. If the profit depends linearly on the number of items, the slope m is called the **marginal profit**. Profit, revenue, and cost are related by the following formula.

$$\text{Profit} = \text{Revenue} - \text{Cost}$$
$$P = R - C$$

If the profit is negative, say $-\$500$, we refer to a **loss** (of $500 in this case). To **break even** means to make neither a profit nor a loss. Thus, break even occurs when $P = 0$, or

$$R = C. \qquad \text{Break even}$$

The **break-even point** is the number of items x at which break even occurs.

Quick Example

If the daily cost (including operating costs) of manufacturing x T-shirts is $C(x) = 8x + 100$, and the revenue obtained by selling x T-shirts is $R(x) = 10x$, then the daily profit resulting from the manufacture and sale of x T-shirts is

$$P(x) = R(x) - C(x) = 10x - (8x + 100) = 2x - 100.$$

Break even occurs when $P(x) = 0$, or $x = 50$.

EXAMPLE 2 Cost, Revenue, and Profit

The annual operating cost of *YSport Fitness* gym is estimated to be

$$C(x) = 100{,}000 + 160x - 0.2x^2 \qquad (0 \le x \le 400)$$

where x is the number of members. Annual revenue from membership averages $800 per member. What is the variable cost? What is the fixed cost? What is the profit function? How many members must *YSport* have to make a profit? What will happen if it has fewer members? If it has more?

Solution The variable cost is the part of the cost function that depends on x:

$$\text{Variable cost} = 160x - 0.2x^2.$$

The fixed cost is the constant term:

$$\text{Fixed cost} = 100{,}000.$$

The annual revenue *YSport* obtains from a single member is $800. So, if it has x members, it earns an annual revenue of

$$R(x) = 800x.$$

For the profit, we use the formula

$$\begin{aligned} P(x) &= R(x) - C(x) & \text{Formula for profit} \\ &= 800x - (100{,}000 + 160x - 0.2x^2) & \text{Substitute } R(x) \text{ and } C(x) \\ &= -100{,}000 + 640x + 0.2x^2. \end{aligned}$$

using Technology

Excel has a feature called "Goal Seek" which can be used to find the point of intersection of the cost and revenue graphs numerically rather than graphically. See the downloadable Excel tutorial for this section at the Web site.

To make a profit, *YSport* needs to do better than break even, so let us find the break-even point: the value of *x* such that $P(x) = 0$. All we have to do is set $P(x) = 0$ and solve for *x*:

$$-100,000 + 640x + 0.2x^2 = 0.$$

Notice that we have a quadratic equation $ax^2 + bx + c = 0$ with $a = 0.2$, $b = 640$, and $c = -100,000$. Its solution is given by the quadratic formula:

$$x = \frac{-b \pm \sqrt{b^2 - 4ac}}{2a} = \frac{-640 \pm \sqrt{640^2 + 4(0.2)(100,000)}}{2(0.2)}$$

$$\approx \frac{-640 \pm 699.71}{2(0.2)}$$

$$\approx 149.3 \text{ or } -3,349.3.$$

We reject the negative solution (as the domain is [0, 400]) and conclude that $x \approx 149.3$ members. To make a profit, should *YSport* have 149 members or 150 members? To decide, take a look at Figure 8, which shows two graphs: On the top we see the graph of revenue and cost, and on the bottom we see the graph of the profit function.

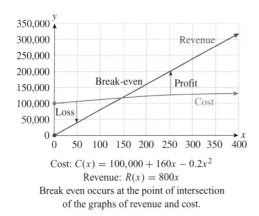

Cost: $C(x) = 100,000 + 160x - 0.2x^2$
Revenue: $R(x) = 800x$
Break even occurs at the point of intersection of the graphs of revenue and cost.

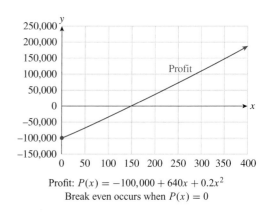

Profit: $P(x) = -100,000 + 640x + 0.2x^2$
Break even occurs when $P(x) = 0$

Figure 8

For values of *x* less than the break-even point of 149.3, $P(x)$ is negative, so the company will have a loss. For values of *x* greater than the break-even point, $P(x)$ is positive, so the company will make a profit. Thus, *YSport Fitness* needs at least 150 members to make a profit. (Note that we rounded 149.3 up to 150 in this case.)

Demand and Supply Models

The demand for a commodity usually goes down as its price goes up. It is traditional to use the letter *q* for the (quantity of) demand, as measured, for example, in sales. Consider the following example.

EXAMPLE 3 Demand: Private Schools

The demand for private schools in Michigan depends on the tuition cost and can be approximated by

$$q = 77.8p^{-0.11} \text{ thousand students} \qquad (200 \le p \le 2,200) \qquad \text{Demand curve}$$

where p is the net tuition cost in dollars.*

a. Use technology to plot the demand function.

b. What is the effect on demand if the tuition cost is increased from $1,000 to $1,500?

Solution

a. The demand function is given by $q(p) = 77.8p^{-0.11}$. Its graph is known as a **demand curve**. (Figure 9)

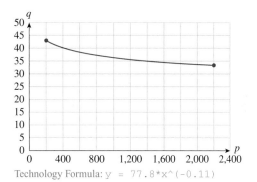

Technology Formula: $y = 77.8*x^{(-0.11)}$

Figure 9

b. The demand at tuition costs of $1,000 and $1,500 are

$$q(1,000) = 77.8(1,000)^{-0.11} \approx 36.4 \text{ thousand students}$$
$$q(1,500) = 77.8(1,500)^{-0.11} \approx 34.8 \text{ thousand students}$$

The change in demand is therefore

$$q(1,500) - q(1,000) \approx 34.8 - 36.4 = -1.6 \text{ thousand students}$$

---

* The tuition cost is net cost: tuition minus tax credit. The model is based on data in "The Universal Tuition Tax Credit: A Proposal to Advance Personal Choice in Education," Patrick L. Anderson, Richard McLellan, J.D., Joseph P. Overton, J.D., Gary Wolfram, Ph.D., Mackinac Center for Public Policy, www.mackinac.org/

We have seen that a demand function gives the number of items consumers are willing to buy at a given price, and a higher price generally results in a lower demand. However, as the price rises, suppliers will be more inclined to produce these items (as opposed to spending their time and money on other products), so supply will generally rise. A **supply function** gives q, the number of items suppliers are willing to make available for sale,* as a function of p, the price per item.

✱ NOTE Although a bit confusing at first, it is traditional to use the same letter q for the quantity of supply and the quantity of demand, particularly when we want to compare them, as in the next example.

Demand, Supply, and Equilibrium Price

A **demand equation** or **demand function** expresses demand q (the number of items demanded) as a function of the unit price p (the price per item). A **supply equation** or **supply function** expresses supply q (the number of items a supplier is willing to make available) as a function of the unit price p (the price per item). It is usually the case that demand decreases and supply increases as the unit price increases.

Demand and supply are said to be in **equilibrium** when demand equals supply. The corresponding values of p and q are called the **equilibrium price** and **equilibrium demand**. To find the equilibrium price, determine the unit price p where the demand and supply curves cross (sometimes we can determine this value analytically by setting demand equal to supply and solving for p). To find the equilibrium demand, evaluate the demand (or supply) function at the equilibrium price.

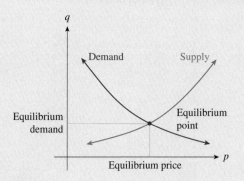

Quick Example

If the demand for your exclusive T-shirts is $q = -20p + 800$ shirts sold per day and the supply is $q = 10p - 100$ shirts per day, then the equilibrium point is obtained when demand = supply:

$$-20p + 800 = 10p - 100$$
$$30p = 900, \text{ giving } p = \$30$$

The equilibrium price is therefore $30 and the equilibrium demand is $q = -20(30) + 800 = 200$ shirts per day. What happens at prices other than the equilibrium price is discussed in Example 4.

EXAMPLE 4 Demand, Supply, and Equilibrium Price

Continuing with Example 3, suppose that private school institutions are willing to create private schools to accommodate

$$q = 30.4 + 0.006p \text{ thousand students} \qquad (200 \leq p \leq 2{,}200) \qquad \text{Supply curve}$$

who pay a net tuition of p dollars.

a. Graph the demand curve of Example 3 and the supply curve given here on the same set of axes. Use your graph to estimate, to the nearest $100, the tuition at which the demand equals the supply. Approximately how many students will be accommodated at that price, known as the **equilibrium price**?

b. What happens if the tuition is higher than the equilibrium price? What happens if it is lower?

c. Estimate the shortage or surplus of openings at private schools if tuition is set at $1,200.

Solution

a. Figure 10 shows the graphs of demand $q = 77.8p^{-0.11}$ and supply $q = 30.4 + 0.006p$. (See the margin note for a brief description of how to plot them.)

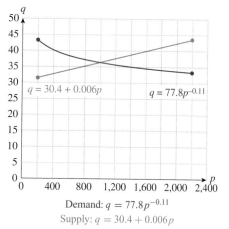

Demand: $q = 77.8p^{-0.11}$
Supply: $q = 30.4 + 0.006p$

Figure 10

The lines cross close to $p = \$1{,}000$, so we conclude that demand = supply when $p \approx \$1{,}000$ (to the nearest 100). This is the (approximate) equilibrium tuition price. At that price, we can estimate the demand or supply at around

Demand: $q = 77.8(1000)^{-0.11} \approx 36.4$

Supply: $q = 30.4 + 0.006(1000) = 36.4$ Demand = Supply at equilibrium

or 36,400 students.

b. Take a look at Figure 11, which shows what happens if schools charge more or less than the equilibrium price. If tuition is, say, $1,800, then the supply will be larger than demand and there will be a surplus of available openings at private schools. Similarly, if tuition is less—say $400—then the supply will be less than the demand, and there will be a shortage of available openings.

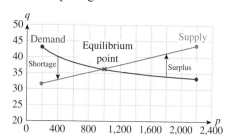

Figure 11

c. The discussion in part (b) shows that if tuition is set at $1,200 there will be a surplus of available openings. To estimate that number, we calculate the projected demand and supply when $p = \$1{,}200$:

Demand: $q = 77.8(1{,}200)^{-0.11} \approx 35.7$ thousand seats

Supply: $q = 30.4 + 0.006(1{,}200) = 37.6$ thousand seats

Surplus = Supply − Demand $\approx 37.6 - 35.7 = 1.9$ thousand seats

So, there would be a surplus of around 1,900 available seats.

using Technology

See the Technology Guide at the end of the chapter for detailed instructions on how to obtain the graph in Example 4 using a TI-83/84 Plus or Excel. Here is an outline:

TI-83/84 Plus

Graphs:

$Y_1 = 77.8 \ast X^{\wedge}(-0.11)$

$Y_2 = 30.4 + 0.006 \ast X$

Xmin = 200, Xmax = 2200;

ZOOM 0 . [More details on page 111.]

Excel

Graphs: Headings p, Demand, Supply in A1–C1; p-values 200, 300, . . . , 2200 in A2–A22.

$= 77.8 \ast A2^{\wedge}(-0.11)$ in B2

$= 30.4 + 0.006 \ast A2$ in C2

copy down through C22. Highlight A1–C22; insert Scatter chart. [More details on page 118.]

Web Site

www.AppliedCalc.org

Go to the Function Evaluator and Grapher under Online Utilities, enter

$77.8 \ast x^{\wedge}(-0.11)$ for y_1 and

$30.4 + 0.006 \ast x$ for y_2.

Graph: Set Xmin = 200 and Xmax = 2200, and press "Plot Graphs."

➡ **Before we go on...** We just saw in Example 4 that if tuition is less than the equilibrium price there will be a shortage. If schools were to raise their tuition toward the equilibrium, they could create and fill more openings and increase revenue, because it is the supply equation—and not the demand equation—that determines what one can sell below the equilibrium price. On the other hand, if they were to charge more than the equilibrium price, they will be left with a possibly costly surplus of unused openings (and will want to lower tuition to reduce the surplus). Prices tend to move toward the equilibrium, so supply tends to equal demand. When supply equals demand, we say that the market **clears**. ■

Modeling Change Over Time

Things around us change with time. Thus, there are many quantities, such as your income or the temperature in Honolulu, that are natural to think of as functions of time. Example 1 on page 44 (on iPod sales) and Example 2 on page 47 (on Facebook membership) in Section 1.1 are models of change over time. Both of those models are curve-fitting models: We used algebraic functions to approximate observed data.

In the next example we are asked to select from among several curve-fitting models for given data.

EXAMPLE 5 **Model Selection: Casino Revenue**

The following table shows annual revenues in 2000–2006 from slot machines and video poker machines at the *Mohegan Sun* casino in Connecticut ($t = 0$ represents 2000).*

t	0	1	2	3	4	5	6
Revenue ($ million)	550	680	750	820	850	890	910

Consider the following four models:

(1) $r(t) = 57t + 607$ Linear model

(2) $r(t) = -9t^2 + 110t + 560$ Quadratic model

(3) $r(t) = 608(1.08)^t$ Exponential model

(4) $r(t) = \dfrac{930}{1 + 0.67(1.7)^{-t}}$ Logistic model

a. Which models fit the data significantly better than the rest?

b. Of the models you selected in part (a), which gives the most reasonable prediction for 2010?

---

* Source: Connecticut Division of Special Revenue/*New York Times*, Sept. 23, 2007, p. C1.

using Technology

See the Technology Guide at the end of the chapter for detailed instructions on how to obtain the table and graphs in Example 5 using a TI-83/84 Plus or Excel. Here is an outline:

TI-83/84 Plus
STAT EDIT; enter the values of t in L_1, and $r(t)$ in L_2. Turn on Plot1 in Y= screen. ZOOM 9
Adding a curve:
$Y_1=-9*X^2+110X+560$
GRAPH
[More details on page 112.]

Excel
Table of values: Headings t, Revenue, $r(t)$ in A1–C1; t-values in A2–A8. Revenues in B2–B8. Formula in C2:
$=-9*A2^2+110*A2+560$
Copy down through C8. Graph: Highlight A1–C8; insert Scatter chart. [More details on page 118.]

Web Site
www.AppliedCalc.org
In the Function Evaluator and Grapher utility, enter the data and model(s) as shown below. Set xMin = 0, xMax = 6 and press "Plot Graphs."

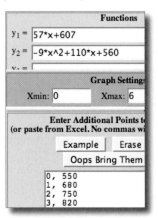

Solution

a. The following table shows the original data together with the values for all four models:

	t	0	1	2	3	4	5	6
Revenue ($ million)		550	680	750	820	850	890	910
Linear: $r(t) = 57t + 607$ Technology: `57*x+607`		607	664	721	778	835	892	949
Quadratic: $r(t) = -9t^2 + 110t + 560$ Technology: `-9*x^2+110*x+560`		560	661	744	809	856	885	896
Exponential: $r(t) = 608(1.08)^t$ Technology: `608*(1.08)^x`		608	657	709	766	827	893	965
Logistic: $r(t) = \dfrac{930}{1 + 0.67(1.7)^{-t}}$ Technology: `930/(1+0.67*1.7^(-x))`		557	667	755	818	861	888	905

Notice first that all the values for the quadratic and logistic models are close to the actual revenue values. This cannot be said for the linear and exponential models. Figure 12 shows the original data together with the graph of each model. Notice

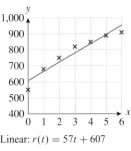

Linear: $r(t) = 57t + 607$

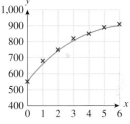

Quadratic: $r(t) = -9t^2 + 110t + 560$

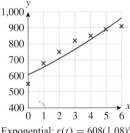

Exponential: $r(t) = 608(1.08)^t$

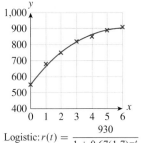

Logistic: $r(t) = \dfrac{930}{1 + 0.67(1.7)^{-t}}$

Figure 12

again that the quadratic and logistic curves appear to follow the data more closely than the other two. We therefore conclude that the quadratic and logistic models fit the data significantly better than the others.

b. Although the quadratic and logistic models both appear to fit the data well, they do not both extrapolate to give reasonable predictions for 2010:

$$\text{Quadratic Model: } r(10) = -9(10)^2 + 110(10) + 560 \approx 760$$

$$\text{Logistic Model: } r(10) = \frac{930}{1 + 0.67(1.7)^{-10}} \approx 927$$

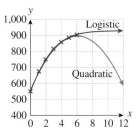

Figure 13

Notice that the quadratic model predicts a significant *decline* in casino revenues whereas the logistic model predicts a more reasonable modest increase. This discrepancy can be seen quite dramatically in Figure 13.

We now derive an analytical model of change over time based on the idea of **compound interest**. Suppose you invest $500 (the **present value**) in an investment account with an annual yield of 15%, and the interest is reinvested at the end of every year (we say that the interest is **compounded** or **reinvested** once a year). Let t represent the number of years since you made the initial $500 investment. Each year, the investment is worth 115% (or 1.15 times) of its value the previous year. The **future value** A of your investment changes over time t, so we think of A as a function of t. The following table illustrates how we can calculate the future value for several values of t:

t	0	1	2	3
FutureValue $A(t)$	500	575	661.25	760.44
A		$500(1.15)$	$500(1.15)^2$	$500(1.15)^3$

$\times 1.15 \qquad \times 1.15 \qquad \times 1.15$

Thus, $A(t) = 500(1.15)^t$. A traditional way to write this formula is

$$A(t) = P(1+r)^t$$

where P is the present value ($P = 500$) and r is the annual interest rate ($r = 0.15$).

If, instead of compounding the interest once a year, we compound it every three months (four times a year), we would earn one quarter of the interest ($r/4$ of the current investment) every three months. Because this would happen $4t$ times in t years, the formula for the future value becomes

$$A(t) = P\left(1 + \frac{r}{4}\right)^{4t}.$$

Compound Interest

If an amount **(present value)** P is invested for t years at an annual rate of r, and if the interest is compounded (reinvested) m times per year, then the **future value** A is

$$A(t) = P\left(1 + \frac{r}{m}\right)^{mt}.$$

A special case is **interest compounded once a year:**

$$A(t) = P(1+r)^t.$$

Quick Example

If $2,000 is invested for two and a half years in a mutual fund with an annual yield of 12.6% and the earnings are reinvested each month, then $P = 2,000$, $r = 0.126$, $m = 12$, and $t = 2.5$, which gives

$$A(2.5) = 2,000\left(1 + \frac{0.126}{12}\right)^{12 \times 2.5}$$

2000*(1+0.126/12)^(12*2.5)

$$= 2,000(1.0105)^{30} = \$2,736.02.$$

EXAMPLE 6 Compound Interest: Investments

Consider the scenario in the preceding Quick Example: You invest $2,000 in a mutual fund with an annual yield of 12.6% and the interest is reinvested each month.

a. Find the associated exponential model.

b. ⊞ Use a table of values to estimate the year during which the value of your investment reaches $5,000.

c. Use a graph to confirm your answer in part (b).

Solution

a. Apply the formula

$$A(t) = P\left(1 + \frac{r}{m}\right)^{mt}$$

with $P = 2,000$, $r = 0.126$, and $m = 12$. We get

$$A(t) = 2,000\left(1 + \frac{0.126}{12}\right)^{12t}$$

$$A(t) = 2,000(1.0105)^{12t} \qquad \texttt{2000*(1+0.126/12)^(12*t)}$$

This is the exponential model. (What would happen if we left out the last set of parentheses in the technology formula?)

b. We need to find the value of t for which $A(t) = \$5,000$, so we need to solve the equation

$$5,000 = 2,000(1.0105)^{12t}$$

In Section 2.3 we will learn how to use logarithms to do this algebraically, but we can answer the question now using a graphing calculator, a spreadsheet, or the Function Evaluator and Grapher utility at the Web site. Just enter the model and compute the balance at the end of several years. Here are examples of tables obtained using three forms of technology:

▦ using Technology

TI-83/84 Plus
Y₁=2000(1+0.126/12)^
(12X)
[2ND] [TABLE]

Excel
Headings t and A in A1–B1;
t-values 0–11 in A2–A13.
=2000*(1+0.126/12)^
(12*A2)
in B2; copy down through B13.

Web Site
www.AppliedCalc.org
Go to the Function Evaluator
and Grapher under Online
Utilities, and enter
2000(1+0.126/12)^(12x)
for y_1. Scroll down to the
Evaluator, enter the values
0–11 under x-values and press
"Evaluate."

TI-83/84 Plus

A	B
t	A
0	$ 2,000.00
1	$ 2,267.07
2	$ 2,569.81
3	$ 2,912.98
4	$ 3,301.97
5	$ 3,742.91
6	$ 4,242.72
7	$ 4,809.29
8	$ 5,451.51
9	$ 6,179.49

Excel

x-Values	y₁-Values
3	2912.98
4	3301.97
5	3742.91
6	4242.72
7	4809.29
8	5451.51

Web site

Because the balance first exceeds $5,000 at $t = 8$ (the end of year 8) your investment has reached $5,000 during year 8.

c. Figure 14 shows the graph of $A(t) = 2,000(1.0105)^{12t}$ together with the horizontal line $y = 5,000$.

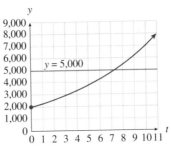

Technology format: `2000*1.0105^(12*x)`

Figure 14

The graphs cross between $t = 7$ and $t = 8$, confirming that year 8 is the first year during which the value of the investment reaches \$5,000.

The compound interest examples we saw above are instances of **exponential growth:** a quantity whose magnitude is an increasing exponential function of time. The decay of unstable radioactive isotopes provides instances of **exponential decay:** a quantity whose magnitude is a *decreasing* exponential function of time. For example, carbon 14, an unstable isotope of carbon, decays exponentially to nitrogen. Because carbon 14 decay is extremely slow, it has important applications in the dating of fossils.

EXAMPLE 7 **Exponential Decay: Carbon Dating**

The amount of carbon 14 remaining in a sample that originally contained A grams is approximately

$$C(t) = A(0.999879)^t$$

where t is time in years.

a. What percentage of the original amount remains after one year? After two years?

b. Graph the function C for a sample originally containing 50g of carbon 14, and use your graph to estimate how long, to the nearest 1,000 years, it takes for half the original carbon 14 to decay.

c. A fossilized plant unearthed in an archaeological dig contains 0.50 gram of carbon 14 and is known to be 50,000 years old. How much carbon 14 did the plant originally contain?

Solution Notice that the given model is exponential as it has the form $f(t) = Ab^t$. (See page 51.)

a. At the start of the first year, $t = 0$, so there are

$$C(0) = A(0.999879)^0 = A \text{ grams.}$$

At the end of the first year, $t = 1$, so there are

$$C(1) = A(0.999879)^1 = 0.999879A \text{ grams;}$$

that is, 99.9879% of the original amount remains. After the second year, the amount remaining is

$$C(2) = A(0.999879)^2 \approx 0.999758A \text{ grams,}$$

or about 99.9758% of the original sample.

b. For a sample originally containing 50g of carbon 14, $A = 50$, so $C(t) = 50(0.999879)^t$. Its graph is shown in Figure 15.

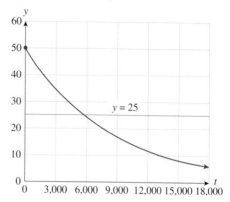

Technology format: `50*0.999879^x`

Figure 15

We have also plotted the line $y = 25$ on the same graph. The graphs intersect at the point where the original sample has decayed to 25g: about $t = 6,000$ years.

c. We are given the following information: $C = 0.50$, $A =$ the unknown, and $t = 50,000$. Substituting gives

$$0.50 = A(0.999879)^{50,000}.$$

Solving for A gives

$$A = \frac{0.5}{0.999879^{50,000}} \approx 212 \text{ grams}.$$

Thus, the plant originally contained 212 grams of carbon 14.

➡ **Before we go on...** The formula we used for A in Example 7(c) has the form

$$A(t) = \frac{C}{0.999879^t},$$

which gives the original amount of carbon 14 t years ago in terms of the amount C that is left now. A similar formula can be used in finance to find the present value, given the future value. ■

1.2 EXERCISES

▼ more advanced   ◆ challenging

⊤ indicates exercises that should be solved using technology

1. Resources You now have 200 sound files on your hard drive, and this number is increasing by 10 sound files each day. Find a mathematical model for this situation. HINT [See Quick Example 1 on page 56.]

2. Resources The amount of free space left on your hard drive is now 50 gigabytes (GB) and is decreasing by 5 GB/month. Find a mathematical model for this situation.

3. Soccer My rectangular soccer field site has a length equal to twice its width. Find its area in terms of its length x. HINT [See Quick Example 3 on page 56.]

4. Cabbage My rectangular cabbage patch has a total area of 100 sq. ft. Find its perimeter in terms of the width x.

5. Vegetables I want to fence in a square vegetable patch. The fencing for the east and west sides costs $4 per foot, and the fencing for the north and south sides costs only $2 per foot. Find the total cost of the fencing as a function of the length of a side x.

6. Orchids My square orchid garden abuts my house so that the house itself forms the northern boundary. The fencing for the southern boundary costs $4 per foot, and the fencing for the east and west sides costs $2 per foot. Find the total cost of the fencing as a function of the length of a side x.

7. Cost A piano manufacturer has a daily fixed cost of $1,200 and a marginal cost of $1,500 per piano. Find the cost $C(x)$ of manufacturing x pianos in one day. Use your function to answer the following questions:

a. On a given day, what is the cost of manufacturing 3 pianos?
b. What is the cost of manufacturing the 3rd piano that day?

c. What is the cost of manufacturing the 11th piano that day?

d. What is the variable cost? What is the fixed cost? What is the marginal cost?

e. Graph C as a function of x. HINT [See Example 1.]

8. *Cost* The cost of renting tuxes for the Choral Society's formal is $20 down, plus $88 per tux. Express the cost C as a function of x, the number of tuxedos rented. Use your function to answer the following questions.

a. What is the cost of renting 2 tuxes?

b. What is the cost of the 2nd tux?

c. What is the cost of the 4,098th tux?

d. What is the variable cost? What is the marginal cost?

e. Graph C as a function of x.

9. *Break-Even Analysis* Your college newspaper, *The Collegiate Investigator*, has fixed production costs of $70 per edition and marginal printing and distribution costs of 40¢ per copy. *The Collegiate Investigator* sells for 50¢ per copy.

a. Write down the associated cost, revenue, and profit functions. HINT [See Examples 1 and 2.]

b. What profit (or loss) results from the sale of 500 copies of *The Collegiate Investigator*?

c. How many copies should be sold in order to break even?

10. *Break-Even Analysis* The Audubon Society at Enormous State University (ESU) is planning its annual fund-raising "Eat-a-thon." The society will charge students 50¢ per serving of pasta. The only expenses the society will incur are the cost of the pasta, estimated at 15¢ per serving, and the $350 cost of renting the facility for the evening.

a. Write down the associated cost, revenue, and profit functions.

b. How many servings of pasta must the Audubon Society sell in order to break even?

c. What profit (or loss) results from the sale of 1,500 servings of pasta?

11. *Break-Even Analysis* Gymnast Clothing manufactures expensive hockey jerseys for sale to college bookstores in runs of up to 200. Its cost (in dollars) for a run of x hockey jerseys is

$$C(x) = 2{,}000 + 10x + 0.2x^2 \quad (0 \le x \le 200)$$

Gymnast Clothing sells the jerseys at $100 each. Find the revenue and profit functions. How many should Gymnast Clothing manufacture to make a profit? HINT [See Example 2.]

12. *Break-Even Analysis* Gymnast Clothing also manufactures expensive soccer cleats for sale to college bookstores in runs of up to 500. Its cost (in dollars) for a run of x pairs of cleats is

$$C(x) = 3{,}000 + 8x + 0.1x^2 \quad (0 \le x \le 500)$$

Gymnast Clothing sells the cleats at $120 per pair. Find the revenue and profit functions. How many should Gymnast Clothing manufacture to make a profit?

13. *Break-Even Analysis: School Construction Costs* The cost, in millions of dollars, of building a two-story high school in New York State was estimated to be

$$C(x) = 1.7 + 0.12x - 0.0001x^2 \quad (20 \le x \le 400)$$

where x is the number of thousands of square feet.[12] Suppose that you are contemplating building a for-profit two-story high school and estimate that your total revenue will be $0.1 million dollars per thousand square feet. What is the profit function? What size school should you build in order to break even?

14. *Break-Even Analysis: School Construction Costs* The cost, in millions of dollars, of building a three-story high school in New York State was estimated to be

$$C(x) = 1.7 + 0.14x - 0.0001x^2 \quad (20 \le x \le 400)$$

where x is the number of thousands of square feet.[13] Suppose that you are contemplating building a for-profit three-story high school and estimate that your total revenue will be $0.2 million dollars per thousand square feet. What is the profit function? What size school should you build in order to break even?

15. ▼ *Profit Analysis—Aviation* The hourly operating cost of a Boeing 747-100, which seats up to 405 passengers, is estimated to be $5,132.[14] If an airline charges each passenger a fare of $100 per hour of flight, find the hourly profit P it earns operating a 747-100 as a function of the number of passengers x. (Be sure to specify the domain.) What is the least number of passengers it must carry in order to make a profit? HINT [The cost function is constant (Variable cost = 0).]

16. ▼ *Profit Analysis—Aviation* The hourly operating cost of a McDonnell Douglas DC 10-10, which seats up to 295 passengers, is estimated to be $3,885.[15] If an airline charges each passenger a fare of $100 per hour of flight, find the hourly profit P it earns operating a DC 10-10 as a function of the number of passengers x. (Be sure to specify the domain.) What is the least number of passengers it must carry in order to make a profit? HINT [The cost function is constant (Variable cost = 0).]

17. ▼ *Break-Even Analysis* (based on a question from a CPA exam) The Oliver Company plans to market a new product. Based on its market studies, Oliver estimates that it can sell up to 5,500 units in 2005. The selling price will be $2 per unit. Variable costs are estimated to be 40% of total revenue. Fixed costs are estimated to be $6,000 for 2005. How many units should the company sell to break even?

18. ▼ *Break-Even Analysis* (based on a question from a CPA exam) The Metropolitan Company sells its latest product at a unit price of $5. Variable costs are estimated to be 30% of the total revenue, while fixed costs amount to $7,000 per month. How many units should the company sell per month in order to break even, assuming that it can sell up to 5,000 units per month at the planned price?

---

[12] The model is the authors'. Source for data: *Project Labor Agreements and Public Construction Cost in New York State*, Paul Bachman and David Tuerck, Beacon Hill Institute at Suffolk University, April 2006, www.beaconhill.org.

[13] Ibid.

[14] In 1992. Source: Air Transportation Association of America.

[15] Ibid.

19. ◆ *Break-Even Analysis (from a CPA exam)* Given the following notations, write a formula for the break-even sales level.

SP = Selling price per unit
FC = Total fixed cost
VC = Variable cost per unit

20. ◆ *Break-Even Analysis (based on a question from a CPA exam)* Given the following notation, give a formula for the total fixed cost.

SP = Selling price per unit
VC = Variable cost per unit
BE = Break even sales level in units

21. ◆ *Break-Even Analysis—Organized Crime* The organized crime boss and perfume king Butch (Stinky) Rose has daily overheads (bribes to corrupt officials, motel photographers, wages for hit men, explosives, and so on) amounting to $20,000 per day. On the other hand, he has a substantial income from his counterfeit perfume racket: He buys imitation French perfume (Chanel № 22.5) at $20 per gram, pays an additional $30 per 100 grams for transportation, and sells it via his street thugs for $600 per gram. Specify Stinky's profit function, $P(x)$, where x is the quantity (in grams) of perfume he buys and sells, and use your answer to calculate how much perfume should pass through his hands per day in order that he break even.

22. ◆ *Break-Even Analysis—Disorganized Crime* Butch (Stinky) Rose's counterfeit Chanel № 22.5 racket has run into difficulties; it seems that the *authentic* Chanel № 22.5 perfume is selling for less than his counterfeit perfume. However, he has managed to reduce his fixed costs to zero, and his overall costs are now $400 per gram plus $30 per gram transportation costs and commission. (The perfume's smell is easily detected by specially trained Chanel Hounds, and this necessitates elaborate packaging measures.) He therefore decides to sell it for $420 per gram in order to undercut the competition. Specify Stinky's profit function, $P(x)$, where x is the quantity (in grams) of perfume he buys and sells, and use your answer to calculate how much perfume should pass through his hands per day in order that he break even. Interpret your answer.

23. *Demand for Monorail Service, Las Vegas* The demand for monorail service in Las Vegas can be approximated by

$q(p) = 64p^{-0.76}$ thousand rides per day $(3 \le p \le 5)$

where p is the cost per ride in dollars.[16]

a. Graph the demand function.
b. What is the result on demand if the cost per ride is increased from $3.00 to $3.50? HINT [See Example 3.]

24. *Demand for Monorail Service, Mars* The demand for monorail service on the Utarek monorail, which links the three urbynes (or districts) of Utarek, Mars, can be approximated by

$q(p) = 30p^{-0.49}$ million rides per day $(3 \le p \le 5)$

where p is the cost per ride in zonars ($\bar{\bar{Z}}$).[17]

a. Graph the demand function.
b. What is the result on demand if the cost per ride is decreased from $\bar{\bar{Z}}5.00$ to $\bar{\bar{Z}}3.50$?

25. ▼ *Demand* The demand for Sigma Mu Fraternity plastic brownie dishes is

$$q(p) = 361{,}201 - (p + 1)^2$$

where q represents the number of brownie dishes Sigma Mu can sell each month at a price of $p¢$. Use this function to determine:

a. The number of brownie dishes Sigma Mu can sell each month if the price is set at 50¢.
b. The number of brownie dishes they can unload each month if they give them away.
c. The lowest price at which Sigma Mu will be unable to sell any dishes.

26. ▼ *Revenue* The total weekly revenue earned at Royal Ruby Retailers is given by

$$R(p) = -\frac{4}{3}p^2 + 80p$$

where p is the price (in dollars) RRR charges per ruby. Use this function to determine:

a. The weekly revenue, to the nearest dollar, when the price is set at $20/ruby.
b. The weekly revenue, to the nearest dollar, when the price is set at $200/ruby. (Interpret your result.)
c. The price RRR should charge in order to obtain a weekly revenue of $1,200.

27. *Equilibrium Price* The demand for your hand-made skateboards, in weekly sales, is $q = -3p + 700$ if the selling price is $$p$. You are prepared to supply $q = 2p - 500$ per week at the price $$p$. At what price should you sell your skateboards so that there is neither a shortage nor a surplus? HINT [See Quick Example on page 62.]

28. *Equilibrium Price* The demand for your factory-made skateboards, in weekly sales, is $q = -5p + 50$ if the selling price is $$p$. If you are selling them at that price, you can obtain $q = 3p - 30$ per week from the factory. At what price should you sell your skateboards so that there is neither a shortage nor a surplus?

29. *Equilibrium Price: Cell Phones* Worldwide quarterly sales of Nokia® cell phones was approximately $q = -p + 156$ million phones when the wholesale price[18] was $$p$.

a. If Nokia was prepared to supply $q = 4p - 394$ million phones per quarter at a wholesale price of $$p$, what would be the equilibrium price?
b. The actual wholesale price was $105 in the fourth quarter of 2004. Estimate the projected shortage or surplus at that price. HINT [See Quick Example on page 62 and also Example 4.]

---

[16] Source: *New York Times*, Februrary 10, 2007, p. A9.
[17] $\bar{\bar{Z}}$ designates Zonars, the official currency of Mars. See www.marsnext .com for details of the Mars colony, its commerce, and its culture.

[18] Source: Embedded.com/Company reports December, 2004.

30. *Equilibrium Price: Cell Phones* Worldwide annual sales of all cell phones is approximately $-10p + 1,600$ million phones when the wholesale price[19] is $\$p$.

   a. If manufacturers are prepared to supply $q = 14p - 800$ million phones per year at a wholesale price of $\$p$, what would be the equilibrium price?

   b. The actual wholesale price was projected to be $80 in the fourth quarter of 2008. Estimate the projected shortage or surplus at that price.

31. ▯ ***Demand for Monorail Service, Las Vegas*** The demand for monorail service in Las Vegas can be modeled by

$$q = 64p^{-0.76} \text{ thousand rides per day}$$

where p is the fare the Las Vegas Monorail Company charges in dollars.[20] Assume the company is prepared to provide service for

$$q = 2.5p + 15.5 \text{ thousand rides per day}$$

at a fare of $\$p$.

   a. Graph the demand and supply equations, and use your graph to estimate the equilibrium price (to the nearest 50¢).

   b. Estimate, to the nearest 10 rides, the shortage or surplus of monorail service at the December 2005 fare of $5 per ride.

32. ▯ ***Demand for Monorail Service, Mars*** The demand for monorail service in the three urbynes (or districts) of Utarek, Mars can be modeled by

$$q = 31p^{-0.49} \text{ million rides per day}$$

where p is the fare the Utarek Monorail Cooperative charges in zonars ($\overline{\overline{Z}}$).[21] Assume the cooperative is prepared to provide service for

$$q = 2.5p + 17.5 \text{ thousand rides per day}$$

at a fare of $\overline{\overline{Z}}p$.

   a. Graph the demand and supply equations, and use your graph to estimate the equilibrium price (to the nearest 0.50 zonars).

   b. Estimate the shortage or surplus of monorail service at the December 2085 fare of $\overline{\overline{Z}}1$ per ride.

33. ▼ ***Toxic Waste Treatment*** The cost of treating waste by removing PCPs goes up rapidly as the quantity of PCPs removed goes up. Here is a possible model:

$$C(q) = 2,000 + 100q^2$$

where q is the reduction in toxicity (in pounds of PCPs removed per day) and $C(q)$ is the daily cost (in dollars) of this reduction.

   a. Find the cost of removing 10 pounds of PCPs per day.

   b. Government subsidies for toxic waste cleanup amount to

$$S(q) = 500q$$

where q is as above and $S(q)$ is the daily dollar subsidy. Calculate the net cost function $N(q)$ (the cost of removing q pounds of PCPs per day after the subsidy is taken into account), given the cost function and subsidy above, and find the net cost of removing 20 pounds of PCPs per day.

34. ▼ ***Dental Plans*** A company pays for its employees' dental coverage at an annual cost C given by

$$C(q) = 1,000 + 100\sqrt{q}$$

where q is the number of employees covered and $C(q)$ is the annual cost in dollars.

   a. If the company has 100 employees, find its annual outlay for dental coverage.

   b. Assuming that the government subsidizes coverage by an annual dollar amount of

$$S(q) = 200q$$

   calculate the net cost function $N(q)$ to the company, and calculate the net cost of subsidizing its 100 employees. Comment on your answer.

35. *Spending on Corrections in the 1990s* The following table shows the annual spending by all states in the United States on corrections ($t = 0$ represents the year 1990):[22]

Year (t)	0	2	4	6	7
Spending ($ billion)	16	18	22	28	30

   a. Which of the following functions best fits the given data? (*Warning:* None of them fits exactly, but one fits more closely than the others.) HINT [See Example 5.]

   (A) $S(t) = -0.2t^2 + t + 16$
   (B) $S(t) = 0.2t^2 + t + 16$
   (C) $S(t) = t + 16$

   b. Use your answer to part (a) to "predict" spending on corrections in 1998, assuming that the trend continued.

36. *Spending on Corrections in the 1990s* Repeat Exercise 35, this time choosing from the following functions:

   a. $S(t) = 16 + 2t$
   b. $S(t) = 16 + t + 0.5t^2$
   c. $S(t) = 16 + t - 0.5t^2$

Freon Production Exercises 37 and 38 are based on the following data in Quick Example 1 on page 42 showing the amount of ozone-damaging Freon (in tons) produced in developing countries in year t since 2000:

---

[19] Wholesale price projections are the authors'. Source for sales prediction: I-Stat/NDR December, 2004.

[20] The model is the authors'. Source for data: *New York Times*, Februrary 10, 2007, p. A9.

[21] $\overline{\overline{Z}}$ designates Zonars, the official currency of Mars. See www. marsnext. com for details of the Mars colony, its commerce, and its culture.

[22] Data are rounded. Source: National Association of State Budget Officers/*The New York Times*, February 28, 1999, p. A1.

t (Year Since 2000)	F (Tons of Freon 22)
0	100
2	140
4	200
6	270
8	400
10	590

Source: *New York Times*, February 23, 2007, p. C1

37. a. Which two of the following models best fit the given data?

(A) $f(t) = 98(1.2^t)$

(B) $f(t) = 4.6t^2 + 1.2t + 109$

(C) $f(t) = 47t + 48$

(D) $f(t) = 98(1.2^{-t})$

b. Of the two models you chose in part (a), which predicts the larger amount of freon in 2020? How much freon does that model predict?

38. Repeat Exercise 37 using the following models:

a. $f(t) = -4.6t^2 + 1.2t + 109$

b. $f(t) = \dfrac{2500}{1 + 22(1.2^{-t})}$

c. $f(t) = 65t - 60$

d. $f(t) = 4.6t^2 + 1.2t + 109$

39. *Soccer Gear* The East Coast College soccer team is planning to buy new gear for its road trip to California. The cost per shirt depends on the number of shirts the team orders as shown in the following table:

x (Shirts ordered)	5	25	40	100	125
A(x) (Cost/shirt, $)	22.91	21.81	21.25	21.25	22.31

a. Which of the following functions best models the data?

(A) $A(x) = 0.005x + 20.75$

(B) $A(x) = 0.01x + 20 + \dfrac{25}{x}$

(C) $A(x) = 0.0005x^2 - 0.07x + 23.25$

(D) $A(x) = 25.5(1.08)^{(x-5)}$

b. 🖥 Graph the model you chose in part (a) for $10 \le x \le 100$. Use your graph to estimate the lowest cost per shirt and the number of shirts the team should order to obtain the lowest price per shirt.

40. *Hockey Gear* The South Coast College hockey team wants to purchase wool hats for its road trip to Alaska. The cost per hat depends on the number of hats the team orders as shown in the following table:

x (Hats ordered)	5	25	40	100	125
A(x) (Cost/hat, $)	25.50	23.50	24.63	30.25	32.70

a. Which of the following functions best models the data?

(A) $A(x) = 0.05x + 20.75$

(B) $A(x) = 0.1x + 20 + \dfrac{25}{x}$

(C) $A(x) = 0.0008x^2 - 0.07x + 23.25$

(D) $A(x) = 25.5(1.08)^{(x-5)}$

b. 🖥 Graph the model you chose in part (a) with $5 \le x \le 30$. Use your graph to estimate the lowest cost per hat and the number of hats the team should order to obtain the lowest price per hat.

41. *Value of Euro* The following table shows the approximate value V of one Euro in U.S. dollars from its introduction in January 2000 to January 2008. ($t = 0$ represents January 2000.)[23]

t (Year)	0	2	8
V (Value in $)	1.00	0.90	1.40

Which of the following kinds of models would best fit the given data? Explain your choice of model. (A, a, b, c, and m are constants.)

(A) Linear: $V(t) = mt + b$

(B) Quadratic: $V(t) = at^2 + bt + c$

(C) Exponential: $V(t) = Ab^t$

42. *Household Income* The following table shows the approximate average household income in the United States in 1990, 1995, and 2003. ($t = 0$ represents 1990.)[24]

t (Year)	0	5	13
H (Household Income in $1,000)	30	35	43

Which of the following kinds of models would best fit the given data? Explain your choice of model. (A, a, b, c, and m are constants.)

(A) Linear: $H(t) = mt + b$

(B) Quadratic: $H(t) = at^2 + bt + c$

(C) Exponential: $H(t) = Ab^t$

43. *Investments* In 2007, **E*TRADE Financial** was offering 4.94% interest on its online savings accounts, with interest reinvested monthly.[25] Find the associated exponential model for the value of a $5,000 deposit after t years. Assuming this rate of return continued for 7 years, how much would a deposit of $5,000 at the beginning of 2007 be worth at the start of 2014? (Answer to the nearest $1.)

---

[23] Source: Bloomberg Financial Markets.

[24] In current dollars, unadjusted for inflation. Source: U.S. Census Bureau; "Table H-5. Race and Hispanic Origin of Householder—Households by Median and Mean Income: 1967 to 2003"; published August 27, 2004; www.census.gov/hhes/income/histinc/h05.html.

[25] Interest rate based on annual percentage yield. Source: www.us.etrade.com, December 2007.

44. *Investments* In 2007, **ING Direct** was offering 4.14% interest on its online Orange Savings Account, with interest reinvested quarterly.[26] Find the associated exponential model for the value of a $4,000 deposit after t years. Assuming this rate of return continued for eight years, how much would a deposit of $4,000 at the beginning of 2007 be worth at the start of 2015? (Answer to the nearest $1.)

45. 🖽 ***Investments*** Refer to Exercise 43. At the start of which year will an investment of $5,000 made at the beginning of 2007 first exceed $7,500?

46. 🖽 ***Investments*** Refer to Exercise 44. In which year will an investment of $4,000 made at the beginning of 2007 first exceed $6,000?

47. *Carbon Dating* A fossil originally contained 104 grams of carbon 14. Refer to the formula for $C(t)$ in Example 7 and estimate the amount of carbon 14 left in the sample after 10,000 years, 20,000 years, and 30,000 years. HINT [See Example 7.]

48. *Carbon Dating* A fossil contains 4.06 grams of carbon 14. Refer to the formula for $C(t)$ in Example 7 and estimate the amount of carbon 14 in the sample 10,000 years, 20,000 years, and 30,000 years ago.

49. *Carbon Dating* A fossil contains 4.06 grams of carbon 14. It is estimated that the fossil originally contained 46 grams of carbon 14. By calculating the amount left after 5,000 years, 10,000 years, . . . , 35,000 years, estimate the age of the sample to the nearest 5,000 years. (Refer to the formula for $C(t)$ in Example 7.)

50. *Carbon Dating* A fossil contains 2.8 grams of carbon 14. It is estimated that the fossil originally contained 104 grams of carbon 14. By calculating the amount 5,000 years, 10,000 years, . . . , 35,000 years ago, estimate the age of the sample to the nearest 5,000 years. (Refer to the formula for $C(t)$ in Example 7.)

51. *Radium Decay* The amount of radium 226 remaining in a sample that originally contained A grams is approximately

$$C(t) = A(0.999567)^t$$

where t is time in years.

a. Find, to the nearest whole number, the percentage of iodine-131 left in an originally pure sample after 1,000 years, 2,000 years, and 3,000 years.

b. Use a graph to estimate, to the nearest 100 years, when one half of a sample of 100 grams will have decayed.

52. *Iodine Decay* The amount of iodine 131 remaining in a sample that originally contained A grams is approximately

$$C(t) = A(0.9175)^t$$

where t is time in days.

a. Find, to the nearest whole number, the percentage of iodine 131 left in an originally pure sample after 2 days, 4 days, and 6 days.

b. Use a graph to estimate, to the nearest day, when one half of a sample of 100 grams will have decayed.

COMMUNICATION AND REASONING EXERCISES

53. If the population of the lunar station at Clavius has a population of $P = 200 + 30t$ where t is time in years since the station was established, then the population is increasing by _____ per year.

54. My bank balance can be modeled by $B(t) = 5,000 - 200t$ dollars, where t is time in days since I opened the account. The balance on my account is _____ by $200 per day.

55. Classify the following model as analytical or curve-fitting, and give a reason for your choice: The price of gold was $700 on Monday, $710 on Tuesday, and $700 on Wednesday. Therefore, the price can be modeled by $p(t) = -10t^2 + 20t + 700$ where t is the day since Monday.

56. Classify the following model as analytical or curve-fitting, and give a reason for your choice: The width of a small animated square on my computer screen is currently 10 mm and is growing by 2 mm per second. Therefore, its area can be modeled by $a(t) = (10 + 2t)^2$ square mm where t is time in seconds.

57. Fill in the missing information for the following *analytical model* (answers may vary): _____. Therefore, the cost of downloading a movie can be modeled by $c(t) = 4 - 0.2t$, where t is time in months since January.

58. Repeat Exercise 57, but this time regard the given model as a *curve-fitting model.*

59. Fill in the blanks: In a linear cost function, the _____ cost is x times the _____ cost.

60. Complete the following sentence: In a linear cost function, the marginal cost is the _____.

61. ▼ We said on page 61 that the demand for a commodity generally goes down as the price goes up. Assume that the demand for a certain commodity goes up as the price goes up. Is it still possible for there to be an equilibrium price? Explain with the aid of a demand and supply graph.

62. ▼ What would happen to the price of a certain commodity if the demand was always greater than the supply? Illustrate with a demand and supply graph.

63. You have a set of data points showing the sales of videos on your Web site versus time that are closely approximated by two different mathematical models. Give one criterion that would lead you to choose one over the other. (Answers may vary.)

64. Would it ever be reasonable to use a quadratic model $s(t) = at^2 + bt + c$ to predict long-term sales if a is negative? Explain.

---

[26] Interest rate based on annual percentage yield. Source: www.home.ingdirect.com, December 2007.

1.3 Linear Functions and Models

Linear functions are among the simplest functions and are perhaps the most useful of all mathematical functions.

Linear Function

A **linear function** is one that can be written in the form

			Quick Example

$$f(x) = mx + b \qquad \text{Function form} \qquad f(x) = 3x - 1$$

or

$$y = mx + b \qquad \text{Equation form} \qquad y = 3x - 1$$

where m and b are fixed numbers. (The names m and b are traditional.*)

✳ NOTE Actually, c is sometimes used instead of b. As for m, there has even been some research lately into the question of its origin, but no one knows exactly why the letter m is used.

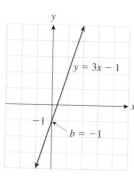

Figure 16

Linear Functions from the Numerical and Graphical Point of View

The following table shows values of $y = 3x - 1 \, (m = 3, b = -1)$ for some values of x:

x	-4	-3	-2	-1	0	1	2	3	4
y	-13	-10	-7	-4	-1	2	5	8	11

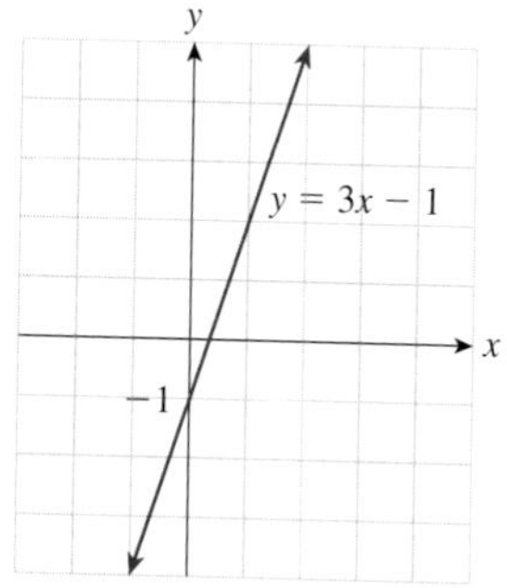

Its graph is shown in Figure 16.

Looking first at the table, notice that that setting $x = 0$ gives $y = -1$, the value of b.

Numerically, b is the value of y when x = 0.

On the graph, the corresponding point $(0, -1)$ is the point where the graph crosses the y-axis, and we say that $b = -1$ is the **y-intercept** of the graph (Figure 17).

What about m? Looking once again at the table, notice that y increases by $m = 3$ units for every increase of 1 unit in x. This is caused by the term $3x$ in the formula: For every increase of 1 in x, we get an increase of $3 \times 1 = 3$ in y.

Numerically, y increases by m units for every 1-unit increase of x.

Likewise, for every increase of 2 in x we get an increase of $3 \times 2 = 6$ in y. In general, if x increases by some amount, y will increase by three times that amount. We write:

y-intercept $= b = -1$
Graphically, b is the y-intercept of the graph.

Figure 17

Change in $y = 3 \times$ Change in x.

The Change in a Quantity: Delta Notation

If a quantity q changes from q_1 to q_2, the **change in q** is just the difference:

$$\text{Change in } q = \text{Second value} - \text{First value}$$
$$= q_2 - q_1$$

Mathematicians traditionally use Δ (delta, the Greek equivalent of the Roman letter D) to stand for change, and write the change in q as Δq.

$$\Delta q = \text{Change in } q = q_2 - q_1$$

Quick Examples

1. If x is changed from 1 to 3, we write

$$\Delta x = \text{Second value} - \text{First value} = 3 - 1 = 2.$$

2. Looking at our linear function, we see that when x changes from 1 to 3, y changes from 2 to 8. So,

$$\Delta y = \text{Second value} - \text{First value} = 8 - 2 = 6.$$

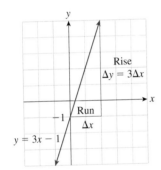

Using delta notation, we can now write, for our linear function,

$$\Delta y = 3\Delta x \qquad \text{Change in } y = 3 \times \text{Change in } x.$$

or

$$\frac{\Delta y}{\Delta x} = 3.$$

Because the value of y increases by exactly 3 units for every increase of 1 unit in x, the graph is a straight line rising by 3 units for every 1 unit we go to the right. We say that we have a **rise** of 3 units for each **run** of 1 unit. Because the value of y changes by $\Delta y = 3\Delta x$ units for every change of Δx units in x, in general we have a rise of $\Delta y = 3\Delta x$ units for each run of Δx units (Figure 18). Thus, we have a rise of 6 for a run of 2, a rise of 9 for a run of 3, and so on. So, $m = 3$ is a measure of the steepness of the line; we call m the **slope of the line:**

$$\text{Slope} = m = \frac{\Delta y}{\Delta x} = \frac{\text{Rise}}{\text{Run}}$$

In general (replace the number 3 by a general number m), we can say the following.

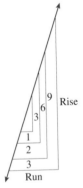

Slope $= m = 3$
Graphically, m is the slope of the graph.

Figure 18

The Roles of m and b in the Linear Function $f(x) = mx + b$

Role of m

Numerically If $y = mx + b$, then y changes by m units for every 1-unit change in x. A change of Δx units in x results in a change of $\Delta y = m\Delta x$ units in y. Thus,

$$m = \frac{\Delta y}{\Delta x} = \frac{\text{Change in } y}{\text{Change in } x}.$$

Graphically m is the slope of the line $y = mx + b$:

$$m = \frac{\Delta y}{\Delta x} = \frac{\text{Rise}}{\text{Run}} = \text{Slope}.$$

For positive m, the graph rises m units for every 1-unit move to the right, and rises $\Delta y = m\Delta x$ units for every Δx units moved to the right. For negative m, the graph drops $|m|$ units for every 1-unit move to the right, and drops $|m|\Delta x$ units for every Δx units moved to the right.

Graph of $y = mx + b$

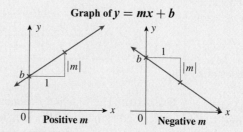

Role of *b*

Numerically When $x = 0$, $y = b$.

Graphically b is the y-intercept of the line $y = mx + b$.

Quick Examples

1. $f(x) = 2x + 1$ has slope $m = 2$ and y-intercept $b = 1$. To sketch the graph, we start at the y-intercept $b = 1$ on the y-axis, and then move 1 unit to the right and up $m = 2$ units to arrive at a second point on the graph. Now connect the two points to obtain the graph on the left.

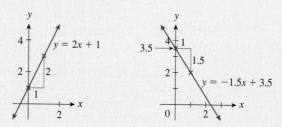

2. The line $y = -1.5x + 3.5$ has slope $m = -1.5$ and y-intercept $b = 3.5$. Because the slope is negative, the graph (above right) goes *down* 1.5 units for every 1 unit it moves to the right.

It helps to be able to picture what different slopes look like, as in Figure 19. Notice that the larger the absolute value of the slope, the steeper is the line.

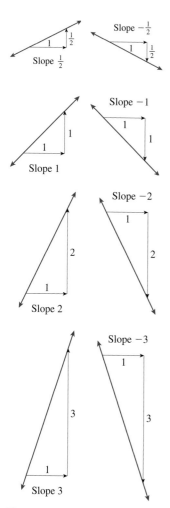

Figure 19

 **using** Technology

See the Technology Guide at the end of the chapter for detailed instructions on how to obtain a table with the successive quotients $m = \Delta y / \Delta x$ for the functions f and g in Example 1 using a TI-83/84 Plus or Excel. These tables show at a glance that f is not linear. Here is an outline:

TI-83/84 Plus

STAT EDIT; Enter values of x and $f(x)$ in lists L_1 and L_2. Highlight the heading L_3 and enter the following formula (including the quotes):
`"ΔList(L₂)/ΔList(L₁)"`
[More details on page 110.]

Excel

Enter headings x, $f(x)$, Df/Dx in cells A1–C1, and the corresponding values from one of the tables in cells A2–B8. Enter `=(B3-B2)/(A3-A2)` in cell C2, and copy down through C8. [More details on page 116.]

EXAMPLE 1 **Recognizing Linear Data Numerically and Graphically**

Which of the following two tables gives the values of a linear function? What is the formula for that function?

x	0	2	4	6	8	10	12
$f(x)$	3	−1	−3	−6	−8	−13	−15

x	0	2	4	6	8	10	12
$g(x)$	3	−1	−5	−9	−13	−17	−21

Solution The function f cannot be linear: If it were, we would have $\Delta f = m \Delta x$ for some fixed number m. However, although the change in x between successive entries in the table is $\Delta x = 2$ each time, the change in f is not the same each time. Thus, the ratio $\Delta f / \Delta x$ is not the same for every successive pair of points.

On the other hand, the ratio $\Delta g / \Delta x$ is the same each time, namely,

$$\frac{\Delta g}{\Delta x} = \frac{-4}{2} = -2$$

| Δx | | $2 - 0 = 2$ | | $4 - 2 = 2$ | | $6 - 4 = 2$ | | $8 - 6 = 2$ | | $10 - 8 = 2$ | | $12 - 10 = 2$ | |

x	0	2	4	6	8	10	12
$g(x)$	3	−1	−5	−9	−13	−17	−21

| Δg | | $(-1) - 3$ $= -4$ | | $-5 - (-1)$ $= -4$ | | $-9 - (-5)$ $= -4$ | | $-13 - (-9)$ $= -4$ | | $-17 - (-13)$ $= -4$ | | $-21 - (-17)$ $= -4$ | |

Thus, g is linear with slope $m = -2$. By the table, $g(0) = 3$, hence $b = 3$. Thus,

$$g(x) = -2x + 3. \qquad \text{Check that this formula gives the values in the table.}$$

If you graph the points in the tables defining f and g above, it becomes easy to see that g is linear and f is not; the points of g lie on a straight line (with slope -2), whereas the points of f do not lie on a straight line (Figure 20).

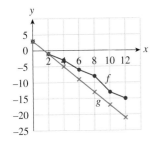

Figure 20

Finding a Linear Equation from Data

If we happen to know the slope and y-intercept of a line, writing down its equation is straightforward. For example, if we know that the slope is 3 and the y-intercept is -1, then the equation is $y = 3x - 1$. Sadly, the information we are given is seldom so convenient. For instance, we may know the slope and a point other than the y intercept, two points on the line, or other information. We therefore need to know how to use the information we are given to obtain the slope and the intercept.

Computing the Slope

We can always determine the slope of a line if we are given two (or more) points on the line, because any two points—say (x_1, y_1) and (x_2, y_2)—determine the line, and hence its slope. To compute the slope when given two points, recall the formula

$$\text{Slope} = m = \frac{\text{Rise}}{\text{Run}} = \frac{\Delta y}{\Delta x}.$$

To find its slope, we need a run Δx and corresponding rise Δy. In Figure 21, we see that we can use $\Delta x = x_2 - x_1$, the change in the x-coordinate from the first point to the second, as our run, and $\Delta y = y_2 - y_1$, the change in the y-coordinate, as our rise. The resulting formula for computing the slope is given in the box.

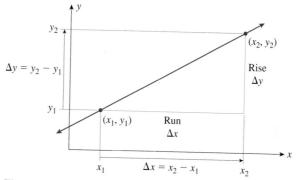

Figure 21

Computing the Slope of a Line

We can compute the slope m of the line through the points (x_1, y_1) and (x_2, y_2) by using

$$m = \frac{\Delta y}{\Delta x} = \frac{y_2 - y_1}{x_2 - x_1}.$$

Quick Examples

1. The slope of the line through $(x_1, y_1) = (1, 3)$ and $(x_2, y_2) = (5, 11)$ is

$$m = \frac{\Delta y}{\Delta x} = \frac{y_2 - y_1}{x_2 - x_1} = \frac{11 - 3}{5 - 1} = \frac{8}{4} = 2.$$

Notice that we can use the points in the reverse order: If we take $(x_1, y_1) = (5, 11)$ and $(x_2, y_2) = (1, 3)$, we obtain the same answer:

$$m = \frac{\Delta y}{\Delta x} = \frac{y_2 - y_1}{x_2 - x_1} = \frac{3 - 11}{1 - 5} = \frac{-8}{-4} = 2.$$

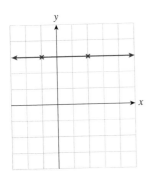

Figure 22

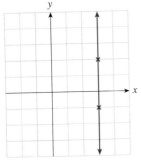

Vertical lines have undefined slope.

Figure 23

2. The slope of the line through $(x_1, y_1) = (1, 2)$ and $(x_2, y_2) = (2, 1)$ is

$$m = \frac{\Delta y}{\Delta x} = \frac{y_2 - y_1}{x_2 - x_1} = \frac{1 - 2}{2 - 1} = \frac{-1}{1} = -1.$$

3. The slope of the line through $(2, 3)$ and $(-1, 3)$ is

$$m = \frac{\Delta y}{\Delta x} = \frac{y_2 - y_1}{x_2 - x_1} = \frac{3 - 3}{-1 - 2} = \frac{0}{-3} = 0.$$

A line of slope 0 has 0 rise, so is a *horizontal* line, as shown in Figure 22.

4. The line through $(3, 2)$ and $(3, -1)$ has slope

$$m = \frac{\Delta y}{\Delta x} = \frac{y_2 - y_1}{x_2 - x_1} = \frac{-1 - 2}{3 - 3} = \frac{-3}{0},$$

which is undefined. The line passing through these points is *vertical*, as shown in Figure 23.

Computing the y-Intercept

Once we know the slope m of a line, and also the coordinates of a point (x_1, y_1), then we can calculate its intercept b as follows: The equation of the line must be

$$y = mx + b,$$

where b is as yet unknown. To determine b we use the fact that the line must pass through the point (x_1, y_1), so that (x_1, y_1) satisfies the equation $y = mx + b$. In other words,

$$y_1 = mx_1 + b.$$

Solving for b gives

$$b = y_1 - mx_1.$$

In summary:

Computing the y-Intercept of a Line

The y-intercept of the line passing through (x_1, y_1) with slope m is

$$b = y_1 - mx_1.$$

Quick Example

The line through $(2, 3)$ with slope 4 has

$$b = y_1 - mx_1 = 3 - (4)(2) = -5.$$

Its equation is therefore

$$y = mx + b = 4x - 5.$$

EXAMPLE 2 Finding Linear Equations

Find equations for the following straight lines.

a. Through the points $(1, 2)$ and $(3, -1)$

b. Through $(2, -2)$ and parallel to the line $3x + 4y = 5$

c. Horizontal and through $(-9, 5)$

d. Vertical and through $(-9, 5)$

Solution

a. To write down the equation of the line, we need the slope m and the y-intercept b.

- **Slope** Because we are given two points on the line, we can use the slope formula:

$$m = \frac{y_2 - y_1}{x_2 - x_1} = \frac{-1 - 2}{3 - 1} = -\frac{3}{2}$$

- **Intercept** We now have the slope of the line, $m = -3/2$, and also a point—we have two to choose from, so let us choose $(x_1, y_1) = (1, 2)$. We can now use the formula for the y-intercept:

$$b = y_1 - mx_1 = 2 - \left(-\frac{3}{2}\right)(1) = \frac{7}{2}$$

Thus, the equation of the line is

$$y = -\frac{3}{2}x + \frac{7}{2}. \qquad y = mx + b$$

using Technology

See the Technology Guide at the end of the chapter for detailed instructions on how to obtain the slope and intercept in Example 2(a) using a TI-83/84 Plus or Excel. Here is an outline:

TI-83/84 Plus

STAT EDIT; Enter values of x and y in lists L_1 and L_2.
Slope: Highlight the heading L_3 and enter
"$\Delta \text{List}(L_2)/\Delta \text{List}(L_1)$"
Intercept: Highlight the heading L_4 and enter
"$L_2-\text{sum}(L_3)*L_1$" [More details on page 110.]

Excel

Enter headings x, y, m, b in cells A1–D1, and the values (x, y) in cells A2–B3. Enter
= (B3-B2)/(A3-A2)
in cell C2, and
=B2-C2*A2
in cell D2. [More details on page 116.]

b. Proceeding as before,

- **Slope** We are not given two points on the line, but we are given a parallel line. We use the fact that *parallel lines have the same slope.* (Why?) We can find the slope of $3x + 4y = 5$ by solving for y and then looking at the coefficient of x:

$$y = -\frac{3}{4}x + \frac{5}{4} \qquad \text{To find the slope, solve for } y.$$

so the slope is $-3/4$.

- **Intercept** We now have the slope of the line, $m = -3/4$, and also a point $(x_1, y_1) = (2, -2)$. We can now use the formula for the y-intercept:

$$b = y_1 - mx_1 = -2 - \left(-\frac{3}{4}\right)(2) = -\frac{1}{2}$$

Thus, the equation of the line is

$$y = -\frac{3}{4}x - \frac{1}{2}. \qquad y = mx + b$$

c. We are given a point: $(-9, 5)$. Furthermore, we are told that the line is horizontal, which tells us that the slope is $m = 0$. Therefore, all that remains is the calculation of the y-intercept:

$$b = y_1 - mx_1 = 5 - (0)(-9) = 5$$

so the equation of the line is

$$y = 5. \qquad {\scriptstyle y = mx + b}$$

d. We are given a point: $(-9, 5)$. This time, we are told that the line is vertical, which means that the slope is undefined. Thus, we can't express the equation of the line in the form $y = mx + b$. (This formula makes sense only when the slope m of the line is defined.) What can we do? Well, here are some points on the desired line:

$$(-9, 1), (-9, 2), (-9, 3), \ldots,$$

so $x = -9$ and $y = anything$. If we simply say that $x = -9$, then these points are all solutions, so the equation is $x = -9$.

Applications: Linear Models

Using linear functions to describe or approximate relationships in the real world is called **linear modeling**.

   Recall from Section 1.2 that a **cost function** specifies the cost C as a function of the number of items x.

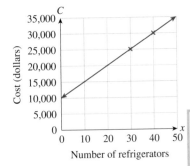

Figure 24

EXAMPLE 3 Linear Cost Function from Data

The manager of the FrozenAir Refrigerator factory notices that on Monday it cost the company a total of $25,000 to build 30 refrigerators and on Tuesday it cost $30,000 to build 40 refrigerators. Find a linear cost function based on this information. What is the daily fixed cost, and what is the marginal cost?

Solution We are seeking the cost C as a linear function of x, the number of refrigerators sold:

$$C = mx + b.$$

We are told that $C = 25,000$ when $x = 30$, and this amounts to being told that $(30, 25,000)$ is a point on the graph of the cost function. Similarly, $(40, 30,000)$ is another point on the line (Figure 24).

   We can use the two points on the line to construct the linear cost equation:

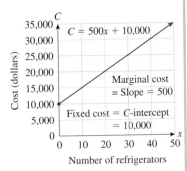

Figure 25

• *Slope* $m = \dfrac{C_2 - C_1}{x_2 - x_1} = \dfrac{30,000 - 25,000}{40 - 30} = 500$ C plays the role of y.

• *Intercept* $b = C_1 - mx_1 = 25,000 - (500)(30) = 10,000$ We used the point $(x_1, C_1) = (30, 25,000)$.

The linear cost function is therefore

$$C(x) = 500x + 10,000.$$

Because $m = 500$ and $b = 10,000$ the factory's fixed cost is $10,000 each day, and its marginal cost is $500 per refrigerator. (See page 58 in Section 1.2.) These are illustrated in Figure 25.

using Technology

To obtain the cost equation for Example 3 with technology, apply the Technology note for Example 2(a) to the given points (30, 25,000) and (40, 30,000) on the graph of the cost equation.

➡ **Before we go on...** Recall that, in general, the slope m measures the number of units of change in y per 1-unit change in x, so it is measured in units of y per unit of x:

$$\text{Units of Slope} = \text{Units of } y \text{ per unit of } x$$

In Example 3, y is the cost C, measured in dollars, and x is the number of items, measured in refrigerators. Hence,

$$\text{Units of Slope} = \text{Units of } y \text{ per Unit of } x = \text{Dollars per refrigerator}$$

The y-intercept b, being a value of y, is measured in the same units as y. In Example 3, b is measured in dollars. ∎

In Section 1.2 we saw that a **demand function** specifies the demand q as a function of the price p per item, whereas a **supply function** specifies the supply q as a function of unit price p.

EXAMPLE 4 **Linear Demand and Supply Functions from Data**

You run a small supermarket, and must determine how much to charge for Hot'n'Spicy brand baked beans. The following chart shows weekly sales figures (the demand) for Hot'n'Spicy at two different prices, as well as the number of cans per week that you are prepared to place on sale (the supply) at these prices.

	Price/Can	\$0.50	\$0.75
Demand (cans sold/week)		400	350
Supply (cans placed on sale/week)		300	500

a. Model these data with linear demand and supply functions. (See Example 4 in Section 1.2.)

b. How do we interpret the slope and q intercept of the demand equation? How do we interpret the slope of the supply equation?

c. Find the equilibrium price and graph demand and supply on the same set of axes. What happens if you charge more than the equilibrium price? What happens if you charge less?

Solution

a. Recall that a demand equation or demand function expresses demand q (in this case, the number of cans of beans sold per week) as a function of the unit price p (in this case, price per can). We model the demand using the two points we are given: (0.50, 400) and (0.75, 350).

$$\textit{Slope: } m = \frac{q_2 - q_1}{p_2 - p_1} = \frac{350 - 400}{0.75 - 0.50} = \frac{-50}{0.25} = -200$$

$$\textit{Intercept: } b = q_1 - mp_1 = 400 - (-200)(0.50) = 500$$

So, the demand equation is

$$q = -200p + 500. \qquad q = mp + b$$

To model the supply, we use the first and third rows of the table. We are again given two points: (0.50, 300) and (0.75, 500).

$$\textbf{\textit{Slope: }} m = \frac{q_2 - q_1}{p_2 - p_1} = \frac{500 - 300}{0.75 - 0.50} = \frac{200}{0.25} = 800$$

$$\textbf{\textit{Intercept: }} b = q_1 - mp_1 = 300 - (800)(0.50) = -100$$

So, the supply equation is

$$q = 800p - 100.$$

b. The key to interpreting the slope in the demand and supply equations is to recall (see the "Before we go on" note at the end of Example 3) that we measure the slope in *units of y per unit of x*. Let us consider the demand and supply equations separately:

Demand equation: Here, $m = -200$, and the units of m are units of q per unit of p, or the number of cans sold per dollar change in the price. Since m is negative, we see that the number of cans sold decreases as the price increases. We conclude that the weekly sales will drop by 200 cans per $1-increase in the price.

To interpret the q intercept for the demand equation, recall that it gives the q-coordinate when $p = 0$. Hence, it is the number of cans the supermarket can "sell" every week if it were to give them away.*

Supply equation: Here, $m = 800$, and the units of m are the number of cans you are prepared to supply per dollar change in the price. We conclude that the weekly supply will increase by 800 cans per $1-increase in the price. (We do not interpret the q-intercept in the case of the supply equation; one cannot have a negative supply. See the "Before we go on" discussion at the end of the example.)

c. To find where the demand equals the supply, we equate the two functions:

$$\text{Demand} = \text{Supply}$$
$$-200p + 500 = 800p - 100$$
$$-1000p = -600,$$

so

$$p = \frac{-600}{-1000} = \$0.60$$

This is the equilibrium price, as discussed in Example 4 of Section 1.2. We can find the corresponding demand by substituting 0.60 for p in the demand (or supply) equation.

$$\text{Equilibrium demand} = -200(0.60) + 500 = 380 \text{ cans per week}$$

So, to balance supply and demand, you should charge $0.60 per can of Hot'n'Spicy beans and you should place 380 cans on sale each week.

✳ NOTE Does this seem realistic? Demand is not always unlimited if items were given away. For instance, campus newspapers are sometimes given away, and yet piles of them are often left untaken. Also see the "Before we go on..." discussion at the end of this example.

▦ using Technology

To obtain the demand and supply equations for Example 4 with technology, apply the Technology note for Example 2(a) to the points (0.50, 400) and (0.75, 350) on the graph of the demand equation, and (0.50, 300) and (0.75, 500) on the graph of the supply equation.

➡ **Before we go on...** As we saw in Example 4 in Section 1.2, charging more than the equilibrium price will result in a surplus of Hot'n'Spicy beans, and charging less will result in a shortage. (See Figure 26.)

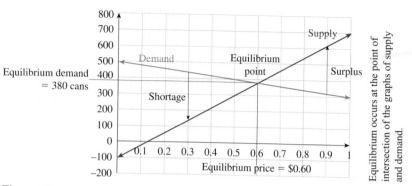

Figure 26

Q : *Just how reliable are the linear models used in Example 4?*

A : The *actual* demand and supply graphs could in principle be obtained by tabulating demand and supply figures for a large number of different prices. If the resulting points were plotted on the *pq* plane, they would probably suggest curves and not a straight line. However, if you looked at a small enough portion of any curve, you could closely *approximate* it by a straight line. In other words, *over a small range of values of p, a linear model is accurate.* Linear models of real-world situations are generally reliable only for small ranges of the variables. (This point will come up again in some of the exercises.)

∎

The next example illustrates modeling change over time *t* with a linear function of *t*.

EXAMPLE 5 Modeling Change Over Time: Growth of Sales

The worldwide market for portable navigation devices was expected to grow from 50 million units in 2007 to around 530 million units in 2015.*

a. Use this information to model annual worldwide sales of portable navigation devices as a linear function of time *t* in years since 2007. What is the significance of the slope?

b. Use the model to predict when annual sales of mobile navigation devices will reach 440 million units.

Solution

a. Since we are interested in worldwide sales *s* of portable navigation devices as a function of time, we take time *t* to be the independent coordinate (playing the role of *x*) and the annual sales *s*, in million of units, to be the dependent coordinate (in the role of *y*). Notice that 2007 corresponds to $t = 0$ and 2015 corresponds to $t = 8$, so we are given

---

* Sales were expected to grow to more than 500 million in 2015 according to a January 2008 press release by Telematics Research Group. Source: www.telematicsresearch.com.

the coordinates of two points on the graph of sales s as a function of time t: $(0, 50)$ and $(8, 530)$. We model the sales using these two points:

$$m = \frac{s_2 - s_1}{t_2 - t_1} = \frac{530 - 50}{8 - 0} = \frac{480}{8} = 60$$

$$b = s_1 - mt_1 = 50 - (60)(0) = 50$$

So, $s = 60t + 50$ million units. $s = mt + b$

The slope m is measured in units of s per unit of t; that is, millions of devices per year, and is thus the *rate of change of annual sales*. To say that $m = 60$ is to say that annual sales are increasing at a rate of 60 million devices per year.

b. Our model of annual sales as a function of time is

$$s = 60t + 50 \text{ million units.}$$

Annual sales of mobile portable devices will reach 440 million when $s = 440$, or

$$440 = 60t + 50$$

Solving for t, $60t = 440 - 50 = 390$

$$t = \frac{390}{60} = 6.5 \text{ years,}$$

which is midway through 2013. Thus annual sales are expected to reach 440 million midway through 2013.

using Technology

To use technology to obtain s as a function of t in Example 5, apply the Technology note for Example 2(a) to the points $(0, 50)$ and $(8, 530)$ on its graph.

EXAMPLE 6 Velocity

You are driving down the Ohio Turnpike, watching the mileage markers to stay awake. Measuring time in hours after you see the 20-mile marker, you see the following markers each half hour:

Time (h)	0	0.5	1	1.5	2
Marker (mi)	20	47	74	101	128

Find your location s as a function of t, the number of hours you have been driving. (The number s is also called your **position** or **displacement**.)

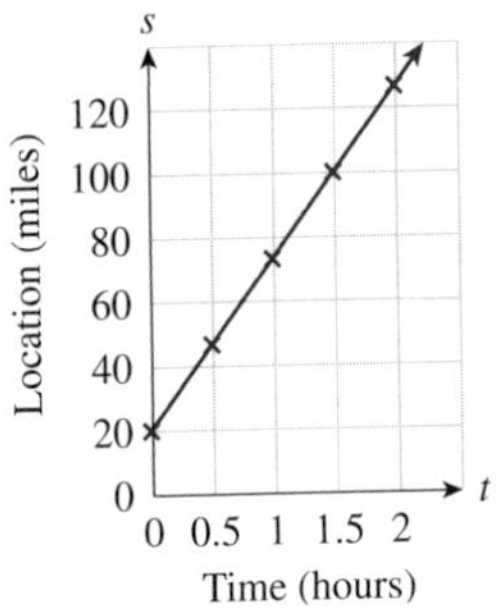

Solution If we plot the location s versus the time t, the five markers listed give us the graph in Figure 27.

These points appear to lie along a straight line. We can verify this by calculating how far you traveled in each half hour. In the first half hour, you traveled $47 - 20 = 27$ miles. In the second half hour you traveled $74 - 47 = 27$ miles also. In fact, you traveled exactly 27 miles each half hour. The points we plotted lie on a straight line that rises 27 units for every 0.5 unit we go to the right, for a slope of $27/0.5 = 54$.

To get the equation of that line, notice that we have the s-intercept, which is the starting marker of 20. Thus, the equation of s as a function of time t is

$$s(t) = 54t + 20.   \text{We used } s \text{ in place of } y \text{ and } t \text{ in place of } x.$$

Notice the significance of the slope: For every hour you travel, you drive a distance of 54 miles. In other words, you are traveling at a constant velocity of 54 mph. We have uncovered a very important principle:

In the graph of displacement versus time, velocity is given by the slope.

using Technology

To use technology to obtain s as a function of t in Example 6, apply the Technology note for Example 2(a) to the points $(0, 20)$ and $(1, 74)$ on its graph.

s

Location (miles)

Time (hours)

Figure 27

Linear Change Over Time

If a quantity q is a linear function of time t,

$$q = mt + b,$$

then the slope m measures the **rate of change** of q, and b is the quantity at time $t = 0$, the **initial quantity**. If q represents the position of a moving object, then the rate of change is also called the **velocity**.

Units of m and b

The units of measurement of m are units of q per unit of time; for instance, if q is income in dollars and t is time in years, then the rate of change m is measured in dollars per year.

The units of b are units of q; for instance, if q is income in dollars and t is time in years, then b is measured in dollars.

Quick Example

If the accumulated revenue from sales of your video game software is given by $R = 2{,}000t + 500$ dollars, where t is time in years from now, then you have earned $500 in revenue so far, and the accumulated revenue is increasing at a rate of $2,000 per year.

Examples 3–6 share the following common theme.

General Linear Models

If $y = mx + b$ is a linear model of changing quantities x and y, then the slope m is the rate at which y is increasing per unit increase in x, and the y-intercept b is the value of y that corresponds to $x = 0$.

Units of m and b

The slope m is measured in units of y per unit of x, and the intercept b is measured in units of y.

Quick Example

If the number n of spectators at a soccer game is related to the number g of goals your team has scored so far by the equation $n = 20g + 4$, then you can expect 4 spectators if no goals have been scored and 20 additional spectators per additional goal scored.

FAQs

What to Use as x and y, and How to Interpret a Linear Model

Q: *In a problem where I must find a linear relationship between two quantities, which quantity do I use as x and which do I use as y?*

A: The key is to decide which of the two quantities is the independent variable, and which is the dependent variable. Then use the independent variable as x and the dependent variable as y. In other words, *y depends on x.*
    Here are examples of phrases that convey this information, usually of the form *Find y [dependent variable] in terms of x [independent variable]:*

• Find the cost in terms of the number of items. $y = \text{Cost}, x = \# \text{ Items}$
• How does color depend on wavelength? $y = \text{Color}, x = \text{Wavelength}$

If no information is conveyed about which variable is intended to be independent, then you can use whichever is convenient.

Q: *How do I interpret a general linear model $y = mx + b$?*

A: The key to interpreting a linear model is to remember the units we use to measure m and b:

The slope m is measured in units of y per unit of x; the intercept b is measured in units of y.

For instance, if $y = 4.3x + 8.1$ and you know that x is measured in feet and y in kilograms, then you can already say, "y is 8.1 kilograms when $x = 0$ feet, and increases at a rate of 4.3 kilograms per foot" without even knowing anything more about the situation!

1.3 EXERCISES

▼ more advanced   ◆ challenging
T indicates exercises that should be solved using technology

In Exercises 1–6, a table of values for a linear function is given. Fill in the missing value and calculate m in each case.

1.

x	−1	0	1
y	5	8	

2.

x	−1	0	1
y	−1	−3	

3.

x	2	3	5
f(x)	−1	−2	

4.

x	2	4	5
f(x)	−1	−2	

5.

x	−2	0	2
f(x)	4		10

6.

x	0	3	6
f(x)	−1		−5

In Exercises 7–10, first find f(0), if not supplied, and then find the equation of the given linear function.

7.

x	−2	0	2	4
f(x)	−1	−2	−3	−4

8.

x	−6	−3	0	3
f(x)	1	2	3	4

9.

x	−4	−3	−2	−1
$f(x)$	−1	−2	−3	−4

10.

x	1	2	3	4
$f(x)$	4	6	8	10

In each of Exercises 11–14, decide which of the two given functions is linear and find its equation. HINT [See Example 1.]

11.

x	0	1	2	3	4
$f(x)$	6	10	14	18	22
$g(x)$	8	10	12	16	22

12.

x	−10	0	10	20	30
$f(x)$	−1.5	0	1.5	2.5	3.5
$g(x)$	−9	−4	1	6	11

13.

x	0	3	6	10	15
$f(x)$	0	3	5	7	9
$g(x)$	−1	5	11	19	29

14.

x	0	3	5	6	9
$f(x)$	2	6	9	12	15
$g(x)$	−1	8	14	17	26

In Exercises 15–24, find the slope of the given line, if it is defined.

15. $y = -\dfrac{3}{2}x - 4$

16. $y = \dfrac{2x}{3} + 4$

17. $y = \dfrac{x+1}{6}$

18. $y = -\dfrac{2x-1}{3}$

19. $3x + 1 = 0$

20. $8x - 2y = 1$

21. $3y + 1 = 0$

22. $2x + 3 = 0$

23. $4x + 3y = 7$

24. $2y + 3 = 0$

In Exercises 25–38, graph the given equation. HINT [See Quick Examples on page 77.]

25. $y = 2x - 1$

26. $y = x - 3$

27. $y = -\frac{2}{3}x + 2$

28. $y = -\frac{1}{2}x + 3$

29. $y + \frac{1}{4}x = -4$

30. $y - \frac{1}{4}x = -2$

31. $7x - 2y = 7$

32. $2x - 3y = 1$

33. $3x = 8$

34. $2x = -7$

35. $6y = 9$

36. $3y = 4$

37. $2x = 3y$

38. $3x = -2y$

In Exercises 39–54, calculate the slope, if defined, of the straight line through the given pair of points. Try to do as many as you can without writing anything down except the answer. HINT [See Quick Examples on page 79.]

39. $(0, 0)$ and $(1, 2)$

40. $(0, 0)$ and $(-1, 2)$

41. $(-1, -2)$ and $(0, 0)$

42. $(2, 1)$ and $(0, 0)$

43. $(4, 3)$ and $(5, 1)$

44. $(4, 3)$ and $(4, 1)$

45. $(1, -1)$ and $(1, -2)$

46. $(-2, 2)$ and $(-1, -1)$

47. $(2, 3.5)$ and $(4, 6.5)$

48. $(10, -3.5)$ and $(0, -1.5)$

49. $(300, 20.2)$ and $(400, 11.2)$

50. $(1, -20.2)$ and $(2, 3.2)$

51. $(0, 1)$ and $\left(-\frac{1}{2}, \frac{3}{4}\right)$

52. $\left(\frac{1}{2}, 1\right)$ and $\left(-\frac{1}{2}, \frac{3}{4}\right)$

53. (a, b) and (c, d) $(a \neq c)$

54. (a, b) and (c, b) $(a \neq c)$

55. In the following figure, estimate the slopes of all line segments.

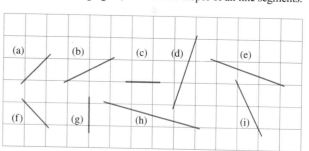

56. In the following figure, estimate the slopes of all line segments.

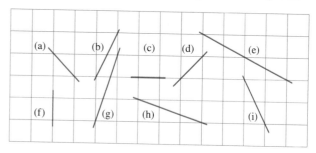

In Exercises 57–74, find a linear equation whose graph is the straight line with the given properties. HINT [See Example 2.]

57. Through $(1, 3)$ with slope 3

58. Through $(2, 1)$ with slope 2

59. Through $(1, -\frac{3}{4})$ with slope $\frac{1}{4}$

60. Through $(0, -\frac{1}{3})$ with slope $\frac{1}{3}$

61. Through $(20, -3.5)$ and increasing at a rate of 10 units of y per unit of x.

62. Through $(3.5, -10)$ and increasing at a rate of 1 unit of y per 2 units of x.

63. Through $(2, -4)$ and $(1, 1)$

64. Through $(1, -4)$ and $(-1, -1)$

65. Through $(1, -0.75)$ and $(0.5, 0.75)$

66. Through $(0.5, -0.75)$ and $(1, -3.75)$

67. Through $(6, 6)$ and parallel to the line $x + y = 4$

68. Through $(1/3, -1)$ and parallel to the line $3x - 4y = 8$

69. Through $(0.5, 5)$ and parallel to the line $4x - 2y = 11$

70. Through $(1/3, 0)$ and parallel to the line $6x - 2y = 11$

71. ▼ Through $(0, 0)$ and (p, q)

72. ▼ Through (p, q) and parallel to $y = rx + s$

73. ▼ Through (p, q) and (r, q) $(p \neq r)$

74. ▼ Through (p, q) and (r, s) $(p \neq r)$

APPLICATIONS

75. *Cost* The RideEm Bicycles factory can produce 100 bicycles in a day at a total cost of $10,500 and it can produce 120 bicycles in a day at a total cost of $11,000. What are the company's daily fixed costs, and what is the marginal cost per bicycle? HINT [See Example 3.]

76. *Cost* A soft-drink manufacturer can produce 1,000 cases of soda in a week at a total cost of $6,000, and 1,500 cases of soda at a total cost of $8,500. Find the manufacturer's weekly fixed costs and marginal cost per case of soda.

77. *Cost: iPods* It cost **Apple** approximately $800 to manufacture 5 30-gigabyte video iPods and $3,700 to manufacture 25.* Obtain the corresponding linear cost function. What was the cost to manufacture each additional iPod? Use the cost function to estimate the cost of manufacturing 100 iPods.

78. *Cost: Xboxes* If it costs **Microsoft** $4,500 to manufacture 8 Xbox 360s and $8,900 to manufacture 16,† obtain the corresponding linear cost function. What was the cost to manufacture each additional Xbox? Use the cost function to estimate the cost of manufacturing 50 Xboxes.

79. *Demand* Sales figures show that your company sold 1,960 pen sets each week when they were priced at $1/pen set and 1,800 pen sets each week when they were priced at $5/pen set. What is the linear demand function for your pen sets? HINT [See Example 4.]

80. *Demand* A large department store is prepared to buy 3,950 of your neon-colored shower curtains per month for $5 each, but only 3,700 shower curtains per month for $10 each. What is the linear demand function for your neon-colored shower curtains?

81. *Demand for Cell Phones* The following table shows worldwide sales of **Nokia** cell phones and their average wholesale prices in 2004:[27]

Quarter	Second	Fourth
Wholesale Price ($)	111	105
Sales (millions)	45.4	51.4

a. Use the data to obtain a linear demand function for (Nokia) cell phones, and use your demand equation to predict sales if Nokia lowered the price further to $103.

b. Fill in the blanks: For every ____ increase in price, sales of cell phones decrease by ____ units.

82. *Demand for Cell Phones* The following table shows projected worldwide sales of (all) cell phones and wholesale prices:[28]

Year	2004	2008
Wholesale Price ($)	100	80
Sales (millions)	600	800

a. Use the data to obtain a linear demand function for cell phones, and use your demand equation to predict sales if the price was set at $85.

b. Fill in the blanks: For every ____ increase in price, sales of cell phones decrease by ____ units.

83. *Demand for Monorail Service, Las Vegas* In 2005, the Las Vegas monorail charged $3 per ride and had an average ridership of about 28,000 per day. In December, 2005 the Las Vegas Monorail Company raised the fare to $5 per ride, and average ridership in 2006 plunged to around 19,000 per day.[29]

a. Use the given information to find a linear demand equation.

b. Give the units of measurement and interpretation of the slope.

c. What would be the effect on ridership of raising the fare to $6 per ride?

---

*Source for cost data: Manufacturing & Technology News, July 31, 2007, Volume 14, No. 14, www.manufacturingnews.com.

†Source for estimate of marginal cost: www.isuppli.com.

[27] Source: Embedded.com/Companyreports December 2004.

[28] Wholesale price projections are the authors'. Source for sales prediction: I-Stat/NDR December, 2004.

[29] Source: *New York Times,* February 10, 2007, p. A9.

84. *Demand for Monorail Service, Mars* The Utarek monorail, which links the three urbynes (or districts) of Utarek, Mars, charged $\bar{\bar{Z}}5$ per ride[30] and sold about 14 million rides per day. When the Utarek City Council lowered the fare to $\bar{\bar{Z}}3$ per ride, the number of rides increased to 18 million per day.

a. Use the given information to find a linear demand equation.

b. Give the units of measurement and interpretation of the slope.

c. What would be the effect on ridership of raising the fare to $\bar{\bar{Z}}10$ per ride?

85. *Equilibrium Price* You can sell 90 pet chias per week if they are marked at $1 each, but only 30 each week if they are marked at $2/chia. Your chia supplier is prepared to sell you 20 chias each week if they are marked at $1/chia, and 100 each week if they are marked at $2 per chia.

a. Write down the associated linear demand and supply functions.

b. At what price should the chias be marked so that there is neither a surplus nor a shortage of chias? HINT [See Example 4.]

86. *Equilibrium Price* The demand for your college newspaper is 2,000 copies each week if the paper is given away free of charge, and drops to 1,000 each week if the charge is 10¢/copy. However, the university is prepared to supply only 600 copies per week free of charge, but will supply 1,400 each week at 20¢ per copy.

a. Write down the associated linear demand and supply functions.

b. At what price should the college newspapers be sold so that there is neither a surplus nor a shortage of papers?

87. *Pasta Imports* During the period 1990–2001, U.S. imports of pasta increased from 290 million pounds in 1990 ($t = 0$) by an average of 40 million pounds/year.[31]

a. Use these data to express q, the annual U.S. imports of pasta (in millions of pounds), as a linear function of t, the number of years since 1990.

b. Use your model to estimate U.S. pasta imports in 2005, assuming the import trend continued.

88. *Mercury Imports* During the period 2210–2220, Martian imports of mercury (from the planet of that name) increased from 550 million kg in 2210 ($t = 0$) by an average of 60 million kg/year.

a. Use these data to express h, the annual Martian imports of mercury (in millions of kilograms), as a linear function of t, the number of years since 2010.

b. Use your model to estimate Martian mercury imports in 2230, assuming the import trend continued.

89. *Satellite Radio Subscriptions* The number of Sirius Satellite Radio subscribers grew from 0.3 million in 2003 to 3.2 million in 2005.[32]

a. Use this information to find a linear model for the number N of subscribers (in millions) as a function of time t in years since 2000.

b. Give the units of measurement and interpretation of the slope.

c. Use the model from part (a) to predict the 2006 figure. (The actual 2006 figure was approximately 6 million subscribers.)

90. *Freon Production* The production of ozone-layer damaging Freon 22 (chlorodifluoromethane) in developing countries rose from 200 tons in 2004 to a projected 590 tons in 2010.[33]

a. Use this information to find a linear model for the amount F of Freon 22 (in tons) as a function of time t in years since 2000.

b. Give the units of measurement and interpretation of the slope.

c. Use the model from part (a) to estimate the 2008 figure and compare it with the actual projection of 400 tons.

91. *Velocity* The position of a model train, in feet along a railroad track, is given by

$$s(t) = 2.5t + 10$$

after t seconds.

a. How fast is the train moving?

b. Where is the train after 4 seconds?

c. When will it be 25 feet along the track?

92. *Velocity* The height of a falling sheet of paper, in feet from the ground, is given by

$$s(t) = -1.8t + 9$$

after t seconds.

a. What is the velocity of the sheet of paper?

b. How high is it after 4 seconds?

c. When will it reach the ground?

93. ▼ *Fast Cars* A police car was traveling down Ocean Parkway in a high speed chase from Jones Beach. It was at Jones Beach at exactly 10 pm ($t = 10$) and was at Oak Beach, 13 miles from Jones Beach, at exactly 10:06 pm.

a. How fast was the police car traveling? HINT [See Example 6.]

b. How far was the police car from Jones Beach at time t?

---

[30] $\bar{\bar{Z}}$ designates Zonars, the official currency in Mars. See www.marsnext.com for details of the Mars colony, its commerce, and its culture.

[31] Data are rounded. Sources: Department of Commerce/*New York Times*, September 5, 1995, p. D4; International Trade Administration, March 31, 2002, www.ita.doc.gov/.

[32] Figures are approximate. Source: Sirius Satellite Radio/*New York Times*, February 20, 2008, p. A1.

[33] Figures are approximate. Source: Lampert Kuijpers (Panel of the Montreal Protocol), National Bureau of Statistics in China, via CEIC DSata/*New York Times*, February 23, 2007, p. C1.

94. ▼ Fast Cars The car that was being pursued by the police in Exercise 93 was at Jones Beach at exactly 9:54 pm ($t = 9.9$) and passed Oak Beach (13 miles from Jones Beach) at exactly 10:06 pm, where it was overtaken by the police.

a. How fast was the car traveling? HINT [See Example 6.]
b. How far was the car from Jones Beach at time *t*?

95. ▼ Fahrenheit and Celsius In the Fahrenheit temperature scale, water freezes at 32°F and boils at 212°F. In the Celsius scale, water freezes at 0°C and boils at 100°C. Assuming that the Fahrenheit temperature F and the Celsius temperature C are related by a linear equation, find F in terms of C. Use your equation to find the Fahrenheit temperatures corresponding to 30°C, 22°C, -10°C, and -14°C, to the nearest degree.

96. ▼ Fahrenheit and Celsius Use the information about Celsius and Fahrenheit given in Exercise 95 to obtain a linear equation for C in terms of F, and use your equation to find the Celsius temperatures corresponding to 104°F, 77°F, 14°F, and -40°F, to the nearest degree.

97. ▼ Income The well-known romance novelist Celestine A. Lafleur (a.k.a. Bertha Snodgrass) has decided to sell the screen rights to her latest book, *Henrietta's Heaving Heart*, to Boxoffice Success Productions for $50,000. In addition, the contract ensures Ms. Lafleur royalties of 5% of the net profits.[34] Express her income I as a function of the net profit N, and determine the net profit necessary to bring her an income of $100,000. What is her marginal income (share of each dollar of net profit)?

98. ▼ Income Due to the enormous success of the movie *Henrietta's Heaving Heart* based on a novel by Celestine A. Lafleur (see the Exercise 97), Boxoffice Success Productions decides to film the sequel, *Henrietta, Oh Henrietta*. At this point, Bertha Snodgrass (whose novels now top the best seller lists) feels she is in a position to demand $100,000 for the screen rights and royalties of 8% of the net profits. Express her income I as a function of the net profit N and determine the net profit necessary to bring her an income of $1,000,000. What is her marginal income (share of each dollar of net profit)?

99. ▼ Biology The Snowtree cricket behaves in a rather interesting way: The rate at which it chirps depends linearly on the temperature. One summer evening you hear a cricket chirping at a rate of 140 chirps/minute, and you notice that the temperature is 80°F. Later in the evening the cricket has slowed down to 120 chirps/minute, and you notice that the temperature has dropped to 75°F. Express the temperature T as a function of the cricket's rate of chirping r. What is the temperature if the cricket is chirping at a rate of 100 chirps/minute?

100. ▼ Muscle Recovery Time Most workout enthusiasts will tell you that muscle recovery time is about 48 hours. But it is not quite as simple as that; the recovery time ought to depend on the number of sets you do involving the muscle group in question. For example, if you do no sets of biceps exercises, then the recovery time for your biceps is (of course) zero. Let's assume that if you do three sets of exercises on a muscle group, then its recovery time is 48 hours. Use these data to write a linear function that gives the recovery time (in hours) in terms of the number of sets affecting a particular muscle. Use this model to calculate how long it would take your biceps to recover if you did 15 sets of curls. Comment on your answer with reference to the usefulness of a linear model.

101. Television Advertising The cost, in millions of dollars, of a 30-second television ad during the Super Bowl in the years 1990 to 2007 can be approximated by the following piecewise linear function ($t = 0$ represents 1990):[35]

$$C(t) = \begin{cases} 0.08t + 0.6 & \text{if } 0 \le t < 8 \\ 0.13t + 0.20 & \text{if } 8 \le t \le 17 \end{cases}$$

How fast and in what direction was the cost of an ad during the Super Bowl changing in 2006?

102. Processor Speeds The processor speed, in megahertz (MHz), of Intel processors could be approximated by the following function of time t in years since the start of 1995:[36]

$$P(t) = \begin{cases} 180t + 200 & \text{if } 0 \le t \le 5 \\ 3000t - 13,900 & \text{if } 5 < t \le 12 \end{cases}$$

How fast and in what direction was processor speed changing in 2005?

103. ▼ Investment in Gold Following are some approximate values of the Amex Gold BUGS Index.[37]

Year	1995	2000	2007
Index	200	50	470

Take t to be the year since 1995 and y to be the BUGS index.

a. Model the 1995 and 2000 data with a linear equation.
b. Model the 2000 and 2007 data with a linear equation.
c. Use the results of parts (a) and (b) to obtain a piecewise linear model of the gold BUGS index for 1995–2007.
d. Use your model to estimate the index in 2002.

104. ▼ Unemployment The following table shows the number of unemployed persons in the U.S. in 1994, 2000, and 2008.[38]

---

[34] Percentages of net profit are commonly called "monkey points." Few movies ever make a net profit on paper, and anyone with any clout in the business gets a share of the *gross*, not the net.

[35] Sources for data: *New York Times*, January 26, 2001, p. C1, http://money.cnn.com.

[36] Sources for data: Sandpile.org/*New York Times*, May 17, 2004, p. C1, www.Intel.com.

[37] BUGS stands for "basket of unhedged gold stocks." Figures are approximate. Sources: www.321gold.com, Bloomberg Financial Markets/*New York Times*, Sept 7, 2003, p. BU8, www.amex.com.

[38] Figures are seasonally adjusted and rounded. Source: U.S. Department of Labor, December, 2004, www.data.bls.gov.

Year	1994	2000	2008
Unemployment (Millions)	9	6	7

Take t to be the year since 1994 and y to be the number (in millions) of unemployed persons.

a. Model the 1994 and 2000 data with a linear equation.
b. Model the 2000 and 2008 data with a linear equation.
c. Use the results of parts (a) and (b) to obtain a piecewise linear model of the number (in millions) of unemployed persons for 1994–2008.
d. Use your model to estimate the number of unemployed persons in 2002.

105. ▼ *Employment in Mexico* The number of workers employed in manufacturing jobs in Mexico was 3 million in 1995, rose to 4.1 million in 2000, and then dropped to 3.5 million in 2004.[39] Model this number N as a piecewise-linear function of the time t in years since 1995, and use your model to estimate the number of manufacturing jobs in Mexico in 2002. (Take the units of N to be millions.)

106. ▼ *Mortgage Delinquencies* The percentage of borrowers in the highest risk category who were delinquent on their payments decreased from 9.7% in 2001 to 4.3% in 2004 and then shot up to 10.3% in 2007.[40] Model this percentage P as a piecewise-linear function of the time t in years since 2001, and use your model to estimate the percentage of delinquent borrowers in 2006.

COMMUNICATION AND REASONING EXERCISES

107. How would you test a table of values of x and y to see if it comes from a linear function?

108. You have ascertained that a table of values of x and y corresponds to a linear function. How do you find an equation for that linear function?

109. To what linear function of x does the linear equation $ax + by = c$ $(b \neq 0)$ correspond? Why did we specify $b \neq 0$?

110. Complete the following. The slope of the line with equation $y = mx + b$ is the number of units that _____ increases per unit increase in _____.

111. Complete the following. If, in a straight line, y is increasing three times as fast as x, then its _____ is _____.

112. Suppose that y is decreasing at a rate of 4 units per 3-unit increase of x. What can we say about the slope of the linear relationship between x and y? What can we say about the intercept?

113. If y and x are related by the linear expression $y = mx + b$, how will y change as x changes if m is positive? negative? zero?

114. Your friend April tells you that $y = f(x)$ has the property that, whenever x is changed by Δx, the corresponding change in y is $\Delta y = -\Delta x$. What can you tell her about f?

115. 🖳 ▼ Consider the following worksheet:

◇	A	B	C	D
1	x	y	m	b
2		1	2	=(B3-B2)/(A3-A2)	=B2-C2*A2
3		3	-1	Slope	Intercept

What is the effect on the slope of increasing the y-coordinate of the second point (the point whose coordinates are in Row 3)? Explain.

116. 🖳 ▼ Referring to the worksheet in Exercise 115, what is the effect on the slope of increasing the x-coordinate of the second point (the point whose coordinates are in row 3)? Explain.

117. If y is measured in bootlags[41] and x is measured in $\overline{\overline{Z}}$ (zonars, the designated currency in Utarek, Mars)[42] and $y = mx + b$, then m is measured in _____ and b is measured in _____.

118. If the slope in a linear relationship is measured in miles per dollar, then the independent variable is measured in _____ and the dependent variable is measured in _____.

119. If a quantity is changing linearly with time, and it increases by 10 units in the first day, what can you say about its behavior in the third day?

120. The quantities Q and T are related by a linear equation of the form

$$Q = mT + b.$$

When $T = 0$, Q is positive, but decreases to a negative quantity when T is 10. What are the signs of m and b. Explain your answers.

121. ▼ The velocity of an object is given by $v = 0.1t + 20$ m/sec, where t is time in seconds. The object is

(A) moving with fixed speed **(B)** accelerating
(C) decelerating **(D)** impossible to say from the given information

122. ▼ The position of an object is given by $x = 0.2t - 4$, where t is time in seconds. The object is

(A) moving with fixed speed **(B)** accelerating
(C) decelerating **(D)** impossible to say from the given information

---

[39] Source: *New York Times*, February 18, 2007, p. WK4.
[40] The 2007 figure is projected from data through October 2006.
Source: *New York Times*, February 18, 2007, p. BU9.

[41] An ancient Martian unit of length; one bootlag is the mean distance from a Martian's foreleg to its rearleg.
[42] Source: www.marsnext.com/comm/zonars.html.

123. ▼ Suppose the cost function is $C(x) = mx + b$ (with m and b positive), the revenue function is $R(x) = kx$ ($k > m$) and the number of items is increased from the break-even quantity. Does this result in a loss, a profit, or is it impossible to say? Explain your answer.

124. ▼ You have been constructing a demand equation, and you obtained a (correct) expression of the form $p = mq + b$, whereas you would have preferred one of the form $q = mp + b$. Should you simply switch p and q in the answer, should you start again from scratch, using p in the role of x and q in the role of y, or should you solve your demand equation for q? Give reasons for your decision.

1.4 Linear Regression

We have seen how to find a linear model given two data points: We find the equation of the line that passes through them. However, we often have more than two data points, and they will rarely all lie on a single straight line, but may often come close to doing so. The problem is to find the line coming *closest* to passing through all of the points.

Suppose, for example, that we are conducting research for a company interested in expanding into Mexico. Of interest to us would be current and projected growth in that country's economy. The following table shows past and projected per capita gross domestic product (GDP)[43] of Mexico for 2000–2012.[44]

Year t ($t = 0$ represents 2000)	0	2	4	6	8	10	12	14
Per Capita GDP y ($1,000)	9	9	10	11	11	12	13	13

A plot of these data suggests a roughly linear growth of the GDP (Figure 28(a)).

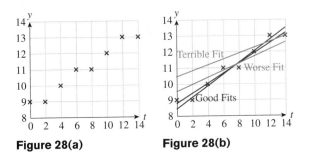

Figure 28(a)   **Figure 28(b)**

These points suggest a roughly linear relationship between t and y, although they clearly do not all lie on a single straight line. Figure 28(b) shows the points together with several lines, some fitting better than others. Can we precisely measure which lines fit better than others? For instance, which of the two lines labeled as "good" fits in Figure 28(b) models the data more accurately? We begin by considering, for each value of t, the difference between the actual GDP (the **observed value**) and the GDP predicted by a linear equation (the **predicted value**). The difference between the predicted value and the observed value is called the **residual**.

$$\text{Residual} = \text{Observed Value} - \text{Predicted Value}$$

---

[43] The GDP is a measure of the total market value of all goods and services produced within a country.

[44] Data are approximate. Sources: CIA World Factbook/www.indexmundi.com, www.economist.com.

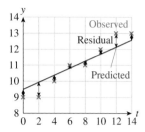

Figure 29

✳ NOTE Why not add the absolute values of the residuals instead? Mathematically, using the squares rather than the absolute values results in a simpler and more elegant solution. Further, using the squares always results in a *single* best-fit line in cases where the *x*-coordinates are all different, whereas this is not the case if we use absolute values.

On the graph, the residuals measure the vertical distances between the (observed) data points and the line (Figure 29) and they tell us how far the linear model is from predicting the actual GDP.

The more accurate our model, the smaller the residuals should be. We can combine all the residuals into a single measure of accuracy by adding their *squares*. (We square the residuals in part to make them all positive.✳) The sum of the squares of the residuals is called the **sum-of-squares error**, **SSE**. Smaller values of SSE indicate more accurate models.

Here are some definitions and formulas for what we have been discussing.

Observed and Predicted Values

Suppose we are given a collection of data points $(x_1, y_1), \ldots, (x_n, y_n)$. The n quantities $y_1, y_2, \ldots, y_n$ are called the **observed y-values**. If we model these data with a linear equation

$$\hat{y} = mx + b, \qquad \hat{y} \text{ stands for "estimated } y \text{" or "predicted } y \text{."}$$

then the y-values we get by substituting the given x-values into the equation are called the **predicted y-values**:

$$\hat{y}_1 = mx_1 + b \qquad \text{Substitute } x_1 \text{ for } x.$$
$$\hat{y}_2 = mx_2 + b \qquad \text{Substitute } x_2 \text{ for } x.$$
$$\ldots$$
$$\hat{y}_n = mx_n + b \qquad \text{Substitute } x_n \text{ for } x.$$

Quick Example

Consider the three data points $(0, 2)$, $(2, 5)$, and $(3, 6)$. The observed y-values are $y_1 = 2$, $y_2 = 5$, and $y_3 = 6$. If we model these data with the equation $\hat{y} = x + 2.5$, then the predicted values are:

$$\hat{y}_1 = x_1 + 2.5 = 0 + 2.5 = 2.5$$
$$\hat{y}_2 = x_2 + 2.5 = 2 + 2.5 = 4.5$$
$$\hat{y}_3 = x_3 + 2.5 = 3 + 2.5 = 5.5$$

Residuals and Sum-of-Squares Error (SSE)

If we model a collection of data $(x_1, y_1), \ldots, (x_n, y_n)$ with a linear equation $\hat{y} = mx + b$, then the **residuals** are the n quantities (Observed Value – Predicted Value):

$$(y_1 - \hat{y}_1), (y_2 - \hat{y}_2), \ldots, (y_n - \hat{y}_n).$$

The **sum-of-squares error (SSE)** is the sum of the squares of the residuals:

$$\text{SSE} = (y_1 - \hat{y}_1)^2 + (y_2 - \hat{y}_2)^2 + \cdots + (y_n - \hat{y}_n)^2.$$

Quick Example

For the data and linear approximation given above, the residuals are:

$$y_1 - \hat{y}_1 = 2 - 2.5 = -0.5$$
$$y_2 - \hat{y}_2 = 5 - 4.5 = 0.5$$
$$y_3 - \hat{y}_3 = 6 - 5.5 = 0.5$$

and $\text{SSE} = (-0.5)^2 + (0.5)^2 + (0.5)^2 = 0.75.$

using Technology

See the Technology Guide at the end of the chapter for detailed instructions on how to obtain the table and graphs in Example 1 using a TI-83/84 Plus or Excel. Here is an outline:

TI-83/84 Plus
STAT EDIT Enter the values of t in L_1, and y (observed) in L_2. Predicted y: Highlight the heading L_3 and enter $0.5*L_1+8$ Squares of residuals: Highlight the heading L_4 and enter " $(L_2-L_3)^2$ " SSE: Enter $\text{sum}(L_4)$ on the home screen.
Graph: $y_1=0.5x+8$ Then turn on Plot1 in Y = screen ZOOM (STAT) [More details on page 110.]

Excel
Enter the headings t, y (observed), y (predicted), Residual^2, m and b in A1–F1. Enter the values of t in A2–A9 and y (observed) in B2–B9. Enter the values 0.25 for m and 9 for b in E2–F2 Predicted y: In C2 enter =$E$2*A2+$F$2 and copy down to C9. Squares of residuals: In D2 enter = (B2-C2) ^2 and copy down to D9. SSE: In any vacant cell to the right of Column D, enter =SUM(D2:D9) Graph: Highlight A1–C9 and insert a Scatter Chart. [More details on page 116.]

EXAMPLE 1 Computing the Sum-of-Squares Error

Using the data above on the GDP in Mexico, compute SSE, the sum-of-squares error, for the linear models $y = 0.5t + 8$ and $y = 0.25t + 9$. Which model is the better fit?

Solution We begin by creating a table showing the values of t, the observed (given) values of y, and the values predicted by the first model.

Year t	Observed y	Predicted $\hat{y} = 0.5t + 8$
0	9	8
2	9	9
4	10	10
6	11	11
8	11	12
10	12	13
12	13	14
14	13	15

We now add two new columns for the residuals and their squares.

Year t	Observed y	Predicted $\hat{y} = 0.5t + 8$	Residual $y - \hat{y}$	Residual^2 $(y - \hat{y})^2$
0	9	8	$9 - 8 = 1$	$1^2 = 1$
2	9	9	$9 - 9 = 0$	$0^2 = 0$
4	10	10	$10 - 10 = 0$	$0^2 = 0$
6	11	11	$11 - 11 = 0$	$0^2 = 0$
8	11	12	$11 - 12 = -1$	$(-1)^2 = 1$
10	12	13	$12 - 13 = -1$	$(-1)^2 = 1$
12	13	14	$13 - 14 = -1$	$(-1)^2 = 1$
14	13	15	$13 - 15 = -2$	$(-2)^2 = 4$

SSE, the sum of the squares of the residuals, is then the sum of the entries in the last column,

$$SSE = 8.$$

Repeating the process using the second model, $0.25t + 9$, yields the following table.

Year t	Observed y	Predicted $\hat{y} = 0.25t + 9$	Residual $y - \hat{y}$	Residual^2 $(y - \hat{y})^2$
0	9	9	$9 - 9 = 0$	$0^2 = 0$
2	9	9.5	$9 - 9.5 = -0.5$	$(-0.5)^2 = 0.25$
4	10	10	$10 - 10 = 0$	$0^2 = 0$
6	11	10.5	$11 - 10.5 = 0.5$	$0.5^2 = 0.25$
8	11	11	$11 - 11 = 0$	$0^2 = 0$
10	12	11.5	$12 - 11.5 = 0.5$	$0.5^2 = 0.25$
12	13	12	$13 - 12 = 1$	$1^2 = 1$
14	13	12.5	$13 - 12.5 = 0.5$	$0.5^2 = 0.25$

This time, SSE $= 2$ and so the second model is a better fit.

Figure 30 shows the data points and the two linear models in question.

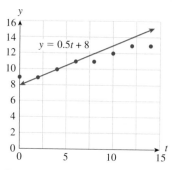
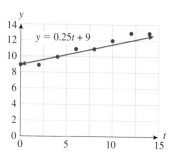

Figure 30

⇒ **Before we go on...**

Q : *It seems clear from the figure that the second model in Example 1 gives a better fit. Why bother to compute SSE to tell me this?*

A : The difference between the two models we chose is so great that it is clear from the graphs which is the better fit. However, if we used a third model with $m = .25$ and $b = 9.1$, then its graph would be almost indistinguishable from that of the second, but a slightly better fit as measured by SSE $= 1.68$.

■

Among all possible lines, there ought to be one with the least possible value of SSE—that is, the greatest possible accuracy as a model. The line (and there is only one such line) that minimizes the sum of the squares of the residuals is called the **regression line**, the **least-squares line**, or the **best-fit line**.

To find the regression line, we need a way to find values of m and b that give the smallest possible value of SSE. As an example, let us take the second linear model in the example above. We said in the "Before we go on" discussion that increasing b from 9 to 9.1 had the desirable effect of decreasing SSE from 2 to 1.68. We could then increase m to 0.26, further reducing SSE to 1.328. Imagine this as a kind of game: Alternately alter the values of m and b by small amounts until SSE is as small as you can make it. This works, but is extremely tedious and time-consuming.

Fortunately, there is an algebraic way to find the regression line. Here is the calculation. To justify it rigorously requires calculus of several variables or linear algebra.

Regression Line

The **regression line (least squares line, best-fit line)** associated with the points $(x_1, y_1), (x_2, y_2), \ldots, (x_n, y_n)$ is the line that gives the minimum sum-of-squares error (SSE). The regression line is

$$y = mx + b,$$

where m and b are computed as follows:

$$m = \frac{n(\sum xy) - (\sum x)(\sum y)}{n(\sum x^2) - (\sum x)^2}$$

$$b = \frac{\sum y - m(\sum x)}{n}$$

$n = $ number of data points.

The quantities m and b are called the **regression coefficients**.

Here, "$\sum$" means "the sum of." Thus, for example,

$$\sum x = \text{Sum of the } x\text{-values} = x_1 + x_2 + \cdots + x_n$$
$$\sum xy = \text{Sum of products} = x_1 y_1 + x_2 y_2 + \cdots + x_n y_n$$
$$\sum x^2 = \text{Sum of the squares of the } x\text{-values} = x_1^2 + x_2^2 + \cdots + x_n^2.$$

On the other hand,

$$\left(\sum x\right)^2 = \text{Square of } \sum x = \text{Square of the sum of the } x\text{-values}.$$

EXAMPLE 2 **Per Capita Gross Domestic Product in Mexico**

In Example 1 we considered the following data on the per capita gross domestic product (GDP) of Mexico:

Year x ($x = 0$ represents 2000)	0	2	4	6	8	10	12	14
Per Capita GDP y ($\$1,000$)	9	9	10	11	11	12	13	13

Find the best-fit linear model for these data and use the model to predict the per capita GDP in Mexico in 2016.

using Technology

See the Technology Guide at the end of the chapter for detailed instructions on how to obtain the regression line and graph in Example 2 using a TI-83/84 Plus or Excel. Here is an outline:

TI-83/84 Plus
STAT EDIT Enter the values of x in L_1, and y in L_2.
Regression equation: STAT
CALC option #4:
LinReg(ax+b)
Graph: Y= VARS 5 EQ 1, then ZOOM 9 [More details on page 110.]

Excel
Enter the values of x in A2–A9 and y in B2–B9.
Graph: Highlight A2–B9 and create a Scatter Plot.
Regression Line: Add a linear trendline with the option "Display equation on chart." OR, after entering x and y,
Regression equation: Enter
=LINEST(B2:B9, A2:A9)
in cells C2–D2 then press Control-Shift-Enter to get m and b. [More details on page 116.]

Web Site
Follow
  Chapter 1
  → Math Tools for Chapter 1
    → Simple Regression Utility

Solution Let's organize our work in the form of a table, where the original data are entered in the first two columns and the bottom row contains the column sums.

x	y	xy	x^2
0	9	0	0
2	9	18	4
4	10	40	16
6	11	66	36
8	11	88	64
10	12	120	100
12	13	156	144
14	13	182	196
$\sum$ (Sum) 56	88	670	560

Because there are $n = 8$ data points, we get

$$m = \frac{n\left(\sum xy\right) - \left(\sum x\right)\left(\sum y\right)}{n\left(\sum x^2\right) - \left(\sum x\right)^2} = \frac{8(670) - (56)(88)}{8(560) - (56)^2} \approx 0.321$$

and

$$b = \frac{\sum y - m\left(\sum x\right)}{n} \approx \frac{88 - (0.321)(56)}{8} \approx 8.75.$$

So, the regression line is

$$y = 0.321x + 8.75.$$

To predict the per capita GDP in Mexico in 2016 we substitute $x = 16$ and get $y \approx 14$, or $14,000 per capita.

Figure 31 shows the data points and the regression line (which has SSE ≈ 0.643; a lot lower than in Example 1.).

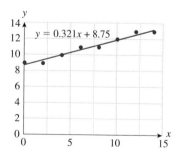

Figure 31

Coefficient of Correlation

If all the data points do not lie on one straight line, we would like to be able to measure how closely they can be approximated by a straight line. Recall that SSE measures the sum of the squares of the deviations from the regression line; therefore it constitutes a measurement of goodness of fit. (For instance, if SSE = 0, then all the points lie on a straight line.) However, SSE depends on the units we use to measure y, and also on the number of data points (the more data points we use, the larger SSE tends to be). Thus, while we can (and do) use SSE to compare the goodness of fit of two lines to the same data, we cannot use it to compare the goodness of fit of one line to one set of data with that of another to a different set of data.

To remove this dependency, statisticians have found a related quantity that can be used to compare the goodness of fit of lines to different sets of data. This quantity, called the **coefficient of correlation** or **correlation coefficient**, and usually denoted r, is between -1 and 1. The closer r is to -1 or 1, the better the fit. For an *exact* fit, we would have $r = -1$ (for a line with negative slope) or $r = 1$ (for a line with positive slope). For a bad fit, we would have r close to 0. Figure 32 shows several collections of data points with least squares lines and the corresponding values of r.

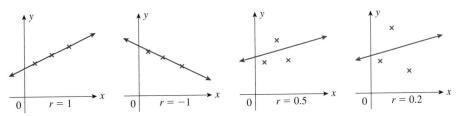

Figure 32

using Technology

See the Technology Guide at the end of the chapter for detailed instructions on how to obtain the correlation coefficient in Example 2 using a TI-83/84 Plus or Excel. Here is an outline:

TI-83/84 Plus

2ND CATALOG

DiagnosticOn Then STAT
CALC option #4:
LinReg(ax+b) [More details on page 110.]

Excel

Graph the data.
Add a trendline and select the option to "Display R-squared value on chart."
OR, after entering the values of x and y,
Enter =LINEST
(B2:B9,A2:A9,TRUE,TRUE)
in cells C2–D6 then press Control-Shift-Enter. [More details on page 116.]

Web Site
Chapter 1
→ Math Tools for Chapter 1
→ Simple Regression Utility

Correlation Coefficient

The coefficient of correlation of the n data points $(x_1, y_1), (x_2, y_2), \ldots, (x_n, y_n)$ is

$$r = \frac{n\left(\sum xy\right) - \left(\sum x\right)\left(\sum y\right)}{\sqrt{n\left(\sum x^2\right) - \left(\sum x\right)^2} \cdot \sqrt{n\left(\sum y^2\right) - \left(\sum y\right)^2}}.$$

It measures how closely the data points $(x_1, y_1), (x_2, y_2), \ldots, (x_n, y_n)$ fit the regression line. (The value r^2 is sometimes called the **coefficient of determination**.)

Interpretation

If r is positive, the regression line has positive slope; if r is negative, the regression line has negative slope.

If $r = 1$ or -1, then all the data points lie exactly on the regression line; if it is close to ± 1, then all the data points are close to the regression line.

If r is close to 0, then y does not depend linearly on x.

EXAMPLE 3 Computing the Coefficient of Correlation

Find the correlation coefficient for the data in Example 2. Is the regression line a good fit?

Solution The formula for r requires $\sum x, \sum x^2, \sum xy, \sum y$, and $\sum y^2$. We have all of these except for $\sum y^2$, which we find in a new column as shown.

x	y	xy	x^2	y^2
0	9	0	0	81
2	9	18	4	81
4	10	40	16	100
6	11	66	36	121
8	11	88	64	121
10	12	120	100	144
12	13	156	144	169
14	13	182	196	169
$\sum$ **(Sum)**	**56**	**88**	**670**	**560**	**986**

Substituting these values into the formula we get

$$r = \frac{n\left(\sum xy\right) - \left(\sum x\right)\left(\sum y\right)}{\sqrt{n\left(\sum x^2\right) - \left(\sum x\right)^2} \cdot \sqrt{n\left(\sum y^2\right) - \left(\sum y\right)^2}}$$

$$= \frac{8(670) - (56)(88)}{\sqrt{8(560) - 56^2} \cdot \sqrt{8(986) - 88^2}}$$

$$\approx 0.982.$$

Thus, the fit is a fairly good one, that is, the original points lie nearly along a straight line, as can be confirmed from the graph in Example 2.

1.4 EXERCISES

▼ more advanced   ◆ challenging

T indicates exercises that should be solved using technology

In Exercises 1–4, compute the sum-of-squares error (SSE) by hand for the given set of data and linear model. HINT [See Example 1.]

1. (1, 1), (2, 2), (3, 4); $y = x - 1$

2. (0, 1), (1, 1), (2, 2); $y = x + 1$

3. (0, −1), (1, 3), (4, 6), (5, 0); $y = -x + 2$

4. (2, 4), (6, 8), (8, 12), (10, 0); $y = 2x - 8$

T *In Exercises 5–8, use technology to compute the sum-of-squares error (SSE) for the given set of data and linear models. Indicate which linear model gives the better fit.*

5. (1, 1), (2, 2), (3, 4);   **a.** $y = 1.5x - 1$ **b.** $y = 2x - 1.5$

6. (0, 1), (1, 1), (2, 2);   **a.** $y = 0.4x + 1.1$ **b.** $y = 0.5x + 0.9$

7. (0, −1), (1, 3), (4, 6), (5, 0);   **a.** $y = 0.3x + 1.1$
   b. $y = 0.4x + 0.9$

8. (2, 4), (6, 8), (8, 12), (10, 0);   **a.** $y = -0.1x + 7$
   b. $y = -0.2x + 6$

Find the regression line associated with each set of points in Exercises 9–12. Graph the data and the best-fit line. (Round all coefficients to 4 decimal places.) HINT [See Example 2.]

9. (1, 1), (2, 2), (3, 4)

10. (0, 1), (1, 1), (2, 2)

11. (0, −1), (1, 3), (4, 6), (5, 0)

12. (2, 4), (6, 8), (8, 12), (10, 0)

In the next two exercises, use correlation coefficients to determine which of the given sets of data is best fit by its associated regression line and which is fit worst. Is it a perfect fit for any of the data sets? HINT [See Example 4.]

13. a. {(1, 3), (2, 4), (5, 6)}
   b. {(0, −1), (2, 1), (3, 4)}
   c. {(4, −3), (5, 5), (0, 0)}

14. a. {(1, 3), (−2, 9), (2, 1)}
   b. {(0, 1), (1, 0), (2, 1)}
   c. {(0, 0), (5, −5), (2, −2.1)}

APPLICATIONS

15. *Worldwide Cell Phone Sales* Following are forecasts of worldwide annual cell phone handset sales:[45]

Year *x*	3	5	7
Sales *y* (millions)	500	600	800

($x = 3$ represents 2003). Complete the following table and obtain the associated regression line. (Round coefficients to 2 decimal places.) HINT [See Example 3.]

	x	*y*	*xy*	x^2
	3	500		
	5	600		
	7	800		
Totals				

Use your regression equation to project the 2008 sales.

16. *Investment in Gold* Following are approximate values of the Amex Gold BUGS Index:[46]

Year *x*	0	4	7
Index *y*	50	250	470

---

[45]Source: In-StatMDR, www.in-stat.com/, July, 2004.

[46]BUGS stands for "basket of unhedged gold stocks." Figures are approximate. Sources: www.321gold.com, Bloomberg Financial Markets/*New York Times*, Sept 7, 2003, p. BU8, www.amex.com.

($x = 0$ represents 2000). Complete the following table and obtain the associated regression line. (Round coefficients to 2 decimal places.)

x	y	xy	x^2
0	50		
4	250		
7	470		
Totals			

Use your regression equation to estimate the 2005 index to the nearest whole number.

17. *E-Commerce* The following chart shows second quarter total retail e-commerce sales in the United States in 2000, 2004, and 2007 ($t = 0$ represents 2000):[47]

Year t	0	4	7
Sales ($ billion)	6	16	32

Find the regression line (round coefficients to two decimal places) and use it to estimate second quarter retail e-commerce sales in 2006.

18. *Retail Inventories* The following chart shows total January retail inventories in the United States in 2000, 2005, and 2007 ($t = 0$ represents 2000):[48]

Year t	0	5	7
Inventory ($ billion)	380	450	480

Find the regression line (round coefficients to two decimal places) and use it to estimate January retail inventories in 2004.

19. *Oil Recovery* The Texas Bureau of Economic Geology published a study on the economic impact of using carbon dioxide enhanced oil recovery (EOR) technology to extract additional oil from fields that have reached the end of their conventional economic life. The following table gives the approximate number of jobs for the citizens of Texas that would be created at various levels of recovery.[49]

Percent Recovery (%)	20	40	80	100
Jobs Created (millions)	3	6	9	15

Find the regression line and use it to estimate the number of jobs that would be created at a recovery level of 50%.

20. *Oil Recovery* (Refer to Exercise 19.) The following table gives the approximate economic value associated with various levels of oil recovery in Texas.[50]

Percent Recovery (%)	10	40	50	80
Economic Value ($ billions)	200	900	1000	2000

Find the regression line and use it to estimate the economic value associated with a recovery level of 70%.

21. 🖩 *Soybean Production* The following table shows soybean production, in millions of tons, in Brazil's *Cerrados* region, as a function of the cultivated area, in millions of acres.[51]

Area (millions of acres)	25	30	32	40	52
Production (millions of tons)	15	25	30	40	60

a. Use technology to obtain the regression line, and to show a plot of the points together with the regression line. (Round coefficients to two decimal places.)
b. Interpret the slope of the regression line.

22. 🖩 *Trade with Taiwan* The following table shows U.S. exports to Taiwan as a function of U.S. imports from Taiwan, based on trade figures in the period 1990–2003.[52]

Imports ($ billions)	22	24	27	35	25
Exports ($ billions)	12	15	20	25	17

a. Use technology to obtain the regression line, and to show a plot of the points together with the regression line. (Round coefficients to two decimal places.)
b. Interpret the slope of the regression line.

🖩 *Exercises 23 and 24 are based on the following table comparing the number of registered automobiles, trucks, and motorcycles in Mexico for various years from 1980 to 2005.[53]*

Year	Automobiles (millions)	Trucks (millions)	Motorcycles (millions)
1980	4.0	1.5	0.28
1985	5.3	2.1	0.25
1990	6.6	3.0	0.25
1995	7.5	3.6	0.13
2000	10.2	4.9	0.29
2005	14.7	7.1	0.61

[47] Figures are rounded. Source: US Census Bureau, www.census.gov, November 2007.

[48] Ibid.

[49] Source: "CO2–Enhanced Oil Recovery Resource Potential in Texas: Potential Positive Economic Impacts," Texas Bureau of Economic Geology, April 2004, www.rrc.state.tx.us/tepc/CO2-EOR_white_paper.pdf.

[50] Ibid.

[51] Source: Brazil Agriculture Ministry/*New York Times*, December 12, 2004, p. N32.

[52] Source: Taiwan Directorate General of Customs/*New York Times*, December 13, 2004, p. C7.

[53] Source: Instituto Nacional de Estadística y Geografía (INEGI), www.inegi.org.mx.

23. 🔢 ▼ *Automobiles and Motorcycles in Mexico*

   a. Use x = Number of automobiles (in millions) and y = Number of motorcycles (in millions), and use technology to obtain the regression equation and graph the associated points and regression line. Round coefficients to two significant digits.

   b. What does the slope tell you about the relationship between the number of automobiles and the number of motorcycles?

   c. Use technology to obtain the coefficient of correlation r. Does the value of r suggest a strong correlation between x and y?

24. 🔢 ▼ *Automobiles and Trucks in Mexico*

   a. Use x = Number of automobiles and y = Number of trucks, and use technology to obtain the regression equation and graph the associated points and regression line. Round coefficients to two significant digits.

   b. What does the slope tell you about the relationship between the number of automobiles and the number of trucks?

   c. Use technology to obtain the coefficient of correlation r. Does the value of r suggest a strong correlation between x and y?

25. 🔢 ▼ *NY City Housing Costs: Downtown* The following table shows the average price of a two-bedroom apartment in downtown New York City from 1994 to 2004. ($t = 0$ represents 1994.[54])

Year t	0	2	4	6	8	10
Price p (\$ million)	0.38	0.40	0.60	0.95	1.20	1.60

   a. Use technology to obtain the linear regression line, with regression coefficients rounded to two decimal places, and plot the regression line and the given points.

   b. Does the graph suggest that a non-linear relationship between t and p would be more appropriate than a linear one? Why?

   c. Use technology to obtain the residuals. What can you say about the residuals in support of the claim in part (b)?

26. 🔢 ▼ *Fiber-Optic Connections* The following table shows the number of fiber-optic cable connections to homes in the U.S. from 2000–2004 ($t = 0$ represents 2000):[55]

Year t	0	1	2	3	4
Connections c (Thousands)	0	10	25	65	150

   a. Use technology to obtain the linear regression line, with regression coefficients rounded to two decimal places, and plot the regression line and the given points.

   b. Does the graph suggest that a non-linear relationship between t and p would be more appropriate than a linear one? Why?

   c. Use technology to obtain the residuals. What can you say about the residuals in support of the claim in part (b)?

COMMUNICATION AND REASONING EXERCISES

27. Why is the regression line associated with the two points (a, b) and (c, d) the same as the line that passes through both? (Assume that $a \neq c$.)

28. What is the smallest possible sum-of-squares error if the given points happen to lie on a straight line? Why?

29. If the points (x_1, y_1), (x_2, y_2), $\ldots$, (x_n, y_n) lie on a straight line, what can you say about the regression line associated with these points?

30. If all but one of the points (x_1, y_1), (x_2, y_2), $\ldots$, (x_n, y_n) lie on a straight line, must the regression line pass through all but one of these points?

31. ▼ Verify that the regression line for the points $(0, 0)$, $(-a, a)$, and (a, a) has slope 0. What is the value of r? (Assume that $a \neq 0$.)

32. ▼ Verify that the regression line for the points $(0, a)$, $(0, -a)$, and $(a, 0)$ has slope 0. What is the value of r? (Assume that $a \neq 0$.)

33. ▼ Must the regression line pass through at least one of the data points? Illustrate your answer with an example.

34. ▼ Why must care be taken when using mathematical models to extrapolate?

---

[54] Data are rounded and 2004 figure is an estimate. Source: Miller Samuel/*New York Times*, March 28, 2004, p. RE 11.

[55] Source: Render, Vanderslice & Associates/*New York Times*, October 11, 2004, p. C1.

KEY CONCEPTS

Web Site www.AppliedCalc.org
Go to the student Web site at
www.AppliedCalc.org to find a
comprehensive and interactive
Web-based summary of Chapter 1.

1.1 Functions from the Numerical and Algebraic Viewpoints

Real-valued function f of a real-valued
variable x, domain *p. 42*
Independent and dependent variables
p. 42
Graph of the function f *p. 42*
Numerically specified function *p. 42*
Graphically specified function *p. 43*
Algebraically defined function *p. 43*
Piecewise-defined function *p. 47*
Vertical line test *p. 49*
Common types of algebraic functions
and their graphs *p. 50*

1.2 Functions and Models

Mathematical model *p. 56*
Analytical model *p. 57*
Curve-fitting model *p. 57*
Cost, revenue, and profit; marginal
cost, revenue, and profit; break-even
point *p. 58–59*
Demand, supply, and equilibrium
price *p. 61–62*
Selecting a model *p. 64*
Compound interest *p. 66*
Exponential growth and decay *p. 68*

1.3 Linear Functions and Models

Linear function $f(x) = mx + b$ *p. 75*
Change in q: $\Delta q = q_2 - q_1$ *p. 76*
Slope of a line:
$$m = \frac{\Delta y}{\Delta x} = \frac{\text{Change in } y}{\text{Change in } x} \quad \textit{p. 76}$$
Interpretations of m *p. 76*

Interpretation of b: y-intercept *p. 77*
Recognizing linear data *p. 78*
Computing the slope of a line *p. 79*
Slopes of horizontal and vertical lines
p. 80
Computing the y-intercept *p. 80*
Linear modeling *p. 82*
Linear cost *p. 82*
Linear demand and supply *p. 83*
Linear change over time; rate of change;
velocity *p. 85*
General linear models *p. 87*

1.4 Linear Regression

Observed and predicted values *p. 95*
Residuals and sum-of-squares error
(SSE) *p. 95*
Regression line (least squares line,
best-fit line) *p. 98*
Correlation coefficient; coefficient of
determination *p. 100*

REVIEW EXERCISES

In each of Exercises 1–4, use the graph of the function f to find approximations of the given values.

1.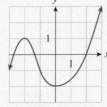

a. $f(-2)$ **b.** $f(0)$
c. $f(2)$ **d.** $f(2) - f(-2)$

2.

a. $f(-2)$ **b.** $f(0)$
c. $f(2)$ **d.** $f(2) - f(-2)$

3.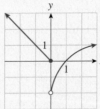

a. $f(-1)$ **b.** $f(0)$
c. $f(1)$ **d.** $f(1) - f(-1)$

4.

a. $f(-1)$ **b.** $f(0)$
c. $f(1)$ **d.** $f(1) - f(-1)$

In each of Exercises 5–8, graph the given function or equation.

5. $y = -2x + 5$

6. $2x - 3y = 12$

7. $y = \begin{cases} \frac{1}{2}x & \text{if } -1 \le x \le 1 \\ x - 1 & \text{if } 1 < x \le 3 \end{cases}$

8. $(x) = 4x - x^2$ with domain $[0, 4]$

In each of Exercises 9–14, decide whether the specified values come from a linear, quadratic, exponential, or absolute value function.

	x	-2	0	1	2	4
9.	$f(x)$	4	2	1	0	2
10.	$g(x)$	-5	-3	-2	-1	1
11.	$h(x)$	1.5	1	0.75	0.5	0
12.	$k(x)$	0.25	1	2	4	16
13.	$u(x)$	0	4	3	0	-12
14.	$w(x)$	32	8	4	2	0.5

In each of Exercises 15–18, find the equation of the specified line.

15. Through $(3, 2)$ with slope -3

16. Through $(-1, 2)$ and $(1, 0)$

17. Through $(1, 2)$ parallel to $x - 2y = 2$

18. With slope $1/2$ crossing $3x + y = 6$ at its x-intercept

In Exercises 19 and 20, determine which of the given lines better fits the given points.

19. $(-1, 1), (1, 2), (2, 0)$; $y = -x/2 + 1$ or $y = -x/4 + 1$

20. $(-2, -1), (-1, 1), (0, 1), (1, 2), (2, 4), (3, 3)$; $y = x + 1$ or $y = x/2 + 1$

In Exercises 21 and 22, find the line that best fits the given points and compute the correlation coefficient.

21. $(-1, 1), (1, 2), (2, 0)$

22. $(-2, -1), (-1, 1), (0, 1), (1, 2), (2, 4), (3, 3)$

Example 3 (page 48)   Obtain a table of values and the graph of the function f specified by

$$f(x) = \begin{cases} -1 & \text{if } -4 \leq x < -1 \\ x & \text{if } -1 \leq x \leq 1 \\ x^2 - 1 & \text{if } 1 < x \leq 2 \end{cases}.$$

Solution with Technology

Enter this function as

$$\underbrace{(\text{X}<-1)*(-1)}_{\text{First part}} + \underbrace{(-1\leq\text{X and X}\leq1)*\text{X}}_{\text{Second part}} + \underbrace{(1<\text{X})*(\text{X}^2-1)}_{\text{Third part}}$$

The logical operator `and` is found in the `TEST  LOGIC` menu. The following alternative formula will also work:

$(\text{X}<-1)*(-1)+(-1\leq\text{X})*(\text{X}\leq1)*\text{X}+(1<\text{X})*(\text{X}^2-1)$

As in Example 1, you can use the Table feature to compute several values of the function at once by pressing [2ND] [TABLE] and obtain the graph by setting $\text{Xmin} = -4$, $\text{Xmax} = 2$, $\text{Ymin} = -1$, and $\text{Ymax} = 5$:

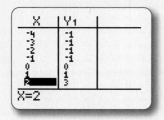

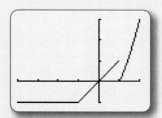

Section 1.2

Example 4(a) (page 62)   The demand and supply curves for private schools in Michigan are $q = 77.8p^{-0.11}$ and $q = 30.4 + 0.006p$ thousand students, respectively $(200 \leq p \leq 2{,}200)$, where p is the net tuition cost in dollars. Graph the demand and supply curves on the same set of axes. Use your graph to estimate, to the nearest \$100, the tuition at which the demand equals the supply (equilibrium price). Approximately how many students will be accommodated at that price?

Solution with Technology

To obtain the graphs of demand and supply:

1. Enter $\text{Y}_1 = 77.8*\text{X}^{\wedge}(-0.11)$ and $\text{Y}_2 = 30.4 + 0.006*\text{X}$ in the "Y=" screen.
2. Press [WINDOW], enter $\text{Xmin} = 200$, $\text{Xmax} = 2200$, $\text{Ymin} = 0$, $\text{Ymax} = 50$; then ([ZOOM] [0]) for the graph:

3. To estimate the equilibrium price, press [TRACE] and use the arrow keys to follow the curve to the approximate point of intersection (around $X = 1008$).

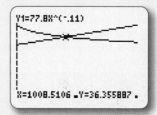

4. For a more accurate estimate, zoom in by pressing [ZOOM] and selecting Option 1 ZBox.
5. Move the curser to a point slightly above and to the left of the intersection, press [ENTER], and then move the curser to a point slightly below and to the right and press [ENTER] again to obtain a box.

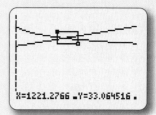

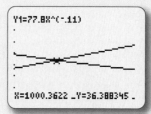

6. Now press ENTER again for a zoomed-in view of the intersection.

7. You can now use TRACE to obtain the intersection coordinates more accurately: $X \approx 1,000$, representing a tuition cost of $1,000. The associated demand is the Y-coordinate: around 36.4 thousand students.

Example 5 (page 64)   The following table shows annual slot machine and video poker machine revenues in 1996–2006 at the *Mohegan Sun* casino ($t = 0$ represents 2000).

t	0	1	2	3	4	5	6
Revenue ($ million)	550	680	750	820	850	890	910

Consider the following four models:

(1) $r(t) = 57t + 607$ Linear model

(2) $r(t) = -9t^2 + 110t + 560$ Quadratic model

(3) $r(t) = 608(1.08)^t$ Exponential model

(4) $r(t) = \dfrac{930}{1 + 0.67(1.7)^{-t}}$ Logistic model

a. Which models fit the data significantly better than the rest?

b. Of the models you selected in part (a), which gives the most reasonable prediction for 2010?

Solution with Technology

1. First enter the actual revenue data in the stat list editor (STAT EDIT) with the values of t in L_1, and the values of $r(t)$ in L_2.

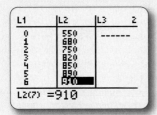

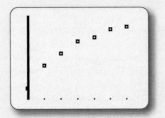

2. Now go to the Y= window and turn Plot1 on by selecting it and pressing ENTER . (You can also turn it on in the 2ND STAT PLOT screen.) Then press ZoomStat (ZOOM 9) to obtain a plot of the points (above).

3. To see any of the four curves plotted along with the points, enter its formula in the Y= screen (for instance, $Y_1 = -9*X^2 + 110X + 560$ for the second model) and press GRAPH (figure on top below).

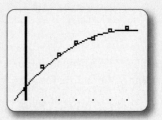

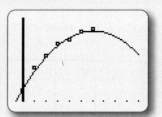

4. To see the extrapolation of the curve to 2010, just change Xmax to 10 (in the WINDOW screen) and press GRAPH again (figure above bottom).

5. Now change Y_1 to see similar graphs for the remaining curves.

6. When you are done, turn Plot1 off again so that the points you entered do not show up in other graphs.

Section **1.3**

Example 1 (page 78)   Which of the following two tables gives the values of a linear function? What is the formula for that function?

x	0	2	4	6	8	10	12
$f(x)$	3	−1	−3	−6	−8	−13	−15

x	0	2	4	6	8	10	12
$g(x)$	3	−1	−5	−9	−13	−17	−21

Solution with Technology

We can use the "List" feature in the TI-83/84 Plus to automatically compute the successive quotients $m = \Delta y/\Delta x$ for either f or g as follows:

1. Use the stat list editor ([STAT] EDIT) to enter the values of x and $f(x)$ in the first two columns, called L_1 and L_2. (If there is already data in a column you want to use, you can clear it by highlighting the column heading (for example, L_1) using the arrow key, and pressing [CLEAR] [ENTER].)

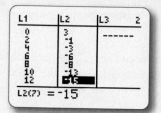

2. Highlight the heading L_3 by using the arrow keys, and enter the following formula (with the quotes, as explained below):

   "ΔList(L_2)/ΔList(L_1)"   ΔList is found under [LIST] OPS; L_1 is [2ND] [1]

   The "ΔList" function computes the differences between successive elements of a list, returning a list with one less element. The formula above then computes the quotients $\Delta y/\Delta x$ in the list L_3.

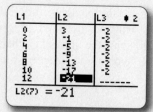

   As you can see in the third column, $f(x)$ is not linear.

3. To redo the computation for $g(x)$, all you need to do is edit the values of L_2 in the stat list editor. By putting quotes around the formula we used for L_3, we told the calculator to remember the formula, so it automatically recalculates the values.

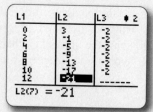

Example 2(a) (page 81) Find the equation of the line through the points $(1, 2)$ and $(3, -1)$.

Solution with Technology

1. Enter the coordinates of the given points in the stat list editor ([STAT] EDIT) with the values of x in L_1, and the values of y in L_2.

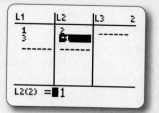

2. To compute the slope $m = \Delta y/\Delta x$, highlight the heading L_3 and enter the following formula (with the quotes—see the discussion of Example 1 above):

   "ΔList(L_2)/ΔList(L_1)"   ΔList is found under [LIST] OPS

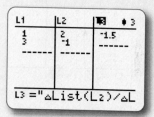

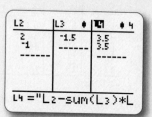

3. To compute the intercept $b = y_1 - mx_1$, highlight the heading L_4 and enter the following formula (again with the quotes):

   "L_2-sum(L_3) * (L_1)"   sum() is found under [LIST] MATH

   The intercept will then appear twice in column L_4. (The calculator computes the intercept twice: using $(x_1, y_1) = (1, 2)$ and $(x_1, y_1) = (3, -1)$: If you used "L_3" instead of "sum(L_3)" in the formula, the TI would return an error, as it cannot multiply columns of different dimensions.)

TECHNOLOGY GUIDE

Section 1.4

Example 1 (page 96)   Using the data on the GDP in Mexico given on page 96, compute SSE, the sum-of-squares error, for the linear models $y = 0.5t + 8$ and $y = 0.25t + 9$, and graph the data with the given models.

Solution with Technology

We can use the "List" feature in the TI-83/84 Plus to automate the computation of SSE.

1. Use the stat list editor (STAT EDIT) to enter the given data in the lists L_1 and L_2. (If there is already data in a list you want to use, you can clear it by highlighting the column heading (for example, L_1) using the arrow key, and pressing CLEAR ENTER.)

2. To compute the predicted values, highlight the heading L_3 using the arrow keys, and enter the formula for the predicted values (figure on the top below):

   $0.5 * L_1 + 8$ L_1 is 2ND 1

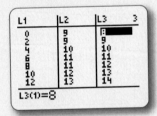

Pressing ENTER again will fill column 3 with the predicted values (above bottom). Note that only seven of the eight data points can be seen on the screen at one time.

3. Highlight the heading L_4 and enter the following formula (including the quotes):

   " $(L_2 - L_3)^2$ "   Squaring the residuals

4. Pressing ENTER will fill column 4 with the squares of the residuals. (Putting quotes around the formula will allow us to easily check the second model, as we shall see.)

5. To compute SSE, the sum of the entries in L_4, go to the home screen and enter $\text{sum}(L_4)$. The sum function is found by pressing 2ND LIST and selecting MATH.

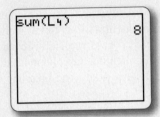

6. To check the second model, go back to the List screen, highlight the heading L_3, enter the formula for the second model, $0.25 * L_1 + 9$, and press ENTER.

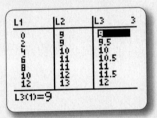

7. Because we put quotes around the formula for the residuals in L_4, the TI-83/84 Plus remembered the formula and automatically recalculated the values. On the home screen we can again calculate $\text{sum}(L_4)$ to get SSE for the second model.

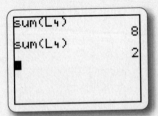

The second model gives a much smaller SSE, and so is the better fit.

8. You can also use the TI-83/84 Plus to plot both the original data points and the two lines. Turn PLOT1 on in the STAT PLOTS window, obtained by pressing 2ND STAT PLOTS. To show the lines, enter them in the "Y=" screen as usual. To obtain a convenient window showing

all the points and the lines, press ZOOM and choose option #9: ZoomStat.

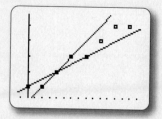

Example 2 (page 98) Consider the following data on the per capita gross domestic product (GDP) of Mexico:

Year x ($x = 0$ represents 2000)	0	2	4	6	8	10	12	14
Per Capita GDP y ($1,000)	9	9	10	11	11	12	13	13

Find the best-fit linear model for these data.

Solution with Technology

1. Enter the data in the TI-83/84 Plus using the List feature, putting the x-coordinates in L_1 and the y-coordinates in L_2, just as in Example 1.

2. Press STAT, select CALC, and choose option #4: LinReg(ax+b). Pressing ENTER will cause the equation of the regression line to be displayed in the home screen:

So, the regression line is $y \approx 0.321x + 8.75$.

3. To graph the regression line without having to enter it by hand in the "Y=" screen, press Y=, clear the contents of Y_1, press VARS, choose option #5: Statistics, select EQ, and then choose #1:RegEQ. The regression equation will then be entered under Y_1.

4. To simultaneously show the data points, press 2ND STATPLOTS and turn PLOT1 on as in Example 1. To obtain a convenient window showing all the points and the line, press ZOOM and choose option #9: ZoomStat.

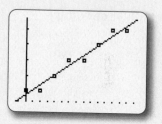

Example 3 (page 100) Find the correlation coefficient for the data in Example 2.

Solution with Technology

To find the correlation coefficient using a TI-83/84 Plus you need to tell the calculator to show you the coefficient at the same time that it shows you the regression line.

1. Press 2ND CATALOG and select "DiagnosticOn" from the list. The command will be pasted to the home screen, and you should then press ENTER to execute the command.

2. Once you have done this, the "LinReg(ax+b)" command (see the previous discussion for Example 2). The example will show you not only a and b, but r and r^2 as well:

TECHNOLOGY GUIDE

EXCEL Technology Guide

Section 1.1

Example 1(a) and (c) (page 44) The number of iPods sold by Apple Inc. each year from 2004 through 2007 can be approximated by $f(x) = -x^2 + 20x + 3$ million iPods ($0 \leq x \leq 3$) where x is the number of years since 2004. Compute $f(0)$, $f(1)$, $f(2)$, and $f(3)$ and obtain the graph of f.

Solution with Technology

To create a table of values of f using Excel:

1. Set up two columns—one for the values of x and one for the values of $f(x)$. Then enter the sequence of values 0, 1, 2, 3 in the x column as shown.

	A	B
1	x	f(x)
2	0	
3	1	
4	2	
5	3	

2. Now enter the formula for f in cell B2. Below are the technology formula for f and the version we use in Excel:

Technology formula
```
-1*x^2+20*x+3
```

Excel formula
```
=-1*A2^2+20*A2+3
```

Notice that we have preceded the Excel formula by an equal sign ($=$) and replaced each occurrence of x by the name of the cell holding the value of x (cell A2 in this case).

	A	B	C
1	x	f(x)	
2	0	=-1*A2^2+20*A2+3	
3	1		
4	2		
5	3		
6			

Note Instead of typing in the name of the cell "A2" each time, you can simply click on the cell A2, and "A2" will be inserted automatically. ■

3. Now highlight cell B2 and drag the **fill handle** (the little dot at the lower right-hand corner of the selection) down

until you reach row 5 as shown below on the left, to obtain the result shown to the right.

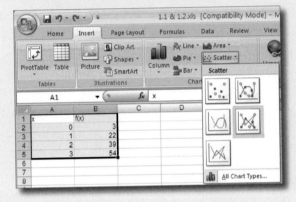

4. To graph the data, highlight A1 through B5, select the Insert tab, and choose a "Scatter" chart:

For a graph with data points connected by line segments, select the style shown on the right to obtain the graph shown below:

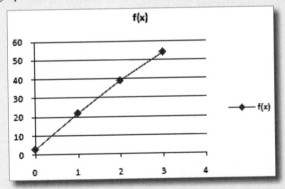

You can then adjust the appearance of the graph by right-clicking on its various elements. (Experiment!)

Q: *The formula* -x^2+20*x+3 *will give the same result as* -1*x^2+20*x+3 *on a graphing calculator (and the Web site). So why did we use* -1*x^2 *in the Excel formula?*

A: Oddly enough, Excel calculates -x^2 as though it were (-x)^2, which is the same as x^2, whereas calculators and computer programs all use the conventional mathematical interpretation: $-x^2$. To avoid having to worry about this, just remember to always use a coefficient in front of powers of x, even if the coefficient is -1.

Example 2 (page 47)   The number $n(t)$ of Facebook members can be approximated by the following function of time t in years ($t = 0$ represents January 2004):

$$n(t) = \begin{cases} 1.5t^2 - t + 1.5 & \text{if } 0 \leq t \leq 3 \\ 46t - 126 & \text{if } 3 < t \leq 5 \end{cases} \text{ million members}$$

(Its graph is shown in Figure 4.) Obtain a table showing the values $n(t)$ for $t = 0, 0.5, 1, \ldots, 5$ and also obtain the graph of n.

Solution with Technology

We can generate a table of values of $n(t)$ for $t = 0, 0.5, 1, \ldots, 5$ as follows:

1. First set up two columns—one for the values of t and one for the values of $n(t)$. To enter the sequence of values 0, 0.5, 1, $\ldots$, 5 in the t column, start by entering the first two values, 0 and 0.5, highlight both of them, and drag the **fill handle** (the little dot at the lower right-hand corner of the selection) down until you reach Row 12. (Why 12?)

2. We must now enter the formula for n in cell B2. The following formula defines the function n in Excel:

   ```
   =(x<=3)*(1.5*x^2-x+1.5)+
   (x>3)*(46*x-126)
   ```

   When x is less than or equal to 3, the logical expression (x<=3) evaluates to 1 because it is true, and the expression (x>3) evaluates to 0 because it is false. The value of the function is therefore given by the expression (1.5*x^2-x+1.5). When x is greater than 3, the expression (x<=3) evaluates to 0 while the expression (x>3) evaluates to 1, so the value of the function is given by the expression (46*x-126). We therefore enter the formula

   ```
   =(A2<=3)*(1.5*A2^2-A2+1.5)
   +(A2>3)*(46*A2-126)
   ```

   in cell B2 and then copy down to cell B12:

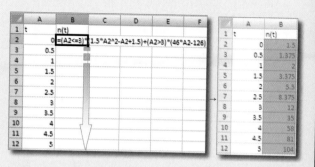

We can now read off the values asked for in the original example: Jan. 2005 ($t = 1$): $n(1) = 2$, Jan. 2007 ($t = 3$): $n(3) = 12$, June 2008 ($t = 4.5$): $n(4.5) = 81$.

3. To graph the data, highlight A1 through B10, select the Insert tab, and choose "Scatter" as in Example 1(c), obtaining the following graph:

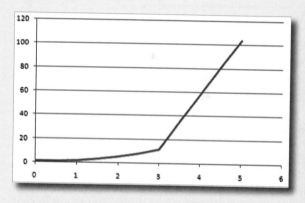

Example 3 (page 48)   Obtain a table of values and the graph of the function f specified by

$$f(x) = \begin{cases} -1 & \text{if } -4 \leq x < -1 \\ x & \text{if } -1 \leq x \leq 1 \\ x^2 - 1 & \text{if } 1 < x \leq 2 \end{cases}.$$

Solution with Technology

The setup in Excel is almost identical to that in Example 2, but because the third part of the formula specifying f is not linear, we need to plot more points in Excel to get a smooth graph.

1. For the values of x in column A, use the values $-4, -3.9, -3.8, \ldots, 2$. For a smoother curve, plot more points. You can find a general purpose Excel Graphing Worksheet that automates some of this on the Web site by following

Chapter 1 → Excel Tutorials → Section 1.1

2. For $f(x)$, use the formula:

$$= \underbrace{(A2<-1)*(-1)}_{\text{First part}} + \underbrace{(-1<=A2)*(A2<=1)*A2}_{\text{Second part}} + \underbrace{(1<A2)*(A2^2-1)}_{\text{Third part}}$$

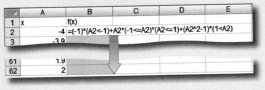

Notice that Excel does not handle the transition at $x = 1$ correctly and connects the two parts of the graph with a spurious line segment.

Section 1.2

Example 4(a) (page 62) The demand and supply curves for private schools in Michigan are $q = 77.8p^{-0.11}$ and $q = 30.4 + 0.006p$ thousand students respectively ($200 \le p \le 2{,}200$) where p is the net tuition cost in dollars. Graph the demand and supply curves on the same set of axes. Use your graph to estimate, to the nearest \$100, the tuition at which the demand equals the supply (equilibrium price). Approximately how many students will be accommodated at that price?

Solution with Technology

To obtain the graphs of demand and supply:

1. Enter the headings p, Demand, and Supply in cells A1–C1 and the p-values 200, 300, . . . , 2,200 in A2–A22.

2. Now enter the formulas for the demand and supply functions in cells B2 and C2:

Demand: `=77.8*A2^(-0.11)`   in cell B2

Supply: `=30.4+0.006*A2`   in cell C2

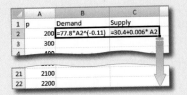

3. Now use the fill handle to copy down to C22 as shown above.

4. To graph the data, highlight A1 through C22, select the Insert tab, and choose a "Scatter" chart:

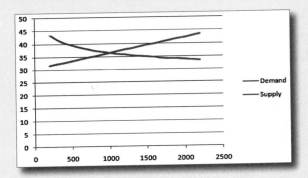

5. If you place the cursor as close as you can get to the intersection point (or just look at the table of values) you will see that the curves cross close to $p = \$1{,}000$ (to the nearest \$100).

6. To more accurately determine where the curves cross, you can narrow down the range of values shown on the x-axis by changing the p-values to 990, 991, . . ., 1010.

Example 5 (page 64) The following table shows annual slot machine and video poker machine revenues in 1996–2006 at the *Mohegan Sun* casino ($t = 0$ represents 2000).

t	0	1	2	3	4	5	6
Reveneue (\$ million)	550	680	750	820	850	890	910

Consider the following four models:

(1) $r(t) = 57t + 607$	Linear model
(2) $r(t) = -9t^2 + 110t + 560$	Quadratic model
(3) $r(t) = 608(1.08)^t$	Exponential model
(4) $r(t) = \dfrac{930}{1 + 0.67(1.7)^{-t}}$	Logistic model

a. Which models fit the data significantly better than the rest?

b. Of the models you selected in part (a), which gives the most reasonable prediction for 2010?

Solution with Technology

1. First create a scatter plot of the given data by tabulating the data as shown below, selecting the Insert tab, and choosing a "Scatter" chart:

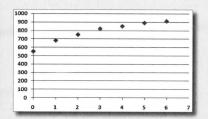

below, with the model represented by a curve, and the actual data points represented by dots:

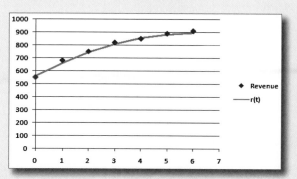

2. In column C use the formula for the model you are interested in seeing; for example, model (2):
$$\texttt{=-9*A2\^2+110*A2+560.}$$

5. To see the extrapolation of the curve to 2010, add the values 7, 8, 9, 10 to Column A (notice that the values of $r(t)$ will automatically be computed in column C as you type), click on the graph, and use the fill handle at the base of column C to include the new data in the graph:

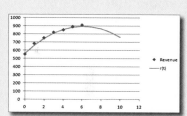

3. To adjust the graph to include the graph of the model you have added, click once on the graph—the effect will be to outline the data you have graphed in columns A and B—and then use the fill handle at the bottom of column B to extend the selection to column C as shown:

6. To see the plots for the remaining curves, change the formula in column B (and don't forget to copy the new formula down to cell C12 when you do so).

Section 1.3

Example 1 (page 78) Which of the following two tables gives the values of a linear function? What is the formula for that function?

x	0	2	4	6	8	10	12
$f(x)$	3	-1	-3	-6	-8	-13	-15

x	0	2	4	6	8	10	12
$g(x)$	3	-1	-5	-9	-13	-17	-21

The graph will now include markers showing the values of both the actual revenue and the model you inserted in column C.

4. Right-click on any of the markers corresponding to column B in the graph, select "Format data series" and, under Line Color select "Solid line," and under Marker Options, select "None." The effect will be as shown

Solution with Technology

The following worksheet shows how you can compute the successive quotients $m = \Delta y / \Delta x$, and hence check whether a given set of data shows a linear relationship, in which case all the quotients will be the same. (The shading indicates that the formula is to be copied down only as far as cell C7. Why not cell C8?)

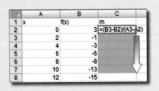

Here are the results for both *f*(*x*) and *g*(*x*):

Example 2(a) (page 81)   Find the equation of the line through the points (1, 2) and (3, −1).

Solution with Technology

1. Enter the *x*- and *y*-coordinates in columns A and B as shown below on the left.

2. Add the headings *m* and *b* in C1–D1, and then the formulas for the slope and intercept in C2–D2 as shown above on the right. The result will be as shown below:

	A	B	C	D
1	x	y	m	b
2		1	2	-1.5	3.5
3		3	-1	Slope	Intercept

Section 1.4

Example 1 (page 96)   Using the data on the GDP in Mexico given on page 96, compute SSE, the sum-of-squares error, for the linear models *y* = 0.5*t* + 8 and *y* = 0.25*t* + 9, and graph the data with the given models.

Solution with Technology

1. Begin by setting up your worksheet with the observed data in two columns, *t* and *y*, and the predicted data for the first model in the third.

Notice that, instead of using the numerical equation for the first model in column C, we used absolute references to the cells containing the slope *m* and the intercept *b*. This way, we can switch from one linear model to the next by changing only *m* and *b* in cells E2 and F2. (We have deliberately left column D empty in anticipation of the next step.)

2. In column D we compute the squares of the residuals using the Excel formula:

$$= (B2-C2)^2 \, .$$

	A	B	C	D	E	F
1	t	y (Observed)	y (Predicted)	Residual^2	m	b
2	0	9	8	=(B2-C2)^2	0.5	8
3	2	9	9			
4	4	10	10			
5	6	11	11			
6	8	11	12			
7	10	12	13			
8	12	13	14			
9	14	13	15			

3. We now compute SSE in cell F4 by summing the entries in column D:

	A	B	C	D	E	F
1	t	y (Observed)	y (Predicted)	Residual^2	m	b
2	0	9	8	1	0.5	8
3	2	9	9	0		
4	4	10	10	0	SSE	=SUM(D2:D9)
5	6	11	11	0		
6	8	11	12	1		
7	10	12	13	1		
8	12	13	14	1		
9	14	13	15	4		

Here is the completed worksheet:

	A	B	C	D	E	F
1	t	y (Observed)	y (Predicted)	Residual^2	m	b
2	0	9	8	1	0.5	8
3	2	9	9	0		
4	4	10	10	0	SSE:	8
5	6	11	11	0		
6	8	11	12	1		
7	10	12	13	1		
8	12	13	14	1		
9	14	13	15	4		

4. Changing m to 0.25 and b to 9 gives the sum of squares error for the second model, SSE = 2.

	A	B	C	D	E	F
1	t	y (Observed)	y (Predicted)	Residual^2	m	b
2	0	9	9	0	0.25	9
3	2	9	9.5	0.25		
4	4	10	10	0	SSE:	2
5	6	11	10.5	0.25		
6	8	11	11	0		
7	10	12	11.5	0.25		
8	12	13	12	1		
9	14	13	12.5	0.25		

Thus, the second model is a better fit.

5. To plot both the original data points and each of the two lines, use a scatterplot to graph the data in columns A through C in each of the previous last two worksheets.

$$y = 0.5t + 8 \qquad\qquad y = 0.25t + 9$$

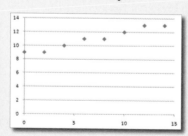

Example 2 (page 98) Consider the following data on the per capita gross domestic product (GDP) of Mexico:

Year x ($x = 0$ represents 2000)	0	2	4	6	8	10	12	14
Per Capita GDP y ($1,000)	9	9	10	11	11	12	13	13

Find the best-fit linear model for these data.

Solution with Technology

Here are two Excel shortcuts for linear regression; one graphical and one based on an Excel formula.

Using the Trendline

1. Start with the original data and a "scatter plot."

2. Click on the chart, select the Layout tab, click the Trendline button, and choose "More Trendline Options." In the Format Trendline dialogue box, select a Linear trendline (the default) and check the option to "Display Equation on chart."

You may have to move the equation to make it readable.

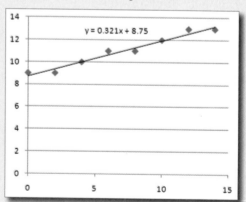

Using a Formula

Alternatively, you can use the "LINEST" function (for "linear estimate").

1. Enter your data as previously, and select a block of unused cells two wide and one tall; for example C2:D2. Then enter the formula

```
=LINEST(B2:B9,A2:A9)
```

as shown.

	A	B	C	D
1	x	y	m	b
2	0	9	=LINEST(B2:B9,A2:A9)	
3	2	9		
4	4	10		
5	6	11		
6	8	11		
7	10	12		
8	12	13		
9	14	13		

2. Press Control-Shift-Enter. The result should look like this.

	A	B	C	D
1	x	y	m	b
2	0	9	0.321429	8.75
3	2	9		
4	4	10		
5	6	11		
6	8	11		
7	10	12		
8	12	13		
9	14	13		

The values of m and b appear in cells C2 and D2 as shown.

Example 3 (page 100)   Find the correlation coefficient for the data in Example 2.

Solution with Technology

1. In Excel, when you add a trendline to a chart you can select the option "Display R-squared value on chart" to show the value of r^2 on the chart (it is common to examine r^2, which takes on values between 0 and 1, instead of r).

2. Alternatively, the LINEST function we used in Example 2 can be used to display quite a few statistics about a best fit line, including r^2. Instead of selecting a block of cells two wide and one tall as we did in Example 2, we select one two wide and *five* tall. We now enter the requisite LINEST formula with two additional arguments set to "TRUE" as shown.

	A	B	C	D	E
1	x	y	m	b	
2	0	9	=LINEST(B2:B9,A2:A9,TRUE,TRUE)		
3	2	9			
4	4	10			
5	6	11			
6	8	11			
7	10	12			
8	12	13			
9	14	13			
10					

3. Press Control-Shift-Enter. The result should look something like this.

	A	B	C	D
1	x	y	m	b
2	0	9	0.321428571	8.75
3	2	9	0.025253814	0.211288564
4	4	10	0.964285714	0.327326835
5	6	11	162	6
6	8	11	17.35714286	0.642857143
7	10	12		
8	12	13		
9	14	13		

The values of m and b appear in cells C2 and D2 as before, and the value of r^2 in cell C4. (Among the other numbers shown is SSE in cell D6. For the meanings of the remaining numbers shown, see the online help for LINEST in Excel; a good course in statistics wouldn't hurt, either.)

2

Nonlinear Functions and Models

Case Study Checking up on Malthus

In 1798 Thomas R. Malthus (1766–1834) published an influential pamphlet, later expanded into a book, titled *An Essay on the Principle of Population as It Affects the Future Improvement of Society*. One of his main contentions was that population grows geometrically (exponentially), while the supply of resources such as food grows only arithmetically (linearly). Some 200 years later, you have been asked to check the validity of Malthus's contention. **How do you go about doing so?**

Web Site
www.AppliedCalc.org

- Inverse functions
- Using and deriving algebraic properties of logarithms

Robert Nickelsberg/Getty Images

Introduction

To see if Malthus was right, we need to see if the data fit the models (linear and exponential) that he suggested or if other models would be better. We saw in Chapter 1 how to fit a linear model. In this chapter we discuss how to construct models that use various *nonlinear* functions.

The nonlinear functions we consider in this chapter are the *quadratic* functions, the simplest nonlinear functions; the *exponential* functions, essential for discussing many kinds of growth and decay, including the growth (and decay) of money in finance and the initial growth of an epidemic; the *logarithmic* functions, needed to fully understand the exponential functions; and the *logistic* functions, used to model growth with an upper limit, such as the spread of an epidemic.

algebra Review

For this chapter, you should be familiar with the algebra reviewed in **Chapter 0, Section 2.**

2.1 Quadratic Functions and Models

In Chapter 1 we studied linear functions. Linear functions are useful, but in real-life applications, they are often accurate for only a limited range of values of the variables. The relationship between two quantities is often best modeled by a curved line rather than a straight line. The simplest function with a graph that is not a straight line is a *quadratic* function.

Quadratic Function

A **quadratic function** of the variable x is a function that can be written in the form

$$f(x) = ax^2 + bx + c \qquad \text{Function form}$$

or

$$y = ax^2 + bx + c \qquad \text{Equation form}$$

where a, b, and c are fixed numbers (with $a \neq 0$).

Quick Examples

1. $f(x) = 3x^2 - 2x + 1$ $a = 3, b = -2, c = 1$
2. $g(x) = -x^2$ $a = -1, b = 0, c = 0$
3. $R(p) = -5{,}600p^2 + 14{,}000p$ $a = -5{,}600, b = 14{,}000, c = 0$

✱ NOTE We shall not fully justify the formula for the vertex and the axis of symmetry until we have studied some calculus, although it is possible to do so with just algebra.

Every quadratic function $f(x) = ax^2 + bx + c$ ($a \neq 0$) has a **parabola** as its graph. Following is a summary of some features of parabolas that we can use to sketch the graph of any quadratic function.*

Features of a Parabola

The graph of $f(x) = ax^2 + bx + c$ $(a \neq 0)$ is a **parabola**. If $a > 0$ the parabola opens upward (concave up) and if $a < 0$ it opens downward (concave down):

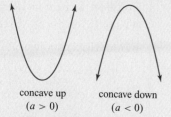

concave up
$(a > 0)$

concave down
$(a < 0)$

Vertex, Intercepts, and Symmetry

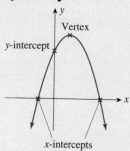

Vertex   The vertex is the turning point of the parabola (see the above figure).
Its x-coordinate is $-\dfrac{b}{2a}$. Its y-coordinate is $f\left(-\dfrac{b}{2a}\right)$.

x-Intercepts (if any)   These occur when $f(x) = 0$; that is, when
$$ax^2 + bx + c = 0.$$
Solve this equation for x by either factoring or using the quadratic formula. The x-intercepts are
$$x = \frac{-b \pm \sqrt{b^2 - 4ac}}{2a}.$$
If the **discriminant** $b^2 - 4ac$ is positive, there are two x-intercepts. If it is zero, there is a single x-intercept (at the vertex). If it is negative, there are no x-intercepts (so the parabola doesn't touch the x-axis at all).

y-Intercept   This occurs when $x = 0$, so
$$y = a(0)^2 + b(0) + c = c.$$

Symmetry   The parabola is symmetric with respect to the vertical line through the vertex, which is the line $x = -\dfrac{b}{2a}$.

Note that the x-intercepts can also be written as
$$x = -\frac{b}{2a} \pm \frac{\sqrt{b^2 - 4ac}}{2a},$$
making it clear that they are located symmetrically on either side of the line $x = -b/(2a)$. This partially justifies the claim that the whole parabola is symmetric with respect to this line.

Figure 1

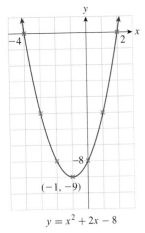

$y = x^2 + 2x - 8$

Figure 2

EXAMPLE 1 Sketching the Graph of a Quadratic Function

Sketch the graph of $f(x) = x^2 + 2x - 8$ by hand.

Solution Here, $a = 1$, $b = 2$, and $c = -8$. Because $a > 0$, the parabola is concave up (Figure 1).

Vertex: The x coordinate of the vertex is

$$x = -\frac{b}{2a} = -\frac{2}{2} = -1.$$

To get its y coordinate, we substitute the value of x back into $f(x)$ to get

$$y = f(-1) = (-1)^2 + 2(-1) - 8 = 1 - 2 - 8 = -9.$$

Thus, the coordinates of the vertex are $(-1, -9)$.

x-Intercepts: To calculate the x-intercepts (if any), we solve the equation

$$x^2 + 2x - 8 = 0.$$

Luckily, this equation factors as $(x + 4)(x - 2) = 0$. Thus, the solutions are $x = -4$ and $x = 2$, so these values are the x-intercepts. (We could also have used the quadratic formula here.)

y-Intercept: The y-intercept is given by $c = -8$.

Symmetry: The graph is symmetric around the vertical line $x = -1$.

   Now we can sketch the curve as in Figure 2. (As we see in the figure, it is helpful to plot additional points by using the equation $y = x^2 + 2x - 8$, and to use symmetry to obtain others.)

EXAMPLE 2 One x-Intercept and No x-Intercepts

Sketch the graph of each quadratic function, showing the location of the vertex and intercepts.

a. $f(x) = 4x^2 - 12x + 9$

b. $g(x) = -\frac{1}{2}x^2 + 4x - 12$

Solution

a. We have $a = 4$, $b = -12$, and $c = 9$. Because $a > 0$, this parabola is concave up.

$$\textit{Vertex:} \quad x = -\frac{b}{2a} = \frac{12}{8} = \frac{3}{2} \qquad x \text{ coordinate of vertex}$$

$$y = f\left(\frac{3}{2}\right) = 4\left(\frac{3}{2}\right)^2 - 12\left(\frac{3}{2}\right) + 9 = 0 \qquad y \text{ coordinate of vertex}$$

Thus, the vertex is at the point $(3/2, 0)$.

$$\textit{x-Intercepts:} \qquad 4x^2 - 12x + 9 = 0$$
$$(2x - 3)^2 = 0$$

The only solution is $2x - 3 = 0$, or $x = 3/2$. Note that this coincides with the vertex, which lies on the x-axis.

y-Intercept: $c = 9$

Symmetry: The graph is symmetric around the vertical line $x = 3/2$.

The graph is the narrow parabola shown in Figure 3. (As we remarked in Example 1, plotting additional points and using symmetry helps us obtain an accurate sketch.)

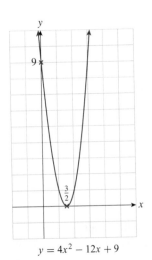

$y = 4x^2 - 12x + 9$

Figure 3

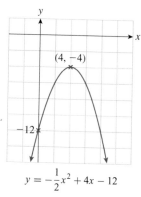

$$y = -\frac{1}{2}x^2 + 4x - 12$$

Figure 4

 **using** Technology

See the Technology Guide at the end of the chapter for detailed instructions on how to do the calculations and the graph in part (a) of Example 2 using a TI-83/84 Plus or Excel.

b. Here, $a = -1/2$, $b = 4$, and $c = -12$. Because $a < 0$, the parabola is concave down. The vertex has x coordinate $-b/(2a) = 4$, with corresponding y coordinate $f(4) = -\frac{1}{2}(4)^2 + 4(4) - 12 = -4$. Thus, the vertex is at $(4, -4)$.

For the x-intercepts, we must solve $-\frac{1}{2}x^2 + 4x - 12 = 0$. If we try to use the quadratic formula, we discover that the discriminant is $b^2 - 4ac = 16 - 24 = -8$. Because the discriminant is negative, there are no solutions of the equation, so there are no x-intercepts.

The y-intercept is given by $c = -12$, and the graph is symmetric around the vertical line $x = 4$.

Because there are no x-intercepts, the graph lies entirely below the x-axis, as shown in Figure 4. (Again, you should plot additional points and use symmetry to ensure that your sketch is accurate.)

APPLICATIONS

Recall that the **revenue** resulting from one or more business transactions is the total payment received. Thus, if q units of some item are sold at p dollars per unit, the revenue resulting from the sale is

revenue = price × quantity

$$R = pq.$$

EXAMPLE 3 Demand and Revenue

Alien Publications, Inc. predicts that the demand equation for the sale of its latest illustrated sci-fi novel *Episode 93: Yoda vs. Alien* is

$$q = -2{,}000p + 150{,}000$$

where q is the number of books it can sell each year at a price of $\$p$ per book. What price should Alien Publications, Inc., charge to obtain the maximum annual revenue?

Solution The total revenue depends on the price, as follows:

$R = pq$	Formula for revenue.
$= p(-2{,}000p + 150{,}000)$	Substitute for q from demand equation.
$= -2{,}000p^2 + 150{,}000p.$	Simplify.

We are after the price p that gives the maximum possible revenue. Notice that what we have is a quadratic function of the form $R(p) = ap^2 + bp + c$, where $a = -2{,}000$, $b = 150{,}000$, and $c = 0$. Because a is negative, the graph of the function is a parabola, concave down, so its vertex is its highest point (Figure 5). The p coordinate of the vertex is

$$p = -\frac{b}{2a} = -\frac{150{,}000}{-4{,}000} = 37.5.$$

This value of p gives the highest point on the graph and thus gives the largest value of $R(p)$. We may conclude that Alien Publications, Inc., should charge $\$37.50$ per book to maximize its annual revenue.

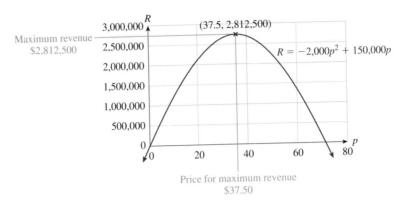

Figure 5

➡ **Before we go on...** You might ask what the maximum annual revenue is for the publisher in Example 3. Because $R(p)$ gives us the revenue at a price of $\$p$, the answer is $R(37.5) = -2,000\,(37.5)^2 + 150,000(37.5) = 2,812,500$. In other words, the company will earn total annual revenues from this book amounting to $\$2,812,500$. ■

EXAMPLE 4 Demand, Revenue, and Profit

As the operator of *YSport Fitness* gym, you calculate your demand equation to be

$$q = -0.06p + 84$$

where q is the number of members in the club and p is the annual membership fee you charge.

a. Your annual operating costs are a fixed cost of $\$20,000$ per year plus a variable cost of $\$20$ per member. Find the annual revenue and profit as functions of the membership price p.

b. At what price should you set the annual membership fee to obtain the maximum revenue? What is the maximum possible revenue?

c. At what price should you set the annual membership fee to obtain the maximum profit? What is the maximum possible profit? What is the corresponding revenue?

Solution

a. The annual revenue is given by

$$R = pq \qquad \text{Formula for revenue.}$$
$$= p(-0.06p + 84) \qquad \text{Substitute for } q \text{ from demand equation.}$$
$$= -0.06p^2 + 84p. \qquad \text{Simplify.}$$

The annual cost C is given by

$$C = 20,000 + 20q. \qquad \$20,000 \text{ plus } \$20 \text{ per member}$$

However, this is a function of q, and not p. To express C as a function of p we substitute for q using the demand equation $q = -0.06p + 84$:

$$C = 20,000 + 20(-0.06p + 84)$$
$$= 20,000 - 1.2p + 1,680$$
$$= -1.2p + 21,680.$$

Thus, the profit function is:

$$P = R - C$$ Formula for profit.

$$= -0.06p^2 + 84p - (-1.2p + 21{,}680)$$ Substitute for revenue and cost.

$$= -0.06p^2 + 85.2p - 21{,}680.$$

b. From part (a) the revenue function is given by

$$R = -0.06p^2 + 84p.$$

This is a quadratic function ($a = -0.06$, $b = 84$, $c = 0$) whose graph is a concave-down parabola (Figure 6).

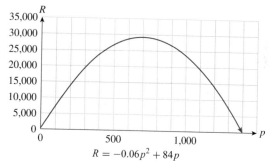

$$R = -0.06p^2 + 84p$$

Figure 6

The maximum revenue corresponds to the highest point of the graph: the vertex, of which the p coordinate is

$$p = -\frac{b}{2a} = -\frac{84}{2(-0.06)} \approx \$700.$$

This is the membership fee you should charge for the maximum revenue. The corresponding maximum revenue is given by the y coordinate of the vertex in Figure 6:

$$R(700) = -0.06(700)^2 + 84(700) = \$29{,}400.$$

c. From part (a), the profit function is given by

$$P = -0.06p^2 + 85.2p - 21{,}680.$$

Like the revenue function, the profit function is quadratic ($a = -0.06$, $b = 85.2$, $c = -21{,}680$). Figure 7 shows both the revenue and profit functions.

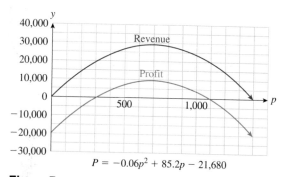

$$P = -0.06p^2 + 85.2p - 21{,}680$$

Figure 7

The maximum profit corresponds to the vertex, whose p coordinate is

$$p = -\frac{b}{2a} = -\frac{85.2}{2(-0.06)} \approx \$710.$$

This is the membership fee you should charge for the maximum profit. The corresponding maximum profit is given by the y coordinate of the vertex of the profit curve in Figure 7:

$$P(710) = -0.06(710)^2 + 85.2(710) - 21{,}680 = \$8{,}566.$$

The corresponding revenue is

$$R(710) = -0.06(710)^2 + 84(710) = \$29{,}394,$$

slightly less than the maximum possible revenue of $29,400.

➡ **Before we go on...** The result of part (c) of Example 4 tells us that the vertex of the profit curve in Figure 7 is slightly to the right of the vertex in the revenue curve. However, the difference is tiny compared to the scale of the graphs, so the graphs appear to be parallel. ■

Q: *Charging $710 membership brings in less revenue than charging $700. So why charge $710?*

A: A membership fee of $700 does bring in slightly larger revenue than a fee of $710, but it also brings in a slightly larger membership, which in turn raises the operating expense and has the effect of *lowering* the profit slightly (to $8,560). In other words, the slightly higher fee, while bringing in less revenue, also lowers the cost, and the net result is a larger profit.

Fitting a Quadratic Function to Data: Quadratic Regression

In Section 1.4 we saw how to fit a regression line to a collection of data points. Here, we see how to use technology to obtain the **quadratic regression curve** associated with a set of points. The quadratic regression curve is the quadratic curve $y = ax^2 + bx + c$ that best fits the data points in the sense that the associated sum-of-squares error (SSE— see Section 1.4) is a minimum. Although there are algebraic methods for obtaining the quadratic regression curve, it is normal to use technology to do this.

EXAMPLE 5 ⓘ Freon Production

The following table shows total and projected production of ozone-layer damaging Freon 22 (chlorodifluoromethane) in developing countries ($t = 0$ represents 2000).*

Year t	0	2	4	6	8	10
Tons of Freon F	100	140	200	270	400	590

a. Is a linear model appropriate for these data?

b. Find the quadratic model

$$F(t) = at^2 + bt + c$$

that best fits the data.

---

* Figures are approximate. Source: Lampert Kuijpers (Panel of the Montreal Protocol), National Bureau of Statistics in China, via CEIC DSata/*New York Times*, February 23, 2007, p. C1.

 **using** Technology

See the Technology Guide at
the end of the chapter for
detailed instructions on how
to obtain the regression curve
and graph for Example 5 using
a TI-83/84 Plus or Excel. Here
is an outline:

TI-83/84 Plus

[STAT] EDIT values of t in L_1
and values of F in L_2
Regression curve: [STAT]
CALC option #5
QuadReg [ENTER]
Graph: [Y=] [VARS] [5]
EQ [1], then [ZOOM] [9]
[More details on page 185.]

Excel

t- and F-values in Columns A
and B
Graph: Highlight data and
insert a Scatter chart.
Regression curve: Right-click a
datapoint and add polynomial
order 2 trendline with option to
show equation on chart.
[More details on page 188.]

Web Site
www.AppliedCalc.org
   Student Home
      → Online Utilities
      → Simple Regression
Enter the data in the x and
y columns and press
"y=ax^2+bx+c" .

Solution

a. To see whether a linear model is appropriate, we plot the data points and the regression line using one of the methods of Example 2 in Section 1.4 (Figure 8).

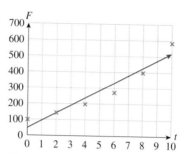

Figure 8

From the graph, we can see that the given data suggest a curve and not a straight line: The observed points are above the regression line at the ends but below in the middle. (We would expect the data points from a linear relation to fall randomly above and below the regression line.)

b. The quadratic model that best fits the data is the quadratic regression model. As with linear regression, there are algebraic formulas to compute a, b, and c, but they are rather involved. However, we exploit the fact that these formulas are built into graphing calculators, spreadsheets, and other technology, and obtain the regression curve using technology (see Figure 9):

$$F(t) = 4.6t^2 + 1.2t + 110 \qquad \text{Coefficients rounded to two significant digits}$$

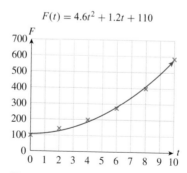

Figure 9

Notice from the previous graphs that the quadratic regression model appears to give a far better fit than the linear regression model. This impression is supported by the values of SSE: For the linear regression model SSE $\approx 13,400$; for the quadratic regression model SSE is much smaller, approximately 730, indicating a much better fit.

2.1 EXERCISES

▼ more advanced   ◆ challenging
🔲 indicates exercises that should be solved using technology

In Exercises 1–10, sketch the graphs of the quadratic functions, indicating the coordinates of the vertex, the y-intercept, and the x-intercepts (if any). HINT [See Example 1.]

1. $f(x) = x^2 + 3x + 2$
2. $f(x) = -x^2 - x$
3. $f(x) = -x^2 + 4x - 4$
4. $f(x) = x^2 + 2x + 1$
5. $f(x) = -x^2 - 40x + 500$
6. $f(x) = x^2 - 10x - 600$
7. $f(x) = x^2 + x - 1$
8. $f(x) = x^2 + \sqrt{2}x + 1$
9. $f(x) = x^2 + 1$
10. $f(x) = -x^2 + 5$

In Exercises 11–14, for each demand equation, express the total revenue R as a function of the price p per item, sketch the graph of the resulting function, and determine the price p that maximizes total revenue in each case. HINT [See Example 3.]

11. $q = -4p + 100$
12. $q = -3p + 300$
13. $q = -2p + 400$
14. $q = -5p + 1{,}200$

🔲 *In Exercises 15–18, use technology to find the quadratic regression curve through the given points. (Round all coefficients to four decimal places.)* HINT [See Example 5.]

15. $\{(1, 2), (3, 5), (4, 3), (5, 1)\}$
16. $\{(-1, 2), (-3, 5), (-4, 3), (-5, 1)\}$
17. $\{(-1, 2), (-3, 5), (-4, 3)\}$
18. $\{(2, 5), (3, 5), (5, 3)\}$

APPLICATIONS

19. *World Military Expenditure* The following chart shows total military and arms trade expenditure from 1990 to 2008 ($t = 0$ represents 1990).[1]

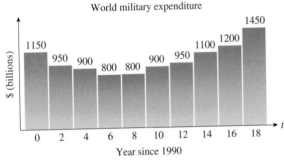

World military expenditure

Source: www.globalissues.org/Geopolitics/ArmsTrade/Spending.asp

_____
[1]Approximate figures in constant 2005 dollars. The 2008 figure is an estimate, based on the increase in U.S. military expenditure.

a. If you want to model the expenditure figures with a function of the form

$$f(t) = at^2 + bt + c,$$

would you expect the coefficient a to be positive or negative? Why? HINT [See "Features of a Parabola," page 125.]

b. Which of the following models best approximates the data given? (Try to answer this without actually computing values.)

(A) $f(t) = 5t^2 - 80t - 1{,}150$
(B) $f(t) = -5t^2 - 80t + 1{,}150$
(C) $f(t) = 5t^2 - 80t + 1{,}150$
(D) $f(t) = -5t^2 - 80t - 1{,}150$

c. What is the nearest year that would correspond to the vertex of the graph of the correct model from part (b)? What is the danger of extrapolating the data in either direction?

20. *Education Expenditure* The following chart shows the percentage of the U.S. Discretionary Budget allocated to education from 2003 to 2009 ($t = 3$ represents the start of 2003).

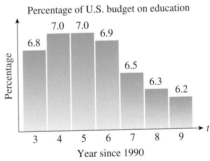

Percentage of U.S. budget on education

Source: www.globalissues.org/Geopolitics/ArmsTrade/Spending.asp

a. If you want to model the percentage figures with a function of the form

$$f(t) = at^2 + bt + c,$$

would you expect the coefficient a to be positive or negative? Why? HINT [See "Features of a Parabola," page 125.]

b. Which of the following models best approximates the data given? (Try to answer this without actually computing values)

(A) $f(t) = 0.04t^2 + 0.3t - 6$
(B) $f(t) = -0.04t^2 + 0.3t + 6$
(C) $f(t) = 0.04t^2 + 0.3t + 6$
(D) $f(t) = -0.04t^2 + 0.3t - 6$

c. What is the nearest year that would correspond to the vertex of the graph of the correct model from part (b)? What is the danger of extrapolating the data in either direction?

21. **Oil Imports from Mexico** Daily oil imports to the United States from Mexico can be approximated by

$$I(t) = -0.015t^2 + 0.1t + 1.4$$
$$\text{million barrels/day} \quad (0 \le t \le 8)$$

where t is time in years since the start of 2000.[2] According to the model, in what year were oil imports to the United States greatest? How many barrels per day were imported that year? HINT [See Example 1.]

22. **Oil Production in Mexico** Daily oil production by Pemex, Mexico's national oil company, for 2001–2009 can be approximated by

$$P(t) = -0.022t^2 + 0.2t + 2.9$$
$$\text{million barrels/day} \quad (1 \le t \le 9)$$

where t is time in years since the start of 2000.[3] According to the model, in what year was oil production by Pemex greatest? How many barrels per day were produced that year?

23. **Fuel Efficiency** The fuel efficiency (in miles per gallon) of an SUV depends on its weight according to the formula[4]

$$E = 0.000\,001\,6x^2 - 0.016x + 54 \quad (1{,}800 \le x \le 5{,}400)$$

where x is the weight of an SUV in pounds. According to the model, what is the weight of the least fuel-efficient SUV? Would you trust the model for weights greater than the answer you obtained? Explain.

24. **Global Warming** The amount of carbon dioxide (in pounds per 15,000 cubic miles) released by a typical SUV depends on its fuel efficiency according to the formula[5]

$$W = 32x^2 - 2{,}080x + 44{,}000 \quad (12 \le x \le 33)$$

where x is the fuel efficiency of an SUV in miles per gallon. According to the model, what is the fuel efficiency of the SUV with the least carbon dioxide pollution? Comment on the reliability of the model for fuel efficiencies that exceed your answer.

25. **Revenue** The market research department of the Better Baby Buggy Co. predicts that the demand equation for its buggies is given by $q = -0.5p + 140$, where q is the number of buggies it can sell in a month if the price is $\$p$ per buggy. At what price should it sell the buggies to get the largest revenue? What is the largest monthly revenue? HINT [See Example 3.]

26. **Revenue** The Better Baby Buggy Co. has just come out with a new model, the Turbo. The market research department predicts that the demand equation for Turbos is given by $q = -2p + 320$, where q is the number of buggies it can sell in a month if the price is $\$p$ per buggy. At what price should it sell the buggies to get the largest revenue? What is the largest monthly revenue?

27. **Revenue** Pack-Em-In Real Estate is building a new housing development. The more houses it builds, the less people will be willing to pay, due to the crowding and smaller lot sizes. In fact, if it builds 40 houses in this particular development, it can sell them for $200,000 each, but if it builds 60 houses, it will only be able to get $160,000 each. Obtain a linear demand equation and hence determine how many houses Pack-Em-In should build to get the largest revenue. What is the largest possible revenue? HINT [See Example 3.]

28. **Revenue** Pack-Em-In has another development in the works. If it builds 50 houses in this development, it will be able to sell them at $190,000 each, but if it builds 70 houses, it will get only $170,000 each. Obtain a linear demand equation and hence determine how many houses it should build to get the largest revenue. What is the largest possible revenue?

29. ▼ **Revenue from Monorail Service, Las Vegas** In 2005, the Las Vegas monorail charged $3 per ride and had an average ridership of about 28,000 per day. In December 2005 the Las Vegas Monorail Company raised the fare to $5 per ride, and average ridership in 2006 plunged to around 19,000 per day.[6]

   a. Use the given information to find a linear demand equation.
   b. Find the price the company should have charged to maximize revenue from ridership. What is the corresponding daily revenue?
   c. The Las Vegas Monorail Company would have needed $44.9 million in revenues from ridership to break even in 2006. Would it have been possible to break even in 2006 by charging a suitable price?

30. ▼ **Revenue from Monorail Service, Mars** The Utarek monorail, which links the three urbynes (or districts) of Utarek, Mars, charged $\overline{\overline{Z}}5$ per ride[7] and sold about 14 million rides per day. When the Utarek City Council lowered the fare to $\overline{\overline{Z}}3$ per ride, the number of rides increased to 18 million per day.

   a. Use the given information to find a linear demand equation.
   b. Find the price the City Council should have charged to maximize revenue from ridership. What is the corresponding daily revenue?
   c. The City Council would have needed to raise $\overline{\overline{Z}}48$ billion in revenues from ridership each Martian year (670 days[8]) to finance the new Mars organism research lab. Would this have been possible by charging a suitable price?

---

[2] Source: Energy Information Administration/Pemex/http://www.eia.doe.gov.

[3] Figures are approximate, and 2008–2009 figures are projections by the Department of Energy. Source: Energy Information Administration: Pemex.

[4] Fuel efficiency assumes 50% city driving and 50% highway driving. The model is based on a quadratic regression using data from 18 models of SUV. Source for data: Environmental Protection Agency, National Highway Traffic Safety Administration, American Automobile Manufacturers' Association, Ford Motor Company/*The New York Times*, November 30, 1997, p. 43.

[5] Ibid.

[6] Source: *New York Times*, Februrary 10, 2007, p. A9.

[7] $\overline{\overline{Z}}$ designates Zonars, the official currency in Mars. See www.marsnext.com for details of the Mars colony, its commerce, and its culture.

[8] As measured in Mars days. The actual length of a Mars year is about 670.55 Mars days, so frequent leap years are designated by the Mars Planetary Authority to adjust.

31. *Web Site Profit* You operate a gaming Web site, www
.mudbeast.net, where users must pay a small fee to log on. When
you charged $2 the demand was 280 log-ons per month. When
you lowered the price to $1.50, the demand increased to 560 log-
ons per month.

  a. Construct a linear demand function for your Web site and
  hence obtain the monthly revenue R as a function of the
  log-on fee x.

  b. Your Internet provider charges you a monthly fee of $30
  to maintain your site. Express your monthly profit P as a
  function of the log-on fee x, and hence determine the log-
  on fee you should charge to obtain the largest possible
  monthly profit. What is the largest possible monthly
  profit? HINT [See Example 4.]

32. *T-Shirt Profit* Two fraternities, Sig Ep and Ep Sig, plan to raise
money jointly to benefit homeless people on Long
Island. They will sell Yoda vs. Alien T-shirts in the student center, but are not sure how much to charge. Sig Ep treasurer
Augustus recalls that they once sold 400 shirts in a week at
$8 per shirt, but Ep Sig treasurer Julius has solid research
indicating that it is possible to sell 600 per week at $4 per shirt.

  a. Based on this information, construct a linear demand
  equation for Yoda vs. Alien T-shirts, and hence obtain the
  weekly revenue R as a function of the unit price x.

  b. The university administration charges the fraternities a
  weekly fee of $500 for use of the Student Center. Write
  down the monthly profit P as a function of the unit price
  x, and hence determine how much the fraternities should
  charge to obtain the largest possible weekly profit. What
  is the largest possible weekly profit? HINT [See Example 4.]

33. *Web Site Profit* The latest demand equation for your gaming
Web site, www.mudbeast.net, is given by

$$q = -400x + 1,200$$

where q is the number of users who log on per month and x is
the log-on fee you charge. Your Internet provider bills you as
follows:

  Site maintenance fee: $20 per month

  High-volume access fee: 50¢ per log-on

Find the monthly cost as a function of the log-on fee x.
Hence, find the monthly profit as a function of x and determine the log-on fee you should charge to obtain the largest
possible monthly profit. What is the largest possible monthly
profit?

34. *T-Shirt Profit* The latest demand equation for your Yoda vs.
Alien T-shirts is given by

$$q = -40x + 600$$

where q is the number of shirts you can sell in one week if
you charge $\$x$ per shirt. The Student Council charges you
$400 per week for use of their facilities, and the T-shirts cost
you $5 each. Find the weekly cost as a function of the unit
price x. Hence, find the weekly profit as a function of x and
determine the unit price you should charge to obtain the

largest possible weekly profit. What is the largest possible
weekly profit?

35. ▼*Nightclub Management* You have just opened a new
nightclub, Russ' Techno Pitstop, but are unsure of how high
to set the cover charge (entrance fee). One week you charged
$10 per guest and averaged 300 guests per night. The next
week you charged $15 per guest and averaged 250 guests
per night.

  a. Find a linear demand equation showing the number of
  guests q per night as a function of the cover charge p.

  b. Find the nightly revenue R as a function of the cover
  charge p.

  c. The club will provide two free non-alcoholic drinks for each
  guest, costing the club $3 per head. In addition, the nightly
  overheads (rent, salaries, dancers, DJ, etc.) amount to
  $3,000. Find the cost C as a function of the cover charge p.

  d. Now find the profit in terms of the cover charge p, and
  hence determine the entrance fee you should charge for a
  maximum profit.

36. ▼*Television Advertising* As sales manager for Montevideo
Productions, Inc., you are planning to review the prices you
charge clients for television advertisement development. You
currently charge each client an hourly development fee of
$2,500. With this pricing structure, the demand, measured by
the number of contracts Montevideo signs per month, is 15
contracts. This is down 5 contracts from the figure last year,
when your company charged only $2,000.

  a. Construct a linear demand equation giving the number of
  contracts q as a function of the hourly fee p Montevideo
  charges for development.

  b. On average, Montevideo bills for 50 hours of production
  time on each contract. Give a formula for the total revenue
  obtained by charging $\$p$ per hour.

  c. The costs to Montevideo Productions are estimated as
  follows:

  Fixed costs: $120,000 per month

  Variable costs: $80,000 per contract

  Express Montevideo Productions' monthly cost **(i)** as a
  function of the number q of contracts and **(ii)** as a function
  of the hourly production charge p.

  d. Express Montevideo Productions' monthly profit as a
  function of the hourly development fee p and hence the
  price it should charge to maximize the profit.

37. ⊡ *World Military Expenditure* The following table shows
total military and arms trade expenditure in 1994, 1998, and
2006. (See Exercise 19; $t = 4$ represents 1994.)[9]

Year t	4	8	16
Military Expenditure ($ billion)	900	800	1,200

---

[9] Approximate figures in constant 2005 dollars. The 2008 figure is
an estimate, based on the increase in U.S. military expenditure.
Source: www.globalissues.org/Geopolitics/ArmsTrade/Spending.asp.

Find a quadratic model for these data, and use your model to estimate world military expenditure in 2008. Compare your answer with the actual figure shown in Exercise 19. HINT [See Example 5.]

38. ⊤ *Education Expenditure* The following table shows the percentage of the U.S. Discretionary Budget allocated to education in 2003, 2005, and 2009. (See Exercise 20; $t = 3$ represents the start of 2003.)[10]

Year t	3	5	9
Percentage	6.8	7	6.2

Find a quadratic model for these data, and use your model to estimate the percentage of the U.S. Discretionary Budget allocated to education in 2008. Compare your answer with the actual figure shown in Exercise 20.

39. ⊤ *iPhone Sales* The following table shows **Apple** iPhone sales from the 2nd quarter in 2007 through the second quarter in 2008 ($t = 2$ represents the second quarter of 2007):[11]

Quarter t	2	3	4	5	6
iPhone Sales (thousands)	270	1,119	2,315	1,703	717

a. Find a quadratic regression model for these data. (Round coefficients to the nearest whole number.) Graph the model together with the data.

b. What does the model predict for iPhone sales in the third quarter of 2008 ($t = 7$) to the nearest 1,000 units? Comment on the answer, and ascertain the actual third quarter sales in 2008 (**Apple**'s fiscal fourth quarter).

40. ⊤ *Facebook Membersip* The following table gives the approximate number of **Facebook** users at various times since its establishment early in 2004.[12]

Year t (since start of 2004)	0	1	2	2.5	3	3.5	4	4.5
Facebook Members n (millions)	0	1	5.5	7	12	30	58	80

a. Find a quadratic regression model for these data. (Round coefficients to the nearest whole number.) Graph the model, together with the data.

---

[10] Source: www.globalissues.org/Geopolitics/ArmsTrade/Spending.asp.

[11] Source: Apple financial statements, www.apple.com.

[12] Sources: Some data are interpolated. (www.facebook.com/, www.insidehighered.com).

b. Assuming the trend had continued, estimate the number of members at the start of 2010 to the nearest 10 million members.

c. Is the quadratic model appropriate for long-term prediction of the number of members? Why?

COMMUNICATION AND REASONING EXERCISES

41. What can you say about the graph of $f(x) = ax^2 + bx + c$ if $a = 0$?

42. What can you say about the graph of $f(x) = ax^2 + bx + c$ if $c = 0$?

43. Multiple choice: Following is the graph of $f(x) = ax^2 + bx + c$:

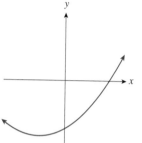

(A) a is positive and c is positive.
(B) a is negative and c is positive.
(C) a is positive and c is negative.
(D) a is negative and c is negative.

44. Multiple choice: Following is the graph of $f(x) = ax^2 + bx + c$:

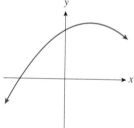

(A) a is positive and c is positive.
(B) a is negative and c is positive.
(C) a is positive and c is negative.
(D) a is negative and c is negative.

45. ▼ Refer to the graph of $f(x) = ax^2 + bx + c$ in Exercise 43. Is b positive or negative? Why?

46. ▼ Refer to the graph of $f(x) = ax^2 + bx + c$ in Exercise 44. Is b positive or negative? Why?

47. Suppose the graph of revenue as a function of unit price is a parabola that is concave down. What is the significance of the coordinates of the vertex, the x-intercepts, and the y-intercept?

48. Suppose the height of a stone thrown vertically upward is given by a quadratic function of time. What is the significance of the coordinates of the vertex, the (possible) x-intercepts, and the y-intercept?

49. How might you tell, roughly, whether a set of data should be modeled by a quadratic rather than by a linear equation?

50. A member of your study group tells you that, because the following set of data does not suggest a straight line, the data are best modeled by a quadratic.

x	0	2	4	6	8
y	1	2	1	0	1

Comment on her suggestion.

51. Is a quadratic model useful for long-term prediction of sales of an item? Why?

52. Of what use is a quadratic model, if not for long-term prediction?

53. ▼ Explain why, if demand is a linear function of unit price p (with negative slope), then there must be a *single value of* p that results in the maximum revenue.

54. ▼ Explain why, if the average cost of a commodity is given by $y = 0.1x^2 - 4x - 2$, where x is the number of units sold, there is a single choice of x that results in the lowest possible average cost.

55. ▼ If the revenue function for a particular commodity is $R(p) = -50p^2 + 60p$, what is the (linear) demand function? Give a reason for your answer.

56. ▼ If the revenue function for a particular commodity is $R(p) = -50p^2 + 60p + 50$, can the demand function be linear? What is the associated demand function?

2.2 Exponential Functions and Models

The quadratic functions we discussed in Section 2.1 can be used to model many nonlinear situations. However, exponential functions give better models in some applications, including population growth, radioactive decay, the growth or depreciation of financial investments, and many other phenomena. (We already saw some of these applications in Section 1.2.)

To work effectively with exponential functions, we need to know the laws of exponents. The following list, taken from the algebra review in Chapter 0, gives the laws of exponents we will be using.

The Laws of Exponents

If b and c are positive and x and y are any real numbers, then the following laws hold:

Law	Quick Examples
1. $b^x b^y = b^{x+y}$	$2^3 2^2 = 2^5 = 32$ $\qquad$ $2^{3-x} = 2^3 2^{-x}$
2. $\dfrac{b^x}{b^y} = b^{x-y}$	$\dfrac{4^3}{4^2} = 4^{3-2} = 4^1 = 4$ $\qquad$ $3^{x-2} = \dfrac{3^x}{3^2} = \dfrac{3^x}{9}$
3. $\dfrac{1}{b^x} = b^{-x}$	$9^{-0.5} = \dfrac{1}{9^{0.5}} = \dfrac{1}{3}$ $\qquad$ $2^{-x} = \dfrac{1}{2^x}$
4. $b^0 = 1$	$(3.3)^0 = 1$ $\qquad$ $x^0 = 1$ if $x \neq 0$
5. $(b^x)^y = b^{xy}$	$(2^3)^2 = 2^6 = 64$ $\qquad$ $\left(\dfrac{1}{2}\right)^x = (2^{-1})^x = 2^{-x}$
6. $(bc)^x = b^x c^x$	$(4 \cdot 2)^2 = 4^2 2^2 = 64$ $\qquad$ $10^x = 5^x 2^x$
7. $\left(\dfrac{b}{c}\right)^x = \dfrac{b^x}{c^x}$	$\left(\dfrac{4}{3}\right)^2 = \dfrac{4^2}{3^2} = \dfrac{16}{9}$ $\qquad$ $\left(\dfrac{1}{2}\right)^x = \dfrac{1^x}{2^x} = \dfrac{1}{2^x}$

Here are the functions we will study in this section.

Exponential Function

An **exponential function** has the form

$$f(x) = Ab^x, \qquad \text{Technology: A*b^x}$$

where A and b are constants with $A \neq 0$ and b positive and not equal to 1. We call b the **base** of the exponential function.

Quick Examples

1. $f(x) = 2^x$ $A = 1, b = 2$; Technology: `2^x`

   $f(1) = 2^1 = 2$ `2^1`

   $f(-3) = 2^{-3} = \dfrac{1}{8}$ `2^(-3)`

   $f(0) = 2^0 = 1$ `2^0`

2. $g(x) = 20(3^x)$ $A = 20, b = 3$; Technology: `20*3^x`

   $g(2) = 20(3^2) = 20(9) = 180$ `20*3^2`

   $g(-1) = 20(3^{-1}) = 20\left(\dfrac{1}{3}\right) = 6\dfrac{2}{3}$ `20*3^(-1)`

3. $h(x) = 2^{-x} = \left(\dfrac{1}{2}\right)^x$ $A = 1, b = \frac{1}{2}$; Technology: `2^(-x)` or `(1/2)^x`

   $h(1) = 2^{-1} = \dfrac{1}{2}$ `2^(-1)` or `(1/2)^1`

   $h(2) = 2^{-2} = \dfrac{1}{4}$ `2^(-2)` or `(1/2)^2`

4. $k(x) = 3 \cdot 2^{-4x} = 3(2^{-4})^x$ $A = 3, b = 2^{-4}$; Technology: `3*2^(-4*x)`

   $k(-2) = 3 \cdot 2^{-4(-2)}$ `3*2^(-4*(-2))`

   $= 3 \cdot 2^8 = 3 \cdot 256 = 768$

Exponential Functions from the Numerical and Graphical Points of View

The following table shows values of $f(x) = 3(2^x)$ for some values of x ($A = 3, b = 2$):

x	-3	-2	-1	0	1	2	3
$f(x)$	$\frac{3}{8}$	$\frac{3}{4}$	$\frac{3}{2}$	3	6	12	24

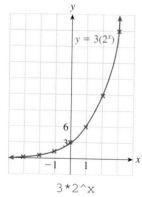

$3*2\text{\^{}}x$

Figure 10

Its graph is shown in Figure 10.

Notice that the y-intercept is $A = 3$ (obtained by setting $x = 0$). In general:

In the graph of $f(x) = Ab^x$, A is the y-intercept, or the value of y when $x = 0$.

What about b? Notice from the table that the value of y is multiplied by $b = 2$ for every increase of 1 in x. If we decrease x by 1, the y coordinate gets *divided* by $b = 2$.

The value of y is multiplied by b for every one-unit increase of x.

x	-3	-2	-1	0	1	2	3
$f(x)$	$\frac{3}{8}$	$\frac{3}{4}$	$\frac{3}{2}$	3	6	12	24

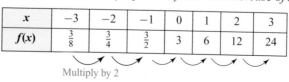

Multiply by 2

On the graph, if we move one unit to the right from any point on the curve, the y coordinate doubles. Thus, the curve becomes dramatically steeper as the value of x increases. This phenomenon is called **exponential growth**. (See Section 1.2.)

Exponential Function Numerically and Graphically

For the exponential function $f(x) = Ab^x$:

Role of A
$f(0) = A$, so A is the y-intercept of the graph of f.

Role of b
If x increases by 1, $f(x)$ is multiplied by b.
If x increases by 2, $f(x)$ is multiplied by b^2.

$\vdots$

If x increases by Δx, $f(x)$ is multiplied by $b^{\Delta x}$.

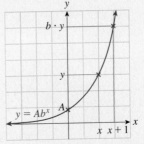

If x increases by 1, y is multiplied by b.

Quick Examples

1. $f_1(x) = 2^x,\ f_2(x) = \left(\dfrac{1}{2}\right)^x = 2^{-x}$

	A	B	C
1	x	2^x	2^(-x)
2	-3	1/8	8
3	-2	1/4	4
4	-1	1/2	2
5	0	1	1
6	1	2	1/2
7	2	4	1/4
8	3	8	1/8

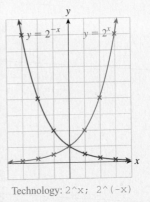

Technology: 2^x; 2^(-x)

When x increases by 1, $f_2(x)$ is multiplied by $\frac{1}{2}$. The function $f_1(x) = 2^x$ illustrates exponential growth, while $f_2(x) = \left(\frac{1}{2}\right)^x$ illustrates the opposite phenomenon: **exponential decay**.

2. $f_1(x) = 2^x,\ f_2(x) = 3^x,\ f_3(x) = 1^x$ (Can you see why f_3 is not an exponential function?)

	A	B	C	D
1	x	2^x	3^x	1^x
2	-3	1/8	1/27	1
3	-2	1/4	1/9	1
4	-1	1/2	1/3	1
5	0	1	1	1
6	1	2	3	1
7	2	4	9	1
8	3	8	27	1

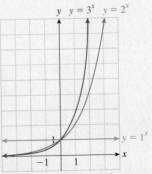

If x increases by 1, 3^x is multiplied by 3. Note also that all the graphs pass through (0, 1). (Why?)

EXAMPLE 1 Recognizing Exponential Data Numerically and Graphically

Some of the values of two functions, f and g, are given in the following table:

x	-2	-1	0	1	2
$f(x)$	-7	-3	1	5	9
$g(x)$	$\frac{2}{9}$	$\frac{2}{3}$	2	6	18

One of these functions is linear, and the other is exponential. Which is which?

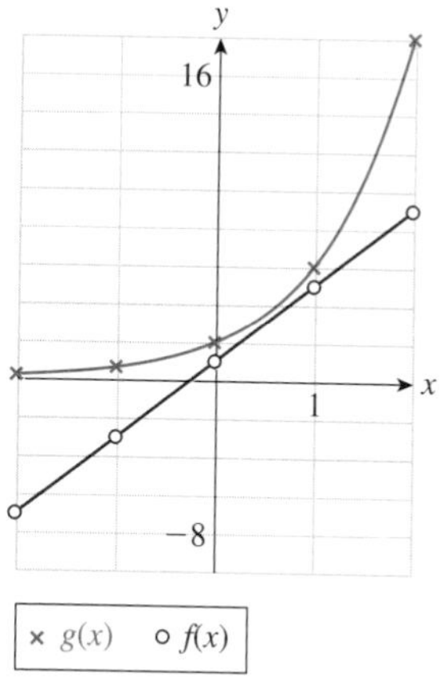

Solution Remember that a linear function increases (or decreases) by the same amount every time x increases by 1. The values of f behave this way: Every time x increases by 1, the value of $f(x)$ increases by 4. Therefore, f is a linear function with a *slope* of 4. Because $f(0) = 1$, we see that

$$f(x) = 4x + 1$$

is a linear formula that fits the data.

On the other hand, every time x increases by 1, the value of $g(x)$ is *multiplied* by 3. Because $g(0) = 2$, we find that

$$g(x) = 2(3^x)$$

is an exponential function fitting the data.

We can visualize the two functions f and g by plotting the data points (Figure 11). The data points for $f(x)$ clearly lie along a straight line, whereas the points for $g(x)$ lie along a curve. The y coordinate of each point for $g(x)$ is 3 times the y coordinate of the preceding point, demonstrating that the curve is an exponential one.

Figure 11

In Section 1.3, we discussed a method for calculating the equation of the line that passes through two given points. In the following example, we show the method for calculating the equation of the exponential curve through two given points.

EXAMPLE 2 Finding the Exponential Curve through Two Points

Find an equation of the exponential curve through $(1, 6.3)$ and $(4, 170.1)$.

Solution We want an equation of the form

$$y = Ab^x \quad (b > 0).$$

Substituting the coordinates of the given points, we get

$$6.3 = Ab^1 \qquad \text{Substitute } (1, 6.3).$$
$$170.1 = Ab^4. \qquad \text{Substitute } (4, 170.1).$$

If we now divide the second equation by the first, we get

$$\frac{170.1}{6.3} = \frac{Ab^4}{Ab} = b^3$$
$$b^3 = 27$$
$$b = 27^{1/3} \qquad \text{Take reciprocal power of both sides.}$$
$$b = 3.$$

Now that we have b, we can substitute its value into the first equation to obtain

$$6.3 = 3A \qquad \text{Substitute } b = 3 \text{ into the equation } 6.3 = Ab^1.$$

$$A = \frac{6.3}{3} = 2.1.$$

We have both constants, $A = 2.1$ and $b = 3$, so the model is

$$y = 2.1(3^x).$$

Example 6 will show how to use technology to fit an exponential function to two or more data points.

APPLICATIONS

Recall some terminology we mentioned earlier: A quantity y experiences **exponential growth** if $y = Ab^t$ with $b > 1$. (Here we use t for the independent variable, thinking of time.) It experiences **exponential decay** if $y = Ab^t$ with $0 < b < 1$. We already saw several examples of exponential growth and decay in Section 1.2.

EXAMPLE 3 Exponential Growth and Decay

a. Compound Interest (See Section 1.2 Example 6.) If $2,000 is invested in a mutual fund with an annual yield of 12.6% and the earnings are reinvested each month, then the future value after t years is

$$A(t) = P\left(1 + \frac{r}{m}\right)^{mt} = 2,000\left(1 + \frac{0.126}{12}\right)^{12t} = 2,000(1.0105)^{12t},$$

which can be written as $2,000(1.0105^{12})^t$, so $A = 2,000$ and $b = 1.0105^{12}$. This is an example of exponential growth, because $b > 1$.

b. Carbon Decay (See Section 1.2 Example 7.) The amount of carbon 14 remaining in a sample that originally contained A grams is approximately

$$C(t) = A(0.999879)^t.$$

This is an instance of exponential decay, because $b < 1$.

➡ **Before we go on...** Refer again to part (a). In Example 6(b) of Section 1.2 we showed how to use technology to answer questions such as the following: "When, to the nearest year, will the value of your investment reach $5,000?" ∎

The next example shows an application to public health.

EXAMPLE 4 Exponential Growth: Epidemics

In the early stages of the AIDS epidemic during the 1980s, the number of cases in the United States was increasing by about 50% every 6 months. By the start of 1983, there were approximately 1,600 AIDS cases in the United States.*

a. Assuming an exponential growth model, find a function that predicts the number of people infected t years after the start of 1983.

b. Use the model to estimate the number of people infected by October 1, 1986, and also by the end of that year.

_____

* Data based on regression of the 1982–1986 figures. Source for data: Centers for Disease Control and Prevention. HIV/AIDS Surveillance Report, 2000;12 (No. 2).

Solution

a. One way of finding the desired exponential function is to reason as follows: At time $t = 0$ (January 1, 1983), the number of people infected was 1,600, so $A = 1,600$. Every 6 months, the number of cases increased to 150% of the number 6 months earlier—that is, to 1.50 times that number. Each year, it therefore increased to $(1.50)^2 = 2.25$ times the number one year earlier. Hence, after t years, we need to multiply the original 1,600 by 2.25^t, so the model is

$$y = 1,600(2.25^t) \text{ cases.}$$

Alternatively, if we wish to use the method of Example 2, we need two data points. We are given one point: (0, 1,600). Because y increased by 50% every 6 months, 6 months later it reached $1,600 + 800 = 2,400$ ($t = 0.5$). This information gives a second point: (0.5, 2,400). We can now apply the method in Example 2 to find the model above.

b. October 1, 1986, corresponds to $t = 3.75$ (because October 1 is 9 months, or $9/12 = 0.75$ of a year after January 1). Substituting this value of t in the model gives

$$y = 1,600(2.25^{3.75}) \approx 33,481 \text{ cases} \qquad \texttt{1600*2.25\textasciicircum3.75}$$

By the end of 1986, the model predicts that

$$y = 1,600(2.25^4) = 41,006 \text{ cases.}$$

(The actual number of cases was around 41,700.)

➡ **Before we go on...** Increasing the number of cases by 50% every 6 months couldn't continue for very long and this is borne out by observations. If increasing by 50% every 6 months did continue, then by January 2003 ($t = 20$), the number of infected people would have been

$$1,600(2.25^{20}) \approx 17,700,000,000$$

a number that is more than 50 times the size of the U.S. population! Thus, although the exponential model is fairly reliable in the early stages of the epidemic, it is unreliable for predicting long-term trends. ■

Epidemiologists use more sophisticated models to measure the spread of epidemics, and these models predict a leveling-off phenomenon as the number of cases becomes a significant part of the total population. We discuss such a model, the **logistic function,** in Section 2.4.

The Number e and More Applications

In nature we find examples of growth that occurs *continuously*, as though "interest" is being added more often than every second or fraction of a second. To model this, we need to see what happens to the compound interest formula of Section 1.2 as we let m (the number of times interest is added per year) become extremely large. Something very interesting does happen: We end up with a more compact and elegant formula than we began with. To see why, let's look at a very simple situation.

Suppose we invest $1 in the bank for 1 year at 100% interest, compounded m times per year. If $m = 1$, then 100% interest is added every year, and so our money doubles at the end of the year. In general, the accumulated capital at the end of the year is

$$A = 1\left(1 + \frac{1}{m}\right)^m = \left(1 + \frac{1}{m}\right)^m. \qquad \texttt{(1+1/m)\textasciicircum m}$$

	A	B
1	m	(1+1/m)^m
2	1	2
3	10	2.59374246
4	100	2.704813829
5	1000	2.716923932
6	10000	2.718145927
7	100000	2.718268237
8	1000000	2.718280469
9	10000000	2.718281694
10	100000000	2.718281786
11	1000000000	2.718282031

Now, we are interested in what A becomes for large values of m. On the left is an Excel sheet showing the quantity $\left(1 + \frac{1}{m}\right)^m$ for larger and larger values of m.

Something interesting *does* seem to be happening! The numbers appear to be getting closer and closer to a specific value. In mathematical terminology, we say that the numbers **converge** to a fixed number, 2.71828..., called the **limiting value*** of the quantities $\left(1 + \frac{1}{m}\right)^m$. This number, called e, is one of the most important in mathematics. The number e is irrational, just as the more familiar number π is, so we cannot write down its exact numerical value. To 20 decimal places,

$$e = 2.71828182845904523536....$$

We now say that, if \$1 is invested for 1 year at 100% interest **compounded continuously**, the accumulated money at the end of that year will amount to $\$e = \$2.72$ (to the nearest cent). But what about the following more general question?

* NOTE See Chapter 3 for more on limits.

Q: *What about a more general scenario: If we invest an amount \$P for t years at an interest rate of r, compounded continuously, what will be the accumulated amount A at the end of that period?*

A: In the special case above (P, t, and r all equal 1), we took the compound interest formula and let m get larger and larger. We do the same more generally, after a little preliminary work with the algebra of exponentials.

$$A = P\left(1 + \frac{r}{m}\right)^{mt}$$

$$= P\left(1 + \frac{1}{(m/r)}\right)^{mt} \qquad \text{Substituting } \tfrac{r}{m} = \tfrac{1}{(m/r)}$$

$$= P\left(1 + \frac{1}{(m/r)}\right)^{(m/r)rt} \qquad \text{Substituting } m = \left(\tfrac{m}{r}\right)r$$

$$= P\left[\left(1 + \frac{1}{(m/r)}\right)^{(m/r)}\right]^{rt} \qquad \text{Using the rule } a^{bc} = (a^b)^c$$

For continuous compounding of interest, we let m, and hence m/r, get very large. This affects only the term in brackets, which converges to e, and we get the formula

$$A = Pe^{rt}.$$

Q: *How do I obtain powers of e or e itself on a TI-83/84 Plus or in Excel?*

A: On the TI-83/84 Plus, enter e^x as e^(x), where e^(can be obtained by pressing [2ND] [LN]. To obtain the number e on the TI-83/84 Plus, enter e^(1). Excel has a built-in function called EXP; EXP(x) gives the value of e^x. To obtain the number e in Excel, enter =EXP(1).

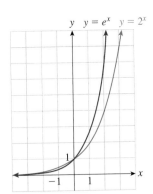

y $y = e^x$ $y = 2^x$

Technology formula: e^(x)
or EXP(x)

Figure 12

Figure 12 shows the graph of $y = e^x$ with that of $y = 2^x$ for comparison.

The Number e and Continuous Compounding

The number e is the limiting value of the quantities $\left(1 + \frac{1}{m}\right)^m$ as m gets larger and larger, and has the value 2.71828182845904523536 ...

If \$P is invested at an annual interest rate r compounded continuously, the accumulated amount after t years is

$$A(t) = Pe^{rt}. \qquad \text{P*e^(r*t) or P*EXP(r*t)}$$

Quick Examples

1. If $100 is invested in an account that bears 15% interest compounded continuously, at the end of 10 years the investment will be worth

$$A(10) = 100e^{(0.15)(10)} = \$448.17. \qquad \texttt{100*e\^{}(0.15*10)} \text{ or}$$
$$\texttt{100*EXP(0.15*10)}$$

2. If $1 is invested in an account that bears 100% interest compounded continuously, at the end of x years, the investment will be worth

$$A(x) = e^x \text{ dollars.}$$

EXAMPLE 5   Continuous Compounding

a. You invest $10,000 at Fastrack Savings & Loan, which pays 6% compounded continuously. Express the balance in your account as a function of the number of years t and calculate the amount of money you will have after 5 years.

b. Your friend has just invested $20,000 in Constant Growth Funds, whose stocks are continuously *declining* at a rate of 6% per year. How much will her investment be worth in 5 years?

c. ⊞ During which year will the value of your investment first exceed that of your friend?

Solution

a. We use the continuous growth formula with $P = 10,000$, $r = 0.06$, and t variable, getting

$$A(t) = Pe^{rt} = 10,000e^{0.06t}.$$

In five years,

$$A(5) = 10,000e^{0.06(5)}$$
$$= 10,000e^{0.3}$$
$$\approx \$13,498.59.$$

b. Because the investment is depreciating, we use a negative value for r and take $P = 20,000$, $r = -0.06$, and $t = 5$, getting

$$A(t) = Pe^{rt} = 20,000e^{-0.06t}$$
$$A(5) = 20,000e^{-0.06(5)}$$
$$= 20,000e^{-0.3}$$
$$\approx \$14,816.36.$$

c. We can answer the question now using a graphing calculator, a spreadsheet, or the Function Evaluator and Grapher tool at the Web site. Just enter the exponential models of parts (a) and (b) and create tables to compute the values at the end of several years:

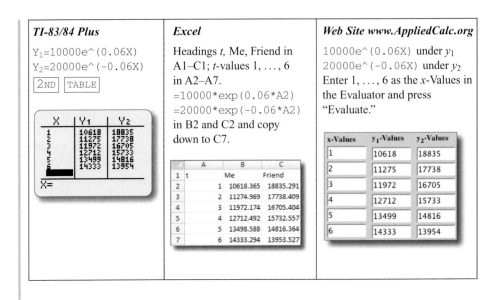

TI-83/84 Plus	Excel	Web Site www.AppliedCalc.org
$Y_1=10000e^\wedge(0.06X)$ $Y_2=20000e^\wedge(-0.06X)$ 2ND TABLE	Headings t, Me, Friend in A1–C1; t-values 1, …, 6 in A2–A7. $=10000*exp(0.06*A2)$ $=20000*exp(-0.06*A2)$ in B2 and C2 and copy down to C7.	$10000e^\wedge(0.06X)$ under y_1 $20000e^\wedge(-0.06X)$ under y_2 Enter 1, …, 6 as the x-Values in the Evaluator and press "Evaluate."

From the table, we see that the value of your investment overtakes that of your friend after $t = 5$ (the end of year 5) and before $t = 6$ (the end of year 6). Thus your investment first exceeds that of your friend sometime during year 6.

➡ **Before we go on…**

Q: *How does continuous compounding compare with monthly compounding?*

A: To repeat the calculation in part (a) of Example 5 using monthly compounding instead of continuous compounding, we use the compound interest formula with $P = 10{,}000$, $r = 0.06$, $m = 12$, and $t = 5$ and find

$$A(5) = 10{,}000(1 + 0.06/12)^{60} \approx \$13{,}488.50.$$

Thus, continuous compounding earns you approximately \$10 more than monthly compounding on a 5-year, \$10,000 investment. This is little to get excited about.

■

If we write the continuous compounding formula $A(t) = Pe^{rt}$ as $A(t) = P(e^r)^t$, we see that $A(t)$ is an exponential function of t, where the base is $b = e^r$, so we have really not introduced a new kind of function. In fact, exponential functions are often written in this way:

Exponential Functions: Alternative Form

We can write any exponential function in the following alternative form:

$$f(x) = Ae^{rx}$$

where A and r are constants. If r is positive, f models exponential growth; if r is negative, f models exponential decay.

Quick Examples

1. $f(x) = 100e^{0.15x}$ Exponential growth $A = 100$, $r = 0.15$

2. $f(t) = Ae^{-0.000\,121\,01t}$ Exponential decay of carbon 14;
   $r = -0.000\,121\,01$

3. $f(t) = 100e^{0.15t} = 100\left(e^{0.15}\right)^t$

   $= 100(1.1618)^t$ Converting Ae^{rt} to the form Ab^t

We will see in Chapter 4 that the exponential function with base e exhibits some interesting properties when we measure its rate of change, and this is the real mathematical importance of e.

Exponential Regression

Starting with a set of data that suggests an exponential curve, we can use technology to compute the exponential regression curve in much the same way as we did for the quadratic regression curve in Example 5 of Section 2.1.

EXAMPLE 6   Exponential Regression: Health Expenditures

The following table shows annual expenditure on health in the United States from 1980 through 2010 ($t = 0$ represents 1980).*

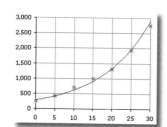

Figure 13

Year t	0	5	10	15	20	25	30
Expenditure ($ billion)	246	427	696	990	1,310	1,920	2,750

a. Find the exponential regression model

$$C(t) = Ab^t$$

for the annual expenditure.

b. Use the regression model to estimate the expenditure in 2002 ($t = 22$; the actual expenditure was approximately $1,550 billion).

Solution

a. We use technology to obtain the exponential regression curve (see Figure 13):

$$C(t) \approx 282.33(1.0808)^t \quad \text{Coefficients rounded}$$

b. Using the model $C(t) \approx 282.33(1.0808)^t$ we find that

$$C(22) \approx 282.33(1.0808)^{22} \approx \$1,560 \text{ billion}$$

which is close to the actual number of around $1,550 billion.

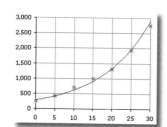

using Technology

See the Technology Guide at the end of the chapter for detailed instructions on how to obtain the regression curve and graph for Example 6 using a TI-83/84 Plus or Excel. Here is an outline:

TI-83/84 Plus

STAT EDIT values of t in L_1 and values of C in L_2
Regression curve: STAT CALC option #0 ExpReg
ENTER
Graph: Y= VARS 5 EQ 1 , then ZOOM 9
[More details on page 186.]

---

* Data are rounded. 2005 and 2010 figures are projections. Source: Centers for Medicare and Medicaid Services, "National Health Expenditures," 2002 version, released January 2004; www.cms.hhs.gov/statistics/nhe/.

Excel

t- and *C*-values in columns A and B

Graph: Highlight data and insert a Scatter chart.

Regression curve: Right-click a datapoint and add exponential Trendline with option to show equation on chart.

[More details on page 189.]

Web Site

www.AppliedCalc.org

Student Home

→ Online Utilities

→ Simple Regression

Enter the data in the *x* and *y* columns and press "y=a(b^x)".

➡ **Before we go on...** We said in the preceding section that the regression curve gives the smallest value of the sum-of-squares error, SSE (the sum of the squares of the residuals). However, exponential regression as computed via technology generally minimizes the sum of the squares of the residuals of the *logarithms* (logarithms are discussed in the next section). Using logarithms allows one easily to convert an exponential function into a linear one and then use linear regression formulas. However, in Section 2.4, we will discuss a way of using Excel's Solver to minimize SSE directly, which allows us to find the best-fit exponential curve directly without the need for devices to simplify the mathematics. If we do this, we obtain a very different equation:

$$C(t) \approx 316.79(1.0747^t).$$

If you plot this function, you will notice that it seems to fit the data more closely than the regression curve. ∎

FAQs

When to Use an Exponential Model for Data Points, and When to Use *e* in Your Model

Q: *Given a set of data points that appear to be curving upward, how can I tell whether to use a quadratic model or an exponential model?*

A: Here are some things to look for:

- Do the data values appear to double at regular intervals? (For example, do the values approximately double every 5 units?) If so, then an exponential model is appropriate. If it takes longer and longer to double, then a quadratic model may be more appropriate.
- Do the values first decrease to a low point and then increase? If so, then a quadratic model is more appropriate.

It is also helpful to use technology to graph both the regression quadratic and exponential curves and to visually inspect the graphs to determine which gives the closest fit to the data.

Q: *We have two ways of writing exponential functions: $f(x) = Ab^x$ and $f(x) = Ae^{rx}$. How do we know which one to use?*

A: The two forms are equivalent, and it is always possible to convert from one form to the other.[*] So, use whichever form seems to be convenient for a particular situation. For instance, $f(t) = A(3^t)$ conveniently models exponential growth that is tripling every unit of time, whereas $f(t) = Ae^{0.06t}$ conveniently models an investment with continuous compounding at 6%.

✱ NOTE Quick Example 3 on page 145 shows how to convert Ae^{rx} to Ab^x. Conversion from Ab^x to Ae^{rx} involves logarithms: $r = \ln b$.

2.2 **EXERCISES**

▼ more advanced   ◆ challenging

T indicates exercises that should be solved using technology

For each function in Exercises 1–12, compute the missing values in the following table and supply a valid technology formula for the given function: HINT [See Quick Examples on page 137.]

x	−3	−2	−1	0	1	2	3
f(x)							

1. $f(x) = 4^x$

2. $f(x) = 3^x$

3. $f(x) = 3^{-x}$

4. $f(x) = 4^{-x}$

5. $g(x) = 2(2^x)$

6. $g(x) = 2(3^x)$

7. $h(x) = -3(2^{-x})$

8. $h(x) = -2(3^{-x})$

9. $r(x) = 2^x - 1$

10. $r(x) = 2^{-x} + 1$

11. $s(x) = 2^{x-1}$

12. $s(x) = 2^{1-x}$

Using a chart of values, graph each of the functions in Exercises 13–18. (Use $-3 \le x \le 3$.)

13. $f(x) = 3^{-x}$ **14.** $f(x) = 4^{-x}$

15. $g(x) = 2(2^x)$ **16.** $g(x) = 2(3^x)$

17. $h(x) = -3(2^{-x})$ **18.** $h(x) = -2(3^{-x})$

In Exercises 19–24, the values of two functions, f and g, are given in a table. One, both, or neither of them may be exponential. Decide which, if any, are exponential, and give the exponential models for those that are. HINT [See Example 1.]

19.

x	-2	-1	0	1	2
$f(x)$	0.5	1.5	4.5	13.5	40.5
$g(x)$	8	4	2	1	$\frac{1}{2}$

20.

x	-2	-1	0	1	2
$f(x)$	$\frac{1}{2}$	1	2	4	8
$g(x)$	3	0	-1	0	3

21.

x	-2	-1	0	1	2
$f(x)$	22.5	7.5	2.5	7.5	22.5
$g(x)$	0.3	0.9	2.7	8.1	16.2

22.

x	-2	-1	0	1	2
$f(x)$	0.3	0.9	2.7	8.1	24.3
$g(x)$	3	1.5	0.75	0.375	0.1875

23.

x	-2	-1	0	1	2
$f(x)$	100	200	400	600	800
$g(x)$	100	20	4	0.8	0.16

24.

x	-2	-1	0	1	2
$f(x)$	0.8	0.2	0.1	0.05	0.025
$g(x)$	80	40	20	10	2

T *For each function in Exercises 25–30, supply a valid technology formula and then use technology to compute the missing values in the following table:* HINT [See Quick Examples on page 137.]

x	-3	-2	-1	0	1	2	3
$f(x)$							

25. $f(x) = e^{-2x}$ **26.** $g(x) = e^{x/5}$

27. $h(x) = 1.01(2.02^{-4x})$ **28.** $h(x) = 3.42(3^{-x/5})$

29. $r(x) = 50\left(1 + \dfrac{1}{3.2}\right)^{2x}$ **30.** $r(x) = 0.043\left(4.5 - \dfrac{5}{1.2}\right)^{-x}$

In Exercises 31–38, supply a valid technology formula for the given function.

31. 2^{x-1} **32.** 2^{-4x} **33.** $\dfrac{2}{1 - 2^{-4x}}$ **34.** $\dfrac{2^{3-x}}{1 - 2^x}$

35. $\dfrac{(3+x)^{3x}}{x+1}$ **36.** $\dfrac{20.3^{3x}}{1 + 20.3^{2x}}$ **37.** $2e^{(1+x)/x}$ **38.** $\dfrac{2e^{2/x}}{x}$

T *On the same set of axes, use technology to graph the pairs of functions in Exercises 39–46 with $-3 \le x \le 3$. Identify which graph corresponds to which function.* HINT [See Quick Examples on page 138.]

39. $f_1(x) = 1.6^x$, $f_2(x) = 1.8^x$

40. $f_1(x) = 2.2^x$, $f_2(x) = 2.5^x$

41. $f_1(x) = 300(1.1^x)$, $f_2(x) = 300(1.1^{2x})$

42. $f_1(x) = 100(1.01^{2x})$, $f_2(x) = 100(1.01^{3x})$

43. $f_1(x) = 2.5^{1.02x}$, $f_2(x) = e^{1.02x}$

44. $f_1(x) = 2.5^{-1.02x}$, $f_2(x) = e^{-1.02x}$

45. $f_1(x) = 1{,}000(1.045^{-3x})$, $f_2(x) = 1{,}000(1.045^{3x})$

46. $f_1(x) = 1{,}202(1.034^{-3x})$, $f_2(x) = 1{,}202(1.034^{3x})$

For Exercises 47–54, model the data using an exponential function $f(x) = Ab^x$. HINT [See Example 1.]

47.

x	0	1	2
$f(x)$	500	250	125

48.

x	0	1	2
$f(x)$	500	1,000	2,000

49.

x	0	1	2
$f(x)$	10	30	90

50.

x	0	1	2
$f(x)$	90	30	10

51.

x	0	1	2
$f(x)$	500	225	101.25

52.

x	0	1	2
$f(x)$	5	3	1.8

53.

x	1	2
$f(x)$	-110	-121

54.

x	1	2
$f(x)$	-41	-42.025

Find equations for exponential functions that pass through the pairs of points given in Exercises 55–62. (Round all coefficients to 4 decimal places when necessary.) HINT [See Example 2.]

55. Through $(2, 36)$ and $(4, 324)$

56. Through $(2, -4)$ and $(4, -16)$

57. Through $(-2, -25)$ and $(1, -0.2)$

58. Through $(1, 1.2)$ and $(3, 0.108)$

59. Through $(1, 3)$ and $(3, 6)$ **60.** Through $(1, 2)$ and $(4, 6)$

61. Through $(2, 3)$ and $(6, 2)$ **62.** Through $(-1, 2)$ and $(3, 1)$

Obtain exponential functions in the form $f(t) = Ae^{rt}$ *in Exercises 63–66.* HINT [See Example 5.]

63. $f(t)$ is the value after t years of a $5,000 investment earning 10% interest compounded continuously.

64. $f(t)$ is the value after t years of a $2,000 investment earning 5.3% interest compounded continuously.

65. $f(t)$ is the value after t years of a $1,000 investment depreciating continuously at an annual rate of 6.3%.

66. $f(t)$ is the value after t years of a $10,000 investment depreciating continuously at an annual rate of 60%.

T *In Exercises 67–70, use technology to find the exponential regression function through the given points. (Round all coefficients to 4 decimal places.)* HINT [See Example 6.]

67. $\{(1, 2), (3, 5), (4, 9), (5, 20)\}$

68. $\{(-1, 2), (-3, 5), (-4, 9), (-5, 20)\}$

69. $\{(-1, 10), (-3, 5), (-4, 3)\}$

70. $\{(3, 3), (4, 5), (5, 10)\}$

APPLICATIONS

71. *Aspirin* Soon after taking an aspirin, a patient has absorbed 300 mg of the drug. After two hours, only 75 mg remain, find an exponential model for the amount of aspirin in the bloodstream after t hours, and use your model to find the amount of aspirin in the bloodstream after 5 hours. HINT [See Example 2.]

72. *Alcohol* After a large number of drinks, a person has a blood alcohol level of 200 mg/dL (milligrams per deciliter). If the amount of alcohol in the blood decays exponentially, and after 2 hours, 112.5 mg/dL remain, find an exponential model for the person's blood alcohol level, and use your model to estimate the person's blood alcohol level after 4 hours. HINT [See Example 2.]

73. *Freon Production* The production of ozone-layer damaging Freon 22 (chlorodifluoromethane) in developing countries rose from 200 tons in 2004 to a projected 590 tons in 2010.[13]

a. Use this information to find both a linear model and an exponential model for the amount F of Freon 22 (in tons) as a function of time t in years since 2000. (Round all coefficients to three significant digits.) HINT [See Example 2.] Which of these models would you judge to be more appropriate to the data shown below:

t (year since 2000)	0	2	4	6	8	10
F (tons of Freon 22)	100	140	200	270	400	590

b. Use the better of the two models from part (a) to predict the 2008 figure and compare it with the projected figure above.

---

[13] Figures are approximate. Source: Lampert Kuijpers (Panel of the Montreal Protocol), National Bureau of Statistics in China, via CEIC DSata/*New York Times*, February 23, 2007, p. C1.

74. *Satellite Radio Subscriptions* The number of **Sirius Satellite Radio** subscribers grew from 0.3 million in 2003 to 3.2 million in 2005.[14]

a. Use this information to find both a linear model and an exponential model for the number N of subscribers (in millions) as a function of time t in years since 2000. (Round all coefficients to three significant digits.) HINT [See Example 2.] Which of these models would you judge to be more appropriate to the data shown below:

t (year since 2000)	3	4	5
N (millions of subscribers)	0.3	1.0	3.2

b. Use the better of the two models from part (a) to predict the 2006 figure. (The actual 2006 figure was approximately 6 million subscribers.)

75. ▼ *U.S. Population* The U.S. population was 180 million in 1960 and 303 million in 2008.[15]

a. Use these data to give an exponential growth model showing the U.S. population P as a function of time t in years since 1960. Round coefficients to 6 significant digits. HINT [See Example 2.]

b. By experimenting, determine the smallest number of significant digits to which you should round the coefficients in part (a) in order to obtain the correct 2008 population figure accurate to three significant digits.

c. Using the model in part (a), predict the population in 2020.

76. ▼ *World Population* World population was estimated at 2.56 billion people in 1950 and 6.72 billion people in 2008.[16]

a. Use these data to give an exponential growth model showing the world population P as a function of time t in years since 1950. Round coefficients to 6 significant digits. HINT [See Example 2.]

b. By experimenting, determine the smallest number of significant digits to which you should round the coefficients in part (a) in order to obtain the correct 2008 population figure to three significant digits.

c. Assuming the exponential growth model from part (a), estimate the world population in the year 1000. Comment on your answer.

77. ▼ *Frogs* Frogs have been breeding like flies at the Enormous State University (ESU) campus! Each year, the pledge class of the Epsilon Delta fraternity is instructed to tag all the frogs residing on the ESU campus. Two years ago they managed to tag all 50,000 of them (with little Epsilon Delta Fraternity tags).

---

[14] Figures are approximate. Source: Sirius Satellite Radio/*New York Times*, February 20, 2008, p. A1.

[15] Figures are rounded to three significant digits. Source: U.S. Census Bureau, www.census.gov/.

[16] Ibid.

This year's pledge class discovered that last year's tags had all fallen off, and they wound up tagging a total of 75,000 frogs.

a. Find an exponential model for the frog population.

b. Assuming exponential population growth, and that all this year's tags have fallen off, how many tags should Epsilon Delta order for next year's pledge class?

78. ▼ *Flies* Flies in Suffolk County have been breeding like frogs! Three years ago the Health Commission caught 4,000 flies in a trap in one hour. This year it caught 7,000 flies in one hour.

a. Find an exponential model for the fly population.

b. Assuming exponential population growth, how many flies should the commission expect to catch next year?

79. *Bacteria* A bacteria culture starts with 1,000 bacteria and doubles in size every 3 hours. Find an exponential model for the size of the culture as a function of time t in hours and use the model to predict how many bacteria there will be after 2 days. HINT [See Example 4.]

80. *Bacteria* A bacteria culture starts with 1,000 bacteria. Two hours later there are 1,500 bacteria. Find an exponential model for the size of the culture as a function of time t in hours, and use the model to predict how many bacteria there will be after 2 days. HINT [See Example 4.]

81. *SARS* In the early stages of the deadly SARS (Severe Acute Respiratory Syndrome) epidemic in 2003, the number of cases was increasing by about 18% each day.[17] On March 17, 2003 (the first day for which statistics were reported by the World Health Organization) there were 167 cases. Find an exponential model that predicts the number of cases t days after March 17, 2003, and use it to estimate the number of cases on March 31, 2003. (The actual reported number of cases was 1,662.)

82. *SARS* A few weeks into the deadly SARS (Severe Acute Respiratory Syndrome) epidemic in 2003, the number of cases was increasing by about 4% each day.[18] On April 1, 2003 there were 1,804 cases. Find an exponential model that predicts the number of cases t days after April 1, 2003, and use it to estimate the number of cases on April 30, 2003. (The actual reported number of cases was 5,663.)

83. *Investments* In 2007, E*TRADE Financial was offering 4.94% interest on its online savings accounts, with interest reinvested monthly.[19] Find the associated exponential model for the value of a $5,000 deposit after t years. Assuming this rate of return continued for seven years, how much would a deposit of $5,000 at the beginning of 2007 be worth at the end of 2014? (Answer to the nearest $1.) HINT [See Example 9; you saw this exercise before in Section 1.2.]

84. *Investments* In 2007, ING Direct was offering 4.14% interest on its online Orange Savings Account, with interest reinvested

quarterly.[20] Find the associated exponential model for the value of a $4,000 deposit after t years. Assuming this rate of return continued for eight years, how much would a deposit of $4,000 at the beginning of 2007 be worth at the end of 2015? (Answer to the nearest $1.) HINT [See Example 9; you saw this exercise before in Section 1.2.]

85. ▯ *Investments* Refer to Exercise 83. At the start of which year will an investment of $5,000 made at the beginning of 2007 first exceed $7,500?

86. ▯ *Investments* Refer to Exercise 84. At the start of which year will an investment of $4,000 made at the beginning of 2007 first exceed $6,000?

87. *Investments* Rock Solid Bank & Trust is offering a CD (certificate of deposit) that pays 4% compounded continuously. How much interest would a $1,000 deposit earn over 10 years? HINT [See Example 5.]

88. *Savings* FlybynightSavings.com is offering a savings account that pays 31% interest compounded continuously. How much interest would a deposit of $2,000 earn over 10 years?

89. *Home Sales* Sales of new houses in the United States declined continuously over the period 2005–2008 at a rate of 30% per year from 1.3 million in 2005.[21] Write down a formula that predicts sales of new houses t years after 2005. Use your model to estimate sales of new houses in 2008 and 2009.

90. *Home Prices* The median price of a home in the United States declined continuously over the period 2005–2008 at a rate of 5.5% per year from around $230 thousand in 2005.[22] Write down a formula that predicts the median price of a home t years after 2005. Use your model to estimate the median home price in 2007 and 2010. HINT [See Example 5.]

91. *Global Warming* The most abundant greenhouse gas is carbon dioxide. According to a United Nations "worst-case scenario" prediction, the amount of carbon dioxide in the atmosphere (in parts of volume per million) can be approximated by

$$C(t) \approx 277e^{0.00353t} \text{ parts per million} \quad (0 \le t \le 350)$$

where t is time in years since 1750.[23]

a. Use the model to estimate the amount of carbon dioxide in the atmosphere in 1950, 2000, 2050, and 2100.

b. According to the model, when, to the nearest decade, will the level surpass 700 parts per million?

---

[17] Source: World Health Organization, www.who.int/.

[18] Ibid.

[19] Interest rate based on annual percentage yield. Source: http://us.etrade .com, December, 2007.

[20] Interest rate based on annual percentage yield. Source: www.home .ingdirect.com, December, 2007.

[21] Based on figures released by the U.S. Census, www.census.gov/.

[22] Based on figures released by the National Association of Realtors, www.realtor.org/.

[23] Exponential regression based on the 1750 figure and the 2100 UN prediction. Sources: Tom Boden/Oak Ridge National Laboratory, Scripps Institute of Oceanography/University of California, International Panel on Climate Change/*New York Times*, December 1, 1997, p. F1.

92. *Global Warming* Repeat Exercise 91 using the United Nations "midrange scenario" prediction:

$$C(t) \approx 277e^{0.00267t} \text{ parts per million} \quad (0 \le t \le 350)$$

where *t* is time in years since 1750.

93. ▣ *New York City Housing Costs: Downtown* The following table shows the average price of a two-bedroom apartment in downtown New York City during the real estate boom from 1994 to 2004.[24]

t	0 (1994)	2	4	6	8	10 (2004)
Price ($ million)	0.38	0.40	0.60	0.95	1.20	1.60

a. Use exponential regression to model the price $P(t)$ as a function of time *t* since 1994. Include a sketch of the points and the regression curve. (Round the coefficients to 3 decimal places.) HINT [See Example 6.]

b. Extrapolate your model to estimate the cost of a two-bedroom downtown apartment in 2005.

94. ▣ *New York City Housing Costs: Uptown* The following table shows the average price of a two-bedroom apartment in uptown New York City during the real estate boom from 1994 to 2004.[25]

t	0 (1994)	2	4	6	8	10 (2004)
Price ($ million)	0.18	0.18	0.19	0.2	0.35	0.4

a. Use exponential regression to model the price $P(t)$ as a function of time *t* since 1994. Include a sketch of the points and the regression curve. (Round the coefficients to 3 decimal places.)

b. Extrapolate your model to estimate the cost of a two-bedroom uptown apartment in 2005.

95. ▣ *Facebook* The following table gives the approximate number of **Facebook** memberships at various times since early in 2005.[26]

Year *t* (since start of 2005)	0	0.5	1	1.5	2	2.5	3	3.5
Facebook Members *n* (millions)	1	2	5.5	7	12	30	58	80

a. Use exponential regression to model **Facebook** membership as a function of time in years since the start of 2005, and graph the data points and regression curve. (Round coefficients to 3 decimal places.)

b. Fill in the missing quantity: According to the model, **Facebook** membership each year was ____ times that of the year before.

c. Use your model to estimate **Facebook** membership in early 2009 to the nearest million.

96. ▣ *Freon Production* (Refer to Exercise 73.) The following table shows estimated total Freon 22 production in various years since 2000.[27]

t (year since 2000)	0	2	4	6	8	10
F (tons of Freon 22)	100	140	200	270	400	590

a. Use exponential regression to model Freon production as a function of time in years since 2000, and graph the data points and regression curve. (Round coefficients to 3 decimal places.)

b. Fill in the missing quantity: According to the model, Freon production each year was ____ times that of the year before.

c. Use your model to estimate Freon production in 2009 to the nearest ton.

COMMUNICATION AND REASONING EXERCISES

97. Which of the following three functions will be largest for large values of *x*?

(A) $f(x) = x^2$ (B) $r(x) = 2^x$ (C) $h(x) = x^{10}$

98. Which of the following three functions will be smallest for large values of *x*?

(A) $f(x) = x^{-2}$ (B) $r(x) = 2^{-x}$ (C) $h(x) = x^{-10}$

99. What limitations apply to using an exponential function to model growth in real-life situations? Illustrate your answer with an example.

100. Explain in words why 5% per year compounded continuously yields more interest than 5% per year compounded monthly.

101. ▽ The following commentary and graph appeared in www.politicalcalculations.blogspot.com on August 30 2005:[28]

One of the neater blogs I've recently encountered is The Real Returns, which offers a wealth of investing, market and economic data. Earlier this month, The Real Returns posted data related to the recent history of U.S. median house prices over the period from 1963 to 2004. The original source of the housing data is the U.S. Census Bureau.

---

[24] Data are rounded and 2004 figure is an estimate. Source: Miller Samuel/*New York Times*, March 28, 2004, p. RE 11.

[25] Ibid.

[26] Sources: www.facebook.com/, www.insidehighered.com (Some data are interpolated.)

[27] Figures are approximate. Source: Lampert Kuijpers (Panel of the Montreal Protocol), National Bureau of Statistics in China, via CEIC DSata/*New York Times*, February 23, 2007, p. C1.

[28] The graph was recreated by the authors using the blog author's data source.
Source for article: www.politicalcalculations.blogspot.com/2005/08/projecting-us-median-housing-prices.html.
Source for data: http://therealreturns.blogspot.com/2005_08_01_archive.html.

Well, that kind of data deserves some curve-fitting and a calculator to estimate what the future U.S. median house price might be, so Political Calculations has extracted the data from 1973 onward to create the following chart:

U.S. median house prices since 1973

$y = 41152e^{0.0551x}$

© Political Calculation 2005

Median house price ($)

Years since 1973

2009

Comment on the article and graph. HINT [See Exercise 90.]

102. ▼ Refer to Exercise 101. Of what possible predictive use, then, is the kind of exponential model given by the blogger in the article referred to?

103. ▼ Describe two real-life situations in which a linear model would be more appropriate than an exponential model, and two situations in which an exponential model would be more appropriate than a linear model.

104. ▼ Describe a real-life situation in which a quadratic model would be more appropriate than an exponential model and one in which an exponential model would be more appropriate than a quadratic model.

105. How would you check whether data points of the form $(1, y_1), (2, y_2), (3, y_3)$ lie on an exponential curve?

106. ▼ You are told that the points $(1, y_1), (2, y_2), (3, y_3)$ lie on an exponential curve. Express y_3 in terms of y_1 and y_2.

107. ▼ Your local banker tells you that the reason his bank doesn't compound interest continuously is that it would be too demanding of computer resources because the computer would need to spend a great deal of time keeping all accounts updated. Comment on his reasoning.

108. ▼ Your other local banker tells you that the reason *her* bank doesn't offer continuously compounded interest is that it is equivalent to offering a fractionally higher interest rate compounded daily. Comment on her reasoning.

2.3 Logarithmic Functions and Models

Logarithms were invented by John Napier (1550–1617) in the late 16th century as a means of aiding calculation. His invention made possible the prodigious hand calculations of astronomer Johannes Kepler (1571–1630), who was the first to describe accurately the orbits and the motions of the planets. Today, computers and calculators have done away with that use of logarithms, but many other uses remain. In particular, the logarithm is used to model real-world phenomena in numerous fields, including physics, finance, and economics.

From the equation

$$2^3 = 8$$

we can see that the power to which we need to raise 2 in order to get 8 is 3. We abbreviate the phrase "the power to which we need to raise 2 in order to get 8" as "$\log_2 8$." Thus, another way of writing the equation $2^3 = 8$ is

$$\log_2 8 = 3 .$$　　The power to which we need to raise 2 in order to get 8 is 3.

This is read "the base 2 logarithm of 8 is 3" or "the log, base 2, of 8 is 3."

Here is the general definition.

> ### Base *b* Logarithm
>
> The **base *b* logarithm of *x*,** $\log_b x$, is the power to which we need to raise *b* in order to get *x*. Symbolically,
>
> $$\log_b x = y \qquad \text{means} \qquad b^y = x .$$
> *Logarithmic form*　　　　　　　　　　　　　　　　　　　*Exponential form*

Quick Examples

1. The following table lists some exponential equations and their equivalent logarithmic forms:

Exponential Form	$10^3 = 1000$	$4^2 = 16$	$3^3 = 27$	$5^1 = 5$	$7^0 = 1$	$4^{-2} = \dfrac{1}{16}$	$25^{1/2} = 5$
Logarithmic Form	$\log_{10} 1000 = 3$	$\log_4 16 = 2$	$\log_3 27 = 3$	$\log_5 5 = 1$	$\log_7 1 = 0$	$\log_4 \dfrac{1}{16} = -2$	$\log_{25} 5 = \dfrac{1}{2}$

2. $\log_3 9 =$ the power to which we need to raise 3 in order to get 9. Because $3^2 = 9$, this power is 2, so $\log_3 9 = 2$.

3. $\log_{10} 10{,}000 =$ the power to which we need to raise 10 in order to get 10,000. Because $10^4 = 10{,}000$, this power is 4, so $\log_{10} 10{,}000 = 4$.

4. $\log_3 \frac{1}{27}$ is the power to which we need to raise 3 in order to get $\frac{1}{27}$. Because $3^{-3} = \frac{1}{27}$ this power is –3, so $\log_3 \frac{1}{27} = -3$.

5. $\log_b 1 = 0$ for every positive number b other than 1 because $b^0 = 1$.

Note The number $\log_b x$ is defined only if b and x are both positive and $b \neq 1$. Thus, it is impossible to compute, say, $\log_3(-9)$ (because there is no power of 3 that equals −9), or $\log_1(2)$ (because there is no power of 1 that equals 2). ■

Logarithms with base 10 and base e are frequently used, so they have special names and notations.

Common Logarithm, Natural Logarithm

The following are standard abbreviations.

		TI-83/84 Plus & Excel Formula
Base 10: $\log_{10} x = \log x$	*Common Logarithm*	`log(x)`
Base e: $\log_e x = \ln x$	*Natural Logarithm*	`ln(x)`

Quick Examples

Logarithmic Form	**Exponential Form**
1. $\log 10{,}000 = 4$	$10^4 = 10{,}000$
2. $\log 10 = 1$	$10^1 = 10$
3. $\log \dfrac{1}{10{,}000} = -4$	$10^{-4} = \dfrac{1}{10{,}000}$
4. $\ln e = 1$	$e^1 = e$
5. $\ln 1 = 0$	$e^0 = 1$
6. $\ln 2 = 0.69314718\ldots$	$e^{0.69314718\ldots} = 2$

Some technologies (such as calculators) do not permit direct calculation of logarithms other than common and natural logarithms. To compute logarithms with other bases with these technologies, we can use the following formula:

✳ **NOTE** Here is a quick explanation of why this formula works: To calculate $\log_b a$, we ask, "to what power must we raise b to get a?" To check the formula, we try using $\log a / \log b$ as the exponent.

$$b^{\frac{\log a}{\log b}} = (10^{\log b})^{\frac{\log a}{\log b}}$$
$$\text{(because } b = 10^{\log b}\text{)}$$
$$= 10^{\log a} = a$$

so this exponent works!

Change-of-Base Formula

$$\log_b a = \frac{\log a}{\log b} = \frac{\ln a}{\ln b} \qquad \text{Change-of-base formula}^*$$

Quick Examples

1. $\log_{11} 9 = \dfrac{\log 9}{\log 11} \approx 0.91631$ `log(9)/log(11)`

2. $\log_{11} 9 = \dfrac{\ln 9}{\ln 11} \approx 0.91631$ `ln(9)/ln(11)`

3. $\log_{3.2} \left(\dfrac{1.42}{3.4} \right) \approx -0.75065$ `log(1.42/3.4)/log(3.2)`

Using Technology to Compute Logarithms

To compute $\log_b x$ using technology, use the following formulas:

TI-83/84 Plus   `log(x)/log(b)`   Example: $\log_2(16)$ is `log(16)/log(2)`

Excel: `=LOG(x,b)`   Example: $\log_2(16)$ is = `LOG(16,2)`

One important use of logarithms is to solve equations in which the unknown is in the exponent.

EXAMPLE 1 Solving Equations with Unknowns in the Exponent

Solve the following equations

a. $5^{-x} = 125$ **b.** $3^{2x-1} = 6$ **c.** $100(1.005)^{3x} = 200$

Solution

a. Write the given equation $5^{-x} = 125$ in logarithmic form:

$$-x = \log_5 125$$

This gives $x = -\log_5 125 = -3$.

b. In logarithmic form, $3^{2x-1} = 6$ becomes

$$2x - 1 = \log_3 6$$
$$2x = 1 + \log_3 6$$

giving $x = \dfrac{1 + \log_3 6}{2} \approx \dfrac{1 + 1.6309}{2} \approx 1.3155.$

c. We cannot write the given equation, $100(1.005)^{3x} = 200$, directly in exponential form. We must first divide both sides by 100:

$$1.005^{3x} = \frac{200}{100} = 2$$
$$3x = \log_{1.005} 2$$
$$x = \frac{\log_{1.005} 2}{3} \approx \frac{138.9757}{3} \approx 46.3252.$$

Now that we know what logarithms are, we can talk about functions based on logarithms:

Logarithmic Function

A **logarithmic function** has the form

$$f(x) = \log_b x + C \qquad \text{(b and C are constants with $b > 0, b \neq 1$)}$$

or, alternatively,

$$f(x) = A \ln x + C. \qquad \text{(A, C constants with $A \neq 0$)}$$

Quick Examples

1. $f(x) = \log x$
2. $g(x) = \ln x - 5$
3. $h(x) = \log_2 x + 1$
4. $k(x) = 3.2 \ln x + 7.2$

Q: *What is the difference between the two forms of the logarithmic function?*

A: None, really, they're equivalent: We can start with an equation in the first form and use the change-of-base formula to rewrite it:

$$f(x) = \log_b x + C$$
$$= \frac{\ln x}{\ln b} + C \qquad \text{Change-of-base formula}$$
$$= \left(\frac{1}{\ln b}\right) \ln x + C.$$

Our function now has the form $f(x) = A \ln x + C$, where $A = 1/\ln b$. We can go the other way as well, to rewrite $A \ln x + C$ in the form $\log_b x + C$.

EXAMPLE 2 Graphs of Logarithmic Functions

a. Sketch the graph of $f(x) = \log_2 x$ by hand.

b. Use technology to compare the graph in part (a) with the graphs of $\log_b x$ for $b = 1/4, 1/2$, and 4.

Solution

a. To sketch the graph of $f(x) = \log_2 x$ by hand, we begin with a table of values. Because $\log_2 x$ is not defined when $x = 0$, we choose several values of x close to zero and also some larger values, all chosen so that their logarithms are easy to compute:

x	$\frac{1}{8}$	$\frac{1}{4}$	$\frac{1}{2}$	1	2	4	8
$f(x) = \log_2 x$	-3	-2	-1	0	1	2	3

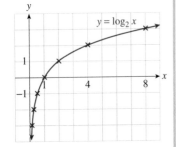

Figure 14

Graphing these points and joining them by a smooth curve gives us Figure 14.

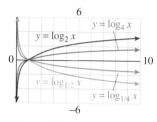

Figure 15

b. We enter the logarithmic functions in graphing utilities as follows (note the use of the change-of-base formula in the TI-83/84 Plus version):

TI-83/84 Plus	Excel
`Y₁=log(X)/log(0.25)`	`=LOG(x,0.25)`
`Y₂=log(X)/log(0.5)`	`=LOG(x,0.5)`
`Y₃=log(X)/log(2)`	`=LOG(x,2)`
`Y₄=log(X)/log(4)`	`=LOG(x,4)`

Figure 15 shows the resulting graphs.

➡ **Before we go on...** Notice that the graphs of the logarithmic functions in Example 2 all pass through the point (1, 0). (Why?) Notice further that the graphs of the logarithmic functions with bases less than 1 are upside-down versions of the others. Finally, how are these graphs related to the graphs of exponential functions? ■

Below are some important algebraic properties of logarithms we shall use throughout the rest of this section.

Logarithm Identities

The following identities hold for all positive bases $a \neq 1$ and $b \neq 1$, all positive numbers x and y, and every real number r. These identities follow from the laws of exponents.

Identity

1. $\log_b(xy) = \log_b x + \log_b y$

2. $\log_b\left(\dfrac{x}{y}\right) = \log_b x - \log_b y$

3. $\log_b(x^r) = r \log_b x$

4. $\log_b b = 1; \log_b 1 = 0$

5. $\log_b\left(\dfrac{1}{x}\right) = -\log_b x$

6. $\log_b x = \dfrac{\log_a x}{\log_a b}$

Quick Examples

$\log_2 16 = \log_2 8 + \log_2 2$

$\log_2\left(\dfrac{5}{3}\right) = \log_2 5 - \log_2 3$

$\log_2(6^5) = 5 \log_2 6$

$\log_2 2 = 1; \ln e = 1; \log_{11} 1 = 0$

$\log_2\left(\dfrac{1}{3}\right) = -\log_2 3$

$\log_2 5 = \dfrac{\log_{10} 5}{\log_{10} 2} = \dfrac{\log 5}{\log 2}$

Relationship with Exponential Functions

The following two identities demonstrate that the operations of taking the base b logarithm and raising b to a power are *inverse* to each other.*

Identity

1. $\log_b(b^x) = x$

In words: The power to which you raise b in order to get b^x is x (!)

2. $b^{\log_b x} = x$

In words: Raising b to the power to which it must be raised to get x, yields x (!)

Quick Example

$\log_2(2^7) = 7$

$5^{\log_5 8} = 8$

Web Site

Go to the student Web site at **www.AppliedCalc.org** and follow the path

 Chapter 2

 → Using and Deriving Algebraic Properties of Logarithms

to find a list of logarithmic identities and a discussion on where they come from.

* NOTE

 Go to the student Web site at **www.AppliedCalc.org** and follow the path

 Chapter 2

 → Inverse Functions

for a general discussion of inverse functions, including further discussion of the relationship between logarithmic and exponential functions.

APPLICATIONS

EXAMPLE 3 Investments: How Long?

Global bonds sold by Mexico are yielding an average of 5.2% per year.* At that interest rate, how long will it take a $1,000 investment to be worth $1,500 if the interest is compounded monthly?

Solution Substituting $A = 1,500$, $P = 1,000$, $r = 0.052$, and $m = 12$ in the compound interest equation gives

$$A(t) = P\left(1 + \frac{r}{m}\right)^{mt}$$

$$1,500 = 1,000\left(1 + \frac{0.052}{12}\right)^{12t}$$

$$\approx 1,000(1.004333)^{12t}$$

and we must solve for t. We first divide both sides by 1,000, getting an equation in exponential form:

$$1.5 = 1.004333^{12t}$$

In logarithmic form, this becomes

$$12t = \log_{1.004333}(1.5).$$

We can now solve for t:

$$t = \frac{\log_{1.004333}(1.5)}{12} \approx 7.8 \text{ years} \qquad \texttt{log(1.5)/(log(1.004333)*12)}$$

Thus, it will take approximately 7.8 years for a $1,000 investment to be worth $1,500.

* In 2008 (bonds maturing 03/03/2015). Source: www.bloomberg.com.

➡ **Before we go on...** We can use the logarithm identities to solve the equation

$$1.5 = 1.004333^{12t}$$

that arose in Example 3 (and also more general equations with unknowns in the exponent) by taking the natural logarithm of both sides:

$$\ln 1.5 = \ln(1.004333^{12t})$$

$$= 12t \ln 1.004333 \qquad \text{By Identity 3}$$

We can now solve this for t to get

$$t = \frac{\ln 1.5}{12 \ln 1.004333}$$

which, by the change-of-base formula, is equivalent to the answer we got in Example 3. ∎

EXAMPLE 4 Half-Life

a. The weight of carbon 14 that remains in a sample that originally contained A grams is given by

$$C(t) = A(0.999879)^t$$

where t is time in years. Find the **half-life**, the time it takes half of the carbon 14 in a sample to decay.

b. Repeat part (a) using the following alternative form of the exponential model in part (a):

$$C(t) = Ae^{-0.000\,121\,01t} \qquad \text{See page 145.}$$

c. Another radioactive material has a half-life of 7,000 years. Find an exponential decay model in the form

$$R(t) = Ae^{-kt}$$

for the amount of undecayed material remaining. (The constant k is called the **decay constant**.)

d. How long will it take for 99.95% of the substance in a sample of the material in part (c) to decay?

Solution

a. We want to find the value of t for which $C(t) =$ the weight of undecayed carbon 14 left = half the original weight = $0.5A$. Substituting, we get

$$0.5A = A(0.999879)^t$$

Dividing both sides by A gives

$$0.5 = 0.999879^t \qquad\qquad \text{Exponential form}$$
$$t = \log_{0.999879} 0.5 \approx 5{,}728 \text{ years} \qquad \text{Logarithmic form}$$

b. This is similar to part (a): We want to solve the equation

$$0.5A = Ae^{-0.000\,121\,01t}$$

for t. Dividing both sides by A gives

$$0.5 = e^{-0.000\,121\,01t}$$

Taking the natural logarithm of both sides gives

$$\ln(0.5) = \ln(e^{-0.000\,121\,01t}) = -0.000\,121\,01t \qquad \text{Identity 3: } \ln(e^a) = a \ln e = a$$
$$t = \frac{\ln(0.5)}{-0.000\,121\,01} \approx 5{,}728 \text{ years}$$

as we obtained in part (a).

c. This time we are given the half-life, which we can use to find the exponential model $R(t) = Ae^{-kt}$. At time $t = 0$, the amount of radioactive material is

$$R(0) = Ae^0 = A$$

Because half of the sample decays in 7,000 years, this sample will decay to $0.5A$ grams in 7,000 years ($t = 7,000$). Substituting this information gives

$$0.5A = Ae^{-k(7,000)}.$$

Canceling A and taking natural logarithms (again using Identity 3) gives

$$\ln(0.5) = -7,000k$$

so the decay constant k is

$$k = -\frac{\ln(0.5)}{7,000} \approx 0.000\,099\,021.$$

Therefore, the model is

$$R(t) = Ae^{-0.000\,099\,021t}.$$

d. If 99.95% of the substance in a sample has decayed, then the amount of undecayed material left is 0.05% of the original amount, or $0.0005A$. We have

$$0.0005A = Ae^{-0.000\,099\,021t}$$
$$0.0005 = e^{-0.000\,099\,021t}$$
$$\ln(0.0005) = -0.000\,099\,021t$$
$$t = \frac{\ln(0.0005)}{-0.000\,099\,021} \approx 76,760 \text{ years.}$$

➡ **Before we go on...**

Q : *In parts (a) and (b) of Example 4 we were given two different forms of the model for carbon 14 decay. How do we convert an exponential function in one form to the other?*

A : We have already seen (See Quick Example 3 on page 145) how to convert from the form $f(t) = Ae^{rt}$ in part (b) to the form $f(t) = Ab^t$ in part (a). To go the other way, start with the model in part (a), and equate it to the desired form:

$$C(t) = A(0.999\,879)^t = Ae^{rt}.$$

To solve for r, cancel the As and take the natural logarithm of both sides:

$$t\ln(0.999\,879) = rt\ln e = rt$$

so $r = \ln(0.999\,879) \approx -0.000\,121\,007,$

giving

$$C(t) = Ae^{-0.000\,121\,007t}$$

as in part (b).

We can use the work we did in parts (b) and (c) of the above example to obtain a formula for the decay constant in an exponential decay model for any radioactive substance when we know its half-life. Write the half-life as t_h. Then the calculation in part (b) gives

$$k = -\frac{\ln(0.5)}{t_h} = \frac{\ln 2}{t_h}.$$ $-\ln(0.5) = -\ln\left(\frac{1}{2}\right) = \ln 2$

Multiplying both sides by t_h gives us the relationship $t_h k = \ln 2$.

Exponential Decay Model and Half-Life

An **exponential decay function** has the form

$$Q(t) = Q_0 e^{-kt}. \qquad Q_0, k \text{ both positive}$$

Q_0 represents the value of Q at time $t = 0$, and k is the **decay constant.** The decay constant k and half-life t_h for Q are related by

$$t_h k = \ln 2.$$

Quick Examples

1. $Q(t) = Q_0 e^{-0.000\,121\,01t}$ is the decay function for carbon 14 (see Example 4b).

2. If $t_h = 10$ years, then $10k = \ln 2$, so $k = \dfrac{\ln 2}{10} \approx 0.06931$ so the decay model is

$$Q(t) = Q_0 e^{-0.06931t}.$$

3. If $k = 0.0123$, then $t_h(0.0123) = \ln 2$, so the half-life is

$$t_h = \frac{\ln 2}{0.0123} \approx 56.35 \text{ years.}$$

We can repeat the analysis above for exponential growth models:

Exponential Growth Model and Doubling Time

An **exponential growth function** has the form

$$Q(t) = Q_0 e^{kt}. \qquad Q_0, k \text{ both positive}$$

Q_0 represents the value of Q at time $t = 0$, and k is the **growth constant.** The growth constant k and doubling time t_d for Q are related by

$$t_d k = \ln 2.$$

Quick Examples

1. $P(t) = 1,000 e^{0.05t}$ $1,000 invested at 5% annually with interest compounded continuously

2. If $t_d = 10$ years, then $10k = \ln 2$, so $k = \dfrac{\ln 2}{10} \approx 0.06931$ and the growth model is

$$Q(t) = Q_0 e^{0.06931t}.$$

3. If $k = 0.0123$, then $t_d(0.0123) = \ln 2$, so the doubling time is

$$t_d = \frac{\ln 2}{0.0123} \approx 56.35 \text{ years.}$$

Logarithmic Regression

If we start with a set of data that suggests a logarithmic curve we can, by repeating the methods from previous sections, use technology to find the logarithmic regression curve $y = \log_b x + C$ approximating the data.

EXAMPLE 5   Research & Development

The following table shows the total spent on research and development in the United States, in billions of dollars, for the period 1995–2009 (t is the year since 1990).*

Year t	5	6	7	8	9	10	11	12
Spending ($ billions)	199	210	222	235	250	268	271	265
Year t	13	14	15	16	17	18	19	
Spending ($ billions)	272	275	289	299	300	304	309	

Find the best-fit logarithmic model of the form

$$S(t) = A \ln t + C$$

and use the model to project total spending on research in 2012, assuming the trend continues.

Solution We use technology to get the following regression model:

$$S(t) = 83.01 \ln t + 64.42. \qquad \text{Coefficients rounded}$$

Because 2012 is represented by $t = 22$, we have

$$S(22) = 83.01 \ln(22) + 64.42 \approx 320. \qquad \text{Why did we round the result to two significant digits?}$$

So, research and development spending is projected to be around $321 billion in 2012.

———————

*Data are approximate and are given in constant 2000 dollars. 2007–2009 figures are projections.
Source: National Science Foundation, Division of Science Resources Statistics, National Patterns of R&D Resources. www.nsf.gov/statistics/, August 2008.

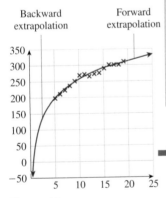

Backward extrapolation   Forward extrapolation

Figure 16

➡ **Before we go on...** The model in Example 5 seems to give reasonable estimates when we extrapolate forward, but extrapolating backward is quite another matter: The logarithm curve drops sharply to the left of the given range and becomes negative for small values of t (Figure 16). ∎

2.3 EXERCISES

▼ more advanced   ◆ challenging
☐ indicates exercises that should be solved using technology

In Exercises 1–4, complete the given tables. HINT [See Quick Examples on page 152.]

1.

Exponential Form	$10^4 = 10,000$	$4^2 = 16$	$3^3 = 27$	$5^1 = 5$	$7^0 = 1$	$4^{-2} = \frac{1}{16}$
Logarithmic Form						

2.

Exponential Form	$4^3 = 64$	$10^{-1} = 0.1$	$2^8 = 256$	$5^0 = 1$	$(0.5)^2 = 0.25$	$6^{-2} = \frac{1}{36}$
Logarithmic Form						

3.

Exponential Form						
Logarithmic Form	$\log_{0.5} 0.25 = 2$	$\log_5 1 = 0$	$\log_{10} 0.1 = -1$	$\log_4 64 = 3$	$\log_2 256 = 8$	$\log_2 \frac{1}{4} = -2$

4.

Exponential Form						
Logarithmic Form	$\log_5 5 = 1$	$\log_4 \frac{1}{16} = -2$	$\log_4 16 = 2$	$\log_{10} 10,000 = 4$	$\log_3 27 = 3$	$\log_7 1 = 0$

In Exercises 5–12, use logarithms to solve the given equation. (Round answers to four decimal places.) HINT [See Example 1.]

5. $3^x = 5$

6. $4^x = 3$

7. $5^{-2x} = 40$

8. $6^{3x+1} = 30$

9. $4.16e^x = 2$

10. $5.3(10^x) = 2$

11. $5(1.06^{2x+1}) = 11$

12. $4(1.5^{2x-1}) = 8$

In Exercises 13–18, graph the given function. HINT [See Example 2.]

13. $f(x) = \log_4 x$

14. $f(x) = \log_5 x$

15. $f(x) = \log_4(x - 1)$

16. $f(x) = \log_5(x + 1)$

17. $f(x) = \log_{1/4} x$

18. $f(x) = \log_{1/5} x$

In Exercises 19–22 find the associated exponential decay or growth model. HINT [See Quick Examples on page 159.]

19. $Q = 1,000$ when $t = 0$; half-life $= 1$

20. $Q = 2,000$ when $t = 0$; half-life $= 5$

21. $Q = 1,000$ when $t = 0$; doubling time $= 2$

22. $Q = 2,000$ when $t = 0$; doubling time $= 5$

In Exercises 23–26 find the associated half-life or doubling time. HINT [See Quick Examples on page 159.]

23. $Q = 1,000e^{0.5t}$

24. $Q = 1,000e^{-0.025t}$

25. $Q = Q_0e^{-4t}$

26. $Q = Q_0e^t$

In Exercises 27–32 convert the given exponential function to the form indicated. Round all coefficients to four significant digits. HINT [See Example 4 "Before we go on."]

27. $f(x) = 4e^{2x}$; $f(x) = Ab^x$

28. $f(x) = 2.1e^{-0.1x}$; $f(x) = Ab^x$

29. $f(t) = 2.1(1.001)^t$; $f(t) = Q_0e^{kt}$

30. $f(t) = 23.4(0.991)^t$; $f(t) = Q_0e^{-kt}$

31. $f(t) = 10(0.987)^t$; $f(t) = Q_0e^{-kt}$

32. $f(t) = 2.3(2.2)^t$; $f(t) = Q_0e^{kt}$

APPLICATIONS

33. *Investments* How long will it take a $500 investment to be worth $700 if it is continuously compounded at 10% per year? (Give the answer to two decimal places.) HINT [See Example 3.]

34. *Investments* How long will it take a $500 investment to be worth $700 if it is continuously compounded at 15% per year? (Give the answer to two decimal places.) HINT [See Example 3.]

35. *Investments* How long, to the nearest year, will it take an investment to triple if it is continuously compounded at 10% per year? HINT [See Example 3.]

36. *Investments* How long, to the nearest year, will it take me to become a millionaire if I invest $1,000 at 10% interest compounded continuously? HINT [See Example 3.]

37. *Investments* I would like my investment to double in value every 3 years. At what rate of interest would I need to invest it, assuming the interest is compounded continuously? HINT [See Quick Examples page 159.]

38. *Depreciation* My investment in OHaganBooks.com stocks is losing half its value every 2 years. Find and interpret the associated decay rate. HINT [See Quick Examples page 159.]

39. *Carbon Dating* The amount of carbon 14 remaining in a sample that originally contained A grams is given by

$$C(t) = A(0.999879)^t$$

where t is time in years. If tests on a fossilized skull reveal that 99.95% of the carbon 14 has decayed, how old, to the nearest 1,000 years, is the skull? HINT [See Example 4.]

40. *Carbon Dating* Refer back to Exercise 39. How old, to the nearest 1,000 years, is a fossil in which only 30% of the carbon 14 has decayed? HINT [See Example 4.]

Long-Term Investments *Exercises 41–48 are based on the following table, which lists interest rates on long-term investments (based on 10-year government bonds) in several countries in 2008.*[29] HINT [See Example 4.]

Country	U.S.	Japan	Canada	Germany	Australia
Yield	3.9%	1.5%	3.8%	4.3%	5.9%

41. Assuming that you invest $10,000 in the United States, how long (to the nearest year) must you wait before your investment is worth $15,000 if the interest is compounded annually?

42. Assuming that you invest $10,000 in Japan, how long (to the nearest year) must you wait before your investment is worth $15,000 if the interest is compounded annually?

43. If you invest $10,400 in Canada and the interest is compounded monthly, how many months will it take for your investment to grow to $20,000?

44. If you invest $10,400 in the United States, and the interest is compounded monthly, how many months will it take for your investment to grow to $20,000?

45. How long, to the nearest year, will it take an investment in Australia to double its value if the interest is compounded every six months?

46. How long, to the nearest year, will it take an investment in Germany to double its value if the interest is compounded every six months?

47. If the interest on a long-term U.S. investment is compounded continuously, how long will it take the value of an investment to double? (Give the answer correct to two decimal places.)

48. If the interest on a long-term Australia investment is compounded continuously, how long will it take the value of an investment to double? (Give an answer correct to two decimal places.)

[29] Approximate interest rates based on 10-year government bonds and similar investments. Source: www.bloomberg.com.

49. *Half-life* The amount of radium 226 remaining in a sample that originally contained A grams is approximately

$$C(t) = A(0.999\ 567)^t$$

where t is time in years. Find the half-life to the nearest 100 years. HINT [See Example 4a.]

50. *Half-life* The amount of iodine 131 remaining in a sample that originally contained A grams is approximately

$$C(t) = A(0.9175)^t$$

where t is time in days. Find the half-life to two decimal places. HINT [See Example 4a.]

51. *Automobiles* The rate of auto thefts triples every 6 months.
a. Determine, to two decimal places, the base b for an exponential model $y = Ab^t$ of the rate of auto thefts as a function of time in months.
b. Find the doubling time to the nearest tenth of a month. HINT [(a) See Section 2.2 Example 2. (b) See Quick Examples page 159.]

52. *Televisions* The rate of television thefts is doubling every 4 months.
a. Determine, to two decimal places, the base b for an exponential model $y = Ab^t$ of the rate of television thefts as a function of time in months.
b. Find the tripling time to the nearest tenth of a month. HINT [(a) See Section 2.2 Example 2. (b) See Quick Examples page 159.]

53. *Half-life* The half-life of cobalt 60 is 5 years.
a. Obtain an exponential decay model for cobalt 60 in the form $Q(t) = Q_0 e^{-kt}$. (Round coefficients to three significant digits.)
b. Use your model to predict, to the nearest year, the time it takes one third of a sample of cobalt 60 to decay. HINT [See Quick Examples page 159.]

54. *Half-life* The half-life of strontium 90 is 28 years.
a. Obtain an exponential decay model for strontium 90 in the form $Q(t) = Q_0 e^{-kt}$. (Round coefficients to three significant digits.)
b. Use your model to predict, to the nearest year, the time it takes three-fifths of a sample of strontium 90 to decay. HINT [See Quick Examples page 159.]

55. *Radioactive Decay* Uranium 235 is used as fuel for some nuclear reactors. It has a half-life of 710 million years. How long will it take 10 grams of uranium 235 to decay to 1 gram? (Round your answer to three significant digits.)

56. *Radioactive Decay* Plutonium 239 is used as fuel for some nuclear reactors, and also as the fissionable material in atomic bombs. It has a half-life of 24,400 years. How long would it take 10 grams of plutonium 239 to decay to 1 gram? (Round your answer to three significant digits.)

57. ▼*Aspirin* Soon after taking an aspirin, a patient has absorbed 300 mg of the drug. If the amount of aspirin in the bloodstream decays exponentially, with half being removed every 2 hours, find, to the nearest 0.1 hour, the time it will take for the amount of aspirin in the bloodstream to decrease to 100 mg.

58. ▼*Alcohol* After a large number of drinks, a person has a blood alcohol level of 200 mg/dL (milligrams per deciliter). If the amount of alcohol in the blood decays exponentially, with one fourth being removed every hour, find the time it will take for the person's blood alcohol level to decrease to 80 mg/dL. HINT [See Example 4.]

59. ▼*Radioactive Decay* You are trying to determine the half-life of a new radioactive element you have isolated. You start with 1 gram, and 2 days later you determine that it has decayed down to 0.7 grams. What is its half-life? (Round your answer to three significant digits.) HINT [First find an exponential model, then see Example 4.]

60. ▼*Radioactive Decay* You have just isolated a new radioactive element. If you can determine its half-life, you will win the Nobel Prize in physics. You purify a sample of 2 grams. One of your colleagues steals half of it, and three days later you find that 0.1 gram of the radioactive material is still left. What is the half-life? (Round your answer to three significant digits.) HINT [First find an exponential model, then see Example 4.]

61. ▮ *Population Aging* The following table shows the percentage of U.S. residents over the age of 65 in 1950, 1960, . . . , 2010 (*t* is time in years since 1900):[30]

t (Year since 1900)	50	60	70	80	90	100	110
P (% over 65)	8.2	9.2	9.9	11.3	12.6	12.6	13

a. Find the logarithmic regression model of the form $P(t) = A \ln t + C$. (Round the coefficients to four significant digits). HINT [See Example 5.]

b. In 1940, 6.9% of the population was over 65. To how many significant digits does the model reflect this figure?

c. Which of the following is correct? The model, if extrapolated into the indefinite future, predicts that

(A) The percentage of U.S. residents over the age of 65 will increase without bound.

(B) The percentage of U.S. residents over the age of 65 will level off at around 14.2%.

(C) The percentage of U.S. residents over the age of 65 will eventually decrease.

62. ▮ *Population Aging* The following table shows the percentage of U.S. residents over the age of 85 in 1950, 1960, . . . , 2010 (*t* is time in years since 1900):[31]

t (Year since 1900)	50	60	70	80	90	100	110
P (% over 85)	0.4	0.5	0.7	1	1.2	1.6	1.9

a. Find the logarithmic regression model of the form $P(t) = A \ln t + C$. (Round the coefficients to four significant digits). HINT [See Example 5.]

b. In 2020, 2.1% of the population is projected to be over 85. To how many significant digits does the model reflect this figure?

c. Which of the following is correct? If you increase A by 0.1 and decrease C by 0.1 in the logarithmic model, then

(A) The new model predicts eventually lower percentages.

(B) The long-term prediction is essentially the same.

(C) The new model predicts eventually higher percentages.

63. ▮ *Research & Development: Industry* The following table shows the total spent on research and development by industry in the United States, billions of dollars, for the period 1995–2009 (*t* is the year since 1990).[32]

Year t	5	6	7	8	9	10	11	12
Spending ($ billions)	118	129	140	150	165	183	181	170
Year t	13	14	15	16	17	18	19	
Spending ($ billions)	172	172	182	191	194	197	200	

Find the logarithmic regression model of the form $S(t) = A \ln t + C$ with coefficients A and C rounded to 2 decimal places. Also obtain a graph showing the data points and the regression curve. In which direction is it more reasonable to extrapolate the model? Why?

64. ▮ *Research & Development: Federal* The following table shows the total spent on research and development by the Federal government in the United States, in billions of dollars, for the period 1995–2009 (*t* is the year since 1990).[33]

Year t	5	6	7	8	9	10	11	12
Spending ($ billions)	17	17	17	17	18	18	20	21
Year t	13	14	15	16	17	18	19	
Spending ($ billions)	23	23	25	24	24	23	23	

Find the logarithmic regression model of the form $S(t) = A \ln t + C$ with coefficients A and C rounded to 2 decimal

---

[30] Source: U.S. Census Bureau.

[31] Ibid.

[32] Non-federal funding by industry. Data are approximate and are given in constant 2000 dollars. 2007–2009 figures are projections. Source: National Science Foundation, Division of Science Resources Statistics, National Patterns of R&D Resources. www.nsf.gov/statistics/, August 2008.

[33] Federal funding excluding grants to industry and nonprofit organizations. Data are approximate and are given in constant 2000 dollars. 2007–2009 figures are projections. Source: National Science Foundation, Division of Science Resources Statistics, National Patterns of R&D Resources. www.nsf.gov/statistics/, August 2008.

places. Also obtain a graph showing the data points and the regression curve. In which direction is it more reasonable to extrapolate the model? Why? HINT [See Example 5.]

65. ▼*Richter Scale* The **Richter scale** is used to measure the intensity of earthquakes. The Richter scale rating of an earthquake is given by the formula

$$R = \frac{2}{3}(\log E - 11.8)$$

where E is the energy released by the earthquake (measured in ergs[34]).

a. The San Francisco earthquake of 1906 registered $R = 8.2$ on the Richter scale. How many ergs of energy were released?

b. In 1989 another San Francisco earthquake registered 7.1 on the Richter scale. Compare the two: The energy released in the 1989 earthquake was what percentage of the energy released in the 1906 quake?

c. Solve the equation given above for E in terms of R.

d. Use the result of part (c) to show that if two earthquakes registering R_1 and R_2 on the Richter scale release E_1 and E_2 ergs of energy, respectively, then

$$\frac{E_2}{E_1} = 10^{1.5(R_2 - R_1)}.$$

e. Fill in the blank: If one earthquake registers 2 points more on the Richter scale than another, then it releases ____ times the amount of energy.

66. ▼*Sound Intensity* The loudness of a sound is measured in **decibels**. The decibel level of a sound is given by the formula

$$D = 10 \log \frac{I}{I_0},$$

where D is the decibel level (dB), I is its intensity in watts per square meter (W/m^2), and $I_0 = 10^{-12}$ W/m^2 is the intensity of a barely audible "threshold" sound. A sound intensity of 90 dB or greater causes damage to the average human ear.

a. Find the decibel levels of each of the following, rounding to the nearest decibel:

Whisper:	115×10^{-12} W/m^2
TV (average volume from 10 feet):	320×10^{-7} W/m^2
Loud music:	900×10^{-3} W/m^2
Jet aircraft (from 500 feet):	100 W/m^2

b. Which of the sounds above damages the average human ear?

c. Solve the given equation to express I in terms of D.

d. Use the answer to part (c) to show that if two sounds of intensity I_1 and I_2 register decibel levels of D_1 and D_2 respectively, then

$$\frac{I_2}{I_1} = 10^{0.1(D_2 - D_1)}.$$

e. Fill in the blank: If one sound registers one decibel more than another, then it is ____ times as intense.

67. ▼*Sound Intensity* The decibel level of a TV set decreases with the distance from the set according to the formula

$$D = 10 \log \left(\frac{320 \times 10^7}{r^2} \right)$$

where D is the decibel level and r is the distance from the TV set in feet.

a. Find the decibel level (to the nearest decibel) at distances of 10, 20, and 50 feet.

b. Express D in the form $D = A + B \log r$ for suitable constants A and B. (Round A and D to two significant digits.)

c. How far must a listener be from a TV so that the decibel level drops to 0? (Round the answer to two significant digits.)

68. ▼*Acidity* The acidity of a solution is measured by its pH, which is given by the formula

$$pH = -\log(H^+)$$

where H^+ measures the concentration of hydrogen ions in moles per liter.[35] The pH of pure water is 7. A solution is referred to as *acidic* if its pH is below 7 and as *basic* if its pH is above 7.

a. Calculate the pH of each of the following substances.

Blood:	3.9×10^{-8} moles/liter
Milk:	4.0×10^{-7} moles/liter
Soap solution:	1.0×10^{-11} moles/liter
Black coffee:	1.2×10^{-7} moles/liter

b. How many moles of hydrogen ions are contained in a liter of acid rain that has a pH of 5.0?

c. Complete the following sentence: If the pH of a solution increases by 1.0, then the concentration of hydrogen ions _____.

COMMUNICATION AND REASONING EXERCISES

69. On the same set of axes, graph $y = \ln x$, $y = A \ln x$, and $y = A \ln x + C$ for various choices of *positive* A and C. What is the effect on the graph of $y = \ln x$ of multiplying by A? What is the effect of then adding C?

70. On the same set of axes, graph $y = -\ln x$, $y = A \ln x$, and $y = A \ln x + C$ for various choices of *negative* A and C. What is the effect on the graph of $y = \ln x$ of multiplying by A? What is the effect of then adding C?

71. Why is the logarithm of a negative number not defined?

72. Of what use are logarithms, now that they are no longer needed to perform complex calculations?

73. Your company's market share is undergoing steady growth. Explain why a logarithmic function is *not* appropriate for long-term future prediction of your market share.

---

[34] An erg is a unit of energy. One erg is the amount of energy it takes to move a mass of one gram one centimeter in one second.

[35] A mole corresponds to about 6.0×10^{23} hydrogen ions. (This number is known as Avogadro's number.)

74. Your company's market share is undergoing steady growth. Explain why a logarithmic function is *not* appropriate for long-term backward extrapolation of your market share.

75. If $y = 4^x$, then $x =$ _____.

76. If $y = \log_6 x$, then $x =$ _____.

77. Simplify: $2^{\log_2 8}$.

78. Simplify: $e^{\ln x}$.

79. Simplify: $\ln(e^x)$.

80. Simplify: $\ln \sqrt{a}$.

81. ▼ If a town's population is increasing exponentially with time, how is time increasing with population? Explain.

82. ▼ If a town's population is increasing logarithmically with time, how is time increasing with population? Explain.

83. ▼ If two quantities Q_1 and Q_2 are logarithmic functions of time t, show that their sum, $Q_1 + Q_2$ is also a logarithmic function of time t.

84. 🔟 ▼ In Exercise 83 we saw that the sum of two logarithmic functions is a logarithmic function. In Exercises 63 and 64 you modeled research and development expenditure by industry and government. Now do a logarithmic regression on the sum of the two sets of figures. Does the result coincide with the sum of the two individual regression models? What does your answer tell you about the sum of logarithmic regression models?

2.4 Logistic Functions and Models

Figure 17 shows the percentage of Internet-connected U.S. households that have broadband connections as a function of time t in years ($t = 0$ represents 2000).[36]

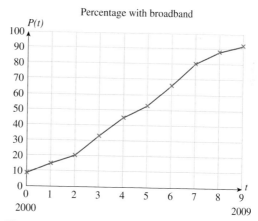

Percentage with broadband

Figure 17

The left-hand part of the curve in Figure 17, from $t = 0$ to, say, $t = 4$, looks roughly like exponential growth: P behaves (roughly) like an exponential function, with the y-coordinates growing by a factor of around 1.5 per year. Then, as the market starts to become saturated, the growth of P slows and its value approaches a "saturation" point near 100%. **Logistic** functions have just this kind of behavior, growing exponentially at first and then leveling off. In addition to modeling the demand for a new technology or product, logistic functions are often used in epidemic and population modeling. In an epidemic, the number of infected people often grows exponentially at first and then slows when a significant proportion of the entire susceptible population is infected and the epidemic has "run its course." Similarly, populations may grow exponentially at first and then slow as they approach the capacity of the available resources.

---

[36] 2009 figure is estimated. Source: www.Nielsen.com.

Logistic Function

A **logistic function** has the form

$$f(x) = \frac{N}{1 + Ab^{-x}}$$

for nonzero constants N, A, and b (A and b positive and $b \neq 1$).

Quick Example

$N = 6, A = 2, b = 1.1$ gives $f(x) = \dfrac{6}{1 + 2(1.1^{-x})}$ `6/(1+2*1.1^-x)`

$$f(0) = \frac{6}{1 + 2} = 2$$ The y-intercept is $N/(1 + A)$.

$$f(1,000) = \frac{6}{1 + 2(1.1^{-1,000})} \approx \frac{6}{1 + 0} = 6 = N$$ When x is large, $f(x) \approx N$.

Graph of a Logistic Function

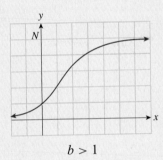   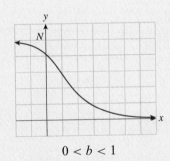

$$b > 1 \qquad\qquad\qquad 0 < b < 1$$

$$y = \frac{N}{1 + Ab^{-x}}$$

Properties of the Logistic Curve $y = \dfrac{N}{1 + Ab^{-x}}$

- The graph is an S-shaped curve sandwiched between the horizontal lines $y = 0$ and $y = N$. N is called the **limiting value** of the logistic curve.
- If $b > 1$ the graph rises; if $b < 1$, the graph falls.
- The y-intercept is $\dfrac{N}{1 + A}$.
- The curve is steepest when $t = \dfrac{\ln A}{\ln b}$.   We will see why in Chapter 5.

Note   If we write b^{-x} as e^{-kx} (where $k = \ln b$), we get the following alternative form of the logistic function:

$$f(x) = \frac{N}{1 + Ae^{-kx}}.$$

Q : *How does the constant b affect the graph?*

A : To understand the role of b, we first rewrite the logistic function by multiplying top and bottom by b^x:

$$f(x) = \frac{N}{1 + Ab^{-x}}$$

$$= \frac{Nb^x}{(1 + Ab^{-x})b^x}$$

$$= \frac{Nb^x}{b^x + A} \qquad \text{Because } b^{-x}b^x = 1$$

For values of x close to 0, the quantity b^x is close to 1, so the denominator is approximately $1 + A$, giving

$$f(x) \approx \frac{Nb^x}{1 + A} = \left(\frac{N}{1 + A}\right)b^x.$$

In other words, $f(x)$ is approximately exponential with base b for values of x close to 0. Put another way, if x represents time, then initially the logistic function behaves like an exponential function.

To summarize:

Logistic Function for Small *x* and the Role of *b*

For small values of x, we have

$$\frac{N}{1 + Ab^{-x}} \approx \left(\frac{N}{1 + A}\right)b^x.$$

Thus, for small x, the logistic function grows approximately exponentially with base b.

Quick Examples

1. Let

$$f(x) = \frac{50}{1 + 24(3^{-x})}. \qquad N = 50, A = 24, b = 3$$

Then

$$f(x) \approx \left(\frac{50}{1 + 24}\right)(3^x) = 2(3^x)$$

for small values of x. The following figure compares their graphs:

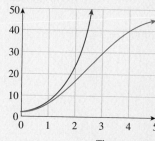
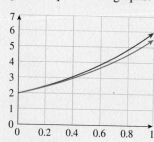

The upper curve is the exponential curve.

Modeling with the Logistic Function

EXAMPLE 1 Epidemics

A flu epidemic is spreading through the U.S. population. An estimated 150 million people are susceptible to this particular strain, and it is predicted that all susceptible people will eventually become infected. There are 10,000 people already infected, and the number is doubling every 2 weeks. Use a logistic function to model the number of people infected. Hence predict when, to the nearest week, 1 million people will be infected.

Solution   Let t be time in weeks, and let $P(t)$ be the total number of people infected at time t. We want to express P as a logistic function of t, so that

$$P(t) = \frac{N}{1 + Ab^{-t}}.$$

We are told that, in the long run, 150 million people will be infected, so that

$$N = 150,000,000. \qquad \text{Limiting value of } P$$

At the current time ($t = 0$), 10,000 people are infected, so

$$10,000 = \frac{N}{1 + A} = \frac{150,000,000}{1 + A} \qquad \text{Value of } P \text{ when } t = 0$$

Solving for A gives

$$10,000(1 + A) = 150,000,000$$
$$1 + A = 15,000$$
$$A = 14,999.$$

What about b? At the beginning of the epidemic (t near 0), P is growing approximately exponentially, doubling every 2 weeks. Using the technique of Section 2.2, we find that the exponential curve passing through the points (0, 10,000) and (2, 20,000) is

$$y = 10,000(\sqrt{2})^t$$

giving us $b = \sqrt{2}$. Now that we have the constants N, A, and b, we can write down the logistic model:

$$P(t) = \frac{150,000,000}{1 + 14,999(\sqrt{2})^{-t}}$$

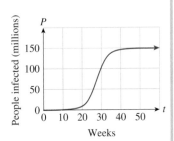

Figure 18

People infected (millions) — P — 150, 100, 50, 0 — Weeks — 0 10 20 30 40 50 — t

The graph of this function is shown in Figure 18.

Now we tackle the question of prediction: When will 1 million people be infected? In other words: When is $P(t) = 1,000,000$?

$$1,000,000 = \frac{150,000,000}{1 + 14,999(\sqrt{2})^{-t}}$$
$$1,000,000[1 + 14,999(\sqrt{2})^{-t}] = 150,000,000$$
$$1 + 14,999(\sqrt{2})^{-t} = 150$$
$$14,999(\sqrt{2})^{-t} = 149$$
$$(\sqrt{2})^{-t} = \frac{149}{14,999}$$
$$-t = \log_{\sqrt{2}}\left(\frac{149}{14,999}\right) \approx -13.31 \qquad \text{Logarithmic form}$$

Thus, 1 million people will be infected by about the 13th week.

➡ **Before we go on...** We said earlier that the logistic curve is steepest when $t = \dfrac{\ln A}{\ln b}$. In Example 1, this occurs when $t = \dfrac{\ln 14{,}999}{\ln\sqrt{2}} \approx 28$ weeks into the epidemic. At that time, the number of cases is growing most rapidly (look at the apparent slope of the graph at the corresponding point). ■

Logistic Regression

Let us go back to the data on the percentage of Internet-connected households with broadband and try to estimate the percentage of households that will have broadband in the long term. In order to be able to make predictions such as this, we require a model for the data, so we will need to do some form of regression.

EXAMPLE 2 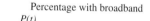 Internet-Connected Households with Broadband

Here are the data graphed in Figure 17:

Year (*t*)	0	1	2	3	4	5	6	7	8	9
Percentage with Broadband (%) (*P*)	8	14	20	33	45	53	66	80	88	92

Find a logistic regression curve of the form

$$P(t) = \frac{N}{1 + Ab^{-t}}.$$

In the long term, what percentage of Internet-connected households with broadband does the model predict?

Solution We can use technology to obtain the following regression model:

$$P(t) \approx \frac{104.047}{1 + 10.453(1.642)^{-t}} \qquad \text{Coefficients rounded to 3 decimal places}$$

Percentage with broadband

Its graph and the original data are shown in Figure 19.

Because $N \approx 104$, the model "predicts" that 104% of all Internet-connected households will have broadband in the long term. Clearly, this makes no sense; a reasonable value of N is 100, as it seems reasonable that, in the long term, all Internet connections will be broadband. There are various curve-fitting procedures that permit one to fix one of the parameters (N in this case) beforehand and adjust the others (A and b here) to obtain the best possible fit. In the Excel Technology Guide at the end of the chapter we show how to do this using Excel's "Solver" Add-in. Here is the best-fit model with N fixed at 100:

$$P(t) \approx \frac{100}{1 + 10.783(1.691)^{-t}} \qquad \text{Coefficients rounded to 3 decimal places}$$

Although this second model is a slightly poorer fit to the data (SSE ≈ 31) than the first one (SSE ≈ 26), it has the advantage that it better predicts the long-term behavior we expect.

Figure 19

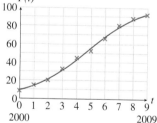

using Technology

See the Technology Guide at the end of the chapter for detailed instructions on how to obtain the regression curve and graph for Example 5 using a TI-83/84 Plus or Excel.

Here is an outline:

TI-83/84 Plus

STAT EDIT values of *t* in L_1
and values of *P* in L_2
Regression curve: STAT
CALC option #B Logistic
ENTER
Graph: Y= VARS 5 EQ 1 ,
then ZOOM 9 [More details
on page 187.]

Excel

Use the Solver Add-in to obtain
the best-fit logistic curves; one
allowing *N* to vary, and another
fixing *N* = 100. [More details
on page 189.]

➡ **Before we go on...** As we noted in Example 2, logistic regression programs generally estimate all three constants *N*, *A*, and *b* for a model $y = \dfrac{N}{1 + Ab^{-x}}$. However, there are times, as in both Examples 1 and 2, when we already know the limiting value *N* and require estimates of only *A* and *b*. In such cases, we can use technology like Excel Solver to find *A* and *b* for the best-fit curve with *N* fixed as described in Example 2. Alternatively, we can use exponential regression to compute estimates of *A* and *b* as follows: First rewrite the logistic equation as

$$\frac{N}{y} = 1 + Ab^{-x},$$

so that

$$\frac{N}{y} - 1 = Ab^{-x} = A(b^{-1})^x.$$

This equation gives $N/y - 1$ as an exponential function of *x*. Thus, if we do exponential regression using the data points $(x, N/y - 1)$, we can obtain estimates for *A* and b^{-1} (and hence *b*). This is done in Exercises 35 and 36.

It is important to note that the resulting curve is not the best-fit curve (in the sense of minimizing SSE; See the "Before we go on" discussion on page 146 after Example 6 in Section 2.2) and will be thus be different from that obtained using the method in Example 2. ∎

2.4 **EXERCISES**

▼ more advanced   ◆ challenging
🔢 indicates exercises that should be solved using technology

In Exercises 1–6, find N, A, and b, give a technology formula for the given function, and use technology to sketch its graph for the given range of values of x. HINT [See Quick Examples on page 166.]

1. $f(x) = \dfrac{7}{1 + 6(2^{-x})}$;   [0, 10]

2. $g(x) = \dfrac{4}{1 + 0.333(4^{-x})}$;   [0, 2]

3. $f(x) = \dfrac{10}{1 + 4(0.3^{-x})}$;   [−5, 5]

4. $g(x) = \dfrac{100}{1 + 5(0.5^{-x})}$;   [−5, 5]

5. $h(x) = \dfrac{2}{0.5 + 3.5(1.5^{-x})}$;   [0, 15]
(First divide top and bottom by 0.5.)

6. $k(x) = \dfrac{17}{2 + 6.5(1.05^{-x})}$;   [0, 100]
(First divide top and bottom by 2.)

In Exercises 7–10, find the logistic function f with the given properties. HINT [See Example 1.]

7. $f(0) = 10$, *f* has limiting value 200, and for small values of *x*, *f* is approximately exponential and doubles with every increase of 1 in *x*.

8. $f(0) = 1$, *f* has limiting value 10, and for small values of *x*, *f* is approximately exponential and grows by 50% with every increase of 1 in *x*.

9. *f* has limiting value 6 and passes through (0, 3) and (1, 4).
HINT [First find *A*, then substitute.]

10. *f* has limiting value 4 and passes through (0, 1) and (1, 2).
HINT [First find *A*, then substitute.]

In Exercises 11–16, choose the logistic function that best approximates the given curve.

11.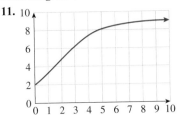

(A) $f(x) = \dfrac{6}{1 + 0.5(3^{-x})}$

(B) $f(x) = \dfrac{9}{1 + 3.5(2^{-x})}$

(C) $f(x) = \dfrac{9}{1 + 0.5(1.01)^{-x}}$

12.

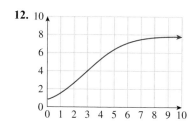

(A) $f(x) = \dfrac{8}{1 + 7(2)^{-x}}$ **(B)** $f(x) = \dfrac{8}{1 + 3(2)^{-x}}$

(C) $f(x) = \dfrac{6}{1 + 11(5)^{-x}}$

13.

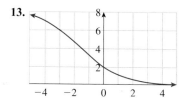

(A) $f(x) = \dfrac{8}{1 + 7(0.5)^{-x}}$ **(B)** $f(x) = \dfrac{8}{1 + 3(0.5)^{-x}}$

(C) $f(x) = \dfrac{8}{1 + 3(2)^{-x}}$

14.

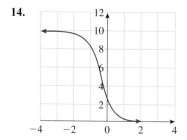

(A) $f(x) = \dfrac{10}{1 + 3(1.01)^{-x}}$ **(B)** $f(x) = \dfrac{8}{1 + 7(0.1)^{-x}}$

(C) $f(x) = \dfrac{10}{1 + 3(0.1)^{-x}}$

15.

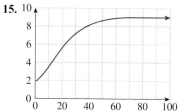

(A) $f(x) = \dfrac{18}{2 + 7(5)^{-x}}$ **(B)** $f(x) = \dfrac{18}{2 + 3(1.1)^{-x}}$

(C) $f(x) = \dfrac{18}{2 + 7(1.1)^{-x}}$

16.

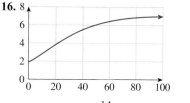

(A) $f(x) = \dfrac{14}{2 + 5(15)^{-x}}$ **(B)** $f(x) = \dfrac{14}{1 + 13(1.05)^{-x}}$

(C) $f(x) = \dfrac{14}{2 + 5(1.05)^{-x}}$

T *In Exercises 17–20, use technology to find a logistic regression curve* $y = \dfrac{N}{1 + Ab^{-x}}$ *approximating the given data. Draw a graph showing the data points and regression curve. (Round b to three significant digits and A and N to two significant digits.)* HINT [See Example 2.]

17.

x	0	20	40	60	80	100
y	2.1	3.6	5.0	6.1	6.8	6.9

18.

x	0	30	60	90	120	150
y	2.8	5.8	7.9	9.4	9.7	9.9

19.

x	0	20	40	60	80	100
y	30.1	11.6	3.8	1.2	0.4	0.1

20.

x	0	30	60	90	120	150
y	30.1	20	12	7.2	3.8	2.4

APPLICATIONS

21. *Subprime Mortgages* The following graph shows the approximate percentage of mortgages issued in the United States that are subprime (normally classified as risky) as well as the logistic regression curve:[37]

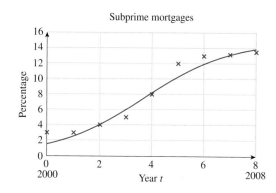

Subprime mortgages

---

[37] 2008 figure is an estimate. Sources: Mortgage Bankers Association, UBS.

a. Which of the following logistic functions best approximates the curve? (*t* is the number of years since the start of 2000.) Try to determine the correct model without actually computing data points. HINT [See Properties of Logistic Curves on page 166.]

(A) $A(t) = \dfrac{15.0}{1 + 8.6(1.8)^{-t}}$

(B) $A(t) = \dfrac{2.0}{1 + 6.8(0.8)^{-t}}$

(C) $A(t) = \dfrac{2.0}{1 + 6.8(1.8)^{-t}}$

(D) $A(t) = \dfrac{15.0}{1 + 8.6(0.8)^{-t}}$

b. According to the model you selected, during which year was the percentage growing fastest? HINT [See the "Before we go on" discussion after Example 1.]

22. *Subprime Mortgage Debt* The following graph shows the approximate value of subprime (normally classified as risky) mortgage debt outstanding in the United States as well as the logistic regression curve:[38]

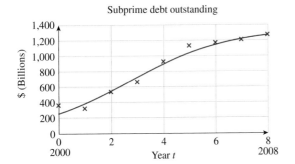

Subprime debt outstanding

a. Which of the following logistic functions best approximates the curve? (*t* is the number of years since the start of 2000.) Try to determine the correct model without actually computing data points. HINT [See Properties of Logistic Curves on page 166.]

(A) $A(t) = \dfrac{1850}{1 + 5.36(1.8)^{-t}}$

(B) $A(t) = \dfrac{1350}{1 + 4.2(1.7)^{-t}}$

(C) $A(t) = \dfrac{1020}{1 + 5.3(1.8)^{-t}}$

(D) $A(t) = \dfrac{1300}{1 + 4.2(0.9)^{-t}}$

b. According to the model you selected, during which year was outstanding debt growing fastest? HINT [See the "Before we go on" discussion after Example 1.]

23. *Scientific Research* The following graph shows the number of research articles in the prominent journal *Physical Review* that were written by researchers in Europe during 1983–2003 (*t* = 0 represents 1983).[39]

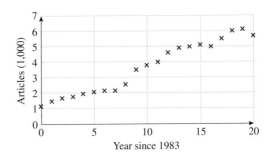

a. Which of the following logistic functions best models the data? (*t* is the number of years since 1983.) Try to determine the correct model without actually computing data points.

(A) $A(t) = \dfrac{7.0}{1 + 5.4(1.2)^{-t}}$

(B) $A(t) = \dfrac{4.0}{1 + 3.4(1.2)^{-t}}$

(C) $A(t) = \dfrac{4.0}{1 + 3.4(0.8)^{-t}}$

(D) $A(t) = \dfrac{7.0}{1 + 5.4(6.2)^{-t}}$

b. According to the model you selected, at what percentage was the number of articles growing around 1985?

24. *Scientific Research* The following graph shows the percentage, above 25%, of research articles in the prominent journal *Physical Review* that were written by researchers in the United States during 1983–2003 (*t* = 0 represents 1983).[40]

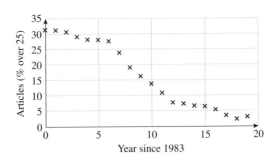

[38] 2008–2009 figures are estimates. Source: www.data360.org/dataset.aspx?Data_Set_Id=9549.

[39] Source: The American Physical Society/*New York Times* May 3, 2003, p. A1.
[40] Ibid.

a. Which of the following logistic functions best models the data? (t is the number of years since 1983 and P is the actual percentage.) Try to determine the correct model without actually computing data points.

(A) $P(t) = \dfrac{36}{1 + 0.06\,(0.02)^{-t}}$

(B) $P(t) = \dfrac{12}{1 + 0.06\,(1.7)^{-t}}$

(C) $P(t) = \dfrac{12}{1 + 0.06(0.7)^{-t}}$

(D) $P(t) = \dfrac{36}{1 + 0.06(0.7)^{-t}}$

b. According to the model you selected, how fast was the value of P declining around 1985?

25. *Computer Use* The following graph shows the actual percentage of U.S. households with a computer as a function of household income (the data points) and a logistic model of these data (the curve).[41]

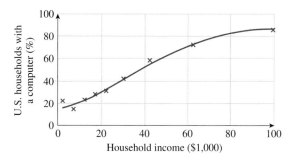

The logistic model is

$$P(x) = \frac{91}{1 + 5.35(1.05)^{-x}} \text{ percent}$$

where x is the household income in thousands of dollars.

a. According to the model, what percentage of extremely wealthy households had computers?

b. For low incomes, the logistic model is approximately exponential. Which exponential model best approximates $P(x)$ for small x?

c. According to the model, 50% of households of what income had computers in 2000? (Round the answer to the nearest $1,000).

26. *Internet Use* The following graph shows the actual percentage of U.S. residents who used the Internet at home as a function of income (the data points) and a logistic model of these data (the curve).[42]

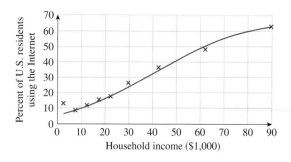

The logistic model is given by

$$P(x) = \frac{64.2}{1 + 9.6(1.06)^{-x}} \text{ percent}$$

where x is an individual's income in thousands of dollars.

a. According to the model, what percentage of extremely wealthy people used the Internet at home?

b. For low incomes, the logistic model is approximately exponential. Which exponential model best approximates $P(x)$ for small x?

c. According to the model, 50% of individuals with what income used the Internet at home in 2000? (Round the answer to the nearest $1,000).

27. *Epidemics* There are currently 1,000 cases of Venusian flu in a total susceptible population of 10,000 and the number of cases is increasing by 25% each day. Find a logistic model for the number of cases of Venusian flu and use your model to predict the number of flu cases a week from now. HINT [Example 1.]

28. *Epidemics* Last year's epidemic of Martian flu began with a single case in a total susceptible population of 10,000. The number of cases was increasing initially by 40% per day. Find a logistic model for the number of cases of Martian flu and use your model to predict the number of flu cases 3 weeks into the epidemic. HINT [Example 1.]

29. *Sales* You have sold 100 "I ♥ Calculus" T-shirts and sales appear to be doubling every five days. You estimate the total market for "I ♥ Calculus" T-shirts to be 3,000. Give a logistic model for your sales and use it to predict, to the nearest day, when you will have sold 700 T-shirts.

30. *Sales* In Russia the average consumer drank two servings of **Coca-Cola®** in 1993. This amount appeared to be increasing exponentially with a doubling time of 2 years.[43] Given a long-range market saturation estimate of 100 servings per year, find a logistic model for the consumption of **Coca-Cola** in Russia and use your model to predict when, to the nearest year, the average consumption will be 50 servings per year.

---

[41] Income levels are midpoints of income brackets. (The top income level is an estimate.) Source: NTIA and ESA, U.S. Department of Commerce, using U.S. Bureau of the Census Current Population, 2000.
[42] Ibid.

[43] The doubling time is based on retail sales of Coca-Cola products in Russia. Sales in 1993 were double those in 1991, and were expected to double again by 1995. Source: *New York Times*, September 26, 1994, p. D2.

31. ⊞ *Scientific Research* The following chart shows some the data shown in the graph in Exercise 23 ($t = 0$ represents 1983).[44]

Year, t	0	5	10	15	20
Research Articles, A (1,000)	1.2	2.1	3.8	5.1	5.7

a. What is the logistic regression model for the data? (Round all coefficients to two significant digits.) At what value does the model predict that the number of research articles will level off? HINT [See Example 2.]

b. According to the model, how many *Physical Review* articles were published by U.S. researchers in 2000 ($t = 17$)? (The actual number was about 5,500 articles.)

32. ⊞ *Scientific Research* The following chart shows some the data shown in the graph in Exercise 24 ($t = 0$ represents 1983).[45]

Year, t	0	5	10	15	20
Percentage, P (over 25)	36	28	16	7	3

a. What is the logistic regression model for the data? (Round all coefficients to two significant digits.) HINT [See Example 2.]

b. According to the model, what percentage of *Physical Review* articles were published by researchers in the United States in 2000 ($t = 17$)? (The actual figure was about 30.1%.)

33. ⊞ *College Basketball: Men* The following table shows the number of NCAA men's college basketball teams in the United States for various years since 1990.[46]

t (year since 1990)	0	5	10	11	12	13	14	15	16	17	18
Teams	767	868	932	937	936	967	981	983	984	994	1,000

a. What is the logistic regression model for the data? (Round all parameters to three significant digits.) At what value does the model predict that the number of basketball teams will level off?

b. According to the model, for what value of t is the regression curve steepest? Interpret the answer.

c. Interpret the coefficient b in the context of the number of men's basketball teams.

34. ⊞ *College Basketball: Women* The following table shows the number of NCAA women's college basketball teams in the United States for various years since 1990.[47]

t (year since 1990)	0	5	10	11	12	13
Teams	1,549	1,732	1,888	1,895	1,911	1,976
t (year since 1990)	14	15	16	17	18	
Teams	1,989	2,019	2,002	2,040	2,060	

a. What is the logistic regression model for the data? (Round all parameters to three significant digits.) At what value does the model predict that the number of basketball teams will level off?

b. According to the model, for what value of t is the regression curve steepest? Interpret the answer.

c. Interpret the coefficient b in the context of the number of women's basketball teams.

⊞ *Exercises 35 and 36 are based on the discussion following Example 2. If the limiting value N is known, then*

$$\frac{N}{y} - 1 = A(b^{-1})^x$$

and so $N/y - 1$ is an exponential function of x. In Exercises 35 and 36, use the given value of N and the data points $(x, N/y - 1)$ to obtain A and b, and hence a logistic model.

35. ⊞ ◆ *Population: Puerto Rico* The following table and graph show the population of Puerto Rico in thousands from 1950 to 2025.[48]

t (year since 1950)	0	10	20	30	40	50
Population (thousands)	2,220	2,360	2,720	3,210	3,540	3,820
t (year since 1950)	55	60	65	70	75	
Population (thousands)	3,910	3,990	4,050	4,080	4,100	

---

[44] Source: The American Physical Society/*New York Times* May 3, 2003, p. A1.

[45] Ibid.

[46] 2007 and 2008 figures are estimates. Source: The 2008 Statistical Abstract, www.census.gov/.

[47] 2007 and 2008 figures are estimates. Source: The 2008 Statistical Abstract, www.census.gov/.

[48] Figures from 2010 on are U.S. census projections. Source: The 2008 Statistical Abstract, www.census.gov/.

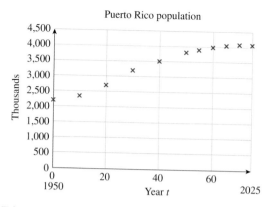

Puerto Rico population

Take t to be the number of years since 1950, and find a logistic model based on the assumption that, eventually, the population of Puerto Rico will grow to 4.5 million. (Round coefficients to 4 decimal places.) In what year does your model predict the population of Puerto Rico will first reach 4.0 million?

36. ▮ ◆ *Population: Virgin Islands* The following table and graph show the population of the Virgin Islands in thousands from 1950 to 2025.[49]

t (year since 1950)	0	10	20	30	40	50
Population (thousands)	27	33	63	98	104	106
t (year since 1950)	55	60	65	70	75	
Population (thousands)	108	108	107	107	108	

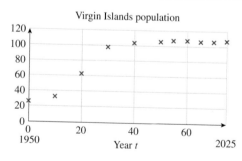

Virgin Islands population

Take t to be the number of years since 1950, and find a logistic model based on the assumption that, eventually, the population of the Virgin Islands will grow to 110,000. (Round coefficients to 4 decimal places.) In what year does your model predict the population of the Virgin Islands first reached 80,000?

COMMUNICATION AND REASONING EXERCISES

37. Logistic functions are commonly used to model the spread of epidemics. Given this fact, explain why a logistic function is also useful to model the spread of a new technology.

38. Why is a logistic function more appropriate than an exponential function for modeling the spread of an epidemic?

39. Give one practical use for logistic regression.

40. Refer to an exercise or example in this section to find a scenario in which a logistic model may not be a good predictor of long-term behavior.

41. What happens to the function $P(t) = \dfrac{N}{1 + Ab^{-t}}$ if we replace b^{-t} by b^t when $b > 1$? If $b < 1$?

42. What happens to the function $P(t) = \dfrac{N}{1 + Ab^{-t}}$ if $A = 0$? If $A < 0$?

43. ▽ We said that the logistic curve $y = \dfrac{N}{1 + Ab^{-t}}$ is steepest when $t = \dfrac{\ln A}{\ln b}$. Show that the corresponding value of y is $N/2$.

HINT [Use the fact that $\dfrac{\ln A}{\ln b} = \ln_b A$.]

44. ▽ We said that the logistic curve $y = \dfrac{N}{1 + Ab^{-t}}$ is steepest when $t = \dfrac{\ln A}{\ln b}$. For which values of A and b is this value of t positive, zero, and negative?

---

[49] Figures from 2010 on are U.S. census projections. Source: The 2008 Statistical Abstract, www.census.gov/.

KEY CONCEPTS

Web Site www.AppliedCalc.org
Go to the student Web site at
www.AppliedCalc.org to find a
comprehensive and interactive
Web-based summary of Chapter 2.

2.1 Quadratic Functions and Models

A **quadratic function** has the form
$f(x) = ax^2 + bx + c$ p. 124
The graph of $f(x) = ax^2 + bx + c$
$(a \neq 0)$ is a **parabola** p. 125
The x coordinate of the **vertex** is $-\frac{b}{2a}$.
The y coordinate is $f\left(-\frac{b}{2a}\right)$ p. 125
x-intercepts (if any) occur at
$$x = \frac{-b \pm \sqrt{b^2 - 4ac}}{2a} \quad \text{p. 125}$$
The **y-intercept** occurs at $y = c$ p. 125
The parabola is **symmetric** with respect to
the vertical line through the vertex p. 125
Sketching the graph of a quadratic
function p. 126
Application to maximizing revenue p. 127
Application to maximizing profit p. 128
Finding the quadratic regression curve
p. 130

2.2 Exponential Functions and Models

An **exponential function** has the form
$f(x) = Ab^x$ p. 137

Roles of the constants A and b in an
exponential function $f(x) = Ab^x$
p. 138
Recognizing exponential data p. 139
Finding the exponential curve through
two points p. 139
Application to compound interest
p. 140
Application to exponential decay (carbon
dating) p. 140
Application to exponential growth
(epidemics) p. 140
The number e and continuous
compounding p. 142
Alternative form of an exponential
function: $f(x) = Ae^{rx}$ p. 144
Finding the exponential regression curve
p. 145

2.3 Logarithmic Functions and Models

The **base b logarithm of x**: $y = \log_b x$
means $b^y = x$ p. 151
Common logarithm, $\log x = \log_{10} x$,
and **natural logarithm**,
$\ln x = \log_e x$ p. 152
Change of base formula p. 153
Solving equations with unknowns in the
exponent p. 153

A **logarithmic function** has the form
$f(x) = Ab^x$ p. 154
Graphs of logarithmic functions p. 154
Logarithm identities p. 155
Application to investments.
(How long?) p. 156
Application to half-life p. 157
Exponential decay models and half-life
p. 159
Exponential growth models and doubling
time p. 159
Finding the logarithmic regression curve
p. 160

2.4 Logistic Functions and Models

A **logistic function** has the form
$$f(x) = \frac{N}{1 + Ab^{-x}} \quad \text{p. 166}$$
Properties of the logistic curve, point
where curve is steepest p. 166
Logistic function for small x, the role of b
p. 167
Application to epidemics p. 168
Finding the logistic regression curve
p. 169

REVIEW EXERCISES

Sketch the graph of the quadratic functions in Exercises 1 and 2, indicating the coordinates of the vertex, the y-intercept, and the x-intercepts (if any).

1. $f(x) = x^2 + 2x - 3$ **2.** $f(x) = -x^2 - x - 1$

In Exercises 3 and 4, the values of two functions, f and g, are given in a table. One, both, or neither of them may be exponential. Decide which, if any, are exponential, and give the exponential models for those that are.

3.

x	-2	-1	0	1	2
$f(x)$	20	10	5	2.5	1.25
$g(x)$	8	4	2	1	0

4.

x	-2	-1	0	1	2
$f(x)$	8	6	4	2	1
$g(x)$	$\frac{3}{4}$	$\frac{3}{2}$	3	6	12

In Exercises 5 and 6 graph given the pairs of functions on the same set of axes with $-3 \leq x \leq 3$.

5. $f(x) = \frac{1}{2}(3^x)$; $g(x) = \frac{1}{2}(3^{-x})$

6. $f(x) = 2(4^x)$; $g(x) = 2(4^{-x})$

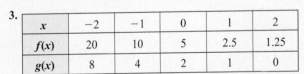 *On the same set of axes, use technology to graph the pairs of functions in Exercises 7 and 8 for the given range of x. Identify which graph corresponds to which function.*

7. $f(x) = e^x$; $g(x) = e^{0.8x}$; $-3 \leq x \leq 3$

8. $f(x) = 2(1.01)^x$; $g(x) = 2(0.99)^x$; $-100 \leq x \leq 100$

In Exercises 9–14, compute the indicated quantity.

9. A $3,000 investment earns 3% interest, compounded monthly. Find its value after 5 years.

10. A $10,000 investment earns 2.5% interest, compounded quarterly. Find its value after 10 years.

11. An investment earns 3% interest, compounded monthly and is worth $5,000 after 10 years. Find its initial value.

12. An investment earns 2.5% interest, compounded quarterly and is worth $10,000 after 10 years. Find its initial value.

13. A $3,000 investment earns 3% interest, compounded continuously. Find its value after 5 years.

14. A $10,000 investment earns 2.5% interest, compounded continuously. Find its value after 10 years.

In Exercises 15–18, find a formula of the form $f(x) = Ab^x$ using the given information.

15. $f(0) = 4.5$; the value of f triples for every half-unit increase in x.

16. $f(0) = 5$; the value of f decreases by 75% for every one-unit increase in x.

17. $f(1) = 2$, $f(3) = 18$.

18. $f(1) = 10$, $f(3) = 5$.

In Exercises 19–22, use logarithms to solve the given equation for x.

19. $3^{-2x} = 4$

20. $2^{2x^2-1} = 2$

21. $300(10^{3x}) = 315$

22. $P(1 + i)^{mx} = A$

On the same set of axes, graph the pairs of functions in Exercises 23 and 24.

23. $f(x) = \log_3 x$; $g(x) = \log_{(1/3)} x$

24. $f(x) = \log x$; $g(x) = \log_{(1/10)} x$

In Exercises 25–28, use the given information to find an exponential model of the form $Q = Q_0e^{-kt}$ or $Q = Q_0e^{kt}$, as appropriate. Round all coefficients to three significant digits when rounding is necessary.

25. Q is the amount of radioactive substance with a half-life of 100 years in a sample originally containing 5g (t is time in years).

26. Q is the number of cats on an island whose cat population was originally 10,000 but is being cut in half every 5 years (t is time in years).

27. Q is the diameter (in cm) of a circular patch of mold on your roommate's damp towel you have been monitoring with morbid fascination. You measured the patch at 2.5 cm across four days ago, and have observed that it is doubling in diameter every two days (t is time in days).

28. Q is the population of cats on another island whose cat population was originally 10,000 but is doubling every 15 months (t is time in months).

In Exercises 29–32, find the time required, to the nearest 0.1 year, for the investment to reach the desired goal.

29. $2,000 invested at 4%, compounded monthly; goal: $3,000.

30. $2,000 invested at 6.75%, compounded daily; goal: $3,000.

31. $2,000 invested at 3.75%, compounded continuously; goal: $3,000.

32. $1,000 invested at 100%, compounded quarterly; goal: $1,200.

In Exercises 33–36, find equations for the logistic functions of x with the stated properties.

33. Through (0, 100), initially increasing by 50% per unit of x, and limiting value 900.

34. Initially exponential of the form $y = 5(1.1)^x$ with limiting value 25.

35. Passing through (0, 5) and decreasing from a limiting value of 20 to 0 at a rate of 20% per unit of x when x is near 0.

36. Initially exponential of the form $y = 2(0.8)^x$ with a value close to 10 when $x = -60$.

APPLICATIONS

37. *Web Site Traffic* The daily traffic ("hits per day") at OHaganBooks.com seems to depend on the monthly expenditure on advertising through banner ads on well-known Internet portals. The following model, based on information collected over the past few months, shows the approximate relationship:

$$h = -0.000005c^2 + 0.085c + 1,750$$

where h is the average number of hits per day at OHaganBooks.com, and c is the monthly advertising expenditure.

a. According to the model, what monthly advertising expenditure will result in the largest volume of traffic at OHaganBooks.com? What is that volume?

b. In addition to predicting a maximum volume of traffic, the model predicts that the traffic will eventually drop to zero if the advertising expenditure is increased too far. What expenditure (to the nearest dollar) results in no Web site traffic?

c. What feature of the formula for this quadratic model indicates that it will predict an eventual decline in traffic as advertising expenditure increases?

38. *Broadband Access* Pablo Pelogrande, a new summer intern at OHaganBooks.com in 2010, was asked by John O'Hagan to research the extent of broadband access in the United States Pelogrande found some old data online on broadband access from the start of 2001 to the end of 2003 and used it to construct the following quadratic model of the growth rate of broadband access:

$$n(t) = 2t^2 - 6t + 12 \text{ million new American adults with broadband per year}$$

(t is time in years; $t = 0$ represents the start 2000).[50]

a. What is an appropriate domain of n?

b. According to the model, when was the growth rate at a minimum?

c. Does the model predict a zero growth rate at any particular time? If so, when?

d. What feature of the formula for this quadratic model indicates that the growth rate eventually increases?

e. Does the fact that $n(t)$ decreases for $t \leq 1.5$ suggest that the number of broadband users actually declined before June 2001? Explain.

---

[50] Based on data for 2001–2003. Source for data: Pew Internet and American Life Project data memos dated May 18, 2003 and April 19, 2004, available at www.pewinternet.org.

f. Pelogande extrapolated the model in order to estimate the growth rate at the beginning of 2010 and 2011. What did he find? Comment on the answer.

39. *Revenue and Profit* Some time ago, a consultant formulated the following linear model of demand for online novels:

$$q = -60p + 950$$

where q is the monthly demand for OHaganBooks.com's online novels at a price of p dollars per novel.

a. Use this model to express the monthly revenue as a function of the unit price p, and hence determine the price you should charge for a maximum monthly revenue.

b. Author royalties and copyright fees cost the company an average of $4 per novel, and the monthly cost of operating and maintaining the online publishing service amounts to $900 per month. Express the monthly profit P as a function of the unit price p, and hence determine the unit price you should charge for a maximum monthly profit. What is the resulting profit (or loss)?

40. *Revenue and Profit* Billy-Sean O'Hagan is John O'Hagan's son and a freshman in college. He notices that the demand for the college newspaper was 2,000 copies each week when the paper was given away free of charge, but dropped to 1,000 each week when the college started charging 10¢/copy.

a. Write down the associated linear demand function.

b. Use your demand function to express the revenue as a function of the unit price p, and hence determine the price the college should charge for a maximum revenue. At that price, what is the revenue from sales of one edition of the newspaper?

c. It costs the college 4¢ to produce each copy of the paper, plus an additional fixed cost of $200. Express the profit P as a function of the unit price p, and hence determine the unit price the college should charge for a maximum monthly profit (or minimum loss). What is the resulting profit (or loss)?

41. *Lobsters* Marjory Duffin, CEO of Duffin Press, is particularly fond of having steamed lobster at working lunches with executives from OHaganBooks.com, and is therefore alarmed by the news that the yearly lobster harvest from New York's Long Island Sound has been decreasing dramatically since 1997. Indeed, the size of the annual harvest can be approximated by

$$n(t) = 10(0.66^t) \text{ million pounds}$$

where t is time in years since June, 1997.[51]

a. The model tells us that the harvest was ____ million pounds in 1997 and decreasing by ___% each year.

b. What does the model predict for the 2005 harvest?

42. *Stock Prices* In the period immediately following its initial public offering (IPO), OHaganBooks.com's stock was doubling in value every three hours. If you bought $10,000 worth of the stock when it was first offered, how much was your stock worth after eight hours?

43. *Lobsters* (See Exercise 41.) Marjory Duffin has just left John O'Hagan, CEO of OHaganBooks.com, a frantic phone message to the effect that yearly lobster harvest from New York's Long Island Sound has just dipped below 100,000 pounds, making that planned lobster working lunch more urgent than ever. What year is it?

44. *Stock Prices* We saw in Exercise 42 that OHaganBooks.com's stock was doubling in value every three hours, following its IPO. If you bought $10,000 worth of the stock when it was first offered, how long from the initial offering did it take your investment to reach $50,000?

45. *Lobsters* We saw in Exercise 41 that the Long Island Sound lobster harvest was given by $n(t) = 10(0.66^t)$ million pounds t years after 1997. However, in 2007, thanks to the efforts of Duffin Press, Inc. it turned around and started increasing by 24% each year.[52] What, to the nearest 1,000 pounds, was the actual size of the harvest in 2010?

46. *Stock Prices* We saw in Exercise 42 that OHaganBooks.com's stock was doubling in value every three hours, following its IPO. After 10 hours of trading, the stock turns around and starts losing one third of its value every four hours. How long (from the initial offering) will it be before your stock is once again worth $10,000?

47. ⊤ *Lobsters* The model in Exercise 41 was based on the data shown in the following chart:

Yearly Lobster Harvest from Long Island Sound

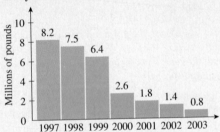

Use the data to obtain an exponential regression curve of the form $n(t) = Ab^t$, with $t = 0$ corresponding to 1997 and coefficients rounded to two significant digits.

48. ⊤ *Stock Prices* The actual stock price of OHaganBooks.com in the hours following its IPO is shown in the following chart:

OHaganBooks.com stock price

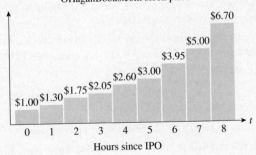

Hours since IPO

51 Based on a regression model. Source for data: NY State Department of Environmental Conservation/*Newsday*, October 6, 2004, p. A4.

52 This claim, like Duffin Press, is fiction.

Use the data to obtain an exponential regression curve of the form $P(t) = Ab^t$, with $t = 0$ the time in hours since the IPO and coefficients rounded to 3 significant digits. At the end of which hour will the stock price first be above $10?

49. Hardware Life *(Based on a question from the GRE economics exam)* To estimate the rate at which new computer hard drives will have to be retired, OHaganBooks.com uses the "survivor curve":

$$L_x = L_0 e^{-x/t}$$

where

L_x = number of surviving hard drives at age x
L_0 = number of hard drives initially
t = average life in years.

All of the following are implied by the curve *except:*

(A) Some of the equipment is retired during the first year of service.
(B) Some equipment survives three average lives.
(C) More than half the equipment survives the average life.
(D) Increasing the average life of equipment by using more durable materials would increase the number surviving at every age.
(E) The number of survivors never reaches zero.

50. Sales OHaganBooks.com modeled its weekly sales over a period of time with the function

$$s(t) = 6{,}050 + \frac{4{,}470}{1 + 14(1.73^{-t})}$$

as shown in the following graph (t is measured in weeks):

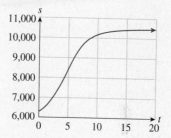

a. As time goes on, it appears that weekly sales are leveling off. At what value are they leveling off?
b. When did weekly sales rise above 10,000?
c. When, to the nearest week, were sales rising most rapidly?

Case Study   Checking up on Malthus

Robert Nickelsberg/Getty Images

In 1798 Thomas R. Malthus (1766–1834) published an influential pamphlet, later expanded into a book, titled *An Essay on the Principle of Population As It Affects the Future Improvement of Society*. One of his main contentions was that population grows geometrically (exponentially) while the supply of resources such as food grows only arithmetically (linearly). This led him to the pessimistic conclusion that population would always reach the limits of subsistence and precipitate famine, war, and ill-health, unless population could be checked by other means. He advocated "moral restraint," which includes the pattern of late marriage common in Western Europe at the time and is now common in most developed countries, and which leads to a lower reproduction rate.

Two hundred years later, you have been asked to check the validity of Malthus's contention. That population grows geometrically, at least over short periods of time, is commonly assumed. That resources grow linearly is more questionable. You decide to check the actual production of a common crop, wheat, in the United States. Agricultural statistics like these are available from the U.S. government on the Internet, through the U.S. Department of Agriculture's National Agricultural Statistics Service (NASS). As of 2008, this service was available at www.nass.usda.gov/. Looking through this site, you locate data on the annual production of all wheat in the United States from 1900 through 2008.

Web Site

www.AppliedCalc.org

To download an Excel sheet with the data used in the case study, go to Everything for Calculus, scroll down to the case study for Chapter 2, and click on "Wheat Production Data (Excel)."

Year	1900	1901	. . .	2007	2008
Thousands of Bushels	599,315	762,546	. . .	2,066,722	2,462,418

Graphing these data (using Excel, for example), you obtain the graph in Figure 20.

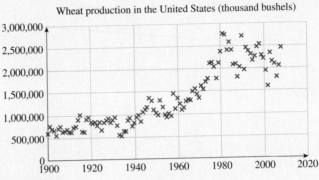

Figure 20

This does not look very linear, particularly in the last half of the 20th century, but you continue checking the mathematics. Using Excel's built-in linear regression capabilities, you find that the line that best fits these data, shown in Figure 21, has $r^2 = 0.7997$. (Recall the discussion of the correlation coefficient r in Section 1.4. A similar statistic is available for other types of regression as well.)

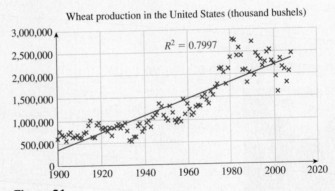

Figure 21

Although that is a fairly high correlation, you notice that the residuals✱ are not distributed randomly: The actual wheat production starts out higher than the line, dips below the line from about 1920 to about 1970, then rises above the line, and finally appears to dip below the line around 2002. This behavior seems to suggest a logistic curve or perhaps a cubic curve. On the other hand, it is also possible that the apparent dip at the end of the data is not statistically significant—it could be nothing more than a transitory fluctuation in the wheat production industry—so perhaps we should also consider models that do not bend downward, like exponential and quadratic models.

Following is a comparison of the four proposed models (with coefficients rounded to three significant digits). For the independent variable, we used t = time in years since 1900. SSE is the sum-of-squares error.

Quadratic

$P(t) \approx 110t^2 - 6,740t + 572,000$

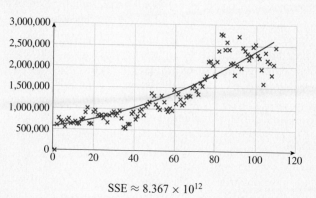

$$\text{SSE} \approx 8.367 \times 10^{12}$$

Cubic

$P(t) \approx -5.25t^3 + 960t^2 - 29,800t + 893,000$

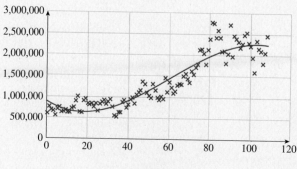

$$\text{SSE} \approx 6.573 \times 10^{12}$$

Exponential

$P(t) \approx 570,000e^{0.0141t}$

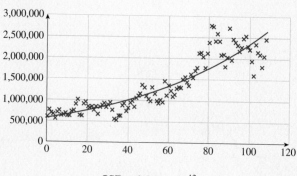

$$\text{SSE} \approx 8.944 \times 10^{12}$$

Logistic

$$P(t) \approx \frac{3,690,000}{1 + 6.91(1.02^{-t})}$$

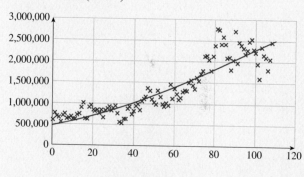

$$\text{SSE} \approx 8.104 \times 10^{12}$$

The model that appears to best fit the data seems to be the cubic model; both visually and by virtue of SSE. Notice also that the cubic model predicts a *decrease* in the production of wheat in the near term (see Figure 22).

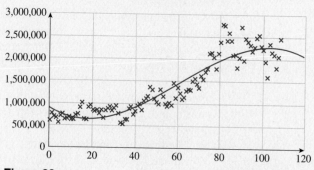

Figure 22

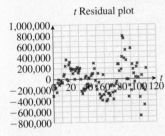

Figure 23

So you prepare a report that documents your findings and concludes that things are even worse than Malthus predicted, at least as far as wheat production in the United States is concerned: The supply is deceasing while the population is still increasing more-or-less exponentially. (See Exercise 75 in Section 2.2.)

You are about to hit "Send," which will dispatch copies of your report to a significant number of people on whom the success of your career depends, when you notice something strange about the pattern of data in Figure 22: The observed data points appear to hug the regression curve quite closely for small values of t, but appear to become more and more scattered as the value of t increases. In the language of residuals, the residuals are small for small values of t but then tend to get larger with increasing t. Figure 23 shows a plot of the residuals that shows this trend even more clearly.

This reminds you vaguely of something that came up in your college business statistics course, so you consult the textbook from that class that (fortunately) you still own and discover that a pattern of residuals with increasing magnitude suggests that, instead of modeling y versus t directly, you instead model $\ln y$ versus t. (The residuals for large values of t will then be scaled down by the logarithm.)

Figure 24 shows the resulting plot together with the regression line (what we call the "linear transformed model").

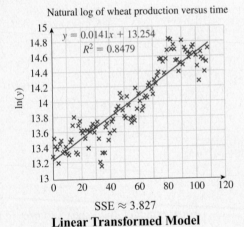

SSE ≈ 3.827

Linear Transformed Model

Figure 24

Notice that this time, the regression patterns no longer suggest an obvious curve. Further, they no longer appear to grow with increasing t. Although SSE is dramatically lower than the values for the earlier models, the contrast is a false one; the units of y are now different, and comparing SSE with that or the earlier models is like comparing apples and oranges. While SSE depends on the units of measurement used, the coefficient of determination r^2 discussed in Section 1.4 is independent of the units used. A similar statistic is available for other types of regression as well, as well as something called "adjusted r^2."

✱ **NOTE** The "adjusted r^2" from statistics that corrects for model size.

The value of r^2 for the transformed model is approximately 0.8497, while r^2 for the cubic model✱ is about 0.8219, which is fairly close.

Q: *If the cubic model and the linear transformed model have similar values of r^2, how do I decide which is more appropriate?*

A: The cubic model, if extrapolated, predicts unrealistically that the production of wheat will plunge in the near future, but the linear transformed model sees the recent drop-off as just one of several market fluctuations that show up in the residuals. You should therefore favor the more reasonable linear transformed model.

Q: *The linear transformed model gives us ln y versus t. What does it say about y versus t?*

A: Accurately write down the equation of the transformed linear model, being careful to replace y by ln y:

$$\ln y = 0.0140613t + 13.2537$$

Rewriting this is exponential form gives

$$y = e^{0.0140613t + 13.2537}$$

$$= e^{13.2537} e^{0.0140613t}$$

$$\approx 570,000 e^{0.0141t}, \qquad \text{Coefficients rounded to 3 digits}$$

which is exactly the exponential model we found earlier! (In fact, using the natural logarithm transformation is the standard method of computing the regression exponential curve.)

Q: *What of the logistic model; should that not be the most realistic?*

A: The logistic model seems as though it *ought* to be the most appropriate, because wheat production cannot reasonably be expected to continue increasing exponentially forever; eventually resource limitations must lead to a leveling-off of wheat production. Such a leveling off, if it occurred before the population started to level off, would seem to vindicate Malthus' pessimistic predictions. However, the logistic regression model looks suspect: It seems to fit the curve more poorly than any of the other models considered, suggesting that, as yet, we do not have significant evidence that any leveling-off is occurring. Wheat production—even if it is logistic—appears still in the early (exponential) stage of growth. In general, for a logistic model to be reliable in its prediction of the leveling-off value N, we would need to see significant evidence of leveling-off in the data. (See, however, Exercise 2 following.)

You now conclude that wheat production for the past 100 years is better described as increasing exponentially than linearly, contradicting Malthus, and moreover that it shows no sign of leveling off as yet.

EXERCISES

1. Use the wheat production data starting at 1950 to construct the exponential regression model in two ways: directly, and using a linear transformed model as above. (Round coefficients to three digits.) Comparing the growth constant k of your model with that of the exponential model based on the data from 1900 on. How would you interpret the difference?

2. Compute the least squares logistic model for the data in the preceding exercise. (Round coefficients to 3 significant digits.) At what level does it predict that wheat production will level off? [Note on using Excel Solver for logistic regression: Before running Solver, press Options in the Solver window and turn "Automatic Scaling" on. This adjusts the algorithm for the fact

that the constants A, N, and b have vastly different orders of magnitude.] Give two graphs: One showing the data with the exponential regression model, and the other showing the data with the logistic regression model. Which model gives a better fit visually? Justify your observation by computing SSE directly for both models. Comment on your answer in terms of Malthus' assertions.

3. Find the production figures for another common crop grown in the United States. Compare the linear, quadratic, cubic, exponential, and logistic models. What can you conclude?

4. Below are the census figures for the population of the United States (in thousands) from 1820 to 2010.[53] Compare the linear, quadratic, and exponential models. What can you conclude?

Population of the United States (1,000)

1820	1830	1840	1850	1860	1870	1880	1890	1900	1910
9,638	12,861	17,063	23,192	31,443	38,558	50,189	62,980	76,212	92,228

1920	1930	1940	1950	1960	1970	1980	1990	2000	2010
106,022	123,203	132,165	151,326	179,323	203,302	226,542	248,710	281,422	308,936

[53] Source: Bureau of the Census, U.S. Department of Commerce.

TI-83/84 Plus Technology Guide

Section 2.1

Example 2 (page 126) Sketch the graph of each quadratic function, showing the location of the vertex and intercepts.

a. $f(x) = 4x^2 - 12x + 9$ **b.** $g(x) = -\frac{1}{2}x^2 + 4x - 12$

Solution with Technology

We will do part (a).

1. Start by storing the coefficients a, b, c using

   $4 \to A : -12 \to B : 9 \to C$

   STO> gives the arrow ALPHA . gives the colon

2. Save your quadratic as Y_1 using the $Y=$ screen:

   $Y_1 = AX^2 + BX + C$

3. To obtain the x-coordinate of the vertex, enter its formula as shown:

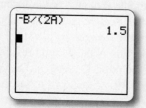

4. The y-coordinate of the vertex can be obtained from the Table screen by entering $x = 1.5$ as shown. (If you can't enter values of x, press 2ND TBLSET, and set Indpnt to Ask.)

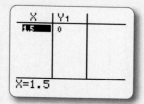

   From the table, we see that the vertex is at the point $(1.5, 0)$.

5. To obtain the x-intercepts, enter the quadratic formula on the home screen as shown:

Because both intercepts agree, we conclude that the graph intersects the x-axis on a single point (at the vertex).

6. To graph the function, we need to select good values for Xmin and Xmax. In general, we would like our graph to show the vertex as well as all the intercepts. To see the vertex, make sure that its x coordinate (1.5) is between Xmin and Xmax. To see the x-intercepts, make sure that they are also between Xmin and Xmax. To see the y-intercept, make sure that $x = 0$ is between Xmin and Xmax. Thus, to see everything, choose Xmin and Xmax so that the interval [xMin, xMax] contains the x coordinate of the vertex, the x-intercepts, and 0. For this example, we can choose an interval like $[-1, 3]$.

7. Once xMin and xMax are chosen, you can obtain convenient values of yMin and yMax by pressing ZOOM and selecting the option ZoomFit. (Make sure that your quadratic equation is entered in the $Y=$ screen before doing this!)

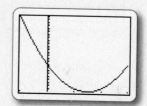

Example 5(b) (page 130) The following table shows total and projected production of ozone-layer damaging Freon 22 (chlorodifluoromethane) in developing countries ($t = 0$ represents 2000).

Year t	0	2	4	6	8	10
Tons of Freon F	100	140	200	270	400	590

Find the quadratic regression model.

Solution with Technology

1. Using STAT EDIT enter the data with the x-coordinates (values of t) in L_1 and the y-coordinates (values of F) in L_2, just as in Section 1.4:

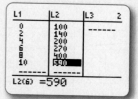

2. Press $\boxed{\text{STAT}}$, select CALC, and choose option #5 QuadReg. Pressing $\boxed{\text{ENTER}}$ gives the quadratic regression curve in the home screen:

$$y \approx 4.598x^2 + 1.161x + 108.9$$ Coefficients rounded to four decimal places

3. Now go to the Y= window and turn Plot1 on by selecting it and pressing $\boxed{\text{ENTER}}$. (You can also turn it on in the $\boxed{\text{2ND}}$ STAT PLOT screen.)

4. Next, enter the regression equation in the $\boxed{\text{Y=}}$ screen by pressing $\boxed{\text{Y=}}$ clearing out whatever function is there, and pressing $\boxed{\text{VARS}}$ $\boxed{5}$ and selecting EQ (Option #1: RegEq):

5. To obtain a convenient window showing all the points and the lines, press $\boxed{\text{ZOOM}}$ and choose option #9: ZoomStat:

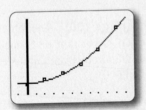

Note When you are done viewing the graph, it is a good idea to turn PLOT1 off again to avoid errors in graphing or data points showing up in your other graphs. ■

Section **2.2**

Example 6(a) (page 145) The following table shows annual expenditure on health in the United States from 1980 through 2010 ($t = 0$ represents 1980).

Year t	0	5	10	15	20	25	30
Expenditure ($ billion)	246	427	696	990	1,310	1,920	2,750

Find the exponential regression model $C(t) = Ab^t$.

Solution with Technology

This is very similar to Example 5 in Section 2.1 (see the Technology Guide for Section 2.1):

1. Use $\boxed{\text{STAT}}$ EDIT to enter the above table of values.

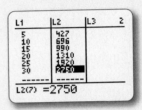

2. Press $\boxed{\text{STAT}}$, select CALC, and choose option #0 ExpReg. Pressing $\boxed{\text{ENTER}}$ gives the exponential regression curve in the home screen:

$$C(t) \approx 282.33(1.0808)^t$$ Coefficients rounded

3. To graph the points and regression line in the same window, turn Stat Plot on (see the Technology Guide for Example 5 in Section 2.1) and enter the regression equation in the Y= screen by pressing $\boxed{\text{Y=}}$, clearing out whatever function is there, and pressing $\boxed{\text{VARS}}$ $\boxed{5}$ and selecting EQ (Option 1: RegEq). Then press $\boxed{\text{ZOOM}}$ and choose option #9: ZoomStat to see the graph.

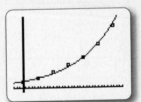

Note When you are done viewing the graph, it is a good idea to turn PLOT1 off again to avoid errors in graphing or data points showing up in your other graphs. ■

Section **2.3**

Example 5 (page 160) The following table shows the total spent in on research and development in the United States, in billions of dollars, for the period 1995–2009 (t is the year since 1990).

Year t	5	6	7	8	9	10	11	12
Spending ($ billions)	199	210	222	235	250	268	271	265
Year t	13	14	15	16	17	18	19	
Spending ($ billions)	272	275	289	299	300	304	309	

Find the best-fit logarithmic model of the form:

$$S(t) = A \ln t + C.$$

Solution with Technology

This is very similar to Example 5 in Section 2.1 (see the Technology Guide for Section 2.1):

1. Use $\boxed{\text{STAT}}$ EDIT to enter the above table of values.
2. Press $\boxed{\text{STAT}}$, select CALC, and choose the #9 LnReg. Pressing $\boxed{\text{ENTER}}$ gives the logarithmic regression curve in the home screen:

$$S(t) = 83.01 \ln t + 64.42 \quad \text{Coefficients rounded}$$

3. To graph the points and regression line in the same window, turn Stat Plot on (see the Technology Guide for Example 5 in Section 2.1) and enter the regression equation in the Y= screen by pressing $\boxed{\text{Y=}}$, clearing out whatever function is there, and pressing $\boxed{\text{VARS}}$ $\boxed{5}$ and selecting EQ (Option 1: RegEq). Then press $\boxed{\text{ZOOM}}$ and choose option #9: ZoomStat to see the graph.

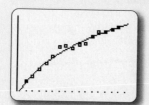

Section 2.4

Example 2 (page 169) The following table shows the percentage of U.S. Internet-connected households that have broadband connections as a function of time t in years ($t = 0$ represents 2000).

Year (t)	0	1	2	3	4	5	6	7	8	9
Percentage with Broadband (%) (P)	8	14	20	33	45	53	66	80	88	92

Find a logistic regression curve of the form

$$P(t) = \frac{N}{1 + Ab^{-t}}.$$

Solution with Technology

This is very similar to Example 5 in Section 2.1 (see the Technology Guide for Section 2.1):

1. Use $\boxed{\text{STAT}}$ EDIT to enter the above table of values.
2. Press $\boxed{\text{STAT}}$, select CALC, and choose the #B Logistic. Pressing $\boxed{\text{ENTER}}$ gives the logistic regression curve in the home screen:

$$P(t) \approx \frac{104.046}{1 + 10.453e^{-0.49578t}} \quad \text{Coefficients rounded}$$

This is not exactly the form we are seeking, but we can convert it to that form by writing

$$e^{-0.49578t} = (e^{0.49578})^{-t} \approx 1.642^{-t}$$

so,

$$P(t) \approx \frac{104.046}{1 + 10.453(1.642)^{-t}}.$$

3. To graph the points and regression line in the same window, turn Stat Plot on (see the Technology Guide for Example 5 in Section 2.1) and enter the regression equation in the Y= screen by pressing $\boxed{\text{Y=}}$, clearing out whatever function is there, and pressing $\boxed{\text{VARS}}$ $\boxed{5}$ and selecting EQ (Option 1: RegEq). Then press $\boxed{\text{ZOOM}}$ and choose option #9: ZoomStat to see the graph.

EXCEL Technology Guide

Section 2.1

Example 2 (page 126)   Sketch the graph of each quadratic function, showing the location of the vertex and intercepts.

a. $f(x) = 4x^2 - 12x + 9$ **b.** $g(x) = -\dfrac{1}{2}x^2 + 4x - 12$

Solution with Technology

We can set up a worksheet so that all we have to enter are the coefficients a, b, and c, and a range of x-values for the graph. Here is a possible layout that will plot 101 points using the coefficients for part (a) (similar to the Excel Graphing Worksheet we mentioned in Example 3 of Section 1.1, which can be found on the Web site by following Chapter 1 → Excel Tutorials → Section 1.1.)

1. First, we compute the x coordinates:

	A	B	C	D	E
1	x	y		a	4
2	=$D$4			b	-12
3	=A2+$D$6			c	9
4				Xmin	-10
5				Xmax	10
6				Delta X	=(D5-D4)/100
7					
101					
102					

2. To add the y coordinates, we use the technology formula

$$a*x^2+b*x+c$$

replacing a, b, and c with (absolute) references to the cells containing their values.

	A	B	C	D
1	x	y		a	4
2		-10	=$D$1*A2^2+$D$2*A2+$D$3	b	-12
3		-9.8		c	9
4		-9.6		Xmin	-10
5		-9.4		Xmax	10
6		-9.2		Delta X	0.2
7					
101					
102		10			

3. Graphing the data in columns A and B gives the graph shown here:

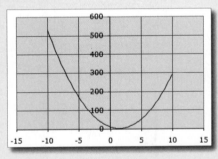

$$y = 4x^2 - 12x + 9$$

4. We can go further and compute the exact coordinates of the vertex and intercepts:

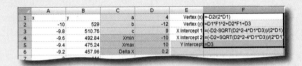

The completed sheet should look like this:

We can now save this sheet as a template to handle all quadratic functions. For instance, to do part (b), we just change the values of a, b, and c in column D to $a = -1/2$, $b = 4$, and $c = -12$.

Example 5(b) (page 130)

The following table shows total and projected production of ozone-layer damaging Freon 22 (chlorodifluoromethane) in developing countries ($t = 0$ represents 2000).

Year t	0	2	4	6	8	10
Tons of Freon F	100	140	200	270	400	590

Find the quadratic regression model.

Solution with Technology

As in Section 1.4, Example 3, we start with a scatter plot of the original data, and add a trendline:

1. Start with the original data and a "Scatter plot." (See Section 1.2 Example 5.)

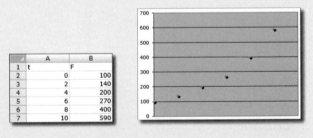

2. Click on the chart, select the Layout tab, click the Trendline button, and choose "More Trendline Options." (Alternatively, right-click on any data point in the chart and select "Add Trendline.") Then select a "Polynomial"

type of order 2 and check the option to "Display Equation on chart."

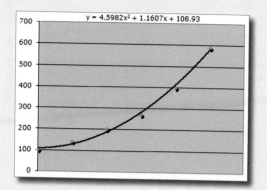

Section 2.2

Example 6(a) (page 145)   The following table shows annual expenditure on health in the United States from 1980 through 2010 ($t = 0$ represents 1980).

Year t	0	5	10	15	20	25	30
Expenditure ($ billion)	246	427	696	990	1,310	1,920	2,750

Find the exponential regression model $C(t) = Ab^t$.

Solution with Technology

This is very similar to Example 5 in Section 2.1 (see the Technology Guide for Section 2.1):

1. Start with a "Scatter plot" of the observed data.
2. Click on the chart, select the Layout tab, click the Trendline button, and choose "More Trendline Options." (Alternatively, right-click on any data point in the chart and select "Add Trendline.") Then select an "Exponential" type and check the option to "Display Equation on chart."

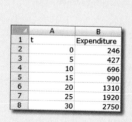

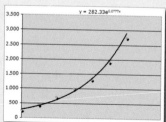

Notice that the regression curve is given in the form Ae^{kt} rather than Ab^t. To transform it, write

$$282.33e^{0.0777t} = 282.33(e^{0.0777})^t$$
$$\approx 282.33(1.0808)^t. \qquad e^{0.0777} \approx 1.0808$$

Section 2.3

Example 5 (page 160)   The following table shows the total spent in on research and development in the United States, in billions of dollars, for the period 1995–2009 (t is the year since 1990).

Year t	5	6	7	8	9	10	11	12
Spending ($ billions)	199	210	222	235	250	268	271	265
Year t	13	14	15	16	17	18	19	
Spending ($ billions)	272	275	289	299	300	304	309	

Find the best-fit logarithmic model of the form

$$S(t) = A \ln t + C.$$

Solution with Technology

This is very similar to Example 5 in Section 2.1 (see the Technology Guide for Section 2.1): We start, as usual, with a "Scatter plot" of the observed data and add a `Logarithmic` trendline. Here is the result:

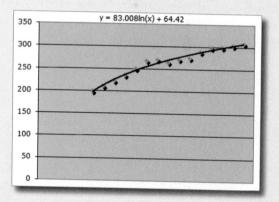

Section 2.4

Example 2 (page 169)   The following table shows the percentage of U.S. Internet-connected households that have broadband connections as a function of time t in years ($t = 0$ represents 2000).

Year (t)	0	1	2	3	4	5	6	7	8	9
Percentage with Broadband (%) (P)	8	14	20	33	45	53	66	80	88	92

Find a logistic regression curve of the form

$$P(t) = \frac{N}{1 + Ab^{-t}}.$$

Solution with Technology

Excel does not have a built-in logistic regression calculation, so we use an alternative method that works for any type of regression curve.

1. First use rough estimates for N, A, and b, and compute the sum-of-squares error (SSE; see Section 1.5) directly:

Cells E2:G2 contain our initial rough estimates of N, A, and b. For N, we used 100 (notice that the y coordinates do appear to level off around 100). For A, we used the fact that the y-intercept is $N/(1 + A)$. In other words,

$$8 = \frac{100}{1 + A}.$$

Because a very rough estimate is all we are after, using $A = 10$ will do just fine. For b, we chose 1.5 as the values of P appear to be increasing by around 50% per year initially (again, this is rough).

2. Cell C2 contains the formula for $P(t)$, and the square of the resulting residual is computed in D2.

3. Cell F6 will contain SSE. The completed spreadsheet should look like this:

	A	B	C	D	E	F	G
1	t	P (Observed)	P (Predicted)	Residual^2	N	A	b
2	0	8	9.090909091	1.19008264	100	10	1.5
3	1	14	13.04347826	0.91493384			
4	2	20	18.36734694	2.66555602			
5	3	33	25.23364486	60.3162722		SSE	
6	4	45	33.60995851	129.733045		1158.4	
7	5	53	43.1616341	96.7934435			
8	6	66	53.25054785	162.54853			
9	7	80	63.08047303	286.270393			
10	8	88	71.93290209	258.151635			
11	9	92	79.35733581	159.836958			

The best-fit curve will result from values of N, A, and b that give a minimum value for SSE. We shall use Excel's "Solver," found in the "Analysis" group on the "Data" tab. (If "Solver" does not appear in the Analysis group, you will have to install the Solver Add-in using the Excel Options dialogue.) Figure 25 shows the Solver

Figure 25

dialogue box with the necessary fields completed to solve the problem.

- The Target Cell refers to the cell that contains SSE.
- "Min" is selected because we are minimizing SSE.
- "Changing Cells" are obtained by selecting the cells that contain the current values of N, A, and b.

4. When you have filled in the values for the three items above, press "Solve" and tell Solver to Keep Solver Solution when done. You will find $N \approx 104.047$, $A \approx 10.453$, and $b \approx 1.642$ so

$$P(t) \approx \frac{104.047}{1 + 10.453(1.642)^{-t}}.$$

If you use a scatter plot to graph the data in columns A, B and C, you will obtain the following graph:

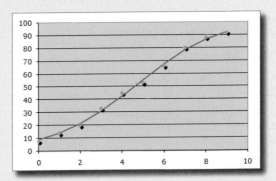

In order to find a model in which $N = 100$, all we need to do is enter 100 in cell E2 and tell Solver that the only cells it should change are F2 and G2, corresponding to A and b, by entering \$F\$2:\$G\$2 in the "By Changing Cells" box.

3

Introduction to the Derivative

Case Study Reducing Sulfur Emissions

The Environmental Protection Agency (EPA) wants to formulate a policy that will encourage utilities to reduce sulfur emissions. Its goal is to reduce annual emissions of sulfur dioxide by a total of 10 million tons from the current level of 25 million tons by imposing a fixed charge for every ton of sulfur released into the environment per year. The EPA has some data showing the marginal cost to utilities of reducing sulfur emissions. As a consultant to the EPA, you must determine the amount to be charged per ton of sulfur emissions in light of these data.

Web Site
At the Web site you will find:

- Section by section tutorials, including game tutorials with randomized quizzes

- A detailed chapter summary

- A true/false quiz

- Additional review exercises

- Graphers, Excel tutorials, and other resources

- The following extra topics:

    Sketching the graph of the derivative

    Continuity and differentiability

Norbert Schaefer/CORBIS

191

Introduction

In the world around us, everything is changing. The mathematics of change is largely about the rate of change: how fast and in which direction the change is occurring. Is the Dow Jones average going up, and if so, how fast? If I raise my prices, how many customers will I lose? If I launch this missile, how fast will it be traveling after two seconds, how high will it go, and where will it come down?

We have already discussed the concept of rate of change for linear functions (straight lines), where the slope measures the rate of change. But this works only because a straight line maintains a constant rate of change along its whole length. Other functions rise faster here than there—or rise in one place and fall in another—so that the rate of change varies along the graph. The first achievement of calculus is to provide a systematic and straightforward way of calculating (hence the name) these rates of change. To describe a changing world, we need a language of change, and that is what calculus is.

The history of calculus is an interesting story of personalities, intellectual movements, and controversy. Credit for its invention is given to two mathematicians: Isaac Newton (1642–1727) and Gottfried Leibniz (1646–1716). Newton, an English mathematician and scientist, developed calculus first, probably in the 1660s. We say "probably" because, for various reasons, he did not publish his ideas until much later. This allowed Leibniz, a German mathematician and philosopher, to publish his own version of calculus first, in 1684. Fifteen years later, stirred up by nationalist fervor in England and on the continent, controversy erupted over who should get the credit for the invention of calculus. The debate got so heated that the Royal Society (of which Newton and Leibniz were both members) set up a commission to investigate the question. The commission decided in favor of Newton, who happened to be president of the society at the time. The consensus today is that both mathematicians deserve credit because they came to the same conclusions working independently. This is not really surprising: Both built on well-known work of other people, and it was almost inevitable that someone would put it all together at about that time.

algebra Review

For this chapter, you should be familiar with the algebra reviewed in **Chapter 0, Section 2.**

3.1 Limits: Numerical and Graphical Approaches

Rates of change are calculated by derivatives, but an important part of the definition of the derivative is something called a **limit**. Arguably, much of mathematics since the 18th century has revolved around understanding, refining, and exploiting the idea of the limit. The basic idea is easy, but getting the technicalities right is not.

Evaluating Limits Numerically

Start with a very simple example: Look at the function $f(x) = 2 + x$ and ask: What happens to $f(x)$ as x approaches 3? The following table shows the value of $f(x)$ for values of x close to and on either side of 3:

		x approaching 3 from the left $\rightarrow$				$\leftarrow x$ approaching 3 from the right			
x	2.9	2.99	2.999	2.9999	3	3.0001	3.001	3.01	3.1
$f(x) = 2 + x$	4.9	4.99	4.999	4.9999		5.0001	5.001	5.01	5.1

We have left the entry under 3 blank to emphasize that when calculating the limit of $f(x)$ as x *approaches* 3, we are not interested in its value when x *equals* 3.

Notice from the table that the closer x gets to 3 from either side, the closer $f(x)$ gets to 5. We write this as

$$\lim_{x \to 3} f(x) = 5. \qquad \text{The limit of } f(x), \text{ as } x \text{ approaches 3, equals 5.}$$

Q : *Why all the fuss? Can't we simply substitute $x = 3$ and avoid having to use a table?*

A : This happens to work for *some* functions, but not for *all* functions. The following example illustrates this point.

EXAMPLE 1 Estimating a Limit Numerically

Use a table to estimate the following limits:

a. $\displaystyle\lim_{x \to 2} \frac{x^3 - 8}{x - 2}$ **b.** $\displaystyle\lim_{x \to 0} \frac{e^{2x} - 1}{x}$

Solution

* **NOTE** However, if you factor $x^3 - 8$, you will find that $f(x)$ can be simplified to a function which *is* defined at $x = 2$. This point will be discussed (and this example redone) in Section 3.3. The function in part (b) cannot be simplified by factoring.

a. We cannot simply substitute $x = 2$, because the function $f(x) = \dfrac{x^3 - 8}{x - 2}$ is not defined at $x = 2$. (Why?)* Instead, we use a table of values as we did above, with x approaching 2 from both sides.

	x approaching 2 from the left →					← x approaching 2 from the right			
x	1.9	1.99	1.999	1.9999	2	2.0001	2.001	2.01	2.1
$f(x) = \dfrac{x^3 - 8}{x - 2}$	11.41	11.9401	11.9940	11.9994		12.0006	12.0060	12.0601	12.61

We notice that as x approaches 2 from either side, $f(x)$ appears to be approaching 12. This suggests that the limit is 12, and we write

$$\lim_{x \to 2} \frac{x^3 - 8}{x - 2} = 12.$$

b. The function $g(x) = \dfrac{e^{2x} - 1}{x}$ is not defined at $x = 0$ (nor can it even be simplified to one which *is* defined at $x = 0$). In the following table, we allow x to approach 0 from both sides:

	x approaching 0 from the left →					← x approaching 0 from the right			
x	−0.1	−0.01	−0.001	−0.0001	0	0.0001	0.001	0.01	0.1
$g(x) = \dfrac{e^{2x} - 1}{x}$	1.8127	1.9801	1.9980	1.9998		2.0002	2.0020	2.0201	2.2140

The table suggests that $\displaystyle\lim_{x \to 0} \frac{e^{2x} - 1}{x} = 2$.

using Technology

We can automate the computations in Example 1 using a graphing calculator or Excel. See the Technology Guides at the end of the section to find out how to create tables like these using a TI-83/84 Plus or Excel. Here is an outline for part (a):

TI-83/84 Plus

Home screen: $Y_1 = (X^3 - 8) / (X - 2)$

2ND TBLSET Indpnt set to Ask

2ND TABLE Enter some values of x from the example: 1.9, 1.99, 1.999 . . .

[More details on page 280.]

Excel

Enter the headings x, $f(x)$ in A1–B1 and again in C1–D1.

In A2–A5 enter 1.9, 1.99, 1.999, 1.9999.

In C1–C5 enter 2.1, 2.01, 2.001, 2.0001. Enter

`=(A2^3-8)/(A2-2)`

in B2 and copy down to B5. Copy and paste the same formula in D2–D5.

[More details on page 282.]

Web Site

www.AppliedCalc.org
Student Home → Online Utilities → Function Evaluator and Grapher Enter `(x^3-8)/(x-2)` for y_1. To obtain a table of values, enter the various x-values in the Evaluator box, and press "Evaluate."

➡ **Before we go on...** Although the table *suggests* that the limit in Example 1 part (b) is 2, it by no means establishes that fact conclusively. It is *conceivable* (though not in fact the case here) that putting $x = 0.000000087$ could result in $g(x) = 426$. Using a table can only suggest a value for the limit. In the next two sections we shall discuss algebraic techniques for finding limits. ∎

Before we continue, let us make a more formal definition.

Definition of a Limit

If $f(x)$ approaches the number L as x approaches (but is not equal to) a from both sides, then we say that $f(x)$ **approaches L as $x \to a$** ("x approaches a") or that the **limit** of $f(x)$ as $x \to a$ is L. More precisely, *we can make $f(x)$ be as close to L as we like by choosing any x sufficiently close to (but not equal to) a on either side.* We write

$$\lim_{x \to a} f(x) = L$$

or

$$f(x) \to L \text{ as } x \to a.$$

If $f(x)$ *fails* to approach *a single fixed number* as x approaches a from both sides, then we say that $f(x)$ **has no limit** as $x \to a$, or

$$\lim_{x \to a} f(x) \text{ does not exist.}$$

Quick Examples

1. $\lim_{x \to 3}(2 + x) = 5$ See discussion before Example 1.

2. $\lim_{x \to -2}(3x) = -6$ As x approaches -2, $3x$ approaches -6.

3. $\lim_{x \to 0}(x^2 - 2x + 1)$ exists.   In fact, the limit is 1.

4. $\lim_{x \to 5} \dfrac{1}{x} = \dfrac{1}{5}$ As x approaches 5, $\dfrac{1}{x}$ approaches $\dfrac{1}{5}$.

5. $\lim_{x \to 2} \dfrac{x^3 - 8}{x - 2} = 12$ See Example 1. (We cannot just put $x = 2$ here.)

(For examples where the limit does not exist, see Example 2.)

Notes

1. It is important that $f(x)$ approach the same number as x approaches a from either side. For instance, if $f(x)$ approaches 5 for $x = 1.9, 1.99, 1.999, \ldots$, but approaches 4 for $x = 2.1, 2.01, 2.001, \ldots$, then the limit as $x \to 2$ does not exist. (See Example 2 for such a situation.)

2. It may happen that $f(x)$ does not approach any fixed number at all as $x \to a$ from either side. In this case, we also say that the limit does not exist.

3. If a happens to be an endpoint of the domain of f, then x can only approach a from one side. In this case, we relax the definition of the limit and require only that x approach a from the side it can. For example, $f(x) = \sqrt{x-1}$ has natural domain $[1, +\infty)$, and we say that

$$\lim_{x \to 1} \sqrt{x - 1} = 0$$

even though x can only approach 1 from the right. ∎

The following example gives instances in which a stated limit does not exist.

EXAMPLE 2 Limits Do Not Always Exist

Do the following limits exist?

a. $\lim\limits_{x \to 0} \dfrac{1}{x^2}$ **b.** $\lim\limits_{x \to 0} \dfrac{|x|}{x}$ **c.** $\lim\limits_{x \to 2} \dfrac{1}{x-2}$

Solution

a. Here is a table of values for $f(x) = \dfrac{1}{x^2}$, with x approaching 0 from both sides.

x approaching 0 from the left $\to$ $\leftarrow$ x approaching 0 from the right

x	-0.1	-0.01	-0.001	-0.0001	0	0.0001	0.001	0.01	0.1
$f(x) = \dfrac{1}{x^2}$	100	10,000	1,000,000	100,000,000		100,000,000	1,000,000	10,000	100

The table shows that as x gets closer to zero on either side, $f(x)$ gets larger and larger **without bound**—that is, if you name any number, no matter how large, $f(x)$ will be even larger than that if x is sufficiently close to 0. Because $f(x)$ is not approaching any real number, we conclude that $\lim\limits_{x \to 0} \dfrac{1}{x^2}$ does not exist. Because $f(x)$ is becoming arbitrarily large, we also say that $\lim\limits_{x \to 0} \dfrac{1}{x^2}$ **diverges to** $+\infty$, or just

$$\lim_{x \to 0} \frac{1}{x^2} = +\infty$$

Note This is not meant to imply that the limit exists; the symbol $+\infty$ does not represent any real number. We write $\lim_{x \to a} f(x) = +\infty$ to indicate two things: (1) the limit does not exist and (2) the function gets large without bound as x approaches a. ■

b. Here is a table of values for $f(x) = \dfrac{|x|}{x}$, with x approaching 0 from both sides.

x approaching 0 from the left $\to$ $\leftarrow$ x approaching 0 from the right

x	-0.1	-0.01	-0.001	-0.0001	0	0.0001	0.001	0.01	0.1
$f(x) = \dfrac{|x|}{x}$	-1	-1	-1	-1		1	1	1	1

The table shows that $f(x)$ does not approach the same limit as x approaches 0 from both sides. There appear to be two *different* limits: the limit as we approach 0 from the left and the limit as we approach from the right. We write

$$\lim_{x \to 0^-} f(x) = -1$$

read as "the limit as x approaches 0 from the left (or from below) is -1" and

$$\lim_{x \to 0^+} f(x) = 1$$

read as "the limit as x approaches 0 from the right (or from above) is 1." These are called the **one-sided limits** of $f(x)$. In order for f to have a **two-sided limit**, the two one-sided limits must be equal. Because they are not, we conclude that $\lim_{x \to 0} f(x)$ does not exist.

c. Near $x = 2$, we have the following table of values for $f(x) = \dfrac{1}{x-2}$:

		x approaching 2 from the left $\rightarrow$				$\leftarrow$ x approaching 2 from the right			
x	1.9	1.99	1.999	1.9999	2	2.0001	2.001	2.01	2.1
$f(x) = \dfrac{1}{x-2}$	-10	-100	-1000	$-10{,}000$		$10{,}000$	1000	100	10

Because $\dfrac{1}{x-2}$ is approaching no (single) real number as $x \to 2$, we see that $\lim\limits_{x \to 2} \dfrac{1}{x-2}$ does not exist. Notice also that $\dfrac{1}{x-2}$ diverges to $+\infty$ as $x \to 2$ from the positive side (right half of the table) and to $-\infty$ as $x \to 2$ from the left (left half of the table). In other words,

$$\lim_{x \to 2^-} \frac{1}{x-2} = -\infty$$

$$\lim_{x \to 2^+} \frac{1}{x-2} = +\infty$$

$$\lim_{x \to 2} \frac{1}{x-2} \text{ does not exist.}$$

In another useful kind of limit, we let x approach either $+\infty$ or $-\infty$, by which we mean that we let x get arbitrarily large or let x become an arbitrarily large negative number. The next example illustrates this.

EXAMPLE 3 Limits at Infinity

Use a table to estimate: **a.** $\lim\limits_{x \to +\infty} \dfrac{2x^2 - 4x}{x^2 - 1}$ and **b.** $\lim\limits_{x \to -\infty} \dfrac{2x^2 - 4x}{x^2 - 1}$.

Solution

a. By saying that x is "approaching $+\infty$," we mean that x is getting larger and larger without bound, so we make the following table:

			x approaching $+\infty$ $\rightarrow$		
x	10	100	1,000	10,000	100,000
$f(x) = \dfrac{2x^2 - 4x}{x^2 - 1}$	1.6162	1.9602	1.9960	1.9996	2.0000

(Note that we are only approaching $+\infty$ from the left because we can hardly approach it from the right!) What seems to be happening is that $f(x)$ is approaching 2. Thus we write

$$\lim_{x \to +\infty} f(x) = 2$$

b. Here, x is approaching $-\infty$, so we make a similar table, this time with x assuming negative values of greater and greater magnitude (read this table from right to left):

$\leftarrow x$ approaching $-\infty$

x	$-100{,}000$	$-10{,}000$	$-1{,}000$	-100	-10
$f(x) = \dfrac{2x^2 - 4x}{x^2 - 1}$	2.0000	2.0004	2.0040	2.0402	2.4242

Once again, $f(x)$ is approaching 2. Thus, $\lim_{x \to -\infty} f(x) = 2$.

Estimating Limits Graphically

We can often estimate a limit from a graph, as the next example shows.

EXAMPLE 4 Estimating Limits Graphically

The graph of a function f is shown in Figure 1. (Recall that the solid dots indicate points on the graph, and the hollow dots indicate points not on the graph.)

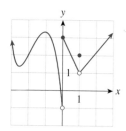

Figure 1

From the graph, analyze the following limits.

a. $\lim_{x \to -2} f(x)$ **b.** $\lim_{x \to 0} f(x)$ **c.** $\lim_{x \to 1} f(x)$ **d.** $\lim_{x \to +\infty} f(x)$

Solution Since we are given only a graph of f, we must analyze these limits graphically.

a. Imagine that Figure 1 was drawn on a graphing calculator equipped with a trace feature that allows us to move a cursor along the graph and see the coordinates as we go. To simulate this, place a pencil point on the graph to the left of $x = -2$, and move it along the curve so that the x-coordinate approaches -2. (See Figure 2.) We evaluate the limit numerically by noting the behavior of the y-coordinates.*

However, we can see directly from the graph that the y-coordinate approaches 2. Similarly, if we place our pencil point to the right of $x = -2$ and move it to the left, the y coordinate will approach 2 from that side as well (Figure 3). Therefore, as x approaches -2 from either side, $f(x)$ approaches 2, so

$$\lim_{x \to -2} f(x) = 2.$$

✱ **NOTE** For a visual animation of this process, look at the online tutorial for this section at the Web site.

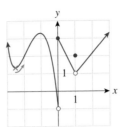

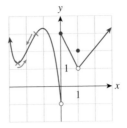

Figure 2   **Figure 3**

b. This time we move our pencil point toward $x = 0$. Referring to Figure 4, if we start from the left of $x = 0$ and approach 0 (by moving right), the y-coordinate approaches -1. However, if we start from the right of $x = 0$ and approach 0 (by moving left), the y-coordinate approaches 3. Thus (see Example 2),

$$\lim_{x \to 0^-} f(x) = -1$$

and

$$\lim_{x \to 0^+} f(x) = 3.$$

Because these limits are not equal, we conclude that

$$\lim_{x \to 0} f(x) \text{ does not exist.}$$

In this case there is a "break" in the graph at $x = 0$, and we say that the function is **discontinuous** at $x = 0$. (See Section 3.2.)

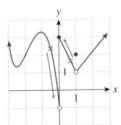

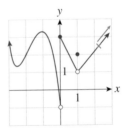

Figure 4   **Figure 5**   **Figure 6**

c. Once more we think about a pencil point moving along the graph with the x-coordinate this time approaching $x = 1$ from the left and from the right (Figure 5). As the x-coordinate of the point approaches 1 from either side, the y-coordinate approaches 1 also. Therefore,

$$\lim_{x \to 1} f(x) = 1.$$

d. For this limit, x is supposed to approach infinity. We think about a pencil point moving along the graph further and further to the right as shown in Figure 6.

As the x-coordinate gets larger, the y-coordinate also gets larger and larger without bound. Thus, $f(x)$ diverges to $+\infty$:

$$\lim_{x \to +\infty} f(x) = +\infty.$$

Similarly,

$$\lim_{x \to -\infty} f(x) = +\infty.$$

➡ **Before we go on...** In Example 4(c) $\lim_{x \to 1} f(x) = 1$ but $f(1) = 2$ (why?). Thus, $\lim_{x \to 1} f(x) \neq f(1)$. In other words, the limit of $f(x)$ as x *approaches* 1 is not the same as the value of f at $x = 1$. Always keep in mind that when we evaluate a limit as $x \to a$, *we do not care about the value of the function at $x = a$*. We only care about the value of $f(x)$ as x *approaches* a. In other words, $f(a)$ may or may not equal $\lim_{x \to a} f(x)$. ■

Here is a summary of the graphical method we used in Example 4, together with some additional information:

Evaluating Limits Graphically

To decide whether $\lim_{x \to a} f(x)$ exists and to find its value if it does:

1. Draw the graph of $f(x)$ by hand or with graphing technology.
2. Position your pencil point (or the Trace cursor) on a point of the graph to the right of $x = a$.
3. Move the point *along the graph* toward $x = a$ from the right and read the y-coordinate as you go. The value the y-coordinate approaches (if any) is the limit $\lim_{x \to a^+} f(x)$.
4. Repeat Steps 2 and 3, this time starting from a point on the graph to the left of $x = a$, and approaching $x = a$ along the graph from the left. The value the y-coordinate approaches (if any) is $\lim_{x \to a^-} f(x)$.
5. If the left and right limits both exist and have the same value L, then $\lim_{x \to a} f(x) = L$. Otherwise, the limit does not exist. The value $f(a)$ has no relevance whatsoever.
6. To evaluate $\lim_{x \to +\infty} f(x)$, move the pencil point toward the far right of the graph and estimate the value the y-coordinate approaches (if any). For $\lim_{x \to -\infty} f(x)$, move the pencil point toward the far left.
7. If $x = a$ happens to be an endpoint of the domain of f, then only a one-sided limit is possible at $x = a$. For instance, if the domain is $(-\infty, 4]$, then $\lim_{x \to 4^-} f(x)$ can be computed, but not $\lim_{x \to 4^+} f(x)$. In this case, we have said that $\lim_{x \to 4} f(x)$ is just the one-sided limit $\lim_{x \to 4^-} f(x)$.

In the next example we use both the numerical and graphical approaches.

EXAMPLE 5 Infinite Limit

Does $\lim\limits_{x \to 0^+} \dfrac{1}{x}$ exist?

Solution

Numerical Method Because we are asked for only the right-hand limit, we need only list values of x approaching 0 from the right.

$\leftarrow x$ approaching 0 from the right

x	0	0.0001	0.001	0.01	0.1
$f(x) = \dfrac{1}{x}$		10,000	1,000	100	10

What seems to be happening as x approaches 0 from the right is that $f(x)$ is increasing without bound, as in Example 4(d). That is, if you name any number, no

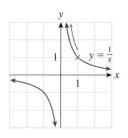

Figure 7

matter how large, $f(x)$ will be even larger than that if x is sufficiently close to zero. Thus, the limit diverges to $+\infty$, so

$$\lim_{x \to 0^+} \frac{1}{x} = +\infty$$

Graphical Method Recall that the graph of $f(x) = \dfrac{1}{x}$ is the standard hyperbola shown in Figure 7. The figure also shows the pencil point moving so that its x-coordinate approaches 0 from the right. Because the point moves along the graph, it is forced to go higher and higher. In other words, its y-coordinate becomes larger and larger, approaching $+\infty$. Thus, we conclude that

$$\lim_{x \to 0^+} \frac{1}{x} = +\infty$$

➡ **Before we go on...** In Example 5(a) you should also check that

$$\lim_{x \to 0^-} \frac{1}{x} = -\infty.$$

We say that as x approaches 0 from the left, $\dfrac{1}{x}$ diverges to $-\infty$. Also, check that

$$\lim_{x \to +\infty} \frac{1}{x} = \lim_{x \to -\infty} \frac{1}{x} = 0. \ \blacksquare$$

APPLICATION

EXAMPLE 6 Broadband

The percentage of U.S. Internet-connected households that have broadband connections can be modeled by

$$P(t) = \frac{100}{1 + 10.8(1.7)^{-t}} \quad (t \ge 0)$$

where t is time in years since 2000.*

a. Estimate $\lim_{t \to +\infty} P(t)$ and interpret the answer.

b. Estimate $\lim_{t \to 0^+} P(t)$ and interpret the answer.

Solution

a. Figure 8 shows a plot of $P(t)$ for $0 \le t \le 20$.

Using either the numerical or the graphical approach, we find

$$\lim_{t \to +\infty} P(t) = \lim_{t \to +\infty} \frac{100}{1 + 10.8(1.7)^{-t}} = 100.$$

Thus, in the long term (as t gets larger and larger), the percentage of U.S. Internet-connected households that have broadband is expected to approach 100%.

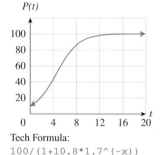

Tech Formula:
`100/(1+10.8*1.7^(-x))`

Figure 8

---

* See Example 2 in Section 2.4. Source for data: www.Nielsen.com.

b. The limit here is

$$\lim_{t \to 0^+} P(t) = \lim_{t \to 0^+} \frac{100}{1 + 10.8(1.7)^{-t}} \approx 8.475.$$

(Notice that in this case, we can simply put $t = 0$ to evaluate this limit.) Thus, the closer t gets to 0 (representing 2000) the closer $P(t)$ gets to 8.475%, meaning that, in 2000, about 8.5% of Internet-connected households had broadband.

FAQs

Determining When a Limit Does or Does Not Exist

Q: *If I substitute $x = a$ in the formula for a function and find that the function is not defined there, it means that $\lim_{x \to a} f(x)$ does not exist, right?*

A: Wrong. The limit may still exist, as in Example 1, or may not exist, as in Example 2. In general, whether or not $\lim_{x \to a} f(x)$ exists has nothing to do with $f(a)$, but rather the value of f when x is *very close to, but not equal to* a.

Q: *Is there a quick and easy way of telling from a graph whether $\lim_{x \to a} f(x)$ exists?*

A: Yes. If you cover up the portion of the graph corresponding to $x = a$, and it appears as though the visible part of the graph could be made into a continuous curve by filling in a suitable point at $x = a$, then the limit exists. (The "suitable point" need not be $(a, f(a))$.) Otherwise, it does not. Try this method with the curves in Example 4.

3.1 EXERCISES

▼ more advanced   ◆ challenging
⊤ indicates exercises that should be solved using technology

Estimate the limits in Exercises 1–18 numerically.
HINT [See Example 1.]

1. $\lim_{x \to 0} \dfrac{x^2}{x + 1}$

2. $\lim_{x \to 0} \dfrac{x - 3}{x - 1}$

3. $\lim_{x \to 2} \dfrac{x^2 - 4}{x - 2}$

4. $\lim_{x \to 2} \dfrac{x^2 - 1}{x - 2}$

5. $\lim_{x \to -1} \dfrac{x^2 + 1}{x + 1}$

6. $\lim_{x \to -1} \dfrac{x^2 + 2x + 1}{x + 1}$

7. $\lim_{x \to +\infty} \dfrac{3x^2 + 10x - 1}{2x^2 - 5x}$ HINT [See Example 3.]

8. $\lim_{x \to +\infty} \dfrac{6x^2 + 5x + 100}{3x^2 - 9}$ HINT [See Example 3.]

9. $\lim_{x \to -\infty} \dfrac{x^5 - 1,000x^4}{2x^5 + 10,000}$

10. $\lim_{x \to -\infty} \dfrac{x^6 + 3,000x^3 + 1,000,000}{2x^6 + 1,000x^3}$

11. $\lim_{x \to +\infty} \dfrac{10x^2 + 300x + 1}{5x + 2}$

12. $\lim_{x \to +\infty} \dfrac{2x^4 + 20x^3}{1,000x^6 + 6}$

13. $\lim_{x \to +\infty} \dfrac{10x^2 + 300x + 1}{5x^3 + 2}$

14. $\lim_{x \to +\infty} \dfrac{2x^4 + 20x^3}{1,000x^3 + 6}$

15. $\lim_{x \to 2} e^{x-2}$

16. $\lim_{x \to +\infty} e^{-x}$

17. $\lim_{x \to +\infty} xe^{-x}$

18. $\lim_{x \to -\infty} xe^{x}$

In each of Exercises 19–30, the graph of f is given. Use the graph to compute the quantities asked for. HINT [See Example 4.]

19. a. $\lim_{x \to 1} f(x)$ **b.** $\lim_{x \to -1} f(x)$

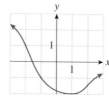

20. a. $\lim_{x \to -1} f(x)$ **b.** $\lim_{x \to 1} f(x)$

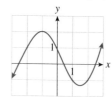

21. a. $\lim_{x\to 0} f(x)$ **b.** $\lim_{x\to 2} f(x)$ **22. a.** $\lim_{x\to -1} f(x)$ **b.** $\lim_{x\to 1} f(x)$

c. $\lim_{x\to -\infty} f(x)$ **d.** $\lim_{x\to +\infty} f(x)$ **c.** $\lim_{x\to +\infty} f(x)$ **d.** $\lim_{x\to -\infty} f(x)$

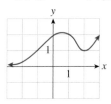   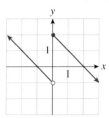

23. a. $\lim_{x\to 2} f(x)$ **b.** $\lim_{x\to 0^+} f(x)$ **24. a.** $\lim_{x\to 3} f(x)$ **b.** $\lim_{x\to 1^+} f(x)$

c. $\lim_{x\to 0^-} f(x)$ **d.** $\lim_{x\to 0} f(x)$ **c.** $\lim_{x\to 1^-} f(x)$ **d.** $\lim_{x\to 1} f(x)$

e. $f(0)$ **f.** $\lim_{x\to -\infty} f(x)$ **e.** $f(1)$ **f.** $\lim_{x\to +\infty} f(x)$

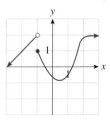   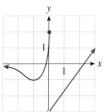

25. a. $\lim_{x\to -2} f(x)$ **b.** $\lim_{x\to -1^+} f(x)$ **26. a.** $\lim_{x\to -1} f(x)$ **b.** $\lim_{x\to 0^+} f(x)$

c. $\lim_{x\to -1^-} f(x)$ **d.** $\lim_{x\to -1} f(x)$ **c.** $\lim_{x\to 0^-} f(x)$ **d.** $\lim_{x\to 0} f(x)$

e. $f(-1)$ **f.** $\lim_{x\to +\infty} f(x)$ **e.** $f(0)$ **f.** $\lim_{x\to -\infty} f(x)$

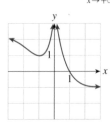   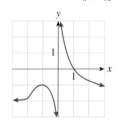

27. a. $\lim_{x\to -1} f(x)$ **b.** $\lim_{x\to 0^+} f(x)$ **28. a.** $\lim_{x\to 1} f(x)$ **b.** $\lim_{x\to 0^+} f(x)$

c. $\lim_{x\to 0^-} f(x)$ **d.** $\lim_{x\to 0} f(x)$ **c.** $\lim_{x\to 0^-} f(x)$ **d.** $\lim_{x\to 0} f(x)$

e. $f(0)$ **f.** $\lim_{x\to +\infty} f(x)$ **e.** $f(0)$ **f.** $\lim_{x\to -\infty} f(x)$

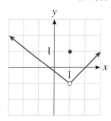

29. a. $\lim_{x\to -1} f(x)$ **b.** $\lim_{x\to 0^+} f(x)$ **30. a.** $\lim_{x\to 0^-} f(x)$ **b.** $\lim_{x\to 1^+} f(x)$

c. $\lim_{x\to 0^-} f(x)$ **d.** $\lim_{x\to 0} f(x)$ **c.** $\lim_{x\to 0} f(x)$ **d.** $\lim_{x\to 1^-} f(x)$

e. $f(0)$ **f.** $f(-1)$ **e.** $f(0)$ **f.** $f(1)$

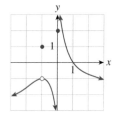   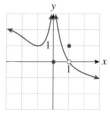

APPLICATIONS

31. *Economic Growth* The value of sold goods in Mexico can be approximated by

$$v(t) = 210 - 62e^{-0.05t} \text{ trillion pesos per month} \quad (t \geq 0)$$

where t is time in months since January 2005.[1] Numerically estimate $\lim_{t\to +\infty} v(t)$ and interpret the answer. HINT [See Example 6.]

32. *Housing Starts* Housing starts in the United States can be approximated by

$$n(t) = \frac{1}{12}(1.1 + 1.2e^{-0.08t}) \text{ million homes per month} \quad (t \geq 0)$$

where t is time in months since January 2006.[2] Numerically estimate $\lim_{t\to +\infty} n(t)$ and interpret the answer. HINT [See Example 6.]

33. *Scientific Research* The number of research articles per year, in thousands, in the prominent journal *Physical Review* written by researchers in Europe can be modeled by

$$A(t) = \frac{7.0}{1 + 5.4(1.2)^{-t}}$$

where t is time in years ($t = 0$ represents 1983).[3] Numerically estimate $\lim_{t\to +\infty} A(t)$ and interpret the answer. HINT [See Example 6.]

34. *Scientific Research* The percentage of research articles in the prominent journal *Physical Review* written by researchers in the United States can be modeled by

$$A(t) = 25 + \frac{36}{1 + 0.6(0.7)^{-t}},$$

where t is time in years ($t = 0$ represents 1983).[4] Numerically estimate $\lim_{t\to +\infty} A(t)$ and interpret the answer. HINT [See Example 6.]

---

[1] Source: Instituto Nacional de Estadística y Geografía (INEGI), www.inegi.org.mx.

[2] Source for data: *New York Times*, February 17, 2007, p. C3.

[3] Based on data from 1983 to 2003. Source: The American Physical Society/*New York Times*, May 3, 2003, p. A1.

[4] Ibid.

35. *SAT Scores by Income* The following bar graph shows U.S. verbal SAT scores as a function of parents' income level:[5]

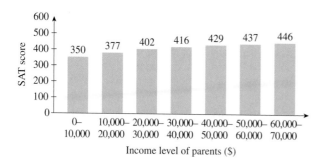

Income level of parents ($)

These data can be modeled by

$$S(x) = 470 - 136(0.974)^x.$$

where $S(x)$ is the average SAT verbal score of a student whose parents' income is x thousand dollars per year. Numerically estimate $\lim_{x \to +\infty} S(x)$ and interpret the result.

36. *SAT Scores by Income* The following bar graph shows U.S. math SAT scores as a function of parents' income level:[6]

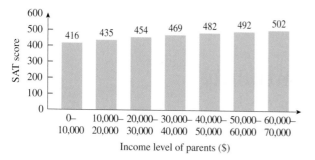

Income level of parents ($)

These data can be modeled by

$$S(x) = 535 - 136(0.979)^x,$$

where $S(x)$ is the average math SAT score of a student whose parents' income is x thousand dollars per year. Numerically estimate $\lim_{x \to +\infty} S(x)$ and interpret the result.

37. *Home Prices* The following graph shows the approximate value of the home price index as a percentage change from 2003.[7]

Home price index

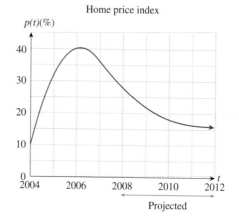

Estimate $\lim_{t \to +\infty} p(t)$ and interpret your answer.

38. *Existing Home Sales* The following graph shows the approximate value of existing home sales as a percentage change from 2003.[8]

Existing home sales

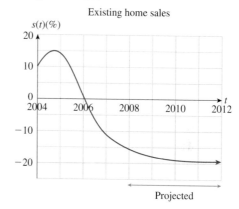

Estimate $\lim_{t \to +\infty} s(t)$ and interpret your answer.

39. *Electric Rates* The cost of electricity in Portland, Oregon, for residential customers increased suddenly on October 1, 2001, from around $0.06 to around $0.08 per kilowatt hour.[9] Let $C(t)$ be this cost at time t, and take $t = 1$ to represent October 1, 2001. What does the given information tell you about $\lim_{t \to 1} C(t)$? HINT [See Example 4(b).]

40. *Airline Stocks* Prior to the September 11, 2001 attacks, **United Airlines** stock was trading at around $35 per share. Immediately following the attacks, the share price dropped by $15.[10] Let $U(t)$ be this cost at time t, and take $t = 11$ to represent September 11, 2001. What does the given information tell you about $\lim_{t \to 11} U(t)$? HINT [See Example 4(b).]

[5] Based on 1994 data. Source: The College Board/*New York Times*, March 5, 1995, p. E16.

[6] Ibid.

[7] S&P/Case-Shiller Home Price Index. Source: Standard & Poors/ *New York Times*, September 29, 2007, p. C3. Projection is the authors'.

[8] Source: Bloomberg Finiancial Markets/*New York Times*, September 29, 2007, p. C3. Projection is the authors'.

[9] Source: Portland General Electric/*New York Times*, February 2, 2002, p. C1.

[10] Stock prices are approximate.

Foreign Trade *Annual U.S. imports from China in the years 1996 through 2003 can be approximated by*

$$I(t) = t^2 + 3.5t + 50 \qquad (1 \le t \le 9)$$

billion dollars, where t represents time in years since 1995. Annual U.S. exports to China in the same years can be approximated by

$$E(t) = 0.4t^2 - 1.6t + 14$$

billion dollars.[11] Exercises 41 and 42 are based on these models.

41. ▼ Assuming the trends shown in the above models continued indefinitely, numerically estimate

$$\lim_{t \to +\infty} I(t) \text{ and } \lim_{t \to +\infty} \frac{I(t)}{E(t)},$$

interpret your answers, and comment on the results.

42. ▼ Repeat Exercise 41, this time calculating

$$\lim_{t \to +\infty} E(t) \text{ and } \lim_{t \to +\infty} \frac{E(t)}{I(t)}.$$

COMMUNICATION AND REASONING EXERCISES

43. Describe the method of evaluating limits numerically. Give at least one disadvantage of this method.

_____

[11] Based on quadratic regression using data from the U.S. Census Bureau Foreign Trade Division Web site www.census.gov/foreign-trade/sitc1/ as of December 2004.

44. Describe the method of evaluating limits graphically. Give at least one disadvantage of this method.

45. Your friend Dion, a business student, claims that the study of limits that do not exist is completely unrealistic and has nothing to do with the world of business. Give two examples from the world of business that might convince him that he is wrong.

46. Your other friend Fiona claims that the study of limits is a complete farce; all you ever need to do to find the limit as x approaches a is substitute $x = a$. Give two examples that show she is wrong.

47. ▼ What is wrong with the following statement? "Because $f(a)$ is not defined, $\lim_{x \to a} f(x)$ does not exist."

48. ▼ What is wrong with the following statement? "Because $f(a)$ is defined, $\lim_{x \to a} f(x)$ exists."

49. ▼ What is wrong with the following statement? "If $f(a)$ is defined, then $\lim_{x \to a} f(x)$ exists and equals $f(a)$."

50. ▼ If $D(t)$ is the Dow Jones Average at time t and $\lim_{t \to +\infty} D(t) = +\infty$, is it possible that the Dow will fluctuate indefinitely into the future?

51. ◆ Give an example of a function f with $\lim_{x \to 1} f(x) = f(2)$.

52. ◆ If $S(t)$ represents the size of the universe in billions of light years at time t years since the big bang and $\lim_{t \to +\infty} S(t) = 130{,}000$, is it possible that the universe will continue to expand forever?

3.2 Limits and Continuity

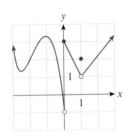

Figure 9

In Section 2.1 we saw examples of graphs that had various kinds of "breaks" or "jumps." For instance, in Example 4 we looked at the graph in Figure 9. This graph appears to have breaks, or **discontinuities**, at $x = 0$ and at $x = 1$. At $x = 0$ we saw that $\lim_{x \to 0} f(x)$ does not exist because the left- and right-hand limits are not the same. Thus, the discontinuity at $x = 0$ seems to be due to the fact that the limit does not exist there. On the other hand, at $x = 1$, $\lim_{x \to 1} f(x)$ *does* exist (it is equal to 1), but is not equal to $f(1) = 2$.

Thus, we have identified two kinds of discontinuity:

1. Points where the limit of the function does not exist.

$x = 0$ in Figure 9 because $\lim_{x \to 0} f(x)$ does not exist.

2. Points where the limit exists but does not equal the value of the function.

$x = 1$ in Figure 9 because $\lim_{x \to 1} f(x) = 1 \ne f(1)$

On the other hand, there is no discontinuity at, say, $x = -2$, where we find that $\lim_{x \to -2} f(x)$ exists and equals 2 and $f(-2)$ is also equal to 2. In other words,

$$\lim_{x \to -2} f(x) = 2 = f(-2).$$

The point $x = -2$ is an example of a point where f is **continuous**. (Notice that you can draw the portion of the graph near $x = -2$ without lifting your pencil from the paper.) Similarly, f is continuous at *every* point other than $x = 0$ and $x = 1$. Here is the mathematical definition.

Continuous Function

Let f be a function and let a be a number in the domain of f. Then f is **continuous at a** if

a. $\lim_{x \to a} f(x)$ exists, and

b. $\lim_{x \to a} f(x) = f(a)$.

The function f is said to be **continuous on its domain** if it is continuous at each point in its domain.

If f is not continuous at a particular a in its domain, we say that f is **discontinuous** at a or that f has a **discontinuity** at a. Thus, a discontinuity can occur at $x = a$ if either

a. $\lim_{x \to a} f(x)$ does not exist, or

b. $\lim_{x \to a} f(x)$ exists but is not equal to $f(a)$.

Quick Examples

1. The function shown in Figure 9 is continuous at $x = -1$ and $x = 2$. It is discontinuous at $x = 0$ and $x = 1$, and so is not continuous on its domain.
2. The function $f(x) = x^2$ is continuous on its domain. (Think of its graph, which contains no breaks).
3. The function f whose graph is shown on the left in the following figure is continuous on its domain. (Although the graph breaks at $x = 2$, that is not a point of its domain.) The function g whose graph is shown on the right is not continuous on its domain because it has a discontinuity at $x = 2$. (Here, $x = 2$ is a point of the domain of g.)

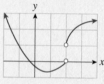

$y = f(x)$: Continuous on its domain

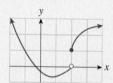

$y = g(x)$: 0 Not continuous on its domain

Note If the number a is not in the domain of f—that is, if $f(a)$ is not defined—we will not consider the question of continuity at a. A function cannot be continuous at a point not in its domain, and it cannot be discontinuous there either. ■

EXAMPLE 1 Continuous and Discontinuous Functions

Which of the following functions are continuous on their domains?

a. $h(x) = \begin{cases} x + 3 & \text{if } x \leq 1 \\ 5 - x & \text{if } x > 1 \end{cases}$

b. $k(x) = \begin{cases} x + 3 & \text{if } x \leq 1 \\ 1 - x & \text{if } x > 1 \end{cases}$

c. $f(x) = \dfrac{1}{x}$

d. $g(x) = \begin{cases} \dfrac{1}{x} & \text{if } x \neq 0 \\ 0 & \text{if } x = 0 \end{cases}$

Solution

a and **b.** The graphs of h and k are shown in Figure 10.

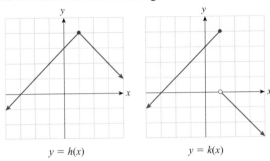

$$y = h(x) \qquad\qquad y = k(x)$$

Figure 10

Even though the graph of h is made up of two different line segments, it is continuous at every point of its domain, including $x = 1$ because

$$\lim_{x \to 1} h(x) = 4 = h(1).$$

On the other hand, $x = 1$ is also in the domain of k, but $\lim_{x \to 1} k(x)$ does not exist. Thus, k is discontinuous at $x = 1$ and thus not continuous on its domain.

c and **d.** The graphs of f and g are shown in Figure 11.

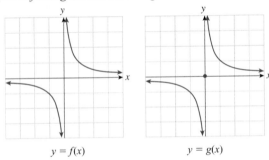

$$y = f(x) \qquad\qquad y = g(x)$$

Figure 11

The domain of f consists of all real numbers except 0 and f is continuous at all such numbers. (Notice that 0 is not in the domain of f, so the question of continuity at 0 does not arise.) Thus, f is continuous on its domain.

The function g, on the other hand, has its domain expanded to include 0, so we now need to check whether g is continuous at 0. From the graph, it is easy to see that g is discontinuous there because $\lim_{x \to 0} g(x)$ does not exist. Thus, g is not continuous on its domain because it is discontinuous at 0.

➡ **Before we go on...**

Q : *Wait a minute! How can a function like $f(x) = 1/x$ be continuous when its graph has a break in it?*

A : We are not claiming that f is continuous *at every real number*. What we are saying is that f is continuous *on its domain;* the break in the graph occurs at a point not in the domain of f. In other words, f is continuous on the set of all nonzero real numbers; it is not continuous on the set of *all* real numbers because it is not even defined on that set.

■

▦ using Technology

We can use technology to draw (approximate) graphs of the functions in Example 1(a), (b), and (c). Here are the technology formulas that will work for the TI-83/84 Plus, Excel, and Web site function evaluator and grapher. (In the TI-83/84 Plus, replace <= by ≤. In Excel, replace x by a cell reference and insert an equals sign in front of the formula.)

a. (x+3)*(x<=1)
+ (5−x)*(x>1)

b. (x+3)*(x<=1)
+ (1−x)*(x>1)

c. (1/x)

Observe in each case how technology handles the breaks in the curves.

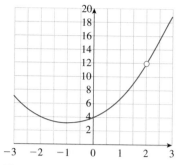

Figure 12

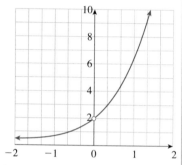

Figure 13

EXAMPLE 2 Continuous Except at a Point

In each case, say what, if any, value of $f(a)$ would make f continuous at a.

a. $f(x) = \dfrac{x^3 - 8}{x - 2}$; $a = 2$ **b.** $f(x) = \dfrac{e^{2x} - 1}{x}$; $a = 0$ **c.** $f(x) = \dfrac{|x|}{x}$; $a = 0$

Solution

a. In Figure 12 we see the graph of $f(x) = \dfrac{x^3 - 8}{x - 2}$. The point corresponding to $x = 2$ is missing because f is not (yet) defined there. (Your graphing utility will probably miss this subtlety and render a continuous curve. See the technology note in the margin.) To turn f into a function that is continuous at $x = 2$, we need to "fill in the gap" so as to obtain a continuous curve. Since the graph suggests that the missing point is (2, 12), let us define $f(2) = 12$.

Does f now become continuous if we take $f(2) = 12$? From the graph, or Example 1(a) of Section 3.1,

$$\lim_{x \to 2} f(x) = \lim_{x \to 2} \frac{x^3 - 8}{x - 2} = 12,$$

which is now equal to $f(2)$. Thus, $\lim_{x \to 2} f(x) = f(2)$, showing that f is now continuous at $x = 2$.

b. In Example 1(b) of the preceding section, we saw that

$$\lim_{x \to 0} f(x) = \lim_{x \to 0} \frac{e^{2x} - 1}{x} = 2$$

and so, as in part (a), we must define $f(0) = 2$. This is confirmed by the graph, shown in Figure 13.

c. We considered the function $f(x) = |x|/x$ in Example 2 in Section 3.1. Its graph is shown in Figure 14.

▦ **using** Technology

It is instructive to see how technology handles the functions in Example 2. Here are the technology formulas that will work for the TI-83/84 Plus, Excel, and Web site function evaluator and grapher. (In Excel, replace x by a cell reference and insert an equal sign in front of the formula.)
a. (x^3-8)/(x-2)
b. (e^(2x)-1)/x

Excel:
=(exp(2*A2)-1)/A2
c. abs(x)/x
In each case, compare the graph rendered by technology with the corresponding figure in Example 2.

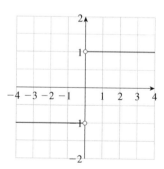

Figure 14

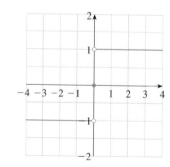

Figure 15

Now we encounter a problem: No matter how we try to fill in the gap at $x = 0$, the result will be a discontinuous function. For example, setting $f(0) = 0$ will result in the discontinuous function shown in Figure 15. We conclude that it is impossible to assign any value to $f(0)$ to turn f into a function that is continuous at $x = 0$.

We can also see this result algebraically: In Example 2 of Section 3.1, we saw that $\lim\limits_{x \to 0} \dfrac{|x|}{x}$ does not exist. Thus, the resulting function will fail to be continuous at 0, no matter how we define $f(0)$.

A function not defined at an isolated point is said to have a **singularity** at that point. The function in part (a) of Example 2 has a singularity at $x = 2$, and the functions in parts (b) and (c) have singularities at $x = 0$. The functions in parts (a) and (b) have *removable* singularities because we can make these functions continuous at $x = a$ by properly defining $f(a)$. The function in part (c) has an **essential singularity** because we cannot make f continuous at $x = a$ just by defining $f(a)$ properly.

3.2 EXERCISES

▼ more advanced   ◆ challenging

🄣 indicates exercises that should be solved using technology

In Exercises 1–12, the graph of a function f is given. Determine whether f is continuous on its domain. If it is not continuous on its domain, say why. HINT [See Quick Examples page 205.]

1.

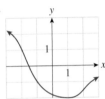

2.

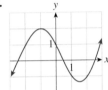

3.

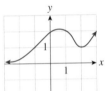

4.

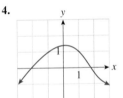

5.

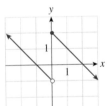

6.

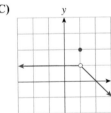

7.

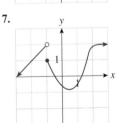

8.

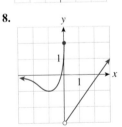

9.

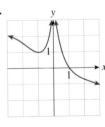

10.

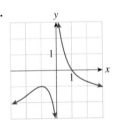

11.

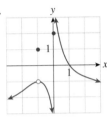

12.

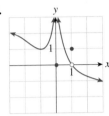

In Exercises 13 and 14, identify which (if any) of the given graphs represent functions continuous on their domains. HINT [See Quick Examples page 205.]

13. (A)

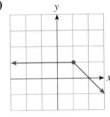

(B)

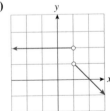

(C)

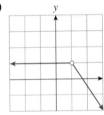

(D)

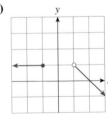

(E)

14. (A)

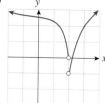

(B)

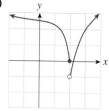

(C)

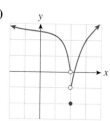

(D)

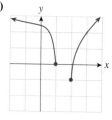

(E)

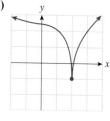

In Exercises 15–22, use a graph of f or some other method to determine what, if any, value to assign to f(a) to make f continuous at x = a. HINT [See Example 2.]

15. $f(x) = \dfrac{x^2 - 2x + 1}{x - 1}; a = 1$

16. $f(x) = \dfrac{x^2 + 3x + 2}{x + 1}; a = -1$

17. $f(x) = \dfrac{x}{3x^2 - x}; a = 0$

18. $f(x) = \dfrac{x^2 - 3x}{x + 4}; a = -4$

19. $f(x) = \dfrac{3}{3x^2 - x}; a = 0$

20. $f(x) = \dfrac{x - 1}{x^3 - 1}; a = 1$

21. $f(x) = \dfrac{1 - e^x}{x}; a = 0$

22. $f(x) = \dfrac{1 + e^x}{1 - e^x}; a = 0$

In Exercises 23–32, use a graph to determine whether the given function is continuous on its domain. If it is not continuous on its domain, list the points of discontinuity. HINT [See Example 1.]

23. $f(x) = |x|$

24. $f(x) = \dfrac{|x|}{x}$

25. $g(x) = \dfrac{1}{x^2 - 1}$

26. $g(x) = \dfrac{x - 1}{x + 2}$

27. $f(x) = \begin{cases} x + 2 & \text{if } x < 0 \\ 2x - 1 & \text{if } x \geq 0 \end{cases}$

28. $f(x) = \begin{cases} 1 - x & \text{if } x \leq 1 \\ x - 1 & \text{if } x > 1 \end{cases}$

29. $h(x) = \begin{cases} \dfrac{|x|}{x} & \text{if } x \neq 0 \\ 0 & \text{if } x = 0 \end{cases}$

30. $h(x) = \begin{cases} \dfrac{1}{x^2} & \text{if } x \neq 0 \\ 2 & \text{if } x = 0 \end{cases}$

31. $g(x) = \begin{cases} x + 2 & \text{if } x < 0 \\ 2x + 2 & \text{if } x \geq 0 \end{cases}$

32. $g(x) = \begin{cases} 1 - x & \text{if } x \leq 1 \\ x + 1 & \text{if } x > 1 \end{cases}$

COMMUNICATION AND REASONING EXERCISES

33. If a function is continuous on its domain, is it continuous at every real number? Explain.

34. True or false? The graph of a function that is continuous on its domain is a continuous curve with no breaks in it. Explain your answer.

35. True or false? The graph of a function that is continuous at every real number is a continuous curve with no breaks in it. Explain your answer.

36. True or false? If the graph of a function is a continuous curve with no breaks in it, then the function is continuous on its domain. Explain your answer.

37. ▼ Give a formula for a function that is continuous on its domain but whose graph consists of three distinct curves.

38. ▼ Give a formula for a function that is not continuous at x = −1 but is not discontinuous there either.

39. ▼ Draw the graph of a function that is discontinuous at every integer.

40. ▼ Draw the graph of a function that is continuous on its domain but whose graph has a break at every integer.

41. ▼ Describe a real-life scenario in the stock market that can be modeled by a discontinuous function.

42. ▼ Describe a real-life scenario in your room that can be modeled by a discontinuous function.

3.3 Limits and Continuity: Algebraic Approach

Although numerical and graphical estimation of limits is effective, the estimates these methods yield may not be perfectly accurate. The algebraic method, when it can be used, will always yield an exact answer. Moreover, algebraic analysis of a function often enables us to take a function apart and see "what makes it tick."

Let's start with the function $f(x) = 2 + x$ and ask: What happens to $f(x)$ as x approaches 3? To answer this algebraically, notice that as x gets closer and closer to 3, the quantity $2 + x$ must get closer and closer to $2 + 3 = 5$. Hence,

$$\lim_{x \to 3} f(x) = \lim_{x \to 3} (2 + x) = 2 + 3 = 5$$

Q: *Is that all there is to the algebraic method? Just substitute x = a?*

A: Under certain circumstances: Notice that by substituting $x = 3$ we *evaluated the function at $x = 3$. In other words, we relied on the fact that

$$\lim_{x \to 3} f(x) = f(3).$$

In Section 3.2 we said that a function satisfying this equation is *continuous* at $x = 3$.

Thus,

> *If we know that the function f is continuous at a point a, we can compute $\lim_{x \to a} f(x)$ by simply substituting $x = a$ into $f(x)$.*

To use this fact, we need to know how to recognize continuous functions when we see them. Geometrically, they are easy to spot: A function is continuous at $x = a$ if its graph has no break at $x = a$. Algebraically, a large class of functions are known to be continuous on their domains—those, roughly speaking, that are *specified by a single formula*.

We can be more precise: A **closed-form function** is any function that can be obtained by combining constants, powers of x, exponential functions, radicals, logarithms, absolute values, trigonometric functions (and some other functions we do not encounter in this text) into a *single* mathematical formula by means of the usual arithmetic operations and composition of functions. (They can be as complicated as we like.)

Closed-Form Functions

A function is **written in closed form** if it is specified by combining constants, powers of x, exponential functions, radicals, logarithms, absolute values, trigonometric functions (and some other functions we do not encounter in this text) into a *single* mathematical formula by means of the usual arithmetic operations and composition of functions. A **closed-form function** is any function that can be written in closed form.

Quick Examples

* NOTE It is possible to rewrite some piecewise defined functions in closed form (using a single formula), but not this particular function, so f(x) is not a closed-form function.

1. $3x^2 - |x| + 1$, $\dfrac{\sqrt{x^2 - 1}}{6x - 1}$, $e^{-\frac{4x^2 - 1}{x}}$, and $\sqrt{\log_3(x^2 - 1)}$ are written in closed form, so they are all closed-form functions.

2. $f(x) = \begin{cases} -1 & \text{if } x \leq -1 \\ x^2 + x & \text{if } -1 < x \leq 1 \\ 2 - x & \text{if } 1 < x \leq 2 \end{cases}$ is not written in closed-form because $f(x)$ is not expressed by a *single* mathematical formula.*

What is so special about closed-form functions is the following theorem.

Theorem 3.1 Continuity of Closed-Form Functions

Every closed-form function is continuous on its domain. Thus, if f is a closed-form function and $f(a)$ is defined, we have $\lim_{x \to a} f(x) = f(a)$.

Quick Example

$f(x) = 1/x$ is a closed-form function, and its natural domain consists of all real numbers except 0. Thus, f is continuous at every nonzero real number. That is,

$$\lim_{x \to a} \frac{1}{x} = \frac{1}{a}$$

provided $a \neq 0$.

Mathematics majors spend a great deal of time studying the proof of this theorem. We ask you to accept it without proof.

EXAMPLE 1 Limit of a Closed-Form Function at a Point in Its Domain

Evaluate $\lim_{x \to 1} \dfrac{x^3 - 8}{x - 2}$ algebraically.

Solution First, notice that $(x^3 - 8)/(x - 2)$ is a closed-form function because it is specified by a single algebraic formula. Also, $x = 1$ is in the domain of this function. Therefore,

$$\lim_{x \to 1} \frac{x^3 - 8}{x - 2} = \frac{1^3 - 8}{1 - 2} = 7.$$

➡ **Before we go on...** In Example 1, the point $x = 2$ is not in the domain of the function $(x^3 - 8)/(x - 2)$, so we cannot evaluate $\lim_{x \to 2} \dfrac{x^3 - 8}{x - 2}$ by substituting $x = 2$. However— and this is the key to finding such limits—some preliminary algebraic simplification will allow us to obtain a closed-form function with $x = 2$ in its domain, as we shall see in Example 2. ∎

EXAMPLE 2 Limit of a Closed-Form Function at a Point Not in Its Domain: Simplifying to Obtain the Limit

Evaluate $\lim_{x \to 2} \dfrac{x^3 - 8}{x - 2}$ algebraically.

Solution Again, although $(x^3 - 8)/(x - 2)$ is a closed-form function, $x = 2$ is not in its domain. Thus, we cannot obtain the limit by substitution. Instead, we first simplify $f(x)$ to obtain a new function with $x = 2$ in its domain. To do this, notice first that the numerator can be factored as

$$x^3 - 8 = (x - 2)(x^2 + 2x + 4).$$

Thus,

$$\frac{x^3 - 8}{x - 2} = \frac{(x - 2)(x^2 + 2x + 4)}{x - 2} = x^2 + 2x + 4.$$

Once we have canceled the offending $(x - 2)$ in the denominator, we are left with a closed-form function *with 2 in its domain.* Thus,

$$\lim_{x \to 2} \frac{x^3 - 8}{x - 2} = \lim_{x \to 2} (x^2 + 2x + 4)$$
$$= 2^2 + 2(2) + 4 = 12. \quad \text{Substitute } x = 2.$$

This confirms the answer we found numerically in Example 1 in Section 3.1.

➡ **Before we go on...** Notice that in Example 2, before simplification, the substitution $x = 2$ yields

$$\frac{x^3 - 8}{x - 2} = \frac{8 - 8}{2 - 2} = \frac{0}{0}.$$

Worse than the fact that 0/0 is undefined, it also conveys absolutely no information as to what the limit might be. (The limit turned out to be 12!) We therefore call the expression 0/0 an **indeterminate form.** Once simplified, the function became $x^2 + 2x + 4$, which, upon the substitution $x = 2$, yielded 12—no longer an indeterminate form. In general, we have the following rule of thumb:

If the substitution $x = a$ yields the indeterminate form 0/0, try simplifying by the method in Example 2.

We will say more about indeterminate forms in Example 3. ∎

Q: *There is something suspicious about Example 2. If 2 was not in the domain before simplifying but was in the domain after simplifying, we must have changed the function, right?*

A: Correct. In fact, when we said that

$$\frac{x^3 - 8}{x - 2} = x^2 + 2x + 4$$

Domain excludes 2   Domain includes 2

we were lying a little bit. What we really meant is that these two expressions are equal *where both are defined.* The functions $(x^3 - 8)/(x - 2)$ and $x^2 + 2x + 4$ are different functions. The difference is that $x = 2$ is not in the domain of $(x^3 - 8)/(x - 2)$ and is in the domain of $x^2 + 2x + 4$. Since $\lim_{x \to 2} f(x)$ explicitly *ignores* any value that f may have at 2, this does not affect the limit. From the point of view of the limit at 2, these functions *are* equal. In general we have the following rule.

Functions with Equal Limits

If $f(x) = g(x)$ for all x except possibly $x = a$, then

$$\lim_{x \to a} f(x) = \lim_{x \to a} g(x).$$

Quick Example

$\dfrac{x^2 - 1}{x - 1} = x + 1$ for all x except $x = 1$.   Write $\dfrac{x^2 - 1}{x - 1}$ as $\dfrac{(x + 1)(x - 1)}{x - 1}$
and cancel the $(x - 1)$

Therefore,

$$\lim_{x \to 1} \frac{x^2 - 1}{x - 1} = \lim_{x \to 1} (x + 1) = 1 + 1 = 2.$$

Q : *How do we find* $\lim_{x \to a} f(x)$ *when* $x = a$ *is not in the domain of the function f, and we cannot simplify the given function to make a a point of the domain?*

A : In such a case, it might be necessary to analyze the function by some other method, such as numerically or graphically. However, if we do not obtain the indeterminate form 0/0 upon substitution, we can often say what the limit is, as the following example shows.

EXAMPLE 3 Limit of a Closed-Form Function at a Point Not in Its Domain: The Determinate Form *k*/0

Evaluate the following limits, if they exist:

a. $\lim\limits_{x \to 1^+} \dfrac{x^2 - 4x + 1}{x - 1}$ **b.** $\lim\limits_{x \to 1} \dfrac{x^2 - 4x + 1}{x - 1}$ **c.** $\lim\limits_{x \to 1} \dfrac{x^2 - 4x + 1}{x^2 - 2x + 1}$

Solution

a. Although the function $f(x) = \dfrac{x^2 - 4x + 1}{x - 1}$ is a closed-form function, $x = 1$ is not in its domain. Notice that substituting $x = 1$ gives

$$\frac{x^2 - 4x + 1}{x - 1} = \frac{1^2 - 4 + 1}{1 - 1} = \frac{-2}{0} \qquad \text{The \textbf{determinate} form } \frac{k}{0}$$

which, although not defined, conveys important information to us: As x gets closer and closer to 1, the numerator approaches -2 and the denominator gets closer and closer to 0. Now, if we divide a number close to -2 by a number close to zero, we get a number of large absolute value; for instance

$$\frac{-2.1}{0.0001} = -21,000 \qquad \text{and} \qquad \frac{-2.1}{-0.0001} = 21,000$$

$$\frac{-2.01}{0.00001} = -201,000 \qquad \text{and} \qquad \frac{-2.01}{-0.00001} = 201,000.$$

(Compare Example 5 in Section 3.1.) In our limit for part (a), x is approaching 1 from the right, so the denominator $x - 1$ is positive (as x is to the right of 1). Thus we have the scenario illustrated previously on the left, and we can conclude that

$$\lim_{x \to 1^+} \frac{x^2 - 4x + 1}{x - 1} = -\infty.$$ Think of this as $\frac{-2}{0^+} = -\infty$.

b. This time, x could be approaching 1 from either side. We already have, from part (a)

$$\lim_{x \to 1^+} \frac{x^2 - 4x + 1}{x - 1} = -\infty.$$

The same reasoning we used in part (a) gives

$$\lim_{x \to 1^-} \frac{x^2 - 4x + 1}{x - 1} = +\infty$$ Think of this as $\frac{-2}{0^-} = +\infty$.

because now the denominator is negative and still approaching zero while the numerator still approaches -2 and therefore is also negative. (See the numerical calculations above on the right.) Because the left and right limits do not agree, we conclude that

$$\lim_{x \to 1} \frac{x^2 - 4x + 1}{x - 1} \text{ does not exist.}$$

c. First notice that the denominator factors:

$$\lim_{x \to 1} \frac{x^2 - 4x + 1}{x^2 - 2x + 1} = \lim_{x \to 1} \frac{x^2 - 4x + 1}{(x - 1)^2}$$

As x approaches 1, the numerator approaches -2 as before, and the denominator approaches 0. However, this time, the denominator $(x - 1)^2$, being a square, is ≥ 0, regardless of from which side x is approaching 1. Thus, the entire function is negative as x approaches 1, and

$$\lim_{x \to 1} \frac{x^2 - 4x + 1}{(x - 1)^2} = -\infty.$$ $\frac{-2}{0^+} = -\infty$

➡ **Before we go on...** In general, the determinate forms $\frac{k}{0^+}$ and $\frac{k}{0^-}$ will always yield $\pm\infty$, with the sign depending on the sign of the overall expression as $x \to a$. (When we write the form $\frac{k}{0}$ we always mean $k \neq 0$.) This and other determinate forms are discussed further after Example 5.

Figure 16 shows the graphs of $\frac{x^2 - 4x + 1}{x - 1}$ and $\frac{x^2 - 4x + 1}{(x - 1)^2}$ from Example 3. You should check that results we obtained above agree with a geometric analysis of these graphs near $x = 1$.

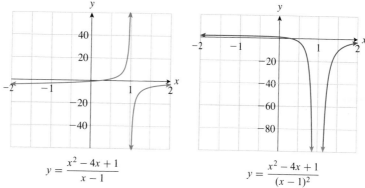

$$y = \frac{x^2 - 4x + 1}{x - 1}$$ $$y = \frac{x^2 - 4x + 1}{(x - 1)^2}$$

Figure 16

We can also use algebraic techniques to analyze functions that are not given in closed form.

EXAMPLE 4 Functions Not Written in Closed Form

For which values of x are the following piecewise defined functions continuous?

a. $f(x) = \begin{cases} x^2 + 2 & \text{if } x < 1 \\ 2x - 1 & \text{if } x \geq 1 \end{cases}$ **b.** $g(x) = \begin{cases} x^2 - x + 1 & \text{if } x \leq 0 \\ 1 - x & \text{if } 0 < x \leq 1 \\ x - 3 & \text{if } x > 1 \end{cases}$

Solution

a. The function $f(x)$ is given in closed form over the intervals $(-\infty, 1)$ and $[1, +\infty)$. At $x = 1$, $f(x)$ suddenly switches from one closed-form formula to another, so $x = 1$ is the only place where there is a potential problem with continuity. To investigate the continuity of $f(x)$ at $x = 1$, let's calculate the limit there:

$$\lim_{x \to 1^-} f(x) = \lim_{x \to 1^-} (x^2 + 2) \qquad f(x) = x^2 + 2 \text{ for } x < 1.$$
$$= (1)^2 + 2 = 3 \qquad x^2 + 2 \text{ is closed-form.}$$
$$\lim_{x \to 1^+} f(x) = \lim_{x \to 1^+} (2x - 1) \qquad f(x) = 2x - 1 \text{ for } x > 1.$$
$$= 2(1) - 1 = 1. \qquad 2x - 1 \text{ is closed-form.}$$

Because the left and right limits are different, $\lim_{x \to 1} f(x)$ does not exist, and so $f(x)$ is discontinuous at $x = 1$.

b. The only potential points of discontinuity for $g(x)$ occur at $x = 0$ and $x = 1$:

$$\lim_{x \to 0^-} g(x) = \lim_{x \to 0^-} (x^2 - x + 1) = 1$$
$$\lim_{x \to 0^+} g(x) = \lim_{x \to 0^+} (1 - x) = 1.$$

Thus, $\lim_{x \to 0} g(x) = 1$. Further, $g(0) = 0^2 - 0 + 1 = 1$ from the formula, and so

$$\lim_{x \to 0} g(x) = g(0),$$

which shows that $g(x)$ is continuous at $x = 0$. At $x = 1$ we have

$$\lim_{x \to 1^-} g(x) = \lim_{x \to 1^-} (1 - x) = 0$$

$$\lim_{x \to 1^+} g(x) = \lim_{x \to 1^+} (x - 3) = -2$$

so that $\lim_{x \to 1} g(x)$ does not exist. Thus, $g(x)$ is discontinuous at $x = 1$. We conclude that $g(x)$ is continuous at every real number x except $x = 1$.

➡ **Before we go on...** Figure 17 shows the graph of g from Example 4(b). Notice how the discontinuity at $x = 1$ shows up as a break in the graph, whereas at $x = 0$ the two pieces "fit together" at the point $(0, 1)$. ■

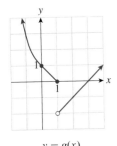

$$y = g(x)$$

Figure 17

Limits at Infinity

Let's look once again at some limits similar to those in Examples 3 and 6 in Section 3.1.

EXAMPLE 5 Limits at Infinity

Compute the following limits, if they exist:

a. $\lim_{x \to +\infty} \dfrac{2x^2 - 4x}{x^2 - 1}$

b. $\lim_{x \to -\infty} \dfrac{2x^2 - 4x}{x^2 - 1}$

c. $\lim_{x \to +\infty} \dfrac{-x^3 - 4x}{2x^2 - 1}$

d. $\lim_{x \to +\infty} \dfrac{2x^2 - 4x}{5x^3 - 3x + 5}$

e. $\lim_{t \to +\infty} e^{0.1t} - 20$

f. $\lim_{t \to +\infty} \dfrac{80}{1 + 2.2(3.68)^{-t}}$

Solution a and **b.** While calculating the values for the tables used in Example 3 in Section 3.1, you might have noticed that the highest power of x in both the numerator and denominator dominated the calculations. For instance, when $x = 100,000$, the term $2x^2$ in the numerator has the value of 20,000,000,000, whereas the term $4x$ has the comparatively insignificant value of 400,000. Similarly, the term x^2 in the denominator overwhelms the term -1. In other words, for large values of x (or negative values with large magnitude),

$$\frac{2x^2 - 4x}{x^2 - 1} \approx \frac{2x^2}{x^2} \qquad \text{Use only the highest powers top and bottom.}$$

$$= 2.$$

Therefore,

$$\lim_{x \to \pm\infty} \frac{2x^2 - 4x}{x^2 - 1} = \lim_{x \to \pm\infty} \frac{2x^2}{x^2}$$

$$= \lim_{x \to \pm\infty} 2 = 2.$$

The procedure of using only the highest powers of x to compute the limit is stated formally and justified after this example.

c. Applying the previous technique of looking only at highest powers gives

$$\lim_{x \to +\infty} \frac{-x^3 - 4x}{2x^2 - 1} = \lim_{x \to +\infty} \frac{-x^3}{2x^2} \qquad \text{Use only the highest powers top and bottom.}$$

$$= \lim_{x \to +\infty} \frac{-x}{2}. \qquad \text{Simplify.}$$

As x gets large, $-x/2$ gets large in magnitude but negative, so the limit is

$$\lim_{x \to +\infty} \frac{-x}{2} = -\infty. \qquad \frac{-\infty}{2} = -\infty \;\; \text{(See below.)}$$

d. $\lim_{x \to +\infty} \dfrac{2x^2 - 4x}{5x^3 - 3x + 5} = \lim_{x \to +\infty} \dfrac{2x^2}{5x^3}$ $\qquad$ Use only the highest powers top and bottom.

$$= \lim_{x \to +\infty} \frac{2}{5x}.$$

As x gets large, $2/(5x)$ gets close to zero, so the limit is

$$\lim_{x \to +\infty} \frac{2}{5x} = 0. \qquad \frac{2}{\infty} = 0 \;\; \text{(See below.)}$$

e. Here we do not have a ratio of polynomials. However, we know that, as t becomes large and positive, so does $e^{0.1t}$, and hence also $e^{0.1t} - 20$. Thus,

$$\lim_{t \to +\infty} e^{0.1t} - 20 = +\infty \qquad e^{+\infty} = +\infty \;\; \text{(See below.)}$$

f. As $t \to +\infty$, the term $(3.68)^{-t} = \dfrac{1}{3.68^t}$ in the denominator, being 1 divided by a very large number, approaches zero. Hence the denominator $1 + 2.2(3.68)^{-t}$ approaches $1 + 2.2(0) = 1$ as $t \to +\infty$. Thus,

$$\lim_{t \to +\infty} \frac{80}{1 + 2.2(3.68)^{-t}} = \frac{80}{1 + 2.2(0)} = 80 \quad {\scriptstyle (3.68)^{-\infty} = 0 \text{ (See below.)}}$$

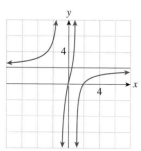

Figure 18

➡ **Before we go on...** Let's now look at the graph of the function $\dfrac{2x^2 - 4x}{x^2 - 1}$ in parts (a) and (b) of Example 5. We say that the graph of f has a **horizontal asymptote** at $y = 2$ because of the limits we have just calculated. This means that the graph approaches the horizontal line $y = 2$ far to the right or left (in this case, to both the right and left). Figure 18 shows the graph of f together with the line $y = 2$.

The graph reveals some additional interesting information: as $x \to 1^+$, $f(x) \to -\infty$, and as $x \to 1^-$, $f(x) \to +\infty$. Thus,

$$\lim_{x \to 1} f(x) \text{ does not exist.}$$

See if you can determine what happens as $x \to -1$.

If you graph the functions in parts (d) and (f) of Example 5, you will again see a horizontal asymptote. Do the limits in parts (c) and (e) show horizontal asymptotes? ■

It is worthwhile looking again at what we did in each of the limits in Example 5:

a and **b.** We saw that $\dfrac{2x^2 - 4x}{x^2 - 1} \approx \dfrac{2x^2}{x^2}$, and then we canceled the x^2. Notice that, before we cancel, letting x approach $\pm\infty$ in the numerator and denominator yields the ratio $\dfrac{\infty}{\infty}$ which, like $\dfrac{0}{0}$, is another *indeterminate form*, and indicates to us that further work is needed—in this case cancellation—before we can write down the limit.

c. We obtained $\dfrac{-x^3 - 4x}{2x^2 - 1} \approx \dfrac{-x^3}{2x^2}$ which results in another indeterminate form, $\dfrac{-\infty}{\infty}$, as $x \to +\infty$. Cancellation of the x^2 gave us $\dfrac{-x}{2}$, resulting in the *determinate* form

$\dfrac{-\infty}{2} = -\infty$ (a very large number divided by 2 is again a very large number).

d. Here, $\dfrac{2x^2 - 4x}{5x^3 - 3x + 5} \approx \dfrac{2x^2}{5x^3} = \dfrac{2}{5x}$, and the cancellation step turns the indeterminate form $\dfrac{\infty}{\infty}$ into the determinate form $\dfrac{2}{\infty} = 0$ (dividing 2 by a very large number yields a very small number).

e. We reasoned that e raised to a large positive number is large and positive. Putting $t = +\infty$ gives us the determinate form $e^{+\infty} = +\infty$.

f. Here we reasoned that 3.68 raised to a large *negative* number is close to zero. Putting $t = +\infty$ gives us the determinate form $3.68^{-\infty} = 1/3.68^{+\infty} = 1/\infty = 0$ (see (d)).

In parts (a)–(d) of Example 5, $f(x)$ was a **rational function**: a quotient of polynomial functions. We calculated the limit of $f(x)$ at $\pm\infty$ by ignoring all powers of x in both the numerator and denominator except for the largest. Following is a theorem that justifies this procedure.

Theorem 3.2 Evaluating the Limit of a Rational Function at $\pm\infty$

If $f(x)$ has the form

$$f(x) = \frac{c_n x^n + c_{n-1} x^{n-1} + \cdots + c_1 x + c_0}{d_m x^m + d_{m-1} x^{m-1} + \cdots + d_1 x + d_0}$$

with the c_i and d_i constants ($c_n \neq 0$ and $d_m \neq 0$), then we can calculate the limit of $f(x)$ as $x \to \pm\infty$ by ignoring all powers of x except the highest in both the numerator and denominator. Thus,

$$\lim_{x \to \pm\infty} f(x) = \lim_{x \to \pm\infty} \frac{c_n x^n}{d_m x^m}.$$

Quick Examples

(See Example 5.)

1. $\displaystyle\lim_{x \to +\infty} \frac{2x^2 - 4x}{x^2 - 1} = \lim_{x \to +\infty} \frac{2x^2}{x^2} = \lim_{x \to +\infty} 2 = 2$

2. $\displaystyle\lim_{x \to +\infty} \frac{-x^3 - 4x}{2x^2 - 1} = \lim_{x \to +\infty} \frac{-x^3}{2x^2} = \lim_{x \to +\infty} \frac{-x}{2} = -\infty$

3. $\displaystyle\lim_{x \to +\infty} \frac{2x^2 - 4x}{5x^3 - 3x + 5} = \lim_{x \to +\infty} \frac{2x^2}{5x^3} = \lim_{x \to +\infty} \frac{2}{5x} = 0$

Proof Our function $f(x)$ is a polynomial of degree n divided by a polynomial of degree m. If n happens to be larger than m, then dividing the top and bottom by the largest power x^n of x gives

$$f(x) = \frac{c_n x^n + c_{n-1}x^{n-1} + \cdots + c_1 x + c_0}{d_m x^m + d_{m-1}x^{m-1} + \cdots + d_1 x + d_0}$$

$$= \frac{c_n x^n/x^n + c_{n-1}x^{n-1}/x^n + \cdots + c_1 x/x^n + c_0/x^n}{d_m x^m/x^n + d_{m-1}x^{m-1}/x^n + \cdots + d_1 x/x^n + d_0/x^n}.$$

Canceling powers of x in each term and remembering that $n > m$ leaves us with

$$f(x) = \frac{c_n + c_{n-1}/x + \cdots + c_1/x^{n-1} + c_0/x^n}{d_m/x^{n-m} + d_{m-1}/x^{n-m+1} + \cdots + d_1/x^{n-1} + d_0/x^n}.$$

As $x \to \pm\infty$, all the terms shown in red approach 0, so we can ignore them in taking the limit. (The first term in the denominator happens to approach 0 as well, but we retain it for convenience.) Thus,

$$\lim_{x \to \pm\infty} f(x) = \lim_{x \to \pm\infty} \frac{c_n}{d_m/x^{n-m}} = \lim_{x \to \pm\infty} \frac{c_n x^n}{d_m x^m},$$

as required. The cases when n is smaller than m and $m = n$ are proved similarly by dividing top and bottom by the largest power of x in each case.

Some Determinate and Indeterminate Forms

The following table brings these ideas together with our observations in Example 3.

Some Determinate and Indeterminate Forms

$\dfrac{0}{0}$ and $\pm\dfrac{\infty}{\infty}$ are **indeterminate**; evaluating limits in which these arise requires simplification or further analysis.

The following are **determinate** forms for any nonzero number k:

* **NOTE** The sign gets switched in these forms if k is negative.

$$\frac{k}{0^{\pm}} = \pm\infty \qquad\qquad \frac{k}{\text{Small}} = \text{Big}^* \text{ (See Example 3.)}$$

$$k(\pm\infty) = \pm\infty \qquad\qquad k \times \text{Big} = \text{Big}^*$$

$$k \pm \infty = \pm\infty \qquad\qquad k \pm \text{Big} = \pm\text{Big}^*$$

$$\pm\frac{\infty}{k} = \pm\infty \qquad\qquad \frac{\text{Big}}{k} = \text{Big}^*$$

$$\pm\frac{k}{\infty} = 0 \qquad\qquad \frac{k}{\text{Big}} = \text{Small}$$

and, if k is positive, then

$$k^{+\infty} = +\infty \qquad\qquad k^{\text{Big positive}} = \text{Big}$$

$$k^{-\infty} = 0 \qquad\qquad k^{\text{Big negative}} = \text{Small}$$

Quick Examples

1. $\displaystyle\lim_{x\to 0}\frac{60}{2x^2} = +\infty$ $\qquad\qquad$ $\dfrac{k}{0^+} = +\infty$

2. $\displaystyle\lim_{x\to -1^-}\frac{2x-6}{x+1} = +\infty$ $\qquad\qquad$ $\dfrac{-4}{0^-} = +\infty$

3. $\displaystyle\lim_{x\to -\infty} 3x - 5 = -\infty$ $\qquad\qquad$ $3(-\infty) - 5 = -\infty - 5 = -\infty$

4. $\displaystyle\lim_{x\to +\infty}\frac{2x}{60} = +\infty$ $\qquad\qquad$ $\dfrac{2(\infty)}{60} = \infty$

5. $\displaystyle\lim_{x\to -\infty}\frac{60}{2x} = 0$ $\qquad\qquad$ $\dfrac{60}{2(-\infty)} = 0$

6. $\displaystyle\lim_{x\to +\infty}\frac{60x}{2x} = 30$ $\qquad\qquad$ $\dfrac{\infty}{\infty}$ is indeterminate but we can cancel.

7. $\displaystyle\lim_{x\to -\infty}\frac{60}{e^x - 1} = \frac{60}{0-1} = -60$ $\qquad$ $e^{-\infty} = 0$

FAQs

Strategy for Evaluating Limits Algebraically

Q: *Is there a systematic way to evaluate a limit* $\lim_{x\to a} f(x)$ *algebraically?*

A: The following approach is often successful:

Case 1: *a* Is a Finite Number (Not $\pm\infty$)

1. Decide whether *f* is a closed-form function. If it is not, then find the left and right limits at the values of *x* where the function changes from one formula to another.

2. If *f* is a closed-form function, try substituting $x = a$ in the formula for $f(x)$. Then one of the following three things may happen:

   $f(a)$ is defined. Then $\lim_{x\to a} f(x) = f(a)$.

   $f(a)$ is not defined and has the indeterminate form 0/0. Try to simplify the expression for *f* to cancel one of the terms that gives 0.

   $f(a)$ is not defined and has one of the determinate forms listed above in the above table. Use the table to determine the limit as in the Quick Examples

Case 2: $a = \pm\infty$

Remember that we can use the determinate forms $k^{+\infty} = \infty$ and $k^{-\infty} = 0$ if k is positive. Further, if the given function is a polynomial or ratio of polynomials, use the technique of Example 5: Focus only on the highest powers of *x* and then simplify to obtain either a number *L*, in which case the limit exists and equals *L*, or one of the determinate forms $\pm\infty/k = \pm\infty$ or $\pm k/\infty = 0$.

There is another technique for evaluating certain difficult limits, called *l'Hospital's Rule*, but this uses derivatives, so we'll have to wait to discuss it until Section 4.1.

3.3 EXERCISES

▼ more advanced   ◆ challenging
T indicates exercises that should be solved using technology

In Exercises 1–4 complete the given sentence.

1. The closed-form function $f(x) = \dfrac{1}{x-1}$ is continuous for all x except _____. HINT [See Quick Example on page 211.]

2. The closed-form function $f(x) = \dfrac{1}{x^2-1}$ is continuous for all x except _____. HINT [See Quick Example on page 211.]

3. The closed-form function $f(x) = \sqrt{x+1}$ has $x = 3$ in its domain. Therefore, $\lim_{x\to 3}\sqrt{x+1} =$ ___. HINT [See Example 1.]

4. The closed-form function $f(x) = \sqrt{x-1}$ has $x = 10$ in its domain. Therefore, $\lim_{x\to 10}\sqrt{x-1} =$ ___. HINT [See Example 1.]

In Exercises 5–20 determine if the given limit leads to a determinate or indeterminate form. Evaluate the limit if it exists, or say why if not. HINT [See Example 3 and Quick Examples on page 220.]

5. $\lim_{x\to 0}\dfrac{60}{x^4}$

6. $\lim_{x\to 0}\dfrac{2x^2}{x^2}$

7. $\lim_{x\to 0}\dfrac{x^3-1}{x^3}$

8. $\lim_{x\to 0}\dfrac{-2}{x^2}$

9. $\lim_{x\to -\infty}(-x^2+5)$

10. $\lim_{x\to 0}\dfrac{2x^2+4}{x}$

11. $\lim_{x\to +\infty}4^{-x}$

12. $\lim_{x\to +\infty}\dfrac{60+e^{-x}}{2-e^{-x}}$

13. $\lim_{x\to 0}\dfrac{-x^3}{3x^3}$

14. $\lim_{x\to -\infty}3x^2+6$

15. $\lim_{x\to -\infty}\dfrac{-x^3}{3x^6}$

16. $\lim_{x\to +\infty}\dfrac{-x^6}{3x^3}$

17. $\lim_{x\to -\infty}\dfrac{4}{-x+2}$

18. $\lim_{x\to -\infty}e^x$

19. $\lim_{x\to -\infty}\dfrac{60}{e^x-1}$

20. $\lim_{x\to -\infty}\dfrac{2}{2x^2+3}$

Calculate the limits in Exercises 21–72 algebraically. If a limit does not exist, say why.

21. $\lim_{x\to 0}(x+1)$
HINT [See Example 1.]

22. $\lim_{x\to 0}(2x-4)$
HINT [See Example 1.]

23. $\lim_{x\to 2}\dfrac{2+x}{x}$

24. $\lim_{x\to -1}\dfrac{4x^2+1}{x}$

25. $\lim_{x\to -1}\dfrac{x+1}{x}$

26. $\lim_{x\to 4}(x+\sqrt{x})$

27. $\lim_{x\to 8}(x-\sqrt[3]{x})$

28. $\lim_{x\to 1}\dfrac{x-2}{x+1}$

29. $\lim_{h\to 1}(h^2+2h+1)$

30. $\lim_{h\to 0}(h^3-4)$

31. $\lim_{h\to 3}2$

32. $\lim_{h\to 0}-5$

33. $\lim_{h\to 0}\dfrac{h^2}{h+h^2}$
HINT [See Example 2.]

34. $\lim_{h\to 0}\dfrac{h^2+h}{h^2+2h}$
HINT [See Example 2.]

35. $\lim_{x\to 1}\dfrac{x^2-2x+1}{x^2-x}$

36. $\lim_{x\to -1}\dfrac{x^2+3x+2}{x^2+x}$

37. $\lim_{x\to 2}\dfrac{x^3-8}{x-2}$

38. $\lim_{x\to -2}\dfrac{x^3+8}{x^2+3x+2}$

39. $\lim_{x\to 0+}\dfrac{1}{x^2}$ HINT [See Example 3.]

40. $\lim_{x\to 0+}\dfrac{1}{x^2-x}$ HINT [See Example 3.]

41. $\lim_{x\to -1}\dfrac{x^2+1}{x+1}$

42. $\lim_{x\to -1-}\dfrac{x^2+1}{x+1}$

43. $\lim_{x\to -2+}\dfrac{x^2+8}{x^2+3x+2}$

44. $\lim_{x\to -1}\dfrac{x^2+3x}{x^2+x}$

45. $\lim_{x\to -2}\dfrac{x^2+8}{x^2+3x+2}$

46. $\lim_{x\to -1}\dfrac{x^2+3x}{x^2+2x+1}$

47. $\lim_{x\to 2}\dfrac{x^2+8}{x^2-4x+4}$

48. $\lim_{x\to -1}\dfrac{x^2+3x}{x^2+3x+2}$

49. $\lim_{x\to +\infty}\dfrac{3x^2+10x-1}{2x^2-5x}$ HINT [See Example 5.]

50. $\lim_{x\to +\infty}\dfrac{6x^2+5x+100}{3x^2-9}$ HINT [See Example 5.]

51. $\lim_{x\to +\infty}\dfrac{x^5-1,000x^4}{2x^5+10,000}$

52. $\lim_{x\to +\infty}\dfrac{x^6+3,000x^3+1,000,000}{2x^6+1,000x^3}$

53. $\lim_{x\to +\infty}\dfrac{10x^2+300x+1}{5x+2}$

54. $\lim_{x\to +\infty}\dfrac{2x^4+20x^3}{1,000x^3+6}$

55. $\lim_{x\to +\infty}\dfrac{10x^2+300x+1}{5x^3+2}$

56. $\lim_{x\to +\infty}\dfrac{2x^4+20x^3}{1,000x^6+6}$

57. $\lim_{x\to -\infty}\dfrac{3x^2+10x-1}{2x^2-5x}$

58. $\lim_{x\to -\infty}\dfrac{6x^2+5x+100}{3x^2-9}$

59. $\lim_{x\to -\infty}\dfrac{x^5-1,000x^4}{2x^5+10,000}$

60. $\lim_{x\to -\infty}\dfrac{x^6+3000x^3+1,000,000}{2x^6+1,000x^3}$

61. $\lim_{x\to -\infty}\dfrac{10x^2+300x+1}{5x+2}$

62. $\lim_{x\to -\infty}\dfrac{2x^4+20x^3}{1,000x^3+6}$

63. $\lim_{x\to -\infty}\dfrac{10x^2+300x+1}{5x^3+2}$

64. $\lim_{x\to -\infty}\dfrac{2x^4+20x^3}{1,000x^6+6}$

65. $\lim_{x\to +\infty}(4e^{-3x}+12)$

66. $\lim_{x\to +\infty}\dfrac{2}{5-5.3e^{-3x}}$

67. $\lim_{t\to +\infty}\dfrac{2}{5-5.3(3^{3t})}$

68. $\lim_{t\to +\infty}(4.1-2e^{3t})$

69. $\lim_{t \to +\infty} \dfrac{2^{3t}}{1 + 5.3e^{-t}}$

70. $\lim_{x \to -\infty} \dfrac{4.2}{2 - 3^{2x}}$

71. $\lim_{x \to -\infty} \dfrac{-3^{2x}}{2 + e^x}$

72. $\lim_{x \to +\infty} \dfrac{2^{-3x}}{1 + 5.3e^{-x}}$

In each of Exercises 73–80, find all points of discontinuity of the given function. HINT [See Example 4.]

73. $f(x) = \begin{cases} x + 2 & \text{if } x < 0 \\ 2x - 1 & \text{if } x \geq 0 \end{cases}$

74. $g(x) = \begin{cases} 1 - x & \text{if } x \leq 1 \\ x - 1 & \text{if } x > 1 \end{cases}$

75. $g(x) = \begin{cases} x + 2 & \text{if } x < 0 \\ 2x + 2 & \text{if } 0 \leq x < 2 \\ x^2 + 2 & \text{if } x \geq 2 \end{cases}$

76. $f(x) = \begin{cases} 1 - x & \text{if } x \leq 1 \\ x + 2 & \text{if } 1 < x < 3 \\ x^2 - 4 & \text{if } x \geq 3 \end{cases}$

77. ▼ $h(x) = \begin{cases} x + 2 & \text{if } x < 0 \\ 0 & \text{if } x = 0 \\ 2x + 2 & \text{if } x > 0 \end{cases}$

78. ▼ $h(x) = \begin{cases} 1 - x & \text{if } x < 1 \\ 1 & \text{if } x = 1 \\ x + 2 & \text{if } x > 1 \end{cases}$

79. ▼ $f(x) = \begin{cases} 1/x & \text{if } x < 0 \\ x & \text{if } 0 \leq x \leq 2 \\ 2^{x-1} & \text{if } x > 2 \end{cases}$

80. ▼ $f(x) = \begin{cases} x^3 + 2 & \text{if } x \leq -1 \\ x^2 & \text{if } -1 < x < 0 \\ x & \text{if } x \geq 0 \end{cases}$

APPLICATIONS

81. *Employment in Mexico* The number N of workers employed in manufacturing jobs in Mexico between 1995 and 2004 can be modeled by

$$N(t) = \begin{cases} 0.22t + 3 & \text{if } 0 \leq t \leq 5 \\ -0.15t + 4.85 & \text{if } 5 < t \leq 9 \end{cases} \text{ million jobs}$$

where t is time in years since 1995.[12]

a. Compute $\lim_{t \to 5^-} N(t)$ and $\lim_{t \to 5^+} N(t)$, and interpret each answer. HINT [See Example 4.]

b. Is the function N continuous at $t = 5$? Did the number of workers employed in manufacturing jobs in Mexico experience any abrupt changes during the period 1995–2004?

82. *Mortgage Delinquencies* The percentage P of borrowers in the highest risk category who were delinquent on their payments between 2001 and 2007 can be approximated by

$$P = \begin{cases} -1.8t + 9.7 & \text{if } 0 \leq t \leq 3 \\ 2t - 1.7 & \text{if } 3 < t \leq 6 \end{cases} \text{ percent}$$

where t is time in years since 2001.[13]

a. Compute $\lim_{t \to 3^-} P(t)$ and $\lim_{t \to 3^+} P(t)$, and interpret each answer.

b. Is the function P continuous at $t = 3$? Did the percentage of borrowers who were delinquent on their payments experience any abrupt changes during the period 2001–2007?

83. *Movie Advertising* Movie expenditures, in billions of dollars, on advertising in newspapers from 1995 to 2004 can be approximated by

$$f(t) = \begin{cases} 0.04t + 0.33 & \text{if } t \leq 4 \\ -0.01t + 1.2 & \text{if } t > 4 \end{cases}$$

where t is time in years since 1995.[14]

a. Compute $\lim_{t \to 4^-} f(t)$ and $\lim_{t \to 4^+} f(t)$, and interpret each answer. HINT [See Example 4.]

b. Is the function f continuous at $t = 4$? What does the answer tell you about movie advertising expenditures?

84. *Movie Advertising* The percentage of movie advertising as a share of newspapers' total advertising revenue from 1995 to 2004 can be approximated by

$$p(t) = \begin{cases} -0.07t + 6.0 & \text{if } t \leq 4 \\ 0.3t + 17.0 & \text{if } t > 4 \end{cases}$$

where t is time in years since 1995.[15]

a. Compute $\lim_{t \to 4^-} p(t)$ and $\lim_{t \to 4^+} p(t)$, and interpret each answer. HINT [See Example 4.]

b. Is the function p continuous at $t = 4$? What does the answer tell you about newspaper revenues?

85. *Law Enforcement* The cost of fighting crime in the United States increased steadily in the period 1982–1999. Total spending on police and courts can be approximated, respectively, by[16]

$P(t) = 1.745t + 29.84$ billion dollars $(2 \leq t \leq 19)$
$C(t) = 1.097t + 10.65$ billion dollars $(2 \leq t \leq 19)$

where t is time in years since 1980. Compute $\lim_{t \to +\infty} \dfrac{P(t)}{C(t)}$ to two decimal places and interpret the result. HINT [See Example 5.]

86. *Law Enforcement* Refer to Exercise 85. Total spending on police, courts, and prisons can be approximated, respectively, by[17]

$P(t) = 1.745t + 29.84$ billion dollars $(2 \leq t \leq 19)$
$C(t) = 1.097t + 10.65$ billion dollars $(2 \leq t \leq 19)$
$J(t) = 1.919t + 12.36$ billion dollars $(2 \leq t \leq 19)$

---

[12] Source: *New York Times*, February 18, 2007, p. WK4.

[13] Ibid.

[14] Model by the authors. Source for data: Newspaper Association of America Business Analysis and Research/*New York Times*, May 16, 2005.

[15] Ibid.

[16] Spending is adjusted for inflation and shown in 1999 dollars. Models are based on a linear regression. Source for data: Bureau of Justice Statistics/*New York Times*, February 11, 2002, p. A14.

[17] Ibid.

where t is time in years since 1980. Compute $\lim_{t \to +\infty} \dfrac{P(t)}{P(t) + C(t) + J(t)}$ to two decimal places and interpret the result.

87. Casino Revenues Annual revenues in 1996–2006 from slot machines and video poker machines at **Foxwoods** casino in Connecticut can be modeled by

$$R(t) = 825 - 240e^{-0.4t} \text{ million dollars} \quad (0 \le t \le 10)$$

where t is time in years since 1996.[18] If we extrapolate this model into the indefinite future, compute and interpret $\lim_{t \to +\infty} R(t)$. **HINT** [See Quick Example on page 220.]

88. Casino Revenues Annual revenues in 1996–2006 from slot machines and video poker machines at the **Mohegan Sun** casino in Connecticut can be modeled by

$$R(t) = 1,260 - 1,030e^{-0.1t} \text{ million dollars} \quad (0 \le t \le 10)$$

where t is time in years since 1996.[19] If we extrapolate this model into the indefinite future, compute and interpret $\lim_{t \to +\infty} R(t)$. **HINT** [See Quick Example on page 220.]

Foreign Trade *Annual U.S. imports from China in the years 1996 through 2003 can be approximated by*

$$I(t) = t^2 + 3.5t + 50 \quad (1 \le t \le 8)$$

billion dollars, where t represents time in years since 1995. Annual U.S. exports to China in the same years can be approximated by

$$E(t) = 0.4t^2 + 1.6t + 14 \quad (0 \le t \le 10)$$

billion dollars.[20] Exercises 89 and 90 are based on these models.

89. Assuming that the trends shown in the above models continue indefinitely, calculate the limits

$$\lim_{t \to +\infty} I(t) \text{ and } \lim_{t \to +\infty} \frac{I(t)}{E(t)}$$

algebraically, interpret your answers, and comment on the results. **HINT** [See Example 5.]

90. Repeat Exercise 89, this time calculating

$$\lim_{t \to +\infty} E(t) \text{ and } \lim_{t \to +\infty} \frac{E(t)}{I(t)} \quad \text{HINT [See Example 5.]}$$

91. ▼ *Acquisition of Language* The percentage $p(t)$ of children who can speak in at least single words by the age of t months can be approximated by the equation[21]

$$p(t) = 100 \left(\frac{1 - 12,200}{t^{4.48}} \right). \quad (t \ge 8.5)$$

Calculate $\lim_{t \to +\infty} p(t)$ and interpret the results. **HINT** [See Example 5(e), (f).]

92. ▼ *Acquisition of Language* The percentage $q(t)$ of children who can speak in sentences of five or more words by the age of t months can be approximated by the equation[22]

$$q(t) = 100 \left(1 - \frac{5.27 \times 10^{17}}{t^{12}} \right). \quad (t \ge 30)$$

If p is the function referred to in the preceding exercise, calculate $\lim_{t \to +\infty} [p(t) - q(t)]$ and interpret the result. **HINT** [See Example 5(e), (f).]

COMMUNICATION AND REASONING EXERCISES

93. Describe the algebraic method of evaluating limits as discussed in this section and give at least one disadvantage of this method.

94. What is a closed-form function? What can we say about such functions?

95. ▼ Your friend Karin tells you that $f(x) = 1/(x - 2)^2$ cannot be a closed-form function because it is not continuous at $x = 2$. Comment on her assertion.

96. ▼ Give an example of a function f specified by means of algebraic formulas such that the domain of f consists of all real numbers and f is not continuous at $x = 2$. Is f a closed-form function?

97. Give examples of two limits that lead to two different indeterminate forms, but where both limits exist.

98. Give examples of two limits; one that leads to a determinate form and another that leads to an indeterminate form, but where neither limit exists.

99. ▼ What is wrong with the following statement? If $f(x)$ is specified algebraically and $f(a)$ is defined, then $\lim_{x \to a} f(x)$ exists and equals $f(a)$.

100. ▼ What is wrong with the following statement? $\lim_{x \to -2} \dfrac{x^2 - 4}{x + 2}$ does not exist because substituting $x = -2$ yields $0/0$, which is undefined.

101. ▼ Give the formula for a function that is continuous everywhere except at two points.

102. ▼ Give the formula for a function that is continuous everywhere except at three points.

103. ◆ *The Indeterminate Form* $\infty - \infty$ An indeterminate form not mentioned in Section 3.3 is $\infty - \infty$. Give examples of three limits that lead to this indeterminate form, and where the first limit exists and equals 5, where the second limit diverges to $+\infty$, and where the third exists and equals -5.

104. ◆ *The Indeterminate Form* 1^∞ An indeterminate form not mentioned in Section 3.3 is 1^∞. Give examples of three limits that lead to this indeterminate form, and where the first limit exists and equals 1, where the second limit exists and equals e, and where the third diverges to $+\infty$. **HINT** [For the third, consider modifying the second.]

---

[18] Source for data: Connecticut Division of Special Revenue/*New York Times*, Sept. 23, 2007, p. C1.

[19] Ibid.

[20] Based on quadratic regression using data from the U.S. Census Bureau Foreign Trade Division Web site www.census.gov/foreign-trade/sitc1/ as of December 2004.

[21] The model is the authors' and is based on data presented in the article *The Emergence of Intelligence* by William H. Calvin, *Scientific American*, October, 1994, pp. 101–107.

[22] Ibid.

3.4　Average Rate of Change

Calculus is the mathematics of change, inspired largely by observation of continuously changing quantities around us in the real world. As an example, the New York metro area consumer confidence index C decreased from 100 points in January 2000 to 80 points in January 2002.[23] As we saw in Chapter 1, the **change** in this index can be measured as the difference:

$$\Delta C = \text{Second value} - \text{First value} = 80 - 100 = -20 \text{ points}$$

(The fact that the confidence index decreased is reflected in the negative sign of the change.) The kind of question we will concentrate on is *how fast* the confidence index was dropping. Because C decreased by 20 points in 2 years, we say it averaged a $20/2 = 10$ point drop each year. (It actually dropped less than 10 points the first year and more the second, giving an average drop of 10 points each year.)

Alternatively, we might want to measure this rate in points per month rather than points per year. Because C decreased by 20 points in 24 months, it went down at an average rate of $20/24 \approx 0.833$ points per month.

In both cases, we obtained the average rate of change by dividing the change by the corresponding length of time:

$$\text{Average rate of change} = \frac{\text{Change in } C}{\text{Change in time}} = \frac{-20}{2} = -10 \text{ points per year}$$

$$\text{Average rate of change} = \frac{\text{Change in } C}{\text{Change in time}} = \frac{-20}{24} \approx -0.833 \text{ points per month}$$

Average Rate of Change of a Function Numerically and Graphically

EXAMPLE 1　Standard and Poor's 500

The following table lists the approximate value of Standard and Poor's 500 stock market index (S&P) during the period 2000–2008* ($t = 0$ represents 2000):

t (year)	0	1	2	3	4	5	6	7	8
$S(t)$ S&P 500 Index (points)	1,450	1,200	950	1,000	1,100	1,200	1,250	1,500	1,300

a. What was the average rate of change in the S&P over the 2-year period 2005–2007 (the period $5 \le t \le 7$ or [5, 7] in interval notation); over the 4-year period 2000–2004 (the period $0 \le t \le 4$ or [0, 4]); and over the period [1, 5]?

b. Graph the values shown in the table. How are the rates of change reflected in the graph?

*The values are approximate values midway through the given year. Source: www.finance.google.com.

[23] Figures are approximate. Source: Siena College Research Institute/*New York Times*, February 10, 2002, p. LI.

Solution

a. During the 2-year period [5, 7], the S&P changed as follows:

Start of the period ($t = 5$): $S(5) = 1,200$
End of the period ($t = 7$): $S(7) = 1,500$

Change during the period [5, 7]: $S(7) - S(5) = 300$

Thus, the S&P increased by 300 points in 2 years, giving an average rate of change of 300/2 = 150 points per year. We can write the calculation this way:

$$\text{Average rate of change of } S = \frac{\text{Change in } S}{\text{Change in } t}$$

$$= \frac{\Delta S}{\Delta t}$$

$$= \frac{S(7) - S(5)}{7 - 5}$$

$$= \frac{1,500 - 1,200}{7 - 5} = \frac{300}{2} = 150 \text{ points per year}$$

Interpreting the result: During the period [5, 7] (that is, 2005–2007), the S&P increased at an average rate of 150 points per year.

Similarly, the average rate of change during the period [0, 4] was

$$\text{Average rate of change of } S = \frac{\Delta S}{\Delta t} = \frac{S(4) - S(0)}{4 - 0} = \frac{1,100 - 1,450}{4 - 0}$$

$$= -\frac{350}{4} = -87.5 \text{ points per year.}$$

Interpreting the result: During the period [0, 4] the S&P *decreased* at an average rate of 87.5 points per year.

Finally, during the period [1, 5], the average rate of change was

$$\text{Average rate of change of } S = \frac{\Delta S}{\Delta t} = \frac{S(5) - S(1)}{5 - 1} = \frac{1,200 - 1,200}{5 - 1}$$

$$= \frac{0}{4} = 0 \text{ points per year.}$$

Interpreting the result: During the period [1, 5] the average rate of change of the S&P was zero points per year (even though its value did fluctuate during that period).

b. In Chapter 1, we saw that the rate of change of a quantity that changes linearly with time is measured by the slope of its graph. However, the S&P index does not change linearly with time. Figure 19 shows the data plotted two different ways: (a) as a bar chart and (b) as a piecewise linear graph. Bar charts are more commonly used in the media, but Figure 19(b) illustrates the changing index more clearly.

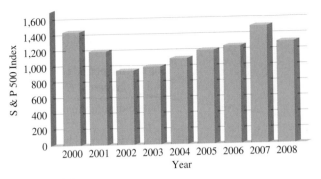

Figure 19(a)

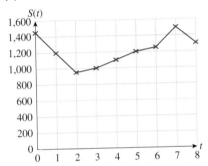

Figure 19(b)

We saw in part (a) that the average rate of change of S over the interval $[5, 7]$ is the ratio

$$\text{Rate of change of } S = \frac{\Delta S}{\Delta t} = \frac{\text{Change in } S}{\text{Change in } t} = \frac{S(7) - S(5)}{7 - 5}.$$

Notice that this rate of change is also the slope of the line through P and Q shown in Figure 20, and we can estimate this slope directly from the graph as shown.

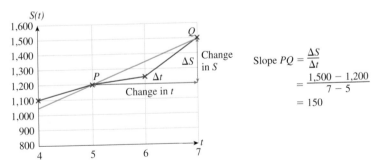

Figure 20

Average Rate of Change as Slope: The average rate of change of the S&P over the interval $[5, 7]$ is the slope of the line passing through the points on the graph where $t = 5$ and $t = 7$.

Similarly, the average rates of change of the S&P over the intervals $[0, 4]$ and $[1, 5]$ are the slopes of the lines through pairs of corresponding points.

Here is the formal definition of the average rate of change of a function over an interval.

Change and Average Rate of Change of *f* over [*a*, *b*]: Difference Quotient

The **change** in $f(x)$ over the interval $[a, b]$ is

Change in $f = \Delta f$

$\qquad$ = Second value − First value

$\qquad$ = $f(b) - f(a)$.

The **average rate of change** of $f(x)$ over the interval $[a, b]$ is

$$\text{Average rate of change of } f = \frac{\text{Change in } f}{\text{Change in } x}$$

$$= \frac{\Delta f}{\Delta x} = \frac{f(b) - f(a)}{b - a}$$

$\qquad\qquad$ = Slope of line through points P and Q (see figure).

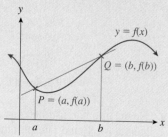

Average rate of change = Slope of PQ

We also call this average rate of change the **difference quotient** of f over the interval $[a, b]$. (It is the *quotient* of the *differences* $f(b) - f(a)$ and $b - a$.) A line through two points of a graph like P and Q is called a **secant line** of the graph.

Units

The units of the change in f are the units of $f(x)$.
The units of the average rate of change of f are units of $f(x)$ per unit of x.

Quick Example

If $f(3) = -1$ billion dollars, $f(5) = 0.5$ billion dollars, and x is measured in years, then the change and average rate of change of f over the interval $[3, 5]$ are given by

$$\text{Change in } f = f(5) - f(3) = 0.5 - (-1) = 1.5 \text{ billion dollars}$$

$$\text{Average rate of change} = \frac{f(5) - f(3)}{5 - 3} = \frac{0.5 - (-1)}{2}$$

$$= 0.75 \text{ billion dollars/year.}$$

Alternative Formula: Average Rate of Change of *f* over [*a*, *a* + *h*]

(Replace b above by $a + h$.) The average rate of change of f over the interval $[a, a + h]$ is

$$\text{Average rate of change of } f = \frac{f(a + h) - f(a)}{h}.$$

In Example 1 we saw that the average rate of change of a quantity can be estimated directly from a graph. Here is an example that further illustrates the graphical approach.

EXAMPLE 2 **Freon Production**

Figure 21 shows a function we looked at in Section 1.1: Let $f(t)$ be the number of tons of ozone-layer damaging Freon 22 (chlorodifluoromethane) produced in year t in developing countries, where $t = 0$ represents the year 2000.*

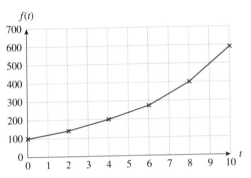

Figure 21

a. Use the graph to estimate the average rate of change of $f(t)$ with respect to t over the interval [4, 8] and interpret the result.

b. Over which 2-year period(s) was the average rate of change of Freon production the greatest?

c. Multiple choice: For the period of time under consideration, Freon production was

(A) increasing at a faster and faster rate.
(B) increasing at a slower and slower rate.
(C) decreasing at a faster and faster rate.
(D) decreasing at a slower and slower rate.

Solution

a. The average rate of change of f over the interval [4, 8] is given by the slope of the line through the points P and Q shown in Figure 22.

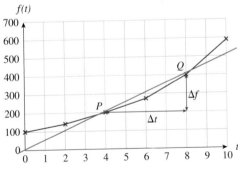

Figure 22

*Source: *New York Times*, February 23, 2007, p. C1.

From the figure,

$$\text{Average rate of change of } f = \frac{\Delta f}{\Delta t} = \text{slope } PQ \approx \frac{400 - 200}{8 - 4} = \frac{200}{4} = 50.$$

Thus, the rate of change of f over the interval $[4, 8]$ is approximately 50.

Q: *How do we interpret the result?*

A: A clue is given by the units of the average rate of change: units of f per unit of t. The units of f are tons of Freon and the units of t are years. Thus, the average rate of change of f is measured in tons of Freon per year, and we can now interpret the result as follows:

Interpreting the average rate of change: Annual production of Freon was increasing at an average rate of 50 tons of Freon per year from 2004 to 2008.

---

b. The rates of change of Freon production over successive 2-year periods are given by the slopes of the individual line segments that make up the graph in Figure 21. Thus, the greatest average rate of change in a single two-year period corresponds to the segment(s) with the largest slope. If you look at the figure, you will notice that the segment corresponding to $[8, 10]$ is the steepest. Thus, the average rate of change of Freon production was largest over the 2-year period from 2008 to 2010.

c. Looking again at the figure, notice that the graph rises as we go from left to right; that is, the value of the function (Freon production) is increasing with increasing t. At the same time, the fact that the curve bends up (is concave up) with increasing t tells us that the successive slopes get steeper, and so the average rates of change increase as well (Choice (A)).

➡ **Before we go on...** Notice in Example 2 that we do not get exact answers from a graph; the best we can do is *estimate* the rates of change: Was the exact answer to part (a) closer to 49 or 51? Two people can reasonably disagree about results read from a graph, and you should bear this in mind when you check the answers to the exercises. ■

Perhaps the most sophisticated way to compute the average rate of change of a quantity is through the use of a mathematical formula or model for the quantity in question.

Average Rate of Change of a Function Using Algebraic Data

EXAMPLE 3 Average Rate of Change from a Formula

You are a commodities trader and you monitor the price of gold on the New York Spot Market very closely during an active morning. Suppose you find that the price of an ounce of gold can be approximated by the function

$$G(t) = -8t^2 + 144t + 150 \text{ dollars} \qquad (7.5 \leq t \leq 10.5)$$

where t is time in hours. (See Figure 23. $t = 8$ represents 8:00 AM.)

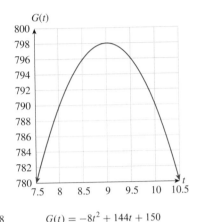

Source: www.kitco.com August 15, 2008

$$G(t) = -8t^2 + 144t + 150$$

Figure 23

Looking at the graph on the right, we can see that the price of gold rose rather rapidly at the beginning of the time period, but by $t = 8.5$ the rise had slowed, until the market faltered and the price began to fall more and more rapidly toward the end of the period. What was the average rate of change of the price of gold over the $1\frac{1}{2}$-hour period starting at 8:00 AM (the interval [8, 9.5] on the t-axis)?

Solution We have

$$\text{Average rate of change of } G \text{ over } [8, 9.5] = \frac{\Delta G}{\Delta t} = \frac{G(9.5) - G(8)}{9.5 - 8}.$$

From the formula for $G(t)$, we find

$$G(9.5) = -8(9.5)^2 + 144(9.5) + 150 = 796$$
$$G(8) = -8(8)^2 + 144(8) + 150 = 790.$$

Thus, the average rate of change of G is given by

$$\frac{G(9.5) - G(8)}{9.5 - 8} = \frac{796 - 790}{1.5} = \frac{6}{1.5} = \$4 \text{ per hour.}$$

In other words, the price of gold was increasing at an average rate of $4 per hour over the given $1\frac{1}{2}$-hour period.

EXAMPLE 4 ▨ **Rates of Change over Shorter Intervals**

Continuing with Example 3, use technology to compute the average rate of change of

$$G(t) = -8t^2 + 144t + 150 \qquad (7.5 \le t \le 10.5)$$

over the intervals $[8, 8 + h]$, where $h = 1, 0.1, 0.01, 0.001,$ and 0.0001. What do the answers tell you about the price of gold?

Solution

We use the alternative formula

$$\text{Average rate of change of } G \text{ over } [a, a+h] = \frac{G(a+h) - G(a)}{h},$$

so

$$\text{Average rate of change of } G \text{ over } [8, 8+h] = \frac{G(8+h) - G(8)}{h}.$$

Let us calculate this average rate of change for some of the values of h listed:

$h = 1$: $G(8+h) = G(8+1) = G(9) = -8(9)^2 + 144(9) + 150 = 798$
$G(8) = -8(8)^2 + 144(8) + 150 = 790$

$$\text{Average rate of change of } G = \frac{G(9) - G(8)}{1} = \frac{798 - 790}{1} = 8$$

$h = 0.1$: $G(8+h) = G(8+0.1) = G(8.1) = -8(8.1)^2 + 144(8.1) + 150 = 791.52$
$G(8) = -8(8)^2 + 144(8) + 150 = 790$

$$\text{Average rate of change of } G = \frac{G(8.1) - G(8)}{0.1} = \frac{791.52 - 790}{0.1} = 15.2$$

$h = 0.01$: $G(8+h) = G(8+0.01) = G(8.01) = -8(8.01)^2 + 144(8.01) + 150$
$= 790.1592$
$G(8) = -8(8)^2 + 144(8) + 150 = 790$

$$\text{Average rate of change of } G = \frac{G(8.01) - G(8)}{0.01} = \frac{790.1592 - 790}{0.01}$$

$$= 15.92$$

Continuing in this way, we get the values in the following table:

h		1	0.1	0.01	0.001	0.0001
Ave. Rate of Change $\dfrac{G(8+h) - G(8)}{h}$		8	15.2	15.92	15.992	15.9992

Each value is an average rate of change of G. For example, the value corresponding to $h = 0.01$ is 15.92, which tells us:

Over the interval [8, 8.01] *the price of gold was increasing at an average rate of* $15.92 *per hour.*

In other words, during the first one-hundredth of an hour (or 36 seconds) starting at $t = 8{:}00$ AM, the price of gold was increasing at an average rate of $15.92 per hour. Put another way, in those 36 seconds, the price of gold increased at a rate that, if continued, would have produced an increase of $15.92 in the price of gold during the next hour. We will return to this example at the beginning of Section 3.5.

using Technology

Example 4 is the kind of example where the use of technology can make a huge difference. See the Technology Guides at the end of the chapter to find out how to do these computations almost effortlessly using a TI-83/84 Plus or Excel. Here is an outline:

TI-83/84 Plus
$Y_1 = -8X^2 + 144X + 150$
Home screen:
$(Y_1(8+1) - Y_1(8))/1$
$(Y_1(8+0.1) - Y_1(8))/0.1$
$(Y_1(8+0.01) - Y_1(8))/0.01$
etc.
[More details on page 280.]

Excel
Headings a, h, t, $G(t)$, Rate of Change in A1–E1
8 in A2, 1 in B2,
=A2 in C2, =A2+B2 in C3
=-8*C2^2+144*C2+150 in D2;
copy down to D3
= (D3-D2)/(C3-C2) in E2
[More details on page 282.]

FAQs

Recognizing When and How to Compute the Average Rate of Change and How to Interpret the Answer

Q : *How do I know, by looking at the wording of a problem, that it is asking for an average rate of change?*

A : If a problem does not ask for an average rate of change directly, it might do so indirectly, as in "On average, how fast is quantity q increasing?"

Q : *If I know that a problem calls for computing an average rate of change, how should I compute it? By hand or using technology?*

A : All the computations can be done by hand, but when hand calculations are not called for, using technology might save time.

Q : *Lots of problems ask us to "interpret" the answer. How do I do that for questions involving average rates of change?*

A : The *units* of the average rate of change are often the key to interpreting the results:

The units of the average rate of change of f(x) are units of f(x) per unit of x.

Thus, for instance, if $f(x)$ is the cost, in dollars, of a trip of x miles in length, and the average rate of change of f is calculated to be 10, then the units of the average rate of change are dollars per mile, and so we can interpret the answer by saying that the cost of a trip rises an average of $10 for each additional mile.

3.4 EXERCISES

▼ more advanced   ◆ challenging
T indicates exercises that should be solved using technology

In Exercises 1–18, calculate the average rate of change of the given function over the given interval. Where appropriate, specify the units of measurement. HINT [See Example 1.]

1.

x	0	1	2	3
$f(x)$	3	5	2	−1

Interval: $[1, 3]$

2.

x	0	1	2	3
$f(x)$	−1	3	2	1

Interval: $[0, 2]$

3.

x	−3	−2	−1	0
$f(x)$	−2.1	0	−1.5	0

Interval: $[−3, −1]$

4.

x	−2	−1	0	1
$f(x)$	−1.5	−0.5	4	6.5

Interval: $[−1, 1]$

5.

t (months)	2	4	6
$R(t)$ ($ millions)	20.2	24.3	20.1

Interval: $[2, 6]$

6.

x (kilos)	1	2	3
$C(x)$ (£)	2.20	3.30	4.00

Interval: $[1, 3]$

7.

p ($)	5.00	5.50	6.00
$q(p)$ (items)	400	300	150

Interval: $[5, 5.5]$

8.

t (hours)	0	0.1	0.2
$D(t)$ (miles)	0	3	6

Interval: $[0.1, 0.2]$

9.

Apple Computer Stock Price ($)

Dec Jan Feb Mar Apr May
2003   2004

Interval: [2, 5]
HINT [See Example 2.]

10.

Cisco Systems Stock Price ($)

Dec   Jan   Feb   Mar   Apr   May
2003   2004

Interval: [1, 5]
HINT [See Example 2.]

11.

Unemployment (%)

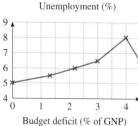

Budget deficit (% of GNP)

Interval: [0, 4]

12.

Inflation (%)

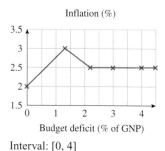

Budget deficit (% of GNP)

Interval: [0, 4]

13. $f(x) = x^2 - 3$; [1, 3] HINT [See Example 3.]

14. $f(x) = 2x^2 + 4$; [−1, 2] HINT [See Example 3.]

15. $f(x) = 2x + 4$; [−2, 0]

16. $f(x) = \dfrac{1}{x}$; [1, 4]

17. $f(x) = \dfrac{x^2}{2} + \dfrac{1}{x}$; [2, 3]   **18.** $f(x) = 3x^2 - \dfrac{x}{2}$; [3, 4]

In Exercises 19–24, calculate the average rate of change of the given function f over the intervals [a, a + h] where h = 1, 0.1, 0.01, 0.001, and 0.0001. (Technology is recommended for the cases h = 0.01, 0.001, and 0.0001) HINT [See Example 4.]

19. $f(x) = 2x^2$; $a = 0$ **20.** $f(x) = \dfrac{x^2}{2}$; $a = 1$

21. $f(x) = \dfrac{1}{x}$; $a = 2$ **22.** $f(x) = \dfrac{2}{x}$; $a = 1$

23. $f(x) = x^2 + 2x$; $a = 3$ **24.** $f(x) = 3x^2 - 2x$; $a = 0$

APPLICATIONS

25. *World Military Expenditure* The following table shows total military and arms trade expenditure in 1994, 1998, and 2006 ($t = 0$ represents 2000).[24]

---

[24] Source: www.globalissues.org/Geopolitics/ArmsTrade/Spending.asp.

Year t	−6	−2	6
Military Expenditure $C(t)$ **($ billion)**	900	800	1,200

Compute and interpret the average rate of change of $C(t)$ **(a)** over the period 1994–2006 (that is, [−6, 6]), and **(b)** over the period [−2, 6]. Be sure to state the units of measurement. HINT [See Example 1.]

26. *Education Expenditure* The following table shows the percentage of the U.S. Discretionary Budget allocated to education in 2003, 2005, and 2009 ($t = 0$ represents 2000).[25]

Year t	3	5	9
Percentage $P(t)$	6.8	7	6.2

Compute and interpret the average rate of change of $P(t)$ **(a)** over the period 2003–2009 (that is, [3, 9]), and **(b)** over the period [5, 9]. Be sure to state the units of measurement. HINT [See Example 1.]

27. *Oil Production in Mexico* The following table shows approximate daily oil production by **Pemex**, Mexico's national oil company, for 2001–2009 ($t = 1$ represents the start of 2001):[26]

t (year since 2000)	1	2	3	4	5	6	7	8	9
$P(t)$ (million barrels)	3.1	3.3	3.4	3.4	3.4	3.3	3.2	3.1	3.0

a. Compute the average rate of change of $P(t)$ over the period 2002–2007. Interpret the result. HINT [See Example 1.]

b. Which of the following is true? From 2001 to 2008, the one-year average rates of change of oil production by **Pemex**

(A) increased in value
(B) decreased in value
(C) never increased in value
(D) never decreased in value
HINT [See Example 2.]

28. *Oil Imports from Mexico* The following table shows U.S. daily oil imports from Mexico, for 2000–2008 ($t = 0$ represents the start of 2000):[27]

t (year since 2000)	0	1	2	3	4	5	6	7	8
$I(t)$ (million barrels)	1.4	1.35	1.5	1.55	1.6	1.5	1.5	1.5	1.2

---

[25] Ibid.

[26] Figures are approximate, and 2008–2009 figures are projections by the Department of Energy. Source: Energy Information Administration/Pemex (http://www.eia.doe.gov).

[27] Ibid.

a. Use the data in the table to compute the average rate of change of $I(t)$ over the period 2001–2006. Interpret the result.

b. Which of the following is true? From 2000 to 2003, the one-year rate of change of oil imports from Mexico

    (A) increased in value
    (B) decreased in value
    (C) never increased in value
    (D) never decreased in value

29. *Subprime Mortgages* The following graph shows the approximate percentage $P(t)$ of mortgages issued in the U.S. that are subprime (normally classified as risky):[28]

Subprime mortgages

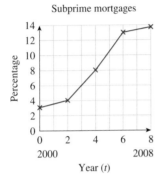

a. Use the graph to estimate, to one decimal place, the average rate of change of $P(t)$ with respect to t over the interval [0, 6] and interpret the result.

b. Over which 2-year period(s) was the average rate of change of $P(t)$ the greatest? **HINT** [See Example 2.]

30. *Subprime Mortgage Debt* The following graph shows the approximate value $V(t)$ of subprime (normally classified as risky) mortgage debt outstanding in the United States:[29]

Subprime debt outstanding

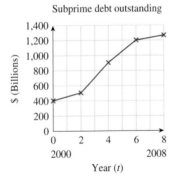

a. Use the graph to estimate, to one decimal place, the average rate of change of $V(t)$ with respect to t over the interval [2, 6] and interpret the result.

b. Over which 2-year period(s) was the average rate of change of $V(t)$ the least? **HINT** [See Example 2.]

31. *iPhone Sales* The following graph shows approximate **Apple** iPhone sales from the 2nd quarter in 2007 through the second quarter in 2008 ($t = 2$ represents the start of the second quarter of 2007):[30]

iPhone sales (thousands)

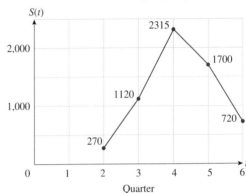

During which 2-quarter interval(s) was the average rate of change of $S(t)$ **(a)** greatest **(b)** least? Interpret your answers by referring to the rates of change. **HINT** [See Example 2.]

32. *Facebook Membership* The following graph gives the approximate number of **Facebook** users at various times since its establishment ($t = 0$ represents the start of 2004).[31]

Facebook membership (millions)

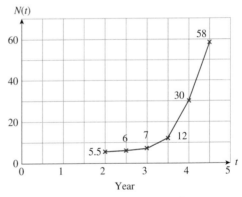

During which 1-year interval(s) was the average rate of change of $N(t)$ **(a)** greatest **(b)** least? Interpret your answers by referring to the rates of change. **HINT** [See Example 2.]

33. ▼ ***Physics Research in the U.S.*** The following table shows the number of research articles in the journal *Physical Review* authored by U.S researchers during the period 1993–2003 ($t = 3$ represents 1993):[32]

t (year since 1990)	3	5	7	9	11	13
$N(t)$ (articles, thousands)	5.1	4.6	4.3	4.3	4.5	4.2

---

[28] Sources: Mortgage Bankers Association, UBS.

[29] 2008 figure is an estimate. Source: www.data360.org/dataset .aspx?Data_Set_Id=9549.

[30] Source: Apple financial statements (www.apple.com).

[31] Sources: Some data are interpolated. (www.facebook.com/, www.insidehighered.com).

[32] Source: The Americal Physical Society/*New York Times*, May 3, 2003, p. A1.

a. Find the interval(s) over which the average rate of change of N was the most negative. What was that rate of change? Interpret your answer.

b. The **percentage change of N over the interval $[a, b]$** is defined to be

$$\text{Percentage change of } N = \frac{\text{Change in } N}{\text{First value}} = \frac{N(b) - N(a)}{N(a)}.$$

Compute the percentage change of N over the interval $[3, 13]$ and also the average rate of change. Interpret the answers.

34. ▼ *Physics Research in Europe* The following table shows the number of research articles in the journal *Physical Review* authored by researchers in Europe during the period 1993–2003 ($t = 3$ represents 1993):[33]

t (year since 1990)	3	5	7	9	11	13
$N(t)$ (articles, thousands)	3.8	4.6	5.0	5.0	6.0	5.7

a. Find the interval(s) over which the average rate of change of N was the most positive. What was that rate of change? Interpret your answer.

b. The **percentage change of N over the interval $[a, b]$** is defined to be

$$\text{Percentage change of } N = \frac{\text{Change in } N}{\text{First value}} = \frac{N(b) - N(a)}{N(a)}.$$

Compute the percentage change of N over the interval $[7, 13]$ and also the average rate of change. Interpret the answers.

35. *College Basketball: Men* The following chart shows the number of NCAA men's college basketball teams in the United States for various years since 2000.[34]

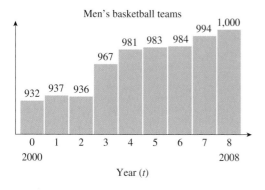

Men's basketball teams

a. On average, how fast was the number of men's college basketball teams growing over the four-year period beginning in 2002?

b. By inspecting the graph, determine whether the four-year average rates of change increased or decreased beginning in 2002. HINT [See Example 2.]

36. *College Basketball: Women* The following chart shows the number of NCAA women's college basketball teams in the United States for various years since 2000.[35]

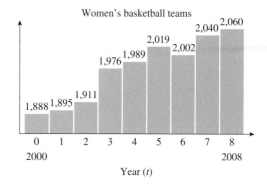

Women's basketball teams

a. On average, how fast was the number of women's college basketball teams growing over the three-year period beginning in 2004?

b. By inspecting the graph, find the three-year period over which the average rate of change was largest. HINT [See Example 2.]

37. ▼ *Funding for the Arts* The following chart shows the total annual support for the arts in the U.S. by federal, state, and local government in 1995–2003 as a function of time in years ($t = 0$ represents 1995) together with the regression line:[36]

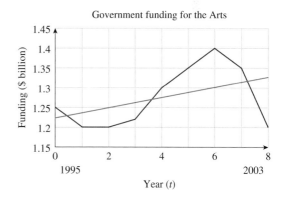

Government funding for the Arts

Multiple choice:

a. Over the period $[0, 4]$ the average rate of change of government funding for the arts was
(A) less than **(B)** greater than **(C)** approximately equal to the rate predicted by the regression line.

b. Over the period $[4, 8]$ the average rate of change of government funding for the arts was
(A) less than **(B)** greater than **(C)** approximately equal to the rate predicted by the regression line.

[33]Source: The Americal Physical Society/*New York Times*, May, 3, 2003, p. A1.

[34]2007 and 2008 figures are estimates. Source: The 2008 Statistical Abstract www.census.gov/.

[35]Ibid.

[36]Figures are adjusted for inflation. Sources: Giving USA, The Foundation Center, Americans for the Arts/*New York Times*, June 19, 2004, p. B7.

c. Over the period [3, 6] the average rate of change of government funding for the arts was
(A) less than   **(B)** greater than   **(C)** approximately equal to the rate predicted by the regression line.

d. Estimate, to two significant digits, the average rate of change of government funding for the arts over the period [0, 8]. (Be careful to state the units of measurement.) How does it compare to the slope of the regression line?

38. ▼ Funding for the Arts The following chart shows the total annual support for the arts in the U.S. by foundation endowments in 1995–2002 as a function of time in years ($t = 0$ represents 1995) together with the regression line:[37]

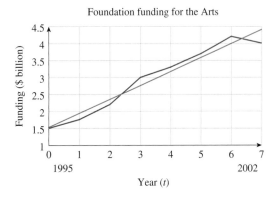

Foundation funding for the Arts

Multiple choice:

a. Over the period [0, 2.5] the average rate of change of government funding for the arts was
(A) less than   **(B)** greater than   **(C)** approximately equal to the rate predicted by the regression line.

b. Over the period [2, 6] the average rate of change of government funding for the arts was
(A) less than **(B)** greater than   **(C)** approximately equal to the rate predicted by the regression line.

c. Over the period [3, 7] the average rate of change of government funding for the arts was
(A) less than   **(B)** greater than   **(C)** approximately equal to the rate predicted by the regression line.

d. Estimate, to two significant digits, the average rate of change of foundation funding for the arts over the period [0, 7]. (Be careful to state the units of measurement.) How does it compare to the slope of the regression line?

39. ▼ Market Volatility During the Dot-com Boom A volatility index generally measures the extent to which a market undergoes sudden changes in value. The volatility of the S&P 500 (as measured by one such index) was decreasing at an average rate of 0.2 points per year during 1991–1995, and was increasing at an average rate of about 0.3 points per year during

1995–1999. In 1995, the volatility of the S&P was 1.1.[38] Use this information to give a rough sketch of the volatility of the S&P 500 as a function of time, showing its values in 1991 and 1999.

40. ▼ Market Volatility During the Dot-com Boom The volatility (see the preceding exercise) of the NASDAQ had an average rate of change of 0 points per year during 1992–1995, and increased at an average rate of 0.2 points per year during 1995–1998. In 1995, the volatility of the NASDAQ was 1.1.[39] Use this information to give a rough sketch of the volatility of the NASDAQ as a function of time.

41. Market Index Joe Downs runs a small investment company from his basement. Every week he publishes a report on the success of his investments, including the progress of the "Joe Downs Index." At the end of one particularly memorable week, he reported that the index for that week had the value $I(t) = 1,000 + 1,500t - 800t^2 + 100t^3$ points, where t represents the number of business days into the week; t ranges from 0 at the beginning of the week to 5 at the end of the week. The graph of I is shown below.

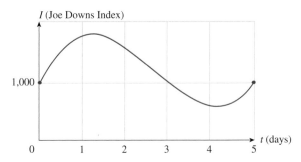

On average, how fast, and in what direction, was the index changing over the first two business days (the interval [0, 2])? HINT [See Example 3.]

42. Market Index Refer to the Joe Downs Index in the preceding exercise. On average, how fast, and in which direction, was the index changing over the last three business days (the interval [2, 5])? HINT [See Example 3.]

43. Crude Oil Prices The price per barrel of crude oil in constant 2008 dollars can be approximated by
$$P(t) = 0.45t^2 - 12t + 105 \text{ dollars} \quad (0 \le t \le 28)$$
where t is time in years since the start of 1980.[40]

a. What, in constant 2008 dollars, was the average rate of change of the price of oil from the start of 1981 ($t = 1$) to the start of 2006 ($t = 26$)? HINT [See Example 3.]

b. Your answer to part (a) is quite small. Can you conclude that the price of oil hardly changed at all over the 25-year period 1981 to 2006? Explain.

[37] Figures are adjusted for inflation. Sources: Giving USA, The Foundation Center, Americans for the Arts/*New York Times*, June 19, 2004, p. B7.

[38] Source for data: Sanford C. Bernstein Company/*New York Times*, March 24, 2000, p. C1.

[39] Ibid.

[40] Source for data: www.inflationdata.com

44. *Median Home Price* The median home price in the U.S. over the period 2004–2009 can be approximated by

$$P(t) = -5t^2 + 75t - 30 \text{ thousand dollars} \qquad (4 \le t \le 9)$$

where t is time in years since the start of 2000.[41]

a. What was the average rate of change of the median home price from the start of 2007 to the start of 2009? HINT [See Example 3.]

b. What, if anything, does your answer to part (a) say about the median home price in 2008? Explain.

45. *SARS* In the early stages of the deadly SARS (Severe Acute Respiratory Syndrome) epidemic in 2003, the number of reported cases can be approximated by

$$A(t) = 167(1.18)^t \qquad (0 \le t \le 20)$$

t days after March 17, 2003 (the first day for which statistics were reported by the World Health Organization).

a. What was the average rate of change of $A(t)$ from March 17 to March 23? Interpret the result.

b. Which of the following is true? For the first 20 days of the epidemic, the number of reported cases
(A) increased at a faster and faster rate
(B) increased at a slower and slower rate
(C) decreased at a faster and faster rate
(D) decreased at a slower and slower rate HINT [See Example 2.]

46. *SARS* A few weeks into the deadly SARS (Severe Acute Respiratory Syndrome) epidemic in 2003, the number of reported cases can be approximated by

$$A(t) = 1,804(1.04)^t \qquad (0 \le t \le 30)$$

t days after April 1, 2003.

a. What was the average rate of change of $A(t)$ from April 19 ($t = 18$) to April 29? Interpret the result.

b. Which of the following is true? During the 30-day period beginning April 1, the number of reported cases
(A) increased at a faster and faster rate
(B) increased at a slower and slower rate
(C) decreased at a faster and faster rate
(D) decreased at a slower and slower rate
HINT [See Example 2.]

47. ▼ *Ecology* Increasing numbers of manatees ("sea sirens") have been killed by boats off the Florida coast. The following graph shows the relationship between the number of boats registered in Florida and the number of manatees killed each year:

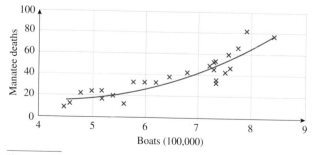

The regression curve shown is given by

$$f(x) = 3.55x^2 - 30.2x + 81 \text{ manatees} \qquad (4.5 \le x \le 8.5)$$

where x is the number of boats (in hundreds of thousands) registered in Florida in a particular year, and $f(x)$ is the number of manatees killed by boats in Florida that year.[42]

a. Compute the average rate of change of f over the intervals [5, 6] and [7, 8].

b. What does the answer to part (a) tell you about the manatee deaths per boat?

48. ▼ *Ecology* Refer to Exercise 47.

a. Compute the average rate of change of f over the intervals [5, 7] and [6, 8].

b. Had we used a linear model instead of a quadratic one, how would the two answers in part (a) be related to each other?

49. ⊞ ▼ *Poverty vs. Income* Based on data from 1988 through 2003, the poverty rate (percentage of households with incomes below the poverty threshold) in the U.S. can be approximated by

$$p(x) = 0.092x^2 - 8.1x + 190 \text{ percentage points} \qquad (38 \le x \le 44)$$

where x is the U.S. median household income in thousands of dollars.[43]

a. Use technology to complete the following table which shows the average rate of change of p over successive intervals of length $\frac{1}{2}$. (Round all answers to two decimal places.) HINT [See Example 4.]

Interval	[39, 39.5]	[39.5, 40]	[40, 40.5]	[40.5, 41]	[41, 41.5]	[41.5, 42]
Average Rate of Change of p						

b. Interpret your answer for the interval [40, 40.5], being sure to indicate the direction of change and the units of measurement.

c. Multiple choice: As the median household income rises, the poverty rate
(A) increases
(B) decreases
(C) increases, then decreases
(D) decreases, then increases

d. Multiple choice: As the median income increases, the effect on the poverty rate is
(A) more pronounced
(B) less pronounced

[42]Regression model is based on data from 1976 to 2000. Sources for data: Florida Department of Highway Safety & Motor Vehicles, Florida Marine Institute/*New York Times*, February 12, 2002, p. F4.

[43]The model is based on a quadratic regression. Household incomes are in constant 2002 dollars. The poverty threshold is approximately $18,000 for a family of four and $9,200 for an individual. Sources: Census Bureau Current Population Survey/*New York Times*, Sept 27, 2003, p. A10/ U.S. Department of Labor Bureau of Labor Statistics www.stats.bls.gov June 17, 2004.

[41]Source for data: www.investmenttools.com.

50. ▣ ▼ *Poverty vs. Unemployment* Based on data from 1988 through 2003, the poverty rate (percentage of households with incomes below the poverty threshold) in the U.S. can be approximated by

$$p(x) = -0.12x^2 + 2.4x + 3.2 \text{ percentage points } (4 \le x \le 8)$$

where x is the unemployment rate in percentage points.[44]

a. Use technology to complete the following table which shows the average rate of change of p over successive intervals of length $\frac{1}{2}$. (Round all answers to two decimal places.)

Interval	[5.0, 5.5]	[5.5, 6.0]	[6.0, 6.5]	[6.5, 7.0]	[7.0, 7.5]	[7.5, 8.0]
Average Rate of Change of p						

b. Interpret your answer for the interval [5.0, 5.5], being sure to indicate the direction of change and the units of measurement. HINT [See Example 4.]

c. Multiple choice: As the median household income rises, the poverty rate
   (A) increases
   (B) decreases
   (C) increases, then decreases
   (D) decreases, then increases

d. Multiple choice: As the unemployment rate increases, the effect on the poverty rate is
   (A) more pronounced
   (B) less pronounced

COMMUNICATION AND REASONING EXERCISES

51. Describe three ways we have used to determine the average rate of change of f over an interval $[a, b]$. Which of the three ways is *least* precise? Explain.

52. If f is a linear function of x with slope m, what is its average rate of change over any interval $[a, b]$?

53. Is the average rate of change of a function over $[a, b]$ affected by the values of the function between a and b? Explain.

54. If the average rate of change of a function over $[a, b]$ is zero, this means that the function has not changed over $[a, b]$, right?

55. Sketch the graph of a function whose average rate of change over $[0, 3]$ is negative but whose average rate of change over $[1, 3]$ is positive.

56. Sketch the graph of a function whose average rate of change over $[0, 2]$ is positive but whose average rate of change over $[0, 1]$ is negative.

[44] The model is based on a quadratic regression. Household incomes are in constant 2002 dollars. The poverty threshold is approximately $18,000 for a family of four and $9,200 for an individual. Sources: Census Bureau Current Population Survey/*New York Times*, Sept 27, 2003, p. A10; U.S. Department of Labor Bureau of Labor Statistics www.stats.bls.gov June 17, 2004.

57. ▼ If the rate of change of quantity A is 2 units of quantity A per unit of quantity B, and the rate of change of quantity B is 3 units of quantity B per unit of quantity C, what is the rate of change of quantity A with respect to quantity C?

58. ▼ If the rate of change of quantity A is 2 units of quantity A per unit of quantity B, what is the rate of change of quantity B with respect to quantity A?

59. ▼ A certain function has the property that its average rate of change over the interval $[1, 1+h]$ (for positive h) increases as h decreases. Which of the following graphs could be the graph of f?

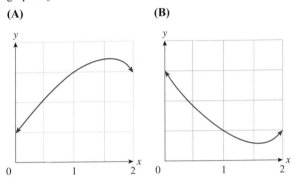

60. ▼ A certain function has the property that its average rate of change over the interval $[1, 1+h]$ (for positive h) decreases as h decreases. Which of the following graphs could be the graph of f?

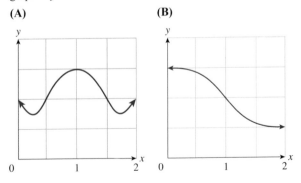

(C)

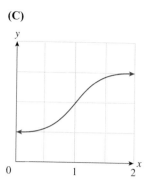

61. ▼ Is it possible for a company's revenue to have a negative 3-year average rate of growth, but a positive average rate of growth in 2 of the 3 years? (If not, explain; if so, illustrate with an example.)

62. ▼ Is it possible for a company's revenue to have a larger 2-year average rate of change than either of the 1-year average rates of change? (If not, explain why with the aid of a graph; if so, illustrate with an example.)

63. ◆ The average rate of change of f over [1, 3] is

(A) always equal to
(B) never equal to
(C) sometimes equal to

the average of its average rates of change over [1, 2] and [2, 3].

64. ◆ The average rate of change of f over [1, 4] is

(A) always equal to
(B) never equal to
(C) sometimes equal to

the average of its average rates of change over [1, 2], [2, 3], and [3, 4].

3.5 Derivatives: Numerical and Graphical Viewpoints

In Example 4 of Section 3.4, we looked at the average rate of change of the function $G(t) = -8t^2 + 144t + 150$, approximating the price of gold on the New York Spot Market, over the intervals $[8, 8 + h]$ for successively smaller values of h. Here are some values we got:

		h getting smaller; interval $[8, 8 + h]$ getting smaller →			
h		1	0.1	0.01	0.001
Average Rate of Change Over $[8, 8 + h]$		8	15.2	15.92	15.992

Rate of change approaching $16 per hour →

The average rates of change of the price of gold over smaller and smaller periods of time, starting at the instant $t = 8$ (8:00 AM), appear to be getting closer and closer to $16 per hour. As we look at these shrinking periods of time, we are getting closer to looking at what happens at the *instant* $t = 8$. So it seems reasonable to say that the average rates of change are approaching the **instantaneous rate of change** at $t = 8$, which the table suggests is $16 per hour. This is how fast the price of gold was changing *exactly* at 8:00 AM.

> *At* $t = 8$, *the instantaneous rate of change of* $G(t)$ *is* 16.

We express this fact mathematically by writing $G'(8) = 16$ (which we read as "G prime of 8 equals 16"). Thus,

> $G'(8) = 16$ *means that, at* $t = 8$, *the instantaneous rate of change of* $G(t)$ *is* 16.

The process of letting h get smaller and smaller is called taking the **limit** as h approaches 0 (as you recognize if you've done the sections on limits). We write $h \to 0$ as shorthand for "h approaches 0." Thus, taking the limit of the average rates of change as $h \to 0$ gives us the instantaneous rate of change.

Q: *All these intervals [8, 8 + h] are intervals to the right of 8. What about small intervals to the left of 8, such as [7.9, 8]?*

A: We can compute the average rate of change of our function for such intervals by choosing h to be negative (h = −0.1, −0.01, etc.) and using the same difference quotient formula we used for positive h:

$$\text{Average rate of change of } G \text{ over } [8 + h, 8] = \frac{G(8) - G(8 + h)}{8 - (8 + h)}$$

$$= \frac{G(8 + h) - G(8)}{h}.$$

Here are the results we get using negative h:

h getting closer to 0; interval $[8 + h, 8]$ getting smaller →

h	−0.1	−0.01	−0.001	−0.0001
Average Rate of Change Over [8 + h, 8]	16.8	16.08	16.008	16.0008

Rate of change approaching $16 per hour →

Notice that the average rates of change are again getting closer and closer to 16 as h approaches 0, suggesting once again that the instantaneous rate of change is $16 per hour.

Instantaneous Rate of Change of f(x) at x = a: Derivative

The **instantaneous rate of change** of $f(x)$ at $x = a$ is defined as

$$f'(a) = \lim_{h \to 0} \frac{f(a + h) - f(a)}{h}.$$

f prime of *a* equals the limit as *h* approaches 0, of the ratio $\dfrac{f(a + h) - f(a)}{h}$

The quantity $f'(a)$ is also called the **derivative of f(x) at x = a.** Finding the derivative of f is called **differentiating f**.

Units
The units of $f'(a)$ are the same as the units of the average rate of change: units of f per unit of x.

Quick Examples

1. If $f(x) = -8x^2 + 144x + 150$, then the two previous tables suggest that

$$f'(8) = \lim_{h \to 0} \frac{f(8 + h) - f(8)}{h} = 16.$$

2. If $f(t)$ is the number of insects in your room at time t hours, and we know that $f(3) = 5$ and $f'(3) = 8$, this means that, at time $t = 3$ hours, there are 5 insects in your room, and this number is growing at an instantaneous rate of 8 insects per hour.

IMPORTANT NOTES

1. Sections 3.1–3.3 discuss limits in some detail. If you have not (yet) covered those sections, you can trust to your intuition.

2. The formula for the derivative tells us that the instantaneous rate of change is the limit of the average rates of change $[f(a + h) - f(a)]/h$ over smaller and smaller intervals. Thus, the value of $f'(a)$ can be approximated by computing the average rate of change for smaller and smaller values of h, both positive and negative.*

3. In this section we will only *approximate* derivatives. In Section 3.6 we will begin to see how we find the *exact* values of derivatives.

4. $f'(a)$ is a number we can calculate, or at least approximate, for various values of a, as we have done in the earlier example. Since $f'(a)$ depends on the value of a, we can think of f' as *a function of a*. (We return to this idea at the end of this section.) An old name for f' is "the function *derived from f*," which has been shortened to the *derivative* of f.

5. It is because f' is a function that we sometimes refer to $f'(a)$ as "the derivative of *f evaluated* at a," or the "derivative of $f(x)$ evaluated at $x = a$."

* **NOTE** If a happens to be an endpoint of the domain of f, then $f'(a)$ can still exist, as the defining limit becomes a one-sided limit; for instance, if f has domain $[2, +\infty)$ then $f'(2)$ would be defined as

$$f'(2) = \lim_{h \to 0^+} \frac{f(2 + h) - f(2)}{h}.$$

It may happen that the average rates of change $[f(a + h) - f(a)]/h$ do not approach any fixed number at all as h approaches zero, or that they approach one number on the intervals using positive h, and another on those using negative h. If this happens, $\lim_{h \to 0}[f(a + h) - f(a)]/h$ does not exist, and we say that f is **not differentiable** at $x = a$, or $f'(a)$ **does not exist**. When the limit *does* exist, we say that f is **differentiable** at the point $x = a$, or $f'(a)$ **exists**. It is comforting to know that all polynomials and exponential functions are differentiable at *every* point. On the other hand, certain functions are not differentiable. Examples are $f(x) = |x|$ and $f(x) = x^{1/3}$, neither of which is differentiable at $x = 0$. (See Section 4.1.)

EXAMPLE 1 Instantaneous Rate of Change: Numerically and Graphically

The air temperature one spring morning, t hours after 7:00 AM, was given by the function $f(t) = 50 + 0.1t^4$ degrees Fahrenheit ($0 \le t \le 4$).

a. How fast was the temperature rising at 9:00 AM?

b. How is the instantaneous rate of change of temperature at 9:00 AM reflected in the graph of temperature vs. time?

Solution

a. We are being asked to find the instantaneous rate of change of the temperature at $t = 2$, so we need to find $f'(2)$. To do this we examine the average rates of change

$$\frac{f(2 + h) - f(2)}{h} \qquad \text{Average rate of change} = \text{difference quotient}$$

for values of h approaching 0. Calculating the average rate of change over $[2, 2 + h]$ for $h = 1, 0.1, 0.01, 0.001$, and 0.0001 we get the following values (rounded to four decimal places):*

* **NOTE** We can quickly compute these values using technology as in Example 4 in Section 3.4. (See the Technology Guides at the end of the chapter.)

h	1	0.1	0.01	0.001	0.0001
Average Rate of Change Over [2, 2 + h]	6.5	3.4481	3.2241	3.2024	3.2002

Here are the values we get using negative values of h:

h	-1	-0.1	-0.01	-0.001	-0.0001
Average Rate of Change Over [2 + h, 2]	1.5	2.9679	3.1761	3.1976	3.1998

The average rates of change are clearly approaching the number 3.2, so we can say that $f'(2) = 3.2$. Thus, at 9:00 in the morning, the temperature was rising at the rate of 3.2 degrees per hour.

b. We saw in Section 3.4 that the average rate of change of f over an interval is the slope of the secant line through the corresponding points on the graph of f. Figure 24 illustrates this for the intervals $[2, 2 + h]$ with $h = 1, 0.5$, and 0.1.

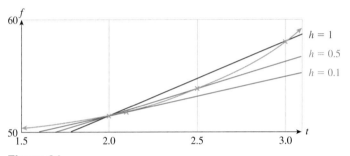

Figure 24

All three secant lines pass though the point $(2, f(2)) = (2, 51.6)$ on the graph of f. Each of them passes through a second point on the curve (the second point is different for each secant line) and this second point gets closer and closer to $(2, 51.6)$ as h gets closer to 0. What seems to be happening is that the secant lines are getting closer and closer to a line that just touches the curve at $(2, 51.6)$: the **tangent line** at $(2, 51.6)$, shown in Figure 25.

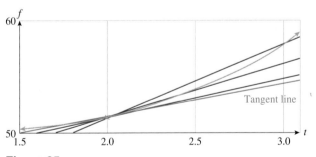

Figure 25

Q: *What is the slope of this tangent line?*

A: Because the slopes of the secant lines are getting closer and closer to 3.2, and because the secant lines are approaching the tangent line, the tangent line must have slope 3.2. In other words,

At the point on the graph where $x = 2$, the slope of the tangent line is $f'(2)$.

Be sure you understand the difference between $f(2)$ and $f'(2)$: Briefly, $f(2)$ is the *value of f* when $t = 2$, while $f'(2)$ is the *rate at which f is changing* when $t = 2$. Here,

$$f(2) = 50 + 0.1(2)^4 = 51.6 \text{ degrees.}$$

Thus, at 9:00 AM ($t = 2$), the temperature was 51.6 degrees. On the other hand,

$$f'(2) = 3.2 \text{ degrees per hour.} \qquad \text{Units of slope are units of } f \text{ per unit of } t.$$

This means that, at 9:00 AM ($t = 2$), the temperature was increasing at a rate of 3.2 degrees per hour.

Because we have been talking about tangent lines, we should say more about what they *are*. A tangent line to a *circle* is a line that touches the circle in just one point. A tangent line gives the circle "a glancing blow," as shown in Figure 26.

For a smooth curve other than a circle, a tangent line may touch the curve at more than one point, or pass through it (Figure 27).

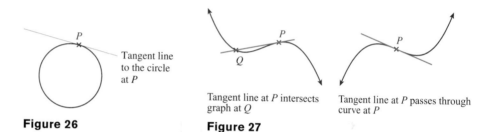

Figure 26

Tangent line to the circle at *P*

Tangent line at *P* intersects graph at *Q*

Tangent line at *P* passes through curve at *P*

Figure 27

However, all tangent lines have the following interesting property in common: If we focus on a small portion of the curve very close to the point *P*—in other words, if we "zoom in" to the graph near the point *P*—the curve will appear almost straight, and almost indistinguishable from the tangent line (Figure 28).

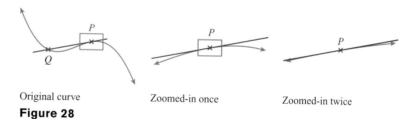

Original curve

Zoomed-in once

Zoomed-in twice

Figure 28

You can check this property by zooming in on the curve shown in Figures 24 and 25 in the previous example near the point where $x = 2$.

Secant and Tangent Lines

The *slope of the secant line* through the points on the graph of f where $x = a$ and $x = a + h$ is given by the average rate of change, or difference quotient,

$$m_{\text{sec}} = \text{slope of secant} = \text{average rate of change} = \frac{f(a + h) - f(a)}{h}.$$

The *slope of the tangent line* through the point on the graph of f where $x = a$ is given by the instantaneous rate of change, or derivative

$$m_{\text{tan}} = \text{slope of tangent} = \text{derivative} = f'(a) = \lim_{h \to 0} \frac{f(a + h) - f(a)}{h}.$$

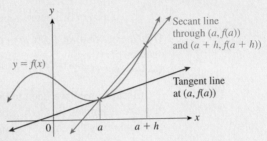

Quick Example

In the following graph, the tangent line at the point where $x = 2$ has slope 3. Therefore, the derivative at $x = 2$ is 3. That is, $f'(2) = 3$.

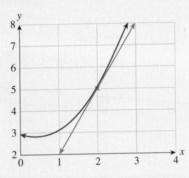

Note It might happen that the tangent line is vertical at some point or does not exist at all. These are the cases in which f is not differentiable at the given point. (See Section 3.6.) ∎

We can now give a more precise definition of what we mean by the tangent line to a point P on the graph of f at a given point: The **tangent line** to the graph of f at the point $P(a, f(a))$ is the straight line passing through P with slope $f'(a)$.

Quick Approximation of the Derivative

Q: *Do we always need to make tables of difference quotients as above in order to calculate an approximate value for the derivative?*

A: We can usually *approximate* the value of the derivative by using a single, small value of h. In the example above, the value $h = 0.0001$ would have given a pretty good approximation. The problems with using a fixed value of h are that (1) we do not get an *exact* answer, only an *approximation* of the derivative, and (2) how good an approximation it is depends on the function we're differentiating.* However, with most of the functions we'll be considering, setting $h = 0.0001$ does give us a good approximation.

✱ **NOTE** In fact, no matter how small the value we decide to use for h, it is possible to craft a function f for which the difference quotient at a is not even close to $f'(a)$.

Calculating a Quick Approximation of the Derivative

We can calculate an approximate value of $f'(a)$ by using the formula

$$f'(a) \approx \frac{f(a+h) - f(a)}{h} \qquad \text{Rate of change over } [a, a+h]$$

with a small value of h. The value $h = 0.0001$ often works (but see the next example for a graphical way of determining a good value to use).

Alternative Formula: The Balanced Difference Quotient

The following alternative formula, which measures the rate of change of f over the interval $[a - h, a + h]$, often gives a more accurate result, and is the one used in many calculators:

$$f'(a) \approx \frac{f(a+h) - f(a-h)}{2h}. \qquad \text{Rate of change over } [a-h, a+h]$$

Note For the quick approximations to be valid, the function f must be differentiable; that is, $f'(a)$ must exist. ∎

EXAMPLE 2 Quick Approximation of the Derivative

a. Calculate an approximate value of $f'(1.5)$ if $f(x) = x^2 - 4x$.

b. Find the equation of the tangent line at the point on the graph where $x = 1.5$.

Solution

a. We shall compute both the ordinary difference quotient and the balanced difference quotient.

Ordinary Difference Quotient: Using $h = 0.0001$, the ordinary difference quotient is:

$$f'(1.5) \approx \frac{f(1.5 + 0.0001) - f(1.5)}{0.0001} \qquad \text{Usual difference quotient}$$

$$= \frac{f(1.5001) - f(1.5)}{0.0001}$$

$$= \frac{(1.5001^2 - 4 \times 1.5001) - (1.5^2 - 4 \times 1.5)}{0.0001} = -0.9999$$

This answer is accurate to 0.0001; in fact, $f'(1.5) = -1$.

Graphically, we can picture this approximation as follows: Zoom in on the curve using the window $1.5 \leq x \leq 1.5001$ and measure the slope of the secant line joining both ends of the curve segment. Figure 29 shows close-up views of the curve and tangent line near the point P in which we are interested, the third view being the zoomed-in view used for this approximation.

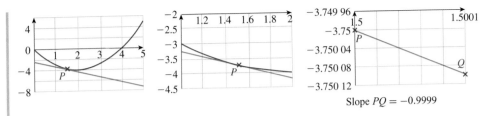

Figure 29

Notice that in the third window the tangent line and curve are indistinguishable. Also, the point P in which we are interested is on the left edge of the window.

Balanced Difference Quotient: For the balanced difference quotient, we get

$$f'(1.5) \approx \frac{f(1.5 + 0.0001) - f(1.5 - 0.0001)}{2(0.0001)} \qquad \text{Balanced difference quotient}$$

$$= \frac{f(1.5001) - f(1.4999)}{0.0002}$$

$$= \frac{(1.5001^2 - 4 \times 1.5001) - (1.4999^2 - 4 \times 1.4999)}{0.0002} = -1.$$

This balanced difference quotient gives the exact answer in this case!* Graphically, it is as though we have zoomed in using a window that puts the point P in the *center* of the screen (Figure 30) rather than at the left edge.

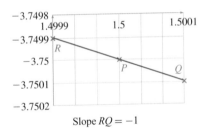

Slope $RQ = -1$

Figure 30

b. We find the equation of the tangent line from a point on the line and its slope, as we did in Chapter 1:

- **Point** $(1.5, f(1.5)) = (1.5, -3.75)$.
- **Slope** $m = f'(1.5) = -1$.   Slope of the tangent line = derivative.

The equation is

$$y = mx + b$$

where $m = -1$ and $b = y_1 - mx_1 = -3.75 - (-1)(1.5) = -2.25$. Thus, the equation of the tangent line is

$$y = -x - 2.25.$$

---

* NOTE The balanced difference quotient always gives the exact derivative for a quadratic function.

using Technology

See the Technology Guides at the end of the chapter to find out how to calculate the quick approximations to the derivative in Example 2 using a TI-83/84 Plus or Excel. Here is an outline:

TI-83/84 Plus

Y_1=X^2-4*X
Home screen:
    (Y_1(1.5001)-Y_1(1.5))/
0.0001
    (Y_1(1.5001)-
Y_1(1.4999))/0.0002
[More details on page 281.]

Excel

Headings a, h, x, f(x), Diff Quotient, Balanced Diff Quotient in A1–F1
    1.5 in A2, 0.0001 in B2,
=A2-B2 in C2, =A2 in C3,
=A2+B2 in C4
=C2^2-4*C2 in D2; copy down to D4
=(D3-D2)/(C3-C2) in E2
=(D4-D2)/(C4-C2) in E3
[More details on page 283.]

Q: Why can't we simply put $h = 0.000\,000\,000\,000\,000\,000\,01$ for an incredibly accurate approximation to the instantaneous rate of change and be done with it?

A: This approach would certainly work if you were patient enough to do the (thankless) calculation by hand! However, doing it with the help of technology—even an ordinary calculator—will cause problems: The issue is that calculators and spreadsheets represent numbers with a maximum number of significant digits (15 in the case of Excel). As the value of h gets smaller, the value of $f(a + h)$ gets closer and closer to the value of $f(a)$. For example, if $f(x) = 50 + 0.1x^4$, Excel might compute

$$f(2 + 0.000\,000\,000\,000\,1) - f(2)$$

$$= 51.600\,000\,000\,000\,3 - 51.6 \qquad \text{Rounded to 15 digits}$$

$$= 0.000\,000\,000\,000\,3$$

and the corresponding difference quotient would be 3, not 3.2 as it should be. If h gets even smaller, Excel will not be able to distinguish between $f(a + h)$ and $f(a)$ at all, in which case it will compute 0 for the rate of change. This loss in accuracy when subtracting two very close numbers is called **subtractive error**.

Thus, there is a trade-off in lowering the value of h: smaller values of h yield *mathematically* more accurate approximations of the derivative, but if h gets too small, subtractive error becomes a problem and decreases the accuracy of computations that use technology.

Leibniz *d* Notation

We introduced the notation $f'(x)$ for the derivative of f at x, but there is another interesting notation. We have written the average rate of change as

$$\text{Average rate of change} = \frac{\Delta f}{\Delta x}. \qquad \frac{\text{Change in } f}{\text{Change in } x}$$

As we use smaller and smaller values for Δx, we approach the instantaneous rate of change, or derivative, for which we also have the notation df/dx, due to Leibniz:

$$\text{Instantaneous rate of change} = \lim_{\Delta x \to 0} \frac{\Delta f}{\Delta x} = \frac{df}{dx}.$$

That is, df/dx is just another notation for $f'(x)$. Do not think of df/dx as an actual quotient of two numbers: remember that we only use an actual quotient $\Delta f/\Delta x$ to *approximate* the value of df/dx.

In Example 3, we apply the quick approximation method of estimating the derivative.

EXAMPLE 3 **Velocity**

* **NOTE** Eric's claim is difficult to believe; 100 ft/s corresponds to around 68 mph, and professional pitchers can throw *forward* at about 100 mph.

My friend Eric, an enthusiastic baseball player, claims he can "probably" throw a ball upward at a speed of 100 feet per second (ft/s).* Our physicist friends tell us that its height s (in feet) t seconds later would be $s = 100t - 16t^2$. Find its average velocity over the interval [2, 3] and its instantaneous velocity exactly 2 seconds after Eric throws it.

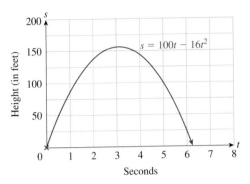

Figure 31

Solution The graph of the ball's height as a function of time is shown in Figure 31. Asking for the velocity is really asking for the rate of change of height with respect to time. (Why?) Consider average velocity first. To compute the **average velocity** of the ball from time 2 to time 3, we first compute the change in height:

$$\Delta s = s(3) - s(2) = 156 - 136 = 20 \text{ ft}$$

Since it rises 20 feet in $\Delta t = 1$ second, we use the defining formula *speed = distance/ time* to get the average velocity:

$$\text{Average velocity} = \frac{\Delta s}{\Delta t} = \frac{20}{1} = 20 \text{ ft/s}$$

from time $t = 2$ to $t = 3$. This is just the difference quotient, so

> *The average velocity is the average rate of change of height.*

To get the **instantaneous velocity** at $t = 2$, we find the instantaneous rate of change of height. In other words, we need to calculate the derivative ds/dt at $t = 2$. Using the balanced quick approximation described earlier, we get

$$\frac{ds}{dt} \approx \frac{s(2 + 0.0001) - s(2 - 0.0001)}{2(0.0001)}$$

$$= \frac{s(2.0001) - s(1.9999)}{0.0002}$$

$$= \frac{100(2.0001) - 16(2.0001)^2 - (100(1.9999) - 16(1.9999)^2)}{0.0002}$$

$$= 36 \text{ ft/s}.$$

In fact, this happens to be the exact answer; the instantaneous velocity at $t = 2$ is exactly 36 ft/s. (Try an even smaller value of h to persuade yourself.)

➡ **Before we go on...** If we repeat the calculation in Example 3 at time $t = 5$, we get

$$\frac{ds}{dt} = -60 \text{ ft/s}$$

The negative sign tells us that the ball is *falling* at a rate of 60 feet per second at time $t = 5$. (How does the fact that it is falling at $t = 5$ show up on the graph?) ■

The preceding example gives another interpretation of the derivative.

Average and Instantaneous Velocity

For an object moving in a straight line with position $s(t)$ at time t, the **average velocity** from time t to time $t + h$ is the average rate of change of position with respect to time:

$$v_{ave} = \frac{s(t+h) - s(t)}{h} = \frac{\Delta s}{\Delta t}$$

Average velocity =
Average rate of change of position

The **instantaneous velocity** at time t is

$$v = \lim_{h \to 0} \frac{s(t+h) - s(t)}{h} = \frac{ds}{dt}$$

Instantaneous velocity =
Instantaneous rate of change of position

In other words, *instantaneous velocity is the derivative of position with respect to time.*

Here is one last comment on Leibniz notation. In Example 3, we could have written the velocity either as s' or as ds/dt, as we chose to do. To write the answer to the question, that the velocity at $t = 2$ sec was 36 ft/s, we can write either

$$s'(2) = 36$$

or

$$\left.\frac{ds}{dt}\right|_{t=2} = 36.$$

The notation "$|_{t=2}$" is read "evaluated at $t = 2$." Similarly, if $y = f(x)$, we can write the instantaneous rate of change of f at $x = 5$ in either functional notation as

$$f'(5) \qquad \text{The derivative of } f, \text{ evaluated at } x = 5$$

or in Leibniz notation as

$$\left.\frac{dy}{dx}\right|_{x=5}. \qquad \text{The derivative of } y, \text{ evaluated at } x = 5$$

The latter notation is obviously more cumbersome than the functional notation $f'(5)$, but the notation dy/dx has compensating advantages. You should practice using both notations.

The Derivative Function

The derivative $f'(x)$ is a number we can calculate, or at least approximate, for various values of x. Because $f'(x)$ depends on the value of x, we may think of f' as a function of x. This function is the **derivative function**.

Derivative Function

If f is a function, its **derivative function** f' is the function whose value $f'(x)$ is the derivative of f at x. Its domain is the set of all x at which f is differentiable. Equivalently, f' associates to each x the slope of the tangent to the graph of the function f at x, or the rate of change of f at x. The formula for the derivative function is

$$f'(x) = \lim_{h \to 0} \frac{f(x+h) - f(x)}{h}.$$ Derivative function

Quick Examples

1. Let $f(x) = 3x - 1$. The graph of f is a straight line that has slope 3 everywhere. In other words, $f'(x) = 3$ for every choice of x; that is, f' is a constant function.

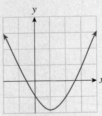

Original Function f
$f(x) = 3x - 1$

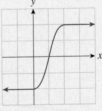

Derivative Function f'
$f'(x) = 3$

2. Given the graph of a function f, we can get a rough sketch of the graph of f' by estimating the slope of the tangent to the graph of f at several points, as illustrated below.*

> **✱ NOTE** This method is discussed in detail on the Web site at Web site → Online Text → Sketching the Graph of the Derivative.

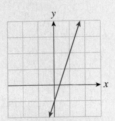

Original Function f
$y = f(x)$

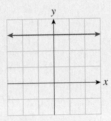

Derivative Function f'
$y = f'(x)$

For x between -2 and 0, the graph of f is linear with slope -2. As x increases from 0 to 2, the slope increases from -2 to 2. For x larger than 2, the graph of f is linear with slope 2. (Notice that, when $x = 1$, the graph of f has a horizontal tangent, so $f'(1) = 0$.)

3. Look again at the graph on the left in Quick Example 2. When $x < 1$ the derivative $f'(x)$ is negative, so the graph has negative slope and f is **decreasing**; its values are going down as x increases. When $x > 1$ the derivative $f'(x)$ is positive, so the graph has positive slope and f is **increasing**; its values are going up as x increases.

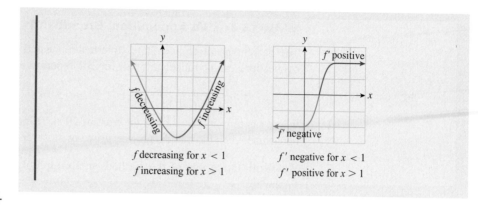

f decreasing for $x < 1$

f increasing for $x > 1$

f' negative for $x < 1$

f' positive for $x > 1$

using Technology

See the Technology Guides at the end of the chapter to find out how to obtain a table of values of and graph the derivative in Example 4 using a TI-83/84 Plus or Excel. Here is an outline:

TI-83/84 Plus

Y₁=-2X^2+6X+5

Y₂=nDeriv(Y₁,X,X)

[More details on page 281.]

Excel

Value of *h* in E2

Values of *x* from A2 down increasing by *h*

-2*A2^2+6*A2+5 from B2 down =(B3-B2)/$E$2 from C2 down

Insert scatter chart using columns A and C [More details on page 283.]

Web Site

www.AppliedCalc.org

Web grapher:

Student Home→Online Utilities→ Function Evaluator and Grapher

Enter

deriv(-2*x^2+6*x+5) for *y₁*. Alternatively, enter -2*x^2+6*x+5 for *y₁* and deriv(y1) for *y₂*.

Excel grapher:

Student Home→Online Utilities→Excel First and Second Derivative Graphing Utility

Function: -2*x^2+6*x+5

The following example shows how we can use technology to graph the (approximate) derivative of a function, where it exists.

EXAMPLE 4 ▯ **Graphing the Derivative with Technology**

Use technology to graph of the derivative of $f(x) = -2x^2 + 6x + 5$ for values of x starting at -5.

Solution The TI-83/84 Plus has a built-in function that approximates the derivative, and we can use it to graph the derivative of a function. In Excel, we need to create the approximation using one of the quick approximation formulas and we can then graph a table of its values. See the Technology Guides at the end of the chapter to find out how to graph the derivative (Figure 32) using the TI-83/84 Plus and Excel.

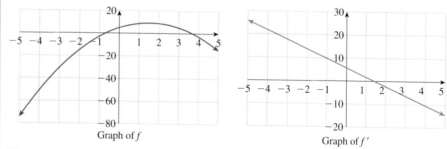

Graph of f

Graph of f'

Figure 32

We said that f' records the slope of (the tangent line to) the function f at each point. Notice that the graph of f' confirms that the slope of the graph of f is decreasing as x increases from -5 to 5. Note also that the graph of f reaches a high point at $x = 1.5$ (the vertex of the parabola). At that point, the slope of the tangent is zero; that is, $f'(1.5) = 0$ as we see in the graph of f'.

EXAMPLE 5 ⓘ An Application: Broadband

The percentage of United States Internet-connected households that have broadband connections can be modeled by the logistic function

$$P(t) = \frac{100}{1 + 10.8(1.7)^{-t}} \qquad (0 \le t \le 9)$$

where t is time in years since the start of 2000.* Graph both P and its derivative, and determine when the percentage was growing most rapidly.

Solution Using one of the methods in Example 4, we obtain the graphs shown in Figure 33.

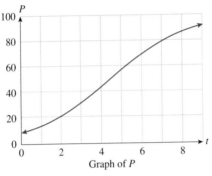
Graph of P

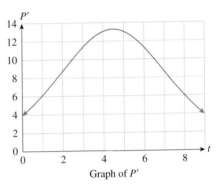
Graph of P'

Figure 33
Technology formula: `100/(1+10.8*1.7^(-x))`

From the graph on the right, we see that P' reaches a peak somewhere between $t = 4$ and $t = 5$ (sometime during 2004). Recalling that P' measures the *slope* of the graph of P, we can conclude that the graph of P is steepest between $t = 4$ and $t = 5$, indicating that, according to the model, the percentage of Internet-connected households with broadband was growing most rapidly during 2004. Notice that this is not so easy to see directly on the graph of P.

To determine the point of maximum growth more accurately, we can zoom in on the graph of P' using the range $4 \le t \le 5$ (Figure 34).

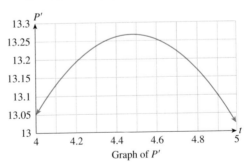
Graph of P'

Figure 34

We can now see that P' reaches its highest point around $t = 4.5$, so we conclude that the percentage of Internet-connected households with broadband was growing most rapidly midway through 2004.

---

*See Example 2 in Section 2.4. Source for data: www.Nielsen.com.

➡ **Before we go on...** Besides helping us to determine the point of maximum growth, the graph of P' in Example 5 gives us a great deal of additional information. As just one example, in Figure 34 we can see that the maximum value of P' is just under 13.3, indicating that the percentage of Internet-connected households that have broadband never grew at a fastest rate of about 13.3 percentage points per quarter. ∎

FAQs

Recognizing When and How to Compute the Instantaneous Rate of Change

Q: *How do I know, by looking at the wording of a problem, that it is asking for an instantaneous rate of change?*

A: If a problem does not ask for an instantaneous rate of change directly, it might do so indirectly, as in "How fast is quantity q increasing?" or "Find the rate of increase of q."

Q: *If I know that a problem calls for estimating an instantaneous rate of change, how should I estimate it: with a table showing smaller and smaller values of h, or by using a quick approximation?*

A: For most practical purposes, a quick approximation is accurate enough. Use a table showing smaller and smaller values of h when you would like to check the accuracy.

Q: *Which should I use in computing a quick approximation: the balanced difference quotient or the ordinary difference quotient?*

A: In general, the balanced difference quotient gives a more accurate answer.

Web Site

At the student Web site at www.AppliedCalc.org you can find the following optional interactive online sections:

- **Continuity and Differentiability**
- **Sketching the Graph of the Derivative**

You can find these sections by following

Chapter 2 → Online Text

3.5 EXERCISES

▼ more advanced   ◆ challenging
T indicates exercises that should be solved using technology

In Exercises 1–4, estimate the derivative from the table of average rates of change. HINT [See discussion at the beginning of the section.]

1.

h	1	0.1	0.01	0.001	0.0001
Average Rate of Change of f Over $[5, 5 + h]$	12	6.4	6.04	6.004	6.0004
h	−1	−0.1	−0.01	−0.001	−0.0001
Average Rate of Change of f Over $[5 + h, 5]$	3	5.6	5.96	5.996	5.9996

Estimate $f'(5)$.

2.

h	1	0.1	0.01	0.001	0.0001
Average Rate of Change of g Over $[7, 7 + h]$	4	4.8	4.98	4.998	4.9998
h	−1	−0.1	−0.01	−0.001	−0.0001
Average Rate of Change of g Over $[7 + h, 7]$	5	5.3	5.03	5.003	5.0003

Estimate $g'(7)$.

3.

h	1	0.1	0.01	0.001	0.0001
Average Rate of Change of r Over $[-6, -6 + h]$	−5.4	−5.498	−5.4998	−5.499982	−5.49999822
h	−1	−0.1	−0.01	−0.001	−0.0001
Average Rate of Change of r Over $[-6 + h, -6]$	−7.52	−6.13	−5.5014	−5.5000144	−5.500001444

Estimate $r'(-6)$.

4.

h	1	0.1	0.01	0.001	0.0001
Average Rate of Change of s Over $[0, h]$	−2.52	−1.13	−0.6014	−0.6000144	−0.600001444
h	−1	−0.1	−0.01	−0.001	−0.0001
Average Rate of Change of s Over $[h, 0]$	−0.4	−0.598	−0.5998	−0.599982	−0.59999822

Estimate $s'(0)$.

Consider the functions in Exercises 5–8 as representing the value of an ounce of palladium in U.S. dollars as a function of the time t in days.[45] Find the average rates of change of R(t) over the time intervals [t, t + h], where t is as indicated and h = 1, 0.1, and 0.01 days. Hence, estimate the instantaneous rate of change of R at time t, specifying the units of measurement. (Use smaller values of h to check your estimates.) HINT [See Example 1.]

5. $R(t) = 60t + 50t - t^2; t = 5$

6. $R(t) = 60t - 2t^2; t = 3$

7. $R(t) = 270 + 20t^3; t = 1$

8. $R(t) = 200 + 50t - t^3; t = 2$

Each of the functions in Exercises 9–12 gives the cost to manufacture x items. Find the average cost per unit of manufacturing h more items (i.e., the average rate of change of the total cost) at a production level of x, where x is as indicated and h = 10 and 1. Hence, estimate the instantaneous rate of change of the total cost at the given production level x, specifying the units of measurement. (Use smaller values of h to check your estimates.) HINT [See Example 1.]

9. $C(x) = 10,000 + 5x - \dfrac{x^2}{10,000}; x = 1,000$

10. $C(x) = 20,000 + 7x - \dfrac{x^2}{20,000}; x = 10,000$

11. $C(x) = 15,000 + 100x + \dfrac{1,000}{x}; x = 100$

12. $C(x) = 20,000 + 50x + \dfrac{10,000}{x}; x = 100$

In Exercises 13–16, the graph of a function is shown together with the tangent line at a point P. Estimate the derivative of f at the corresponding x value. HINT [See Quick Example page 244.]

13.
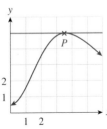

14.
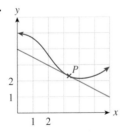

15.
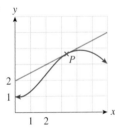

16.
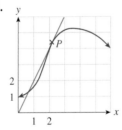

*In each of the graphs given in Exercises 17–22, say at which labeled point the slope of the tangent is **(a)** greatest and **(b)** least (in the sense that −7 is less than 1).* HINT [See Quick Example page 244.]

17.
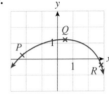

18.
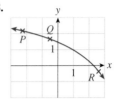

19.
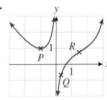

20.
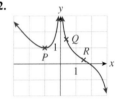

21.
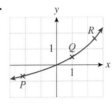

22.
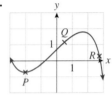

In each of Exercises 23–26, three slopes are given. For each slope, determine at which of the labeled points on the graph the tangent line has that slope.

23. **a.** 0   **b.** 4   **c.** −1
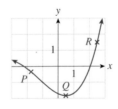

24. **a.** 0   **b.** 1   **c.** −1
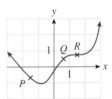

25. **a.** 0   **b.** 3   **c.** −3
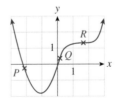

26. **a.** 0   **b.** 3   **c.** 1
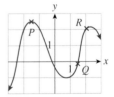

---

[45] Palladium was trading at around $290 in August 2008.

*In each of Exercises 27–30, find the approximate coordinates of all points (if any) where the slope of the tangent is: **(a)** 0, **(b)** 1, **(c)** −1. HINT [See Quick Example page 244.]*

27.

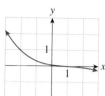

28.

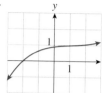

29.

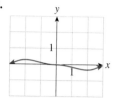

30.

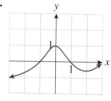

31. Complete the following: The tangent to the graph of the function f at the point where $x = a$ is the line passing through the point _____ with slope _____ .

32. Complete the following: The difference quotient for f at the point where $x = a$ gives the slope of the _____ line that passes through _____ .

33. Which is correct? The derivative function assigns to each value x

(A) the average rate of change of f at x
(B) the slope of the tangent to the graph of f at $(x, f(x))$
(C) the rate at which f is changing over the interval $[x, x + h]$ for $h = 0.0001$
(D) the balanced difference quotient $[f(x + h) - f(x - h)]/(2h)$ for $h \approx 0.0001$

34. Which is correct? The derivative function $f'(x)$ tells us
(A) the slope of the tangent line at each of the points $(x, f(x))$
(B) the approximate slope of the tangent line at each of the points $(x, f(x))$
(C) the slope of the secant line through $(x, f(x))$ and $(x + h, f(x + h))$ for $h = 0.0001$
(D) the slope of a certain secant line through each of the points $(x, f(x))$

35. ▼ Let f have the graph shown.

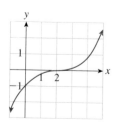

a. The average rate of change of f over the interval $[2, 4]$ is
(A) greater than $f'(2)$ **(B)** less than $f'(2)$
(C) approximately equal to $f'(2)$

b. The average rate of change of f over the interval $[-1, 1]$ is
(A) greater than $f'(0)$ **(B)** less than $f'(0)$
(C) approximately equal to $f'(0)$

c. Over the interval $[0, 2]$, the instantaneous rate of change of f is
(A) increasing   **(B)** decreasing   **(C)** neither

d. Over the interval $[0, 4]$, the instantaneous rate of change of f is
(A) increasing, then decreasing
(B) decreasing, then increasing
(C) always increasing
(D) always decreasing

e. When $x = 4$, $f(x)$ is
(A) approximately 0, and increasing at a rate of about 0.7 units per unit of x
(B) approximately 0, and decreasing at a rate of about 0.7 units per unit of x
(C) approximately 0.7, and increasing at a rate of about 1 unit per unit of x
(D) approximately 0.7, and increasing at a rate of about 3 units per unit of x

36. ▼ A function f has the following graph.

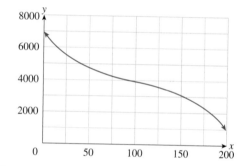

a. The average rate of change of f over $[0, 200]$ is
(A) greater than
(B) less than
(C) approximately equal to
the instantaneous rate of change at $x = 100$.

b. The average rate of change of f over $[0, 200]$ is
(A) greater than
(B) less than
(C) approximately equal to
the instantaneous rate of change at $x = 150$.

c. Over the interval $[0, 50]$ the instantaneous rate of change of f is
(A) increasing, then decreasing
(B) decreasing, then increasing
(C) always increasing
(D) always decreasing

d. On the interval $[0, 200]$, the instantaneous rate of change of f is
(A) always positive   **(B)** always negative
(C) negative, positive, and then negative

e. $f'(100)$ is

    (A) greater than $f'(25)$ **(B)** less than $f'(25)$

    (C) approximately equal to $f'(25)$

In Exercises 37–40, use a quick approximation to estimate the derivative of the given function at the indicated point. HINT [See Example 2(a).]

37. $f(x) = 1 - 2x\,;\, x = 2$ **38.** $f(x) = \dfrac{x}{3} - 1\,;\, x = -3$

39. $f(x) = \dfrac{x^2}{4} - \dfrac{x^3}{3}\,;\, x = -1$ **40.** $f(x) = \dfrac{x^2}{2} + \dfrac{x}{4}\,;\, x = 2$

In Exercises 41–48, estimate the indicated derivative by any method. HINT [See Example 2.]

41. $g(t) = \dfrac{1}{t^5}\,;$ estimate $g'(1)$

42. $s(t) = \dfrac{1}{t^3}\,;$ estimate $s'(-2)$

43. $y = 4x^2\,;$ estimate $\left.\dfrac{dy}{dx}\right|_{x=2}$

44. $y = 1 - x^2\,;$ estimate $\left.\dfrac{dy}{dx}\right|_{x=-1}$

45. $s = 4t + t^2\,;$ estimate $\left.\dfrac{ds}{dt}\right|_{t=-2}$

46. $s = t - t^2\,;$ estimate $\left.\dfrac{ds}{dt}\right|_{t=2}$

47. $R = \dfrac{1}{p}\,;$ estimate $\left.\dfrac{dR}{dp}\right|_{p=20}$

48. $R = \sqrt{p}\,;$ estimate $\left.\dfrac{dR}{dp}\right|_{p=400}$

*In Exercises 49–54, **(a)** use any method to estimate the slope of the tangent to the graph of the given function at the point with the given x-coordinate and **(b)** find an equation of the tangent line in part (a). In each case, sketch the curve together with the appropriate tangent line.* HINT [See Example 2(b).]

49. $f(x) = x^3\,;\, x = -1$ **50.** $f(x) = x^2\,;\, x = 0$

51. $f(x) = x + \dfrac{1}{x}\,;\, x = 2$ **52.** $f(x) = \dfrac{1}{x^2}\,;\, x = 1$

53. $f(x) = \sqrt{x}\,;\, x = 4$ **54.** $f(x) = 2x + 4\,;\, x = -1$

In each of Exercises 55–58, estimate the given quantity.

55. $f(x) = e^x\,;$ estimate $f'(0)$

56. $f(x) = 2e^x\,;$ estimate $f'(1)$

57. $f(x) = \ln x\,;$ estimate $f'(1)$

58. $f(x) = \ln x\,;$ estimate $f'(2)$

In Exercises 59–64, match the graph of f to the graph of f' (the graphs of f' are shown after Exercise 64).

59. ▼

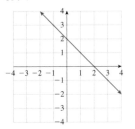

60. ▼

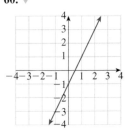

61. ▼

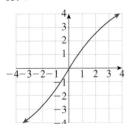

62. ▼

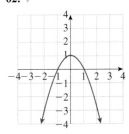

63. ▼

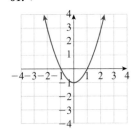

64. ▼

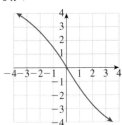

Graphs of derivatives for Exercises 59–64:

(A)

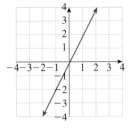

(B)

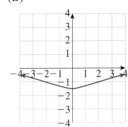

(C)

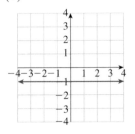

(D)

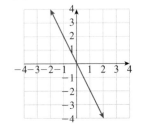

(E)

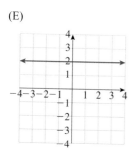

(F)

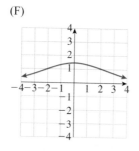

In Exercises 65–68 the graph of a function is given. For which x in the range shown is the function increasing? For which x is the function decreasing? HINT [See Quick Example 3 page 250.]

65.

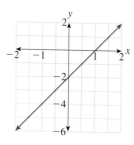

66.

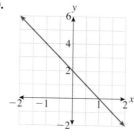

67.

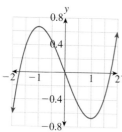

68.

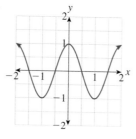

In Exercises 69–72 the graph of the derivative of a function is given. For which x is the (original) function increasing? For which x is the (original) function decreasing? HINT [See Quick Example 3 page 250.]

69.

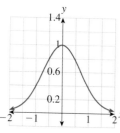

70.

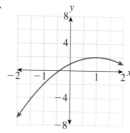

71.

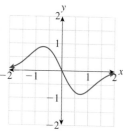

72.

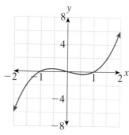

⊤ In Exercises 73 and 74, use technology to graph the derivative of the given function for the given range of values of x. Then use your graph to estimate all values of x (if any) where the tangent line to the graph of the given function is horizontal. Round answers to one decimal place. HINT [See Example 4.]

73. $f(x) = x^4 + 2x^3 - 1$; $-2 \le x \le 1$

74. $f(x) = -x^3 - 3x^2 - 1$; $-3 \le x \le 1$

⊤ In Exercises 75 and 76, use the method of Example 4 to list approximate values of $f'(x)$ for x in the given range. Graph f(x) together with $f'(x)$ for x in the given range.

75. $f(x) = \dfrac{x+2}{x-3}$; $4 \le x \le 5$

76. $f(x) = \dfrac{10x}{x-2}$; $2.5 \le x \le 3$

APPLICATIONS

77. Demand Suppose the demand for a new brand of sneakers is given by

$$q = \frac{5,000,000}{p}$$

where p is the price per pair of sneakers, in dollars, and q is the number of pairs of sneakers that can be sold at price p. Find $q(100)$ and estimate $q'(100)$. Interpret your answers. HINT [See Example 1.]

78. Demand Suppose the demand for an old brand of TV is given by

$$q = \frac{100,000}{p + 10}$$

where p is the price per TV set, in dollars, and q is the number of TV sets that can be sold at price p. Find $q(190)$ and estimate $q'(190)$. Interpret your answers. HINT [See Example 1.]

79. Oil Imports from Mexico The following graph shows approximate daily oil imports to the U.S. from Mexico.[46] Also shown is the tangent line (and its slope) at the point corresponding to year 2005.

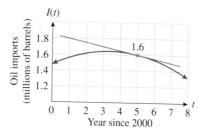

[46] Figures are approximate, and 2008–2009 figures are projections by the Department of Energy. Source: Energy Information Administration/Pemex (http://www.eia.doe.gov).

a. Estimate the slope of the tangent line shown on the graph. What does the graph tell you about oil imports from Mexico in 2005? HINT [Identify two points on the tangent line. Then see Quick Example page 244.]

b. According to the graph, is the rate of change of oil imports from Mexico increasing, decreasing, or increasing then decreasing? Why?

80. *Oil Production in Mexico* The following graph shows approximate daily oil production by **Pemex**, Mexico's national oil company.[47] Also shown is the tangent line (and its slope) at the point corresponding to year 2003.

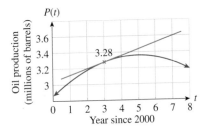

P(t)

Oil production (millions of barrels) vs. Year since 2000

a. Estimate the slope of the tangent line shown on the graph. What does the graph tell you about oil production by **Pemex** in 2003? HINT [Identify two points on the tangent line. Then see Quick Example page 244.]

b. According to the graph, is the rate of change of oil production by **Pemex** increasing or decreasing over the range [0, 4]? Why?

81. ▼ *Prison Population* The following curve is a model of the total population in state prisons as a function of time in years (*t* = 0 represents 1980).[48]

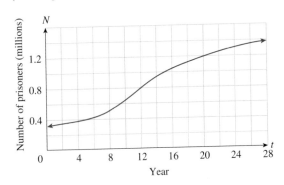

N

Number of prisoners (millions) vs. Year

a. Which is correct? Over the period [16, 20] the instantaneous rate of change of *N* is

(A) increasing   **(B)** decreasing

b. Which is correct? The instantaneous rate of change of prison population at *t* = 12 was

(A) less than   **(B)** greater than
(C) approximately equal to

the average rate of change over the interval [0, 24].

c. Which is correct? Over the period [0, 28] the instantaneous rate of change of *N* is

(A) increasing, then decreasing
(B) decreasing, then increasing
(C) always increasing
(D) always decreasing

d. According to the model, the total state prison population was increasing fastest around what year?

e. Roughly estimate the instantaneous rate of change of *N* at *t* = 16 by using a balanced difference quotient with *h* = 4. Interpret the result.

82. ▼ *Demand for Freon* The demand for chlorofluorocarbon-12 (CFC-12)—the ozone-depleting refrigerant commonly known as Freon[49]—has been declining significantly in response to regulation and concern about the ozone layer. The graph below represents a model for the projected demand for CFC-12 as a function of time in years (*t* = 0 represents 1990).[50]

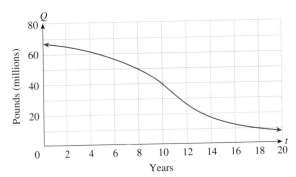

Q

Pounds (millions) vs. Years

a. Which is correct? Over the period [12, 20] the instantaneous rate of change of *Q* is

(A) increasing   **(B)** decreasing

b. Which is correct? The instantaneous rate of change of demand for Freon at *t* = 10 was

(A) less than   **(B)** greater than
(C) approximately equal to

the average rate of change over the interval [0, 20].

c. Which is correct? Over the period [0, 20] the instantaneous rate of change of *Q* is

(A) increasing, then decreasing
(B) decreasing, then increasing
(C) always increasing
(D) always decreasing

d. According to the model, the demand for Freon was decreasing most rapidly around what year?

---

[47] Figures are approximate, and 2008–2009 figures are projections by the Department of Energy. Source: Energy Information Administration/Pemex (http://www.eia.doe.gov).

[48] The prison population represented excludes federal prisons. Source for 1980–2000 data: Bureau of Justice Statistics/*New York Times*, June 9, 2001, p. A10.

[49] The name given to it by DuPont.

[50] Source for data: The Automobile Consulting Group (*New York Times*, December 26, 1993, p. F23). The exact figures were not given, and the chart is a reasonable facsimile of the chart that appeared in *New York Times*.

e. Roughly estimate the instantaneous rate of change of Q at $t = 13$ by using a balanced difference quotient with $h = 5$. Interpret the result.

83. *Velocity* If a stone is dropped from a height of 400 feet, its height after t seconds is given by $s = 400 - 16t^2$.
  a. Find its average velocity over the period $[2, 4]$.
  b. Estimate its instantaneous velocity at time $t = 4$. HINT [See Example 3.]

84. *Velocity* If a stone is thrown down at 120 ft/s from a height of 1,000 feet, its height after t seconds is given by $s = 1,000 - 120t - 16t^2$.
  a. Find its average velocity over the period $[1, 3]$.
  b. Estimate its instantaneous velocity at time $t = 3$. HINT [See Example 3.]

85. *Crude Oil Prices* The price per barrel of crude oil in constant 2008 dollars can be approximated by
$$P(t) = 0.45t^2 - 12t + 105 \text{ dollars} \quad (0 \le t \le 28)$$
where t is time in years since the start of 1980.[51]
  a. Compute the average rate of change of $P(t)$ over the interval $[0, 28]$, and interpret your answer. HINT [See Section 3.4 Example 3.]
  b. Estimate the instantaneous rate of change of $P(t)$ at $t = 0$, and interpret your answer. HINT [See Example 2(a).]
  c. The answers to part (a) and part (b) have opposite signs. What does this indicate about the price of oil?

86. *Median Home Price* The median home price in the U.S. over the period 2004–2009 can be approximated by
$$P(t) = -5t^2 + 75t - 30 \text{ thousand dollars} \quad (4 \le t \le 9)$$
where t is time in years since the start of 2000.[52]
  a. Compute the average rate of change of $P(t)$ over the interval $[5, 9]$, and interpret your answer. HINT [See Section 3.4 Example 3.]
  b. Estimate the instantaneous rate of change of $P(t)$ at $t = 5$, and interpret your answer. HINT [See Example 2(a).]
  c. The answer to part (b) has larger absolute value than the answer to part (a). What does this indicate about the median home price?

87. *SARS* In the early stages of the deadly SARS (Severe Acute Respiratory Syndrome) epidemic in 2003, the number of reported cases can be approximated by
$$A(t) = 167(1.18)^t \quad (0 \le t \le 20)$$
t days after March 17, 2003 (the first day in which statistics were reported by the World Health Organization).
  a. What, approximately, was the instantaneous rate of change of $A(t)$ on March 27 ($t = 10$)? Interpret the result.
  b. Which of the following is true? For the first 20 days of the epidemic, the instantaneous rate of change of the number of cases
    (A) increased   **(B)** decreased
    (C) increased and then decreased
    (D) decreased and then increased

88. *SARS* A few weeks into the deadly SARS (Severe Acute Respiratory Syndrome) epidemic in 2003, the number of reported cases can be approximated by
$$A(t) = 1,804(1.04)^t \quad (0 \le t \le 30)$$
t days after April 1, 2003.
  a. What, approximately, was the instantaneous rate of change of $A(t)$ on April 21 ($t = 20$)? Interpret the result.
  b. Which of the following is true? During April, the instantaneous rate of change of the number of cases
    (A) increased   **(B)** decreased
    (C) increased and then decreased
    (D) decreased and then increased

89. *Sales* Weekly sales of a new brand of sneakers are given by
$$S(t) = 200 - 150e^{-t/10}$$
pairs sold per week, where t is the number of weeks since the introduction of the brand. Estimate $S(5)$ and $\left.\dfrac{dS}{dt}\right|_{t=5}$ and interpret your answers.

90. *Sales* Weekly sales of an old brand of TV are given by
$$S(t) = 100e^{-t/5}$$
sets per week, where t is the number of weeks after the introduction of a competing brand. Estimate $S(5)$ and $\left.\dfrac{dS}{dt}\right|_{t=5}$ and interpret your answers.

91. *Early Internet Online Services* On January 1, 1996, **America Online** was the biggest online service provider, with 4.5 million subscribers, and was adding new subscribers at a rate of 60,000 per week.[53] If $A(t)$ is the number of **America Online** subscribers t weeks after January 1, 1996, what do the given data tell you about values of the function A and its derivative? HINT [See Quick Example 2 on page 240.]

92. *Early Internet Online Services* On January 1, 1996, **Prodigy** was the third-biggest online service provider, with 1.6 million subscribers, but was losing subscribers.[54] If $P(t)$ is the number of **Prodigy** subscribers t weeks after January 1, 1996, what do the given data tell you about values of the function P and its derivative? HINT [See Quick Example 2 on page 240.]

93. ▼ *Learning to Speak* Let $p(t)$ represent the percentage of children who are able to speak at the age of t months.
  a. It is found that $p(10) = 60$ and $\left.\dfrac{dp}{dt}\right|_{t=10} = 18.2$. What does this mean?[55] HINT [See Quick Example 2 on page 240.]
  b. As t increases, what happens to p and $\dfrac{dp}{dt}$?

---

[51] Source for data: www.inflationdata.com.
[52] Source for data: www.investmenttools.com.
[53] Source: Information and Interactive Services Report/*New York Times*, January 2, 1996, p. C14.
[54] Ibid.
[55] Based on data presented in the article *The Emergence of Intelligence* by William H. Calvin, *Scientific American*, October, 1994, pp. 101–107.

94. ▼ *Learning to Read* Let $p(t)$ represent the number of children in your class who learned to read at the age of t years.

    a. Assuming that everyone in your class could read by the age of 7, what does this tell you about $p(7)$ and $\dfrac{dp}{dt}\Big|_{t=7}$?

    HINT [See Quick Example 2 on page 240.]

    b. Assuming that 25.0% of the people in your class could read by the age of 5, and that 25.3% of them could read by the age of 5 years and one month, estimate $\dfrac{dp}{dt}\Big|_{t=5}$.

    Remember to give its units.

95. *Subprime Mortgages* (Compare Exercise 29 of Section 3.4.) The percentage of mortgages issued in the United States that are subprime (normally classified as risky) can be approximated by

$$A(t) = \frac{15}{1 + 8.6(1.8)^{-t}} \quad (0 \le t \le 9)$$

where t is the number of years since the start of 2000.

    a. Estimate $A(6)$ and $A'(6)$. (Round answers to two significant digits.) What do the answers tell you about subprime mortgages?

    b. 🔲 Graph the extrapolated function and its derivative for $0 \le t \le 16$ and use your graphs to describe how the derivative behaves as t becomes large. (Express this behavior in terms of limits if you have studied the sections on limits.) What does this tell you about subprime mortgages? HINT [See Example 5.]

96. *Subprime Mortgage Debt* (Compare Exercise 30 of Section 3.4.) The value of subprime (normally classified as risky) mortgage debt outstanding in the U.S. can be approximated by

$$A(t) = \frac{1{,}350}{1 + 4.2(1.7)^{-t}} \text{ billion dollars} \quad (0 \le t \le 9)$$

where t is the number of years since the start of 2000.

    a. Estimate $A(7)$ and $A'(7)$. (Round answers to three significant digits.) What do the answers tell you about subprime mortgages?

    b. 🔲 Graph the function and its derivative and use your graphs to estimate when, to the nearest year, $A'(t)$ is greatest. What does this tell you about subprime mortgages? HINT [See Example 5.]

97. 🔲 ▼ *Embryo Development* The oxygen consumption of a turkey embryo increases from the time the egg is laid through the time the turkey chick hatches. In a brush turkey, the oxygen consumption (in milliliters per hour) can be approximated by

$$c(t) = -0.0012t^3 + 0.12t^2 - 1.83t + 3.97 \quad (20 \le t \le 50)$$

where t is the time (in days) since the egg was laid.[56] (An egg will typically hatch at around $t = 50$.) Use technology to graph $c'(t)$ and use your graph to answer the following questions. HINT [See Example 5.]

    a. Over the interval [20, 32] the derivative c' is
      (A) increasing, then decreasing
      (B) decreasing, then increasing
      (C) decreasing   **(D)** increasing

    b. When, to the nearest day, is the oxygen consumption increasing at the fastest rate?

    c. When, to the nearest day, is the oxygen consumption increasing at the slowest rate?

98. 🔲 ▼ *Embryo Development* The oxygen consumption of a bird embryo increases from the time the egg is laid through the time the chick hatches. In a typical galliform bird, the oxygen consumption (in milliliters per hour) can be approximated by

$$c(t) = -0.0027t^3 + 0.14t^2 - 0.89t + 0.15 \quad (8 \le t \le 30)$$

where t is the time (in days) since the egg was laid.[57] (An egg will typically hatch at around $t = 28$.) Use technology to graph $c'(t)$ and use your graph to answer the following questions. HINT [See Example 5.]

    a. Over the interval [8, 30] the derivative c' is
      (A) increasing, then decreasing
      (B) decreasing, then increasing
      (C) decreasing   **(D)** increasing

    b. When, to the nearest day, is the oxygen consumption increasing the fastest?

    c. When, to the nearest day, is the oxygen consumption increasing at the slowest rate?

The next two exercises are applications of Einstein's Special Theory of Relativity and relate to objects that are moving extremely fast. In science fiction terminology, a speed of warp 1 is the speed of light—about 3×10^8 meters per second. (Thus, for instance, a speed of warp 0.8 corresponds to 80% of the speed of light—about 2.4×10^8 meters per second.)

99. ◆ *Lorentz Contraction* According to Einstein's Special Theory of Relativity, a moving object appears to get shorter to a stationary observer as its speed approaches the speed of light. If a spaceship that has a length of 100 meters at rest travels at a speed of warp p, its length in meters, as measured by a stationary observer, is given by

$$L(p) = 100\sqrt{1 - p^2}$$

with domain [0, 1). Estimate $L(0.95)$ and $L'(0.95)$. What do these figures tell you?

100. ◆ *Time Dilation* Another prediction of Einstein's Special Theory of Relativity is that, to a stationary observer, clocks (as well as all biological processes) in a moving object appear to go more and more slowly as the speed of the object approaches that of light. If a spaceship travels at a speed of warp p, the time it takes for an onboard clock to register

---

[56] The model approximates graphical data published in the article *The Brush Turkey* by Roger S. Seymour, *Scientific American*, December, 1991, pp. 108–114.

[57] Ibid.

one second, as measured by a stationary observer, will be given by

$$T(p) = \frac{1}{\sqrt{1 - p^2}} \text{ seconds}$$

with domain [0, 1). Estimate $T(0.95)$ and $T'(0.95)$. What do these figures tell you?

COMMUNICATION AND REASONING EXERCISES

101. Explain why we cannot put $h = 0$ in the approximation

$$f'(x) \approx \frac{f(x + h) - f(x)}{h}$$

for the derivative of f.

102. The balanced difference quotient

$$f'(a) \approx \frac{f(a + 0.0001) - f(a - 0.0001)}{0.0002}$$

is the average rate of change of f on what interval?

103. Let $H(t)$ represent the number of Handbook members in millions t years after its inception in 2020. It is found that $H(10) = 50$ and $H'(10) = -6$. This means that, in 2030 (Multiple Choice):

(A) There were 6 million members and this number was decreasing at a rate of 50 million per year

(B) There were –6 million members and this number was increasing at a rate of 50 million per year.

(C) Membership had dropped by 6 million since the previous year, but was now increasing at a rate of 50 million per year

(D) There were 50 million members and this number was decreasing at a rate of 6 million per year.

(E) There were 50 million members and membership had dropped by 6 million since the previous year.

104. Let $F(t)$ represent the net earnings of Footbook Inc. in millions of dollars t years after its inception in 3020. It is found that $F(100) = -10$ and $F'(100) = 60$. This means that, in 3120 (Multiple Choice):

(A) Footbook lost $10 million but its net earnings were increasing at a rate of $60 million per year.

(B) Footbook earned $60 million but its earnings were decreasing at a rate of $10 million per year.

(C) Footbook's net earnings had increased by $60 million since the year before, but it still lost $10 million.

(D) Footbook earned $10 million but its net earnings were decreasing at a rate of $60 million per year.

(E) Footbook's net earnings had decreased by $10 million since the year before, but it still earned $60 million.

105. It is now eight months since the Garden City lacrosse team won the national championship, and sales of team paraphernalia, while still increasing, have been leveling off. What does this tell you about the derivative of the sales curve?

106. Having been soundly defeated in the national lacrosse championships, Brakpan High has been faced with decreasing sales of its team paraphernalia. However, sales, while still decreasing, appear to be bottoming out. What does this tell you about the derivative of the sales curve?

107. ▼ Company A's profits are given by $P(0) = \$1$ million and $P'(0) = -\$1$ million/month. Company B's profits are given by $P(0) = -\$1$ million and $P'(0) = \$1$ million/month. In which company would you rather invest? Why?

108. ▼ Company C's profits are given by $P(0) = \$1$ million and $P'(0) = \$0.5$ million/month. Company D's profits are given by $P(0) = \$0.5$ million and $P'(0) = \$1$ million/month. In which company would you rather invest? Why?

109. ▼ During the one-month period starting last January 1, your company's profits increased at an average rate of change of $4 million per month. On January 1, profits were increasing at an instantaneous rate of $5 million per month. Which of the following graphs could represent your company's profits? Why?

(A)

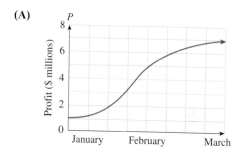

(B)

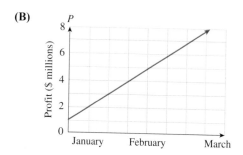

(C)

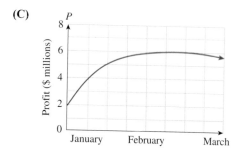

110. ▼ During the one-month period starting last January 1, your company's sales increased at an average rate of change of $3,000 per month. On January 1, sales were changing at an instantaneous rate of –$1,000 per month. Which of the following graphs could represent your company's sales? Why?

(A)

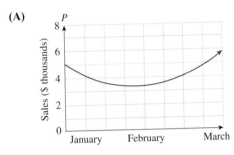

(B)

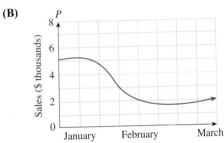

(C)

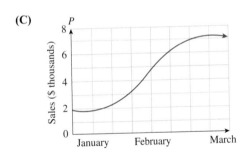

111. ▼ If the derivative of f is zero at a point, what do you know about the graph of f near that point?

112. ▼ Sketch the graph of a function whose derivative never exceeds 1.

113. ▼ Sketch the graph of a function whose derivative exceeds 1 at every point.

114. ▼ Sketch the graph of a function whose derivative is exactly 1 at every point.

115. ▼ Use the difference quotient to explain the fact that if f is a linear function, then the average rate of change over any interval equals the instantaneous rate of change at any point.

116. ▼ Give a numerical explanation of the fact that if f is a linear function, then the average rate of change over any interval equals the instantaneous rate of change at any point.

117. ◆ Consider the following values of the function f from Exercise 1.

h	0.1	0.01	0.001	0.0001
Average Rate of Change of f over $[5, 5+h]$	6.4	6.04	6.004	6.0004
h	−0.1	−0.01	−0.001	−0.0001
Average Rate of Change of f over $[5+h, 5]$	5.6	5.96	5.996	5.9996

Does the table suggests that the instantaneous rate of change of f is

(A) increasing   **(B)** decreasing

as x increases toward 5?

118. ◆ Consider the following values of the function g from Exercise 2.

h	0.1	0.01	0.001	0.0001
Average Rate of Change of g over $[7, 7+h]$	4.8	4.98	4.998	4.9998
h	−0.1	−0.01	−0.001	−0.0001
Average Rate of Change of g over $[7+h, 7]$	5.3	5.03	5.003	5.0003

Does the table suggest that the instantaneous rate of change of g is

(A) increasing   **(B)** decreasing

as x increases toward 7?

119. ▼ Sketch the graph of a function whose derivative is never zero but decreases as x increases.

120. ▼ Sketch the graph of a function whose derivative is never negative but is zero at exactly two points.

121. ◆ Here is the graph of the derivative f' of a function f. Give a rough sketch of the graph of f, given that $f(0) = 0$.

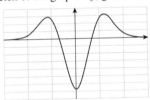

122. ◆ Here is the graph of the derivative f' of a function f. Give a rough sketch of the graph of f, given that $f(0) = 0$.

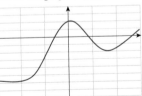

123. ◆ Professor Talker of the physics department drove a 60-mile stretch of road in exactly one hour. The speed limit along that stretch was 55 miles per hour. Which of the following must be correct:

(A) He exceeded the speed limit at no point of the journey.

(B) He exceeded the speed limit at some point of the journey.

(C) He exceeded the speed limit throughout the journey.

(D) He traveled slower than the speed limit at some point of the journey.

124. ◆ Professor Silent, another physics professor, drove a 50-mile stretch of road in exactly one hour. The speed limit along that stretch was 55 miles per hour. Which of the following must be correct:

(A) She exceeded the speed limit at no point of the journey.

(B) She exceeded the speed limit at some point of the journey.

(C) She traveled slower than the speed limit throughout the journey.

(D) She traveled slower than the speed limit at some point of the journey.

125. ◆ Draw the graph of a function f with the property that the balanced difference quotient gives a more accurate approximation of $f'(1)$ than the ordinary difference quotient.

126. ◆ Draw the graph of a function f with the property that the balanced difference quotient gives a less accurate approximation of $f'(1)$ than the ordinary difference quotient.

3.6 The Derivative: Algebraic Viewpoint

In Section 3.5 we saw how to estimate the derivative of a function using numerical and graphical approaches. In this section we use an algebraic approach that will give us the *exact value* of the derivative, rather than just an approximation, when the function is specified algebraically.

This algebraic approach is quite straightforward: Instead of subtracting numbers to estimate the average rate of change over smaller and smaller intervals, we subtract algebraic expressions. Our starting point is the definition of the derivative in terms of the difference quotient:

$$f'(a) = \lim_{h \to 0} \frac{f(a+h) - f(a)}{h}.$$

EXAMPLE 1 Calculating the Derivative at a Point Algebraically

Let $f(x) = x^2$. Use the definition of the derivative to compute $f'(3)$ algebraically.

Solution Substituting $a = 3$ into the definition of the derivative, we get:

$$f'(3) = \lim_{h \to 0} \frac{f(3+h) - f(3)}{h} \qquad \text{Formula for the derivative}$$

$$= \lim_{h \to 0} \frac{\overbrace{(3+h)^2}^{f(3+h)} - \overbrace{3^2}^{f(3)}}{h} \qquad \text{Substitute for } f(3) \text{ and } f(3+h).$$

$$= \lim_{h \to 0} \frac{(9 + 6h + h^2) - 9}{h} \qquad \text{Expand } (3+h)^2.$$

$$= \lim_{h \to 0} \frac{6h + h^2}{h} \qquad \text{Cancel the 9.}$$

$$= \lim_{h \to 0} \frac{h(6+h)}{h} \qquad \text{Factor out } h.$$

$$= \lim_{h \to 0} (6 + h) \qquad \text{Cancel the } h.$$

Now we let h approach 0. As h gets closer and closer to 0, the sum $6 + h$ clearly gets closer and closer to $6 + 0 = 6$. Thus,

$$f'(3) = \lim_{h \to 0} (6 + h) = 6. \qquad \text{As } h \to 0, (6+h) \to 6$$

(Calculations of limits like this are discussed and justified more fully in Sections 3.2 and 3.3.)

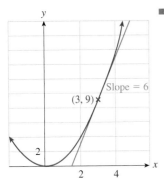

Figure 35

➡ **Before we go on...** We did the following calculation in Example 1: If $f(x) = x^2$, then $f'(3) = 6$. In other words, the tangent to the graph of $y = x^2$ at the point $(3, 9)$ has slope 6 (Figure 35). ∎

There is nothing very special about $a = 3$ in Example 1. Let's try to compute $f'(x)$ for general x.

EXAMPLE 2 Calculating the Derivative Function Algebraically

Let $f(x) = x^2$.

a. Use the definition of the derivative to compute $f'(x)$ algebraically.
b. Use the answer to evaluate $f'(3)$.

Solution
a. Once again, our starting point is the definition of the derivative in terms of the difference quotient:

$$f'(x) = \lim_{h \to 0} \frac{f(x+h) - f(x)}{h} \qquad \text{Formula for the derivative}$$

$$= \lim_{h \to 0} \frac{\overbrace{(x+h)^2}^{f(x+h)} - \overbrace{x^2}^{f(x)}}{h} \qquad \text{Substitute for } f(x) \text{ and } f(x+h).$$

$$= \lim_{h \to 0} \frac{(x^2 + 2xh + h^2) - x^2}{h} \qquad \text{Expand } (x+h)^2.$$

$$= \lim_{h \to 0} \frac{2xh + h^2}{h} \qquad \text{Cancel the } x^2.$$

$$= \lim_{h \to 0} \frac{h(2x+h)}{h} \qquad \text{Factor out } h.$$

$$= \lim_{h \to 0} (2x+h) \qquad \text{Cancel the } h.$$

Now we let h approach 0. As h gets closer and closer to 0, the sum $2x + h$ clearly gets closer and closer to $2x + 0 = 2x$. Thus,

$$f'(x) = \lim_{h \to 0} (2x+h) = 2x.$$

This is the derivative function.

b. Now that we have a *formula* for the derivative of f, we can obtain $f'(a)$ for any value of a we choose by simply evaluating f' there. For instance,

$$f'(3) = 2(3) = 6$$

as we saw in Example 1.

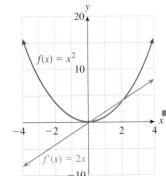

Figure 36

➡ **Before we go on...** The graphs of $f(x) = x^2$ and $f'(x) = 2x$ from Example 2 are familiar. Their graphs are shown in Figure 36.

When $x < 0$, the parabola slopes downward, which is reflected in the fact that the derivative $2x$ is negative there. When $x > 0$, the parabola slopes upward, which is reflected in the fact that the derivative is positive there. The parabola has a horizontal tangent line at $x = 0$, reflected in the fact that $2x = 0$ there. ∎

EXAMPLE 3 More Computations of Derivative Functions

Compute the derivative $f'(x)$ for each of the following functions:

a. $f(x) = x^3$ **b.** $f(x) = 2x^2 - x$ **c.** $f(x) = \dfrac{1}{x}$

Solution

a. $f'(x) = \lim\limits_{h \to 0} \dfrac{f(x+h) - f(x)}{h}$ Derivative formula

$$= \lim_{h \to 0} \frac{\overbrace{(x+h)^3}^{f(x+h)} - \overbrace{x^3}^{f(x)}}{h}$$ Substitute for $f(x)$ and $f(x+h)$.

$$= \lim_{h \to 0} \frac{(x^3 + 3x^2h + 3xh^2 + h^3) - x^3}{h}$$ Expand $(x+h)^3$.

$$= \lim_{h \to 0} \frac{3x^2h + 3xh^2 + h^3}{h}$$ Cancel the x^3.

$$= \lim_{h \to 0} \frac{h(3x^2 + 3xh + h^2)}{h}$$ Factor out h.

$$= \lim_{h \to 0} (3x^2 + 3xh + h^2)$$ Cancel the h.

$$= 3x^2.$$ Let h approach 0.

b. $f'(x) = \lim\limits_{h \to 0} \dfrac{f(x+h) - f(x)}{h}$ Derivative formula

$$= \lim_{h \to 0} \frac{\overbrace{(2(x+h)^2 - (x+h))}^{f(x+h)} - \overbrace{(2x^2 - x)}^{f(x)}}{h}$$ Substitute for $f(x)$ and $f(x+h)$.

$$= \lim_{h \to 0} \frac{(2x^2 + 4xh + 2h^2 - x - h) - (2x^2 - x)}{h}$$ Expand.

$$= \lim_{h \to 0} \frac{4xh + 2h^2 - h}{h}$$ Cancel the $2x^2$ and x.

$$= \lim_{h \to 0} \frac{h(4x + 2h - 1)}{h}$$ Factor out h.

$$= \lim_{h \to 0} (4x + 2h - 1)$$ Cancel the h.

$$= 4x - 1.$$ Let h approach 0.

c. $f'(x) = \lim\limits_{h \to 0} \dfrac{f(x+h) - f(x)}{h}$ Derivative formula

$$= \lim_{h \to 0} \frac{\left[\overbrace{\dfrac{1}{x+h}}^{f(x+h)} - \overbrace{\dfrac{1}{x}}^{f(x)} \right]}{h}$$ Substitute for $f(x)$ and $f(x+h)$.

$$= \lim_{h \to 0} \frac{\left[\dfrac{x - (x+h)}{(x+h)x} \right]}{h}$$ Subtract the fractions.

$$= \lim_{h \to 0} \frac{1}{h} \left[\frac{x - (x + h)}{(x + h)x} \right]$$ Dividing by h = Multiplying by $1/h$.

$$= \lim_{h \to 0} \left[\frac{-h}{h(x + h)x} \right]$$ Simplify.

$$= \lim_{h \to 0} \left[\frac{-1}{(x + h)x} \right]$$ Cancel the h.

$$= \frac{-1}{x^2}$$ Let h approach 0.

In Example 4, we redo Example 3 of Section 3.5, this time getting an exact, rather than approximate, answer.

EXAMPLE 4 Velocity

My friend Eric, an enthusiastic baseball player, claims he can "probably" throw a ball upward at a speed of 100 feet per second (ft/s). Our physicist friends tell us that its height s (in feet) t seconds later would be $s(t) = 100t - 16t^2$. Find the ball's instantaneous velocity function and its velocity exactly 2 seconds after Eric throws it.

Solution The instantaneous velocity function is the derivative ds/dt, which we calculate as follow:

$$\frac{ds}{dt} = \lim_{h \to 0} \frac{s(t + h) - s(t)}{h}$$

Let us compute $s(t + h)$ and $s(t)$ separately:

$$s(t) = 100t - 16t^2$$
$$s(t + h) = 100(t + h) - 16(t + h)^2$$
$$= 100t + 100h - 16(t^2 + 2th + h^2)$$
$$= 100t + 100h - 16t^2 - 32th - 16h^2.$$

Therefore,

$$\frac{ds}{dt} = \lim_{h \to 0} \frac{s(t + h) - s(t)}{h}$$
$$= \lim_{h \to 0} \frac{100t + 100h - 16t^2 - 32th - 16h^2 - (100t - 16t^2)}{h}$$
$$= \lim_{h \to 0} \frac{100h - 32th - 16h^2}{h}$$
$$= \lim_{h \to 0} \frac{h(100 - 32t - 16h)}{h}$$
$$= \lim_{h \to 0} (100 - 32t - 16h)$$
$$= 100 - 32t \text{ ft/s}.$$

Thus, the velocity exactly 2 seconds after Eric throws it is

$$\frac{ds}{dt}\bigg|_{t=2} = 100 - 32(2) = 36 \text{ ft/s}.$$

This verifies the accuracy of the approximation we made in Section 3.5.

➡ **Before we go on...** From the derivative function in Example 4, we can now describe the behavior of the velocity of the ball: Immediately on release ($t = 0$) the ball is traveling at 100 feet per second upward. The ball then slows down; precisely, it loses 32 feet per second of speed every second. When, exactly, does the velocity become zero and what happens after that? ■

Q : *Do we always have to calculate the limit of the difference quotient to find a formula for the derivative function?*

A : As it turns out, no. In Section 4.1 we will start to look at shortcuts for finding derivatives that allow us to bypass the definition of the derivative in many cases.

A Function Not Differentiable at a Point

Recall from Section 3.5 that a function is **differentiable** at a point a if $f'(a)$ exists; that is, if the difference quotient $[f(a + h) - f(a)]/h$ approaches a fixed value as h approaches 0. In Section 3.5, we mentioned that the function $f(x) = |x|$ is not differentiable at $x = 0$. In Example 5, we find out why.

EXAMPLE 5 A Function Not Differentiable at 0

Numerically, graphically, and algebraically investigate the differentiability of the function $f(x) = |x|$ at the points **(a)** $x = 1$ and **(b)** $x = 0$.

Solution

a. We compute

$$f'(1) = \lim_{h \to 0} \frac{f(1 + h) - f(1)}{h}$$

$$= \lim_{h \to 0} \frac{|1 + h| - 1}{h}.$$

Numerically, we can make tables of the values of the average rate of change $(|1 + h| - 1)/h$ for h positive or negative and approaching 0:

h	1	0.1	0.01	0.001	0.0001
Average Rate of Change Over [1, 1 + h]	1	1	1	1	1

h	−1	−0.1	−0.01	−0.001	−0.0001
Average Rate of Change Over [1 + h, 1]	1	1	1	1	1

From these tables it appears that $f'(1)$ is equal to 1. We can verify that algebraically: For h that is sufficiently small, $1 + h$ is positive (even if h is negative) and so

$$f'(1) = \lim_{h \to 0} \frac{1 + h - 1}{h}$$

$$= \lim_{h \to 0} \frac{h}{h} \qquad \text{Cancel the 1s.}$$

$$= \lim_{h \to 0} 1 \qquad \text{Cancel the } h.$$

$$= 1$$

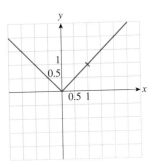

Figure 37

Graphically, we are seeing the fact that the tangent line at the point $(1, 1)$ has slope 1 because the graph is a straight line with slope 1 near that point (Figure 37).

b. $f'(0) = \lim_{h \to 0} \dfrac{f(0 + h) - f(0)}{h}$

$= \lim_{h \to 0} \dfrac{|0 + h| - 0}{h}$

$= \lim_{h \to 0} \dfrac{|h|}{h}$

If we make tables of values in this case we get the following:

h	1	0.1	0.01	0.001	0.0001
Average Rate of Change over $[0, 0 + h]$	1	1	1	1	1

h	−1	−0.1	−0.01	−0.001	−0.0001
Average Rate of Change over $[0 + h, 0]$	−1	−1	−1	−1	−1

For the limit and hence the derivative $f'(0)$ to exist, the average rates of change should approach the same number for both positive and negative h. Because they do not, f is not differentiable at $x = 0$. We can verify this conclusion algebraically: If h is positive, then $|h| = h$, and so the ratio $|h|/h$ is 1, regardless of how small h is. Thus, according to the values of the difference quotients with $h > 0$, the limit should be 1. On the other hand if h is negative, then $|h| = -h$ (positive) and so $|h|/h = -1$, meaning that the limit should be −1. Because the limit cannot be both −1 and 1 (it must be a single number for the derivative to exist), we conclude that $f'(0)$ does not exist.

To see what is happening graphically, take a look at Figure 38, which shows zoomed-in views of the graph of f near $x = 0$.

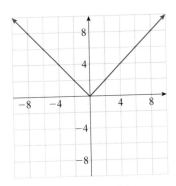
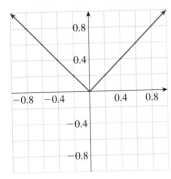
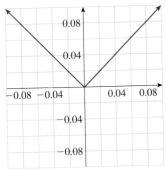

Figure 38

No matter what scale we use to view the graph, it has a sharp corner at $x = 0$ and hence has no tangent line there. Since there is no tangent line at $x = 0$, the function is not differentiable there.

➡ **Before we go on...** Notice that $|x| = \begin{cases} -x & \text{if } x < 0 \\ x & \text{if } x \geq 0 \end{cases}$ is an example of a piecewise-

linear function whose graph comes to a point at $x = 0$. In general, if $f(x)$ is any piecewise linear function whose graph comes to a point at $x = a$, it will be non-differentiable at $x = a$ for the same reason that $|x|$ fails to be differentiable at $x = 0$.

If we repeat the computation in Example 5(a) using any nonzero value for a in place of 1, we see that f is differentiable there as well. If a is positive, we find that $f'(a) = 1$ and, if a is negative, $f'(a) = -1$. In other words, the derivative function is

$$f'(x) = \begin{cases} -1 & \text{if } x < 0 \\ 1 & \text{if } x > 0 \end{cases}.$$

Immediately to the left of $x = 0$, we see that $f'(x) = -1$, immediately to the right, $f'(x) = 1$, and when $x = 0$, $f'(x)$ is not defined. ∎

FAQ

Computing Derivatives Algebraically

Q: The algebraic computation of $f'(x)$ seems to require a number of steps. How do I remember what to do, and when?

A: If you examine the computations in the previous examples, you will find the following pattern:

1. Write out the formula for $f'(x)$, as the limit of the difference quotient, then substitute $f(x + h)$ and $f(x)$.
2. Expand and simplify the *numerator* of the expression, but not the denominator.
3. After simplifying the numerator, factor out an h to cancel with the h in the denominator. If h does not factor out of the numerator, you might have made an error. (A frequent error is a wrong sign.)
4. After canceling the h, you should be able to see what the limit is by letting $h \to 0$.

3.6 EXERCISES

▼ more advanced   ◆ challenging
Ⅰ indicates exercises that should be solved using technology

In Exercises 1–14, compute $f'(a)$ algebraically for the given value of a. HINT [See Example 1.]

1. $f(x) = x^2 + 1$; $a = 2$

2. $f(x) = x^2 - 3$; $a = 1$

3. $f(x) = 3x - 4$; $a = -1$

4. $f(x) = -2x + 4$; $a = -1$

5. $f(x) = 3x^2 + x$; $a = 1$

6. $f(x) = 2x^2 + x$; $a = -2$

7. $f(x) = 2x - x^2$; $a = -1$

8. $f(x) = -x - x^2$; $a = 0$

9. $f(x) = x^3 + 2x$; $a = 2$

10. $f(x) = x - 2x^3$; $a = 1$

11. $f(x) = \dfrac{-1}{x}$; $a = 1$ HINT [See Example 3.]

12. $f(x) = \dfrac{2}{x}$; $a = 5$ HINT [See Example 3.]

13. ▼ $f(x) = mx + b$; $a = 43$

14. ▼ $f(x) = \dfrac{x}{k} - b$ $(k \neq 0)$; $a = 12$

In Exercises 15–28, compute the derivative function $f'(x)$ algebraically. (Notice that the functions are the same as those in Exercises 1–14.) HINT [See Examples 2 and 3.]

15. $f(x) = x^2 + 1$

16. $f(x) = x^2 - 3$

17. $f(x) = 3x - 4$

18. $f(x) = -2x + 4$

19. $f(x) = 3x^2 + x$

20. $f(x) = 2x^2 + x$

21. $f(x) = 2x - x^2$

22. $f(x) = -x - x^2$

23. $f(x) = x^3 + 2x$

24. $f(x) = x - 2x^3$

25. ▼ $f(x) = \dfrac{-1}{x}$

26. ▼ $f(x) = \dfrac{2}{x}$

27. ▼ $f(x) = mx + b$

28. ▼ $f(x) = \dfrac{x}{k} - b$ $(k \neq 0)$

In Exercises 29–38, compute the indicated derivative.

29. $R(t) = -0.3t^2$; $R'(2)$

30. $S(t) = 1.4t^2$; $S'(-1)$

31. $U(t) = 5.1t^2 + 5.1$; $U'(3)$

32. $U(t) = -1.3t^2 + 1.1$; $U'(4)$

33. $U(t) = -1.3t^2 - 4.5t$; $U'(1)$

34. $U(t) = 5.1t^2 - 1.1t$; $U'(1)$

35. $L(r) = 4.25r - 5.01$; $L'(1.2)$

36. $L(r) = -1.02r + 5.7$; $L'(3.1)$

37. ▼ $q(p) = \dfrac{2.4}{p} + 3.1$; $q'(2)$

38. ▼ $q(p) = \dfrac{1}{0.5p} - 3.1$; $q'(2)$

In Exercises 39–44, find the equation of the tangent to the graph at the indicated point. HINT [Compute the derivative algebraically; then see Example 2(b) in Section 3.5.]

39. ▼ $f(x) = x^2 - 3$; $a = 2$ **40.** ▼ $f(x) = x^2 + 1$; $a = 2$

41. ▼ $f(x) = -2x - 4$; $a = 3$ **42.** ▼ $f(x) = 3x + 1$; $a = 1$

43. ▼ $f(x) = x^2 - x$; $a = -1$ **44.** ▼ $f(x) = x^2 + x$; $a = -1$

APPLICATIONS

45. *Velocity* If a stone is dropped from a height of 400 feet, its height after t seconds is given by $s = 400 - 16t^2$. Find its instantaneous velocity function and its velocity at time $t = 4$. HINT [See Example 4.]

46. *Velocity* If a stone is thrown down at 120 feet per second from a height of 1,000 feet, its height after t seconds is given by $s = 1,000 - 120t - 16t^2$. Find its instantaneous velocity function and its velocity at time $t = 3$. HINT [See Example 4.]

47. *Oil Imports from Mexico* Daily oil imports to the United States from Mexico can be approximated by

$$I(t) = -0.015t^2 + 0.1t + 1.4 \text{ million barrels} \quad (0 \le t \le 8)$$

where t is time in years since the start of 2000.[58] Find the derivative function $\dfrac{dI}{dt}$. At what rate were oil imports changing at the start of 2007 ($t = 7$)? HINT [See Example 4.]

48. *Oil Production in Mexico* Daily oil production by **Pemex**, Mexico's national oil company, can be approximated by

$$P(t) = -0.022t^2 + 0.2t + 2.9 \text{ million barrels} \quad (1 \le t \le 9)$$

where t is time in years since the start of 2000.[59] Find the derivative function $\dfrac{dP}{dt}$. At what rate was oil production changing at the start of 2004 ($t = 4$)? HINT [See Example 4.]

49. *Bottled Water Sales* Annual U.S. sales of bottled water rose through the period 2000–2008 as shown in the following chart.[60]

[58] Source for data: Energy Information Administration/Pemex (http://www.eia.doe.gov).

[59] Ibid.

[60] The 2008 figure is an estimate. Source: Beverage Marketing Corporation, www.bottledwater.org.

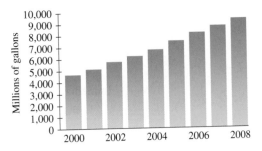

Bottled water sales in the U.S.

The function

$$R(t) = 12t^2 + 500t + 4{,}700 \text{ million gallons} \quad (0 \le t \le 8)$$

gives a good approximation, where t is time in years since 2000. Find the derivative function $R'(t)$. According to the model, how fast were annual sales of bottled water increasing in 2005?

50. *Bottled Water Sales* Annual U.S. per capita sales of bottled water rose through the period 2000–2008 as shown in the following chart.[61]

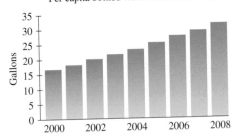

Per capita bottled water sales in the U.S.

The function

$$Q(t) = 0.04t^2 + 1.5t + 17 \text{ gallons} \quad (0 \le t \le 8)$$

gives a good approximation, where t is the time in years since 2000. Find the derivative function $Q'(t)$. According to the model, how fast were annual per capita sales of bottled water increasing in 2008?

51. ▼ *Ecology* Increasing numbers of manatees ("sea sirens") have been killed by boats off the Florida coast. The following graph shows the relationship between the number of boats registered in Florida and the number of manatees killed each year.

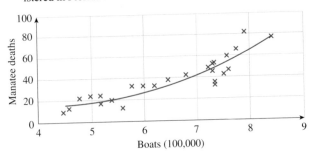

[61] Ibid.

The regression curve shown is given by

$$f(x) = 3.55x^2 - 30.2x + 81 \text{ manatee deaths}$$
$$(4.5 \leq x \leq 8.5)$$

where x is the number of boats (hundreds of thousands) registered in Florida in a particular year and $f(x)$ is the number of manatees killed by boats in Florida that year.[62] Compute and interpret $f'(8)$.

52. ▼ *SAT Scores by Income* The following graph shows U.S. verbal SAT scores as a function of parents' income level.[63]

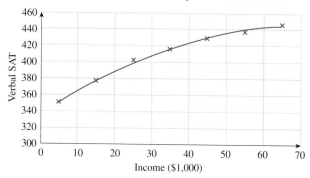

The regression curve shown is given by

$$f(x) = -0.021x^2 + 3.0x + 336 \quad (5 \leq x \leq 65)$$

where $f(x)$ is the average SAT verbal score of a student whose parents earn x thousand dollars per year. Compute and interpret $f'(30)$.

53. ▼ *Television Advertising* The cost, in millions of dollars, of a 30-second television ad during the Super Bowl in the years 1990 to 2007 can be approximated by the following piecewise linear function ($t = 0$ represents 1990):[64]

$$C(t) = \begin{cases} 0.08t + 0.6 & \text{if } 0 \leq t < 8 \\ 0.13t + 0.20 & \text{if } 8 \leq t \leq 17 \end{cases}$$

a. Is C a continuous function of t? Why? HINT [See Example 4 of Section 3.3.]

b. Is C a differentiable function of t? Compute $\lim_{t \to 8^-} C'(t)$ and $\lim_{t \to 8^+} C'(t)$ and interpret the results. HINT [See *Before we go on...* after Example 5.]

54. ▼ *Processor Speeds* The processor speed, in megahertz (MHz), of **Intel** processors can be approximated by the following function of time t in years since the start of 1995:[65]

$$P(t) = \begin{cases} 180t + 200 & \text{if } 0 \leq t \leq 5 \\ 3,000t - 13,900 & \text{if } 5 < t \leq 12 \end{cases}$$

a. Is P a continuous function of t? Why? HINT [See Example 4 of Section 3.3.]

b. Is P a differentiable function of t? Compute $\lim_{t \to 5^-} P'(t)$ and $\lim_{t \to 5^+} P'(t)$ and interpret the results. HINT [See *Before we go on...* after Example 5.]

COMMUNICATION AND REASONING EXERCISES

55. Of the three methods (numerical, graphical, algebraic) we can use to estimate the derivative of a function at a given value of x, which is always the most accurate? Explain.

56. Explain why we cannot put $h = 0$ in the formula

$$f'(a) = \lim_{h \to 0} \frac{f(a + h) - f(a)}{h}$$

for the derivative of f.

57. You just got your derivatives test back and you can't understand why that teacher of yours deducted so many points for what you thought was your best work:

$$\lim_{h \to 0} \frac{f(x + h) - f(x)}{h}$$
$$= \lim_{h \to 0} \frac{f(x) + h - f(x)}{h}$$
$$= \lim_{h \to 0} \frac{h}{h} \qquad \text{Canceled the } f(x)$$
$$= 1 \qquad \text{✗ WRONG } -10$$

What was wrong with your answer?

58. Your friend just got his derivatives test back and can't understand why that teacher of his deducted so many points for the following:

$$\lim_{h \to 0} \frac{f(x + h) - f(x)}{h}$$
$$= \lim_{h \to 0} \frac{f(x) + f(h) - f(x)}{h}$$
$$= \lim_{h \to 0} \frac{f(h)}{h} \qquad \text{Canceled the } f(x)$$
$$= \lim_{h \to 0} \frac{f(h)}{h} \qquad \text{Now cancel the } h.$$
$$= f() \qquad \text{✗ WRONG } -50$$

What was wrong with his answer?

59. Your other friend just got her derivatives test back and can't understand why that teacher of hers took off so many points for the following:

$$\lim_{h \to 0} \frac{f(x + h) - f(x)}{h}$$
$$= \lim_{h \to 0} \frac{f(x + h) - f(x)}{h} \qquad \text{Now cancel the } h.$$
$$= \lim_{h \to 0} f(x) - f(x) \qquad \text{Canceled the } f(x)$$
$$= 0 \qquad \text{✗ WRONG } -15$$

What was wrong with his answer?

---

[62] Regression model is based on data from 1976 to 2000. Sources for data: Florida Department of Highway Safety & Motor Vehicles, Florida Marine Institute/*New York Times*, February 12, 2002, p. F4.

[63] Based on 1994 data. Source: The College Board/*New York Times*, March 5, 1995, p. E16.

[64] Sources for data: *New York Times*, January 26, 2001, p. C1., www.money.cnn.com.

[65] Sources for data: Sandpile.org/*New York Times*, May 17, 2004, p. C1 and www.Intel.com.

60. Your third friend just got her derivatives test back and can't understand why that teacher of hers took off so many points for the following:

$$\lim_{h \to 0} \frac{f(x+h) - f(x)}{h}$$

$$= \lim_{h \to 0} \frac{f(x) + h - f(x)}{h}$$

$$= \lim_{h \to 0} \frac{f(x) + h - f(x)}{h} \qquad \text{Now cancel the } h.$$

$$= \lim_{h \to 0} f(x) - f(x) \qquad \text{Canceled the } f(x)$$

$$= 0 \qquad \qquad \text{✗ WRONG} \quad -25$$

What was wrong with her answer?

61. Your friend Muffy claims that, because the balanced difference quotient is more accurate, it would be better to use that instead of the usual difference quotient when computing the derivative algebraically. Comment on this advice.

62. Use the balanced difference quotient formula,

$$f'(a) = \lim_{h \to 0} \frac{f(a+h) - f(a-h)}{2h}$$

to compute $f'(3)$ when $f(x) = x^2$. What do you find?

63. ▼ A certain function f has the property that $f'(a)$ does not exist. How is that reflected in the attempt to compute $f'(a)$ algebraically?

64. ▼ One cannot put $h = 0$ in the formula

$$f'(a) = \lim_{h \to 0} \frac{f(a+h) - f(a)}{h}$$

for the derivative of f. (See Exercise 56.) However, in the last step of each of the computations in the text, we are effectively setting $h = 0$ when taking the limit. What is going on here?

KEY CONCEPTS

REVIEW EXERCISES

T indicates exercises that must be solved using technology

Numerically *estimate whether the limits in Exercises 1–4 exist. If a limit does exist, give its approximate value.*

1. $\lim_{x \to 3} \dfrac{x^2 - x - 6}{x - 3}$

2. $\lim_{x \to 3} \dfrac{x^2 - 2x - 6}{x - 3}$

3. $\lim_{x \to -1} \dfrac{|x + 1|}{x^2 - x - 2}$

4. $\lim_{x \to -1} \dfrac{|x + 1|}{x^2 + x - 2}$

In Exercises 5 and 6, the graph of a function f is shown. Graphically determine whether the given limits exist. If a limit does exist, give its approximate value.

5.

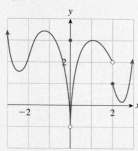

a. $\lim_{x \to 0} f(x)$ **b.** $\lim_{x \to 1} f(x)$
c. $\lim_{x \to 2} f(x)$

6.

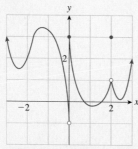

a. $\lim_{x \to 0} f(x)$ **b.** $\lim_{x \to -2} f(x)$
c. $\lim_{x \to 2} f(x)$

Calculate the limits in Exercises 7–24 algebraically. If a limit does not exist, say why.

7. $\lim_{x \to -2} \dfrac{x^2}{x - 3}$

8. $\lim_{x \to 3} \dfrac{x^2 - 9}{2x - 6}$

9. $\lim_{x \to 0} \dfrac{x}{2x^2 - x}$

10. $\lim_{x \to 1} \dfrac{x^2 - 9}{x - 1}$

11. $\lim_{x \to -1} \dfrac{x^2 + 3x}{x^2 - x - 2}$

12. $\lim_{x \to -1^+} \dfrac{x^2 + 1}{x^2 + 3x + 2}$

13. $\lim_{x \to 4} \dfrac{x^2 + 8}{x^2 - 2x - 8}$

14. $\lim_{x \to 4} \dfrac{x^2 + 3x}{x^2 - 8x + 16}$

15. $\lim_{x \to 1/2} \dfrac{x^2 + 8}{4x^2 - 4x + 1}$

16. $\lim_{x \to 1/2} \dfrac{x^2 + 3x}{2x^2 + 3x - 1}$

17. $\lim_{x \to -\infty} \dfrac{x^2 - x - 6}{x - 3}$

18. $\lim_{x \to \infty} \dfrac{x^2 - x - 6}{4x^2 - 3}$

19. $\lim_{t \to +\infty} \dfrac{-5}{5 + 5.3(3^{2t})}$

20. $\lim_{t \to +\infty} \left(3 + \dfrac{2}{e^{4t}}\right)$

21. $\lim_{x \to +\infty} \dfrac{2}{5 + 4e^{-3x}}$

22. $\lim_{x \to +\infty} (4e^{3x} + 12)$

23. $\lim_{t \to +\infty} \dfrac{1 + 2^{-3t}}{1 + 5.3e^{-t}}$

24. $\lim_{x \to -\infty} \dfrac{8 + 0.5^x}{2 - 3^{2x}}$

273

In Exercises 25–28, find the average rate of change of the given function over the interval $[a, a + h]$ for $h = 1, 0.01,$ and 0.001. (Round answers to four decimal places.) Then estimate the slope of the tangent line to the graph of the function at a.

25. $f(x) = \frac{1}{x+1}$; $a = 0$ **26.** $f(x) = x^x$; $a = 2$

27. $f(x) = e^{2x}$; $a = 0$ **28.** $f(x) = \ln(2x)$; $a = 1$

In Exercises 29–32 you are given the graph of a function with four points marked. Determine at which (if any) of these points the derivative of the function is: (i) −1 (ii) 0 (iii) 1, and (iv) 2.

29.

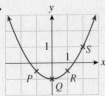

30.

31.

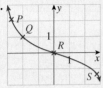

32.

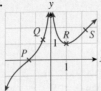

33. Let f have the graph shown.

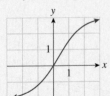

Select the correct answer.

a. The average rate of change of f over the interval $[0, 2]$ is
   (A) greater than $f'(0)$ **(B)** less than $f'(0)$
   (C) approximately equal to $f'(0)$
b. The average rate of change of f over the interval $[−1, 1]$ is
   (A) greater than $f'(0)$ **(B)** less than $f'(0)$
   (C) approximately equal to $f'(0)$
c. Over the interval $[0, 2]$, the instantaneous rate of change of f is
   (A) increasing   **(B)** decreasing
   (C) neither increasing nor decreasing
d. Over the interval $[−2, 2]$, the instantaneous rate of change of f is
   (A) increasing, then decreasing
   (B) decreasing, then increasing
   (C) approximately constant
e. When $x = 2$, $f(x)$ is
   (A) approximately 1 and increasing at a rate of about 2.5 units per unit of x
   (B) approximately 1.2 and increasing at a rate of about 1 unit per unit of x

(C) approximately 2.5 and increasing at a rate of about 0.5 units per unit of x
(D) approximately 2.5 and increasing at a rate of about 2.5 units per unit of x

34. Let f have the graph shown.

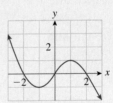

Select the correct answer.

a. The average rate of change of f over the interval $[0, 1]$ is
   (A) greater than $f'(0)$ **(B)** less than $f'(0)$
   (C) approximately equal to $f'(0)$
b. The average rate of change of f over the interval $[0, 2]$ is
   (A) greater than $f'(1)$ **(B)** less than $f'(1)$
   (C) approximately equal to $f'(1)$
c. Over the interval $[−2, 0]$, the instantaneous rate of change of f is
   (A) increasing   **(B)** decreasing
   (C) neither increasing nor decreasing
d. Over the interval $[−2, 2]$, the instantaneous rate of change of f is
   (A) increasing, then decreasing
   (B) decreasing, then increasing
   (C) approximately constant
e. When $x = 0$, $f(x)$ is
   (A) approximately 0 and increasing at a rate of about 1.5 units per unit of x
   (B) approximately 0 and decreasing at a rate of about 1.5 units per unit of x
   (C) approximately 1.5 and neither increasing nor decreasing
   (D) approximately 0 and neither increasing nor decreasing

In Exercises 35–38, use the definition of the derivative to calculate the derivative of each of the given functions algebraically.

35. $f(x) = x^2 + x$ **36.** $f(x) = 3x^2 − x + 1$

37. $f(x) = 1 − \frac{2}{x}$ **38.** $f(x) = \frac{1}{x} + 1$

🅣 *In Exercises 39–42, use technology to graph the derivative of the given function. In each case, choose a range of x-values and y-values that shows the interesting features of the graph.*

39. $f(x) = 10x^5 + \frac{1}{2}x^4 − x + 2$

40. $f(x) = \frac{10}{x^5} + \frac{1}{2x^4} − \frac{1}{x} + 2$

41. $f(x) = 3x^3 + 3\sqrt[3]{x}$

42. $f(x) = \frac{2}{x^{2.1}} − \frac{x^{0.1}}{2}$

APPLICATIONS

43. Stock Investments OHaganBooks.com CEO John O'Hagan has terrible luck with stocks. The following graph shows the value of Fly-By-Night Airlines stock that he bought acting on a "hot tip" from Marjory Duffin (CEO of Duffin Press and a close business associate):

Fly-by-night stock

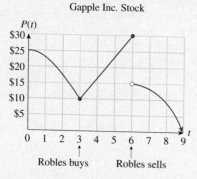

O'Hagan buys   O'Hagan sells

a. Compute $P(3)$, $\lim_{t \to 3^-} P(t)$ and $\lim_{t \to 3^+} P(t)$. Does $\lim_{t \to 3} P(t)$ exist? Interpret your answers in terms of Fly-By-Night stock.

b. Is P continuous at $t = 6$? Is P differentiable at $t = 6$? Interpret your answers in terms of Fly-By-Night stock.

44. Stock Investments John O'Hagan's golf partner Juan Robles seems to have had better luck with his investment in Gapple Gomputer Inc. stocks as shown in the following graph:

Gapple Inc. Stock

Robles buys   Robles sells

a. Compute $P(6)$, $\lim_{t \to 6^-} P(t)$ and $\lim_{t \to 6^+} P(t)$. Does $\lim_{t \to 6} P(t)$ exist? Interpret your answers in terms of Gapple stock.

b. Is P continuous at $t = 3$? Is P differentiable at $t = 3$? Interpret your answers in terms of Gapple stock.

45. Real Estate Marjory Duffin has persuaded John O'Hagan to consider investing a portion of OHaganBooks.com profits in real estate, now that the real estate market seems to have bottomed out. A real estate broker friend of hers e-mailed her the following (somewhat optimistic) graph from brokersadvocacy.com:[66]

[66] Authors' note: As of August 2008, brokersadvocacy.com is unregistered.

Home price index

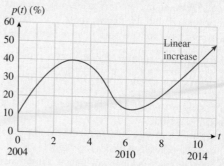

Here, $p(t)$ is the home price percentage over the 2003 level.

a. Assuming the trend shown in the graph were to continue indefinitely, estimate $\lim_{t \to 3} p(t)$ and $\lim_{t \to +\infty} p(t)$ and interpret the results.

b. Estimate $\lim_{t \to +\infty} p'(t)$ and interpret the result.

46. Advertising Costs OHaganBooks.com has (on further advice from Marjory Duffin) mounted an aggressive online marketing strategy. The following graph shows the weekly cost of this campaign for the six-week period since the start of July (t is time in weeks):

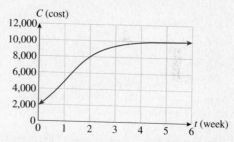

a. Assuming the trend shown in the graph were to continue indefinitely, estimate $\lim_{t \to 2} C(t)$ and $\lim_{t \to +\infty} C(t)$ and interpret the results.

b. Estimate $\lim_{t \to +\infty} C'(t)$ and interpret the result.

47. Sales Since the start of July, OHaganBooks.com has seen its weekly sales increase, as shown in the following table:

Week	1	2	3	4	5	6
Sales (books)	6,500	7,000	7,200	7,800	8,500	9,000

a. What was the average rate of increase of weekly sales over this entire period?

b. During which 1-week interval(s) did the rate of increase of sales exceed the average rate?

c. During which 2-week interval(s) did the weekly sales rise at the highest average rate, and what was that average rate?

48. Rising Sea Level Marjory Duffin recently purchased a beach-front condominium in New York and is now in a panic, having just seen some disturbing figures about rising sea levels (sea levels as measured in New York relative to the 1900 level).[67]

Year since 1900	0	25	50	75	100	125
Sea Level (mm)	0	60	140	240	310	390

a. What was the average rate of increase of the sea level over this entire period?

b. During which 25-year interval(s) did the rate of increase of the sea level exceed the average rate?

c. Marjory Duffin's condominium is about 2 meters above sea level. Using the average rate of change from part (a), estimate how long she has before the sea rises to her condominium.

49. Real Estate The following graph (see Exercise 45) shows the home price index chart e-mailed to Marjory Duffin by a real estate broker:

Home price index

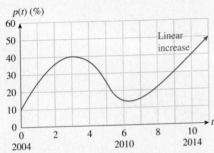

Use the graph to answer the following questions:

a. What was the average rate of change of the index over the 10-year period beginning 2004?

b. What was the average rate of change of the index over the period [3, 10]?

c. Which of the following is correct? Over the period [4, 6],

   (A) The rate of change of the index increased.
   (B) The rate of change of the index increased and then decreased.
   (C) The rate of change of the index decreased.
   (D) The rate of change of the index decreased and then increased.

50. Advertising Costs The following graph (see Exercise 46) shows the weekly cost of OHaganBooks.com's online ad campaign for the six-week period since the start of July (t is time in weeks).

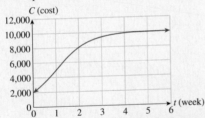

Use the graph to answer the following questions:

a. What was the average rate of change of cost over the entire six-week period?

b. What was the average rate of change of cost over the period [2, 6]?

c. Which of the following is correct? Over the period [2, 6],

   (A) The rate of change of cost increased and the cost increased.
   (B) The rate of change of cost decreased and the cost increased.
   (C) The rate of change of cost increased and the cost decreased.
   (D) The rate of change of cost decreased and the cost decreased.

51. Sales OHaganBooks.com fits the curve

$$w(t) = 36t^2 + 250t + 6240 \quad (0 \le t \le 6)$$

to its weekly sales figures from Exercise 47, as shown in the following graph:

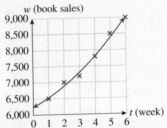

a. Compute the derivative function $w'(t)$.

b. According to the model, what was the rate of increase of sales at the beginning of the second week ($t = 1$)?

c. If we extrapolate the model, what would be the rate of increase of weekly sales at the beginning of the 8th week ($t = 7$)?

52. Sea Levels Marjory Duffin fit the curve

$$s(t) = 0.002t^2 + 3t - 6.4 \quad (0 \le t \le 125)$$

to her sea level figures from Exercise 48, as shown in the following graph:

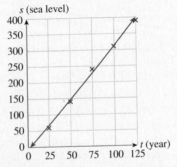

a. Compute the derivative function $s'(t)$.

b. According to the model, what was the rate of increase of the sea level in 2000 ($t = 100$)?

c. If we extrapolate the model, what would be the rate of increase of the sea level in 2100 ($t = 200$)?

Case Study   Reducing Sulfur Emissions

The Environmental Protection Agency (EPA) wishes to formulate a policy that will encourage utilities to reduce sulfur emissions. Its goal is to reduce annual emissions of sulfur dioxide by a total of 10 million tons from the current level of 25 million tons by imposing a fixed charge for every ton of sulfur released into the environment per year. As a consultant to the EPA, you must determine the amount to be charged per ton of sulfur emissions.

You would like first to know the cost to the utility industry of reducing sulfur emissions. In other words, you would like to have a cost function of the form

$$C(q) = \text{Cost of removing } q \text{ tons of sulfur dioxide.}$$

Unfortunately, you do not have such a function handy. You do, however, have the following data, which show the *marginal* cost (that is, the *rate of change* of cost) to the utility industry of reducing sulfur emissions at several levels of reduction.[68]

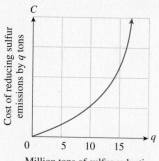

Figure 39

Reduction (tons) q	8,000,000	10,000,000	12,000,000
Marginal Cost ($ per ton) $C'(q)$	270	360	779

The table tells you that $C'(8,000,000) = \$270$ per ton, $C'(10,000,000) = \$360$ per ton, and $C'(12,000,000) = \$779$ per ton. Recalling that $C'(q)$ is the slope of the tangent to the graph of the cost function, you can see from the table that this slope is positive and increasing as q increases, so the graph of the cost function has the general shape shown in Figure 39.

Notice that the slope (additional cost) is increasing as you move to the right, so the utility industry has no cost incentive to reduce emissions further, as it costs the industry significantly more per ton for each additional ton of sulfur it removes. What you would like—if the goal of reducing total emissions by 10 million tons is to be reached—is that, somehow, the imposition of a fixed charge for every ton of sulfur dioxide released will *alter* the form of the cost curve so that it has the general shape shown in Figure 40. In this ideal curve, the cost D to utilities is lowest at a reduction level of 10 million tons, so if the utilities act to minimize cost, they can be expected to reduce emissions by 10 million tons, which is exactly the EPA goal! From the graph, you can see that the tangent line to the curve at the point where $q = 10$ million tons is horizontal, and thus has zero slope: $D'(10,000,000) = \$0$ per ton. Further, the slope $D'(q)$ is negative for values of q to the left of 10 million tons and positive for values to the right.

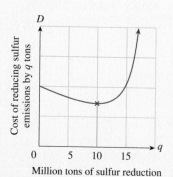

Figure 40

So, how much should the EPA charge per ton of sulfur released into the environment? Suppose the EPA charges $\$k$ per ton, so that

$$\text{Emission charge to utilities} = k \times \text{Sulfur emission}$$

It is your job to calculate k. Because you are working with q as the independent variable, you decide that it would be best to formulate the emission charge as a function of q. However, q represents the amount by which sulfur emissions have been reduced from the original 25 million tons; that is, the amount by which sulfur emissions are *lower than* the original 25 million tons:

$$q = 25,000,000 - \text{Sulfur emissions}$$

---

[68] These figures were produced in a computerized study of reducing sulfur emissions from the 1980 level by the given amounts. Source: Congress of the United States, Congressional Budget Office, *Curbing Acid Rain: Cost, Budget and Coal Market Effects* (Washington, DC: Government Printing Office, 1986): xx, xxii, 23, 80.

Thus, the total annual emission charge to the utilities is

$$k \times \text{Sulfur emission} = k(25,000,000 - q) = 25,000,000k - kq$$

This results in a total cost to the utilities of

$$\text{Total cost} = \text{Cost of reducing emissions} + \text{Emission charge}$$
$$D(q) = C(q) + 25,000,000k - kq$$

You now recall from calculus that the derivative of a sum of two functions is the sum of their derivatives (you will see why in Section 4.1*), so the derivative of D is given by

$$D'(q) = \text{Derivative of } C + \text{Derivative of } (25,000,000k - kq)$$

The function $y = 25,000,000k - kq$ is a linear function of q with slope $-k$ and intercept $25,000,000k$. Thus its derivative is just its slope: $-k$. Therefore:

$$D'(q) = C'(q) - k$$

Remember that you want

$$D'(10,000,000) = 0.$$

Thus,

$$C'(10,000,000) - k = 0$$

Referring to the table, you see that

$$360 - k = 0$$

or

$$k = \$360 \text{ per ton.}$$

In other words, all you need to do is set the emission charge at $k = \$360$ per ton of sulfur emitted. Further, to ensure that the resulting curve will have the general shape shown in Figure 40, you would like to have $D'(q)$ negative for $q < 10,000,000$ and positive for $q > 10,000,000$. To check this, write

$$D'(q) = C'(q) - k$$
$$= C'(q) - 360$$

and refer to the table to obtain

$$D'(8,000,000) = 270 - 360 = -90 < 0 \checkmark$$

and

$$D'(12,000,000) = 779 - 360 = 419 > 0 \checkmark$$

Thus, based on the given data, the resulting curve will have the shape you require. You therefore inform the EPA that an annual emissions charge of $360 per ton of sulfur released into the environment will create the desired incentive: to reduce sulfur emissions by 10 million tons per year.

One week later, you are informed that this charge would be unrealistic because the utilities cannot possibly afford such a cost. You are asked whether there is an alternative plan that accomplishes the 10-million-ton reduction goal and yet is cheaper to the utilities by $5 billion per year. You then look at your expression for the emission charge

$$25,000,000k - kq$$

✶ NOTE This statement makes intuitive sense: For instance, if C is changing at a rate of 3 units per second and D is changing at a rate of 2 units per second, then their sum is changing at a rate of $3 + 2 = 5$ units per second.

and notice that, if you decrease this amount by $5 billion, the derivative will not change at all because it will still have the same slope (only the intercept is affected). Thus, you propose the following revised formula for the emission charge:

$$25,000,000k - kq - 5,000,000,000$$
$$= 25,000,000(360) - 360q - 5,000,000,000$$
$$= 4,000,000,000 - 360q$$

At the expected reduction level of 10 million tons, the total amount paid by the utilities will then be

$$4,000,000,000 - 360(10,000,000) = \$400,000,000$$

Thus, your revised proposal is the following: Impose an annual emissions charge of $360 per ton of sulfur released into the environment and hand back $5 billion in the form of subsidies. The effect of this policy will be to cause the utilities industry to reduce sulfur emissions by 10 million tons per year and will result in $400 million in annual revenues to the government.

Notice that this policy also provides an incentive for the utilities to search for cheaper ways to reduce emissions. For instance, if they lowered costs to the point where they could achieve a reduction level of 12 million tons, they would have a total emission charge of

$$4,000,000,000 - 360(12,000,000) = -\$320,000,000.$$

The fact that this is negative means that the government would be paying the utilities industry $320 million more in annual subsidies than the industry is paying in per ton emission charges.

EXERCISES

1. Excluding subsidies, what should the annual emission charge be if the goal is to reduce sulfur emissions by 8 million tons?
2. Excluding subsidies, what should the annual emission charge be if the goal is to reduce sulfur emissions by 12 million tons?
3. What is the *marginal emission charge* (derivative of emission charge) in your revised proposal (as stated before the exercise set)? What is the relationship between the marginal cost of reducing sulfur emissions before emissions charges are implemented and the marginal emission charge, at the optimal reduction under your revised proposal?
4. We said that the revised policy provided an incentive for utilities to find cheaper ways to reduce emissions. How would $C(q)$ have to change to make 12 million tons the optimum reduction?
5. What change in $C(q)$ would make 8 million tons the optimum reduction?
6. If the scenario in Exercise 5 took place, what would the EPA have to do in order to make 10 million tons the optimal reduction once again?
7. Due to intense lobbying by the utility industry, you are asked to revise the proposed policy so that the utility industry will pay no charge if sulfur emissions are reduced by the desired 10 million tons. How can you accomplish this?
8. Suppose that instead of imposing a fixed charge per ton of emission, you decide to use a sliding scale, so that the total charge to the industry for annual emissions of x tons will be $\$kx^2$ for some k. What must k be to again make 10 million tons the optimum reduction? HINT [The derivative of kx^2 is $2kx$.]

TI-83/84 Plus   **Technology Guide**

Section **3.1**

Example 1 (page 193)   Use a table to estimate the following limits.

a. $\lim\limits_{x \to 2} \dfrac{x^3 - 8}{x - 2}$ **b.** $\lim\limits_{x \to 0} \dfrac{e^{2x} - 1}{x}$

Solution with Technology

On the TI-83/84 Plus, use the table feature to automate these computations as follows:

1. Define $Y_1=(X^3-8)/(X-2)$ for part (a) or $Y_1=(e^(2X)-1)/X$ for part (b).

2. Press $\boxed{2ND}$ $\boxed{TABLE}$ to list its values for the given values of x. (If the calculator does not allow you to enter values of x, press $\boxed{2ND}$ $\boxed{TBLSET}$ and set Indpnt to Ask).

Here is the table showing some of the values for part (a):

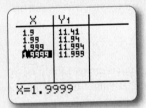

3. For part (b) use $Y_1=(e^(2X)-1)/X$ and use values of x approaching 0 from either side.

Section **3.4**

Example 3 (page 229)   The price of an ounce of gold can be approximated by the function

$G(t) = -8t^2 + 144t + 150$ dollars $(7.5 \le t \le 10.5)$

where t is time in hours. What was the average rate of change of the price of gold over the $1\frac{1}{2}$-hour period starting at 8:00 AM (the interval [8, 9.5] on the t-axis)?

Solution with Technology

On the TI-83/84 Plus:

1. Enter the function G as Y_1 (using X for t):
$Y_1=-8X^2+144X+150$

2. Now find the average rate of change over [8, 9.5] by evaluating the following on the home screen:
$(Y_1(9.5)-Y_1(8))/(9.5-8)$

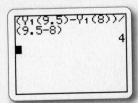

As shown on the screen, the average rate is of change is 4.

Example 4 (page 230)   Continuing with Example 3, use technology to compute the average rate of change of

$G(t) = -8t^2 + 144t + 150$ $(7.5 \le t \le 10.5)$

over the intervals [8, 8 + h], where $h = 1, 0.1, 0.01, 0.001,$ and 0.0001.

Solution with Technology

1. As in Example 3, enter the function G as Y_1 (using X for t):

$Y_1=-8X^2+144X+150$

2. Now find the average rate of change for $h = 1$ by evaluating, on the home screen,

$(Y_1(8+1)-Y_1(8))/1$

which gives 8.

3. To evaluate for $h = 0.1$, recall the expression using $\boxed{2ND}$ $\boxed{ENTER}$ and then change the 1, both places it occurs, to 0.1, getting

$(Y_1(8+0.1)-Y_1(8))/0.1$

which gives 15.2.

4. Continuing, we can evaluate the average rate of change for all the desired values of h:

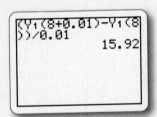

We get the values in the following table:

h	1	0.1	0.01	0.001	0.0001
Ave. Rate of Change $\dfrac{G(8+h) - G(8)}{h}$	8	15.2	15.92	15.992	15.9992

Section 3.5

Example 2 (page 245) Calculate an approximate value of $f'(1.5)$ if $f(x) = x^2 - 4x$, and then find the equation of the tangent line at the point on the graph where $x = 1.5$.

Solution with Technology

1. In the TI-83/84 Plus, enter the function f as Y_1

$$Y_1 = X^2 - 4*X$$

2. Go to the home screen to compute the approximations:

$(Y_1(1.5001) - Y_1(1.5))/0.0001$

Usual difference quotient

$(Y_1(1.5001) - Y_1(1.4999))/0.0002$

Balanced difference quotient

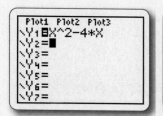

From the display on the right, we find that the difference quotient quick approximation is -0.9999 and the balanced difference quotient quick approximation is -1, which is in fact the exact value of $f'(1.5)$. See the discussion in the text for the calculation of the equation of the tangent line.

Example 4 (page 251) Use technology to graph of the derivative of $f(x) = -2x^2 + 6x + 5$ for values of x in starting at -5.

Solution with Technology

On the TI-83/84 Plus, the easiest way to obtain quick approximations of the derivative of a given function is to use the built-in `nDeriv` function, which calculates balanced difference quotients.

1. On the $Y=$ screen, first enter the function:

$$Y_1 = -2X^2 + 6X + 5$$

2. Then set

$Y_2 = nDeriv(Y_1, X, X)$ For `nDeriv` press [MATH] [8]

which is the TI-83's approximation of $f'(x)$.

Alternatively, we can enter the balanced difference quotient directly:

$Y_2 = (Y_1(X+0.001) - Y_1(X-0.001))/0.002$

(The TI-83 uses $h = 0.001$ by default in the balanced difference quotient when calculating `nDeriv`, but this can be changed by giving a value of h as a fourth argument, like `nDeriv(Y_1,X,X,0.0001)`.) To see a table of approximate values of the derivative, we press [2ND] [TABLE] and choose a collection of values for x:

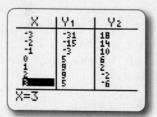

Here, Y_1 shows the value of f and Y_2 shows the values of f'.

To graph the function or its derivative, we can graph Y_1 or Y_2 in a window showing the given domain $[-5, 5]$:

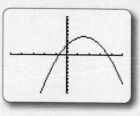
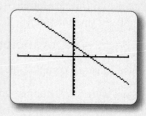

Graph of f Graph of f'

EXCEL **Technology Guide**

Section 3.1

Example 1 (page 193)   Use a table to estimate the following limits.

a. $\lim_{x \to 2} \dfrac{x^3 - 8}{x - 2}$ **b.** $\lim_{x \to 0} \dfrac{e^{2x} - 1}{x}$

Solution with Technology

1. Set up your spreadsheet to duplicate the table in part (a) as follows:

	A	B	C	D
1	x	f(x)	x	f(x)
2	1.9	=(A2^3-8)/(A2-2)	2.1	
3	1.99		2.01	
4	1.999		2.001	
5	1.9999		2.0001	

	A	B	C	D
1	x	f(x)	x	f(x)
2	1.9	11.41	2.1	12.61
3	1.99	11.9401	2.01	12.0601
4	1.999	11.994001	2.001	12.006001
5	1.9999	11.99940001	2.0001	12.00060001

(The formula in cell B2 is copied to columns B and D as indicated by the shading.) The values of $f(x)$ will be calculated in columns B and D.

2. For part (b), use the formula $= (\text{EXP}(2*\text{A2})-1)/\text{A2}$ in cell B2 and, in columns A and C, use values of x approaching 0 from either side.

Section 3.4

Example 3 (page 229)   The price of an ounce of gold can be approximated by the function

$$G(t) = -8t^2 + 144t + 150 \text{ dollars}   (7.5 \le t \le 10.5)$$

where t is time in hours. What was the average rate of change of the price of gold over the $1\frac{1}{2}$-hour period starting at 8:00 AM (the interval [8, 9.5] on the t-axis)?

Solution with Technology

To use Excel to compute the average rate of change of G:

1. Start with two columns, one for values of t and one for values of $G(t)$, which you enter using the formula for G:

	A	B
1	t	G(t)
2	8	=-8*A2^2+144*A2+150
3	9.5	

2. Next, calculate the average rate of change as shown here:

	A	B	C
1	t	G(t)	
2	8	790	Rate of change over [8, 9.5]:
3	9.5	796	=(B3-B2)/(A3-A2)

	A	B	C	D
1	t	G(t)		
2	8	790	Rate of change over [8, 9.5]:	
3	9.5	796	4	

In Example 4, we describe another, more versatile Excel template for computing rates of change. ■

Example 4 (page 230)   Continuing with Example 3, use technology to compute the average rate of change of

$$G(t) = -8t^2 + 144t + 150   (7.5 \le t \le 10.5)$$

over the intervals [8, 8 + h], where h = 1, 0.1, 0.01, 0.001, and 0.0001.

Solution with Technology

The template we can use to compute the rates of change is an extension of what we used in Example 3:

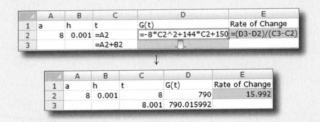

1. Column C contains the values $t = a$ and $t = a + h$ we are using for the independent variable.

2. The formula in cell E2 is the average rate of change formula $\Delta G/\Delta t$. Entering the different values h = 1, 0.1, 0.01, 0.001, and 0.0001 in cell B2 gives the results shown in the following table:

h	1	0.1	0.01	0.001	0.0001
Ave. Rate of Change $\dfrac{G(8 + h) - G(8)}{h}$	8	15.2	15.92	15.992	15.9992

Section 3.5

Example 2 (page 245) Calculate an approximate value of $f'(1.5)$ if $f(x) = x^2 - 4x$, and then find the equation of the tangent line at the point on the graph where $x = 1.5$.

Solution with Technology

You can compute both the difference quotient and the balanced difference quotient approximations in Excel using the following extension of the worksheet in Example 4 in Section 3.4.

	A	B	C	D	E	F
1	a	h	x	f(x)	Diff Quotients	Balanced Diff Quotient
2		1.5	0.0001	=A2-B2	=C2^2-4*C2	=(D3-D2)/(C3-C2)	=(D4-D2)/(C4-C2)
3				=A2		
4				=A2+B2		

Notice that we get two difference quotients in column E. The first uses $h = -0.0001$ while the second uses $h = 0.0001$ and is the one we use for our quick approximation. The balanced quotient is their average (column F). The results are as follows.

	A	B	C	D	E	F
1	a	h	x	f(x)	Diff Quotients	Balanced Diff Quotient
2		1.5	0.0001	1.4999	-3.7499	-1.0001	-1
3				1.5	-3.75	-0.9999	
4				1.5001	-3.7501		

From the results shown above, we find that the difference quotient quick approximation is -0.9999 and that the balanced difference quotient quick approximation is -1, which is in fact the exact value of $f'(1.5)$. See the discussion in the text for the calculation of the equation of the tangent line.

Example 4 (page 251) Use technology to graph of the derivative of $f(x) = -2x^2 + 6x + 5$ for values of x in starting at -5.

Solution with Technology

1. Start with a table of values for the function f:

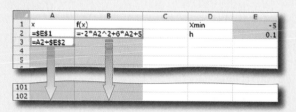

	A	B	C	D	E
1	x	f(x)		Xmin	-5
2	=$E$1	=-2*A2^2+6*A2+5		h	0.1
3	=A2+$E$2				
4					
5					
101					
102					

2. Next, compute approximate derivatives in Column C:

	A	B	C	D	E
1	x	f(x)	f'(x)	Xmin	-5
2	-5	-75	=(B3-B2)/$E$2	h	0.1
3	-4.9	-72.42			
4	-4.8	-69.88			
5	-4.7	-67.38			
101	4.9	-13.62			
102	5	-15			

	A	B	C	D	E
1	x	f(x)	f'(x)	Xmin	-5
2	-5	-75	25.8	h	0.1
3	-4.9	-72.42	25.4		
4	-4.8	-69.88	25		
5	-4.7	-67.38	24.6		
101	4.9	-13.62	-13.8		
102	5	-15			

You cannot paste the difference quotient formula into cell C102. (Why?) Notice that this worksheet uses the ordinary difference quotients, $[f(x + h) - f(x)]/h$. If you prefer, you can use balanced difference quotients $[f(x + h) - f(x - h)]/(2h)$, in which case cells C2 and C102 would both have to be left blank.

We then graph the function and the derivative on different graphs as follows:

1. First, graph the function f in the usual way, using Columns A and B.

2. Make a copy of this graph and click on it once. Columns A and B should be outlined, indicating that these are the columns used in the graph.

TECHNOLOGY GUIDE

3. By dragging from the center of the bottom edge of the box, move the Column B box over to Column C as shown:

	A	B	C
96	4.4	-7.32	-11.8
97	4.5	-8.5	-12.2
98	4.6	-9.72	-12.6
99	4.7	-10.98	-13
100	4.8	-12.28	-13.4
101	4.9	-13.62	-13.8
102	5	-15	

→

	A	B	C
96	4.4	-7.32	-11.8
97	4.5	-8.5	-12.2
98	4.6	-9.72	-12.6
99	4.7	-10.98	-13
100	4.8	-12.28	-13.4
101	4.9	-13.62	-13.8
102	5	-15	

The graph will then show the derivative (Columns A and C):

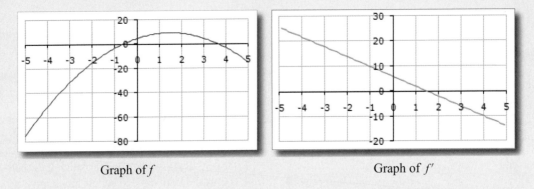

Graph of f Graph of f'

4

Techniques of Differentiation with Applications

Case Study Projecting Market Growth

You are on the board of directors at Fullcourt Academic Press. The sales director of the high school division has just burst into your office with a proposal for an expansion strategy based on the assumption that the number of high school seniors in the United States will be growing at a rate of at least 5,600 per year through the year 2015. Because the figures actually appear to be leveling off, you are suspicious about this estimate. You would like to devise a model that predicts this trend before tomorrow's scheduled board meeting.

How do you go about doing this?

Web Site

At the Web site you will find:

- Section by section tutorials, including game tutorials with randomized quizzes

- A detailed chapter summary

- A true/false quiz

- Additional review exercises

- Graphers, Excel tutorials, and other resources

- The following extra topic:

    Linear Approximation and Error Estimation

Yuri Arcurs, 2009/Used under license from Shutterstock.com

Introduction

In Chapter 3 we studied the concept of the derivative of a function, and we saw some of the applications for which derivatives are useful. However, computing the derivative of a function algebraically seemed to be a time-consuming process, forcing us to restrict attention to fairly simply functions.

In this chapter we develop shortcut techniques that will allow us to write down the derivative of a function directly without having to calculate any limit. These techniques will also enable us to differentiate any closed-form function—that is, any function, no matter how complicated, that can be specified by a formula involving powers, radicals, absolute values, exponents, and logarithms. (In a later chapter, we will discuss how to add trigonometric functions to this list.) We also show how to find the derivatives of functions that are only specified *implicitly*—that is, functions for which we are not given an explicit formula for y in terms of x but only an equation relating x and y.

algebra Review

For this chapter, you should be familiar with the algebra reviewed in **Chapter 0, Sections 3 and 4.**

4.1 Derivatives of Powers, Sums, and Constant Multiples

Up to this point we have approximated derivatives using difference quotients, and we have done exact calculations using the definition of the derivative as the limit of a difference quotient. In general, we would prefer to have an exact calculation, and it is also very useful to have a formula for the derivative function when we can find one. However, the calculation of a derivative as a limit is often tedious, so it would be nice to have a quicker method. We discuss the first of the shortcut rules in this section. By the end of this chapter, we will be able to find fairly quickly the derivative of almost any function we can write.

Shortcut Formula: The Power Rule

If you look at Examples 2 and 3 in Section 3.6, you may notice a pattern:

$$f(x) = x^2 \quad \Rightarrow \quad f'(x) = 2x$$
$$f(x) = x^3 \quad \Rightarrow \quad f'(x) = 3x^2$$

This pattern generalizes to any power of x:

Theorem 4.1 The Power Rule

If n is any constant and $f(x) = x^n$, then

$$f'(x) = nx^{n-1}.$$

Quick Examples

1. If $f(x) = x^2$, then $f'(x) = 2x^1 = 2x$.
2. If $f(x) = x^3$, then $f'(x) = 3x^2$.
3. If $f(x) = x$, rewrite as $f(x) = x^1$, so $f'(x) = 1x^0 = 1$.
4. If $f(x) = 1$, rewrite as $f(x) = x^0$, so $f'(x) = 0x^{-1} = 0$.

Web Site
www.AppliedCalc.org
At the Web site you can find
a proof of the power rule by
following:

Everything for Calculus
→ Chapter 4
→ Proof of the Power Rule

The proof of the power rule involves first studying the case when n is a positive integer, and then studying the cases of other types of exponents (negative integer, rational number, irrational number). You can find a proof at the Web site.

EXAMPLE 1 Using the Power Rule for Negative and Fractional Exponents

Calculate the derivatives of the following:

a. $f(x) = \dfrac{1}{x}$ **b.** $f(x) = \dfrac{1}{x^2}$ **c.** $f(x) = \sqrt{x}$

Solution

＊ NOTE See the section on exponents in the algebra review to brush up on negative and fractional exponents.

a. Rewrite＊ as $f(x) = x^{-1}$. Then $f'(x) = (-1)x^{-2} = -\dfrac{1}{x^2}$.

b. Rewrite as $f(x) = x^{-2}$. Then $f'(x) = (-2)x^{-3} = -\dfrac{2}{x^3}$.

c. Rewrite as $f(x) = x^{0.5}$. Then $f'(x) = 0.5x^{-0.5} = \dfrac{0.5}{x^{0.5}}$. Alternatively, rewrite $f(x)$ as $x^{1/2}$, so that $f'(x) = \dfrac{1}{2}x^{-1/2} = \dfrac{1}{2x^{1/2}} = \dfrac{1}{2\sqrt{x}}$.

By rewriting the given functions in Example 1 before taking derivatives, we converted them from **rational** or **radical form** (as in, say, $\dfrac{1}{x^2}$ and $\sqrt{x}$) to **exponent form** (as in x^{-2} and $x^{0.5}$; see the Algebra Review, Section 0.2) to enable us to use the power rule. (See the Caution below.)

Caution

We cannot apply the power rule to terms in the denominators or under square roots. For example:

1. The derivative of $\dfrac{1}{x^2}$ is **NOT** $\dfrac{1}{2x}$; it is $-\dfrac{2}{x^3}$.   See Example 1(b).

2. The derivative of $\sqrt{x^3}$ is **NOT** $\sqrt{3x^2}$; it is $1.5x^{0.5}$.   Rewrite $\sqrt{x^3}$ as $x^{3/2}$ or $x^{1.5}$ and apply the power rule.

Table 1 Table of Derivative Formulas

$f(x)$	$f'(x)$
1	0
x	1
x^2	$2x$
x^3	$3x^2$
x^n	nx^{n-1}
$\dfrac{1}{x}$	$-\dfrac{1}{x^2}$
$\dfrac{1}{x^2}$	$-\dfrac{2}{x^3}$
$\sqrt{x}$	$\dfrac{1}{2\sqrt{x}}$

Some of the derivatives in Example 1 are very useful to remember, so we summarize them in Table 1. We suggest that you add to this table as you learn more derivatives. It is *extremely* helpful to remember the derivatives of common functions such as $1/x$ and $\sqrt{x}$, even though they can be obtained by using the power rule as in the above example.

Another Notation: Differential Notation

Here is a useful notation based on the "d-notation" we discussed in Section 3.5. **Differential notation** is based on an abbreviation for the phrase "the derivative with respect to x." For example, we learned that if $f(x) = x^3$, then $f'(x) = 3x^2$. When we say "$f'(x) = 3x^2$," we mean the following:

The derivative of x^3 with respect to x equals $3x^2$.

✱ NOTE This may seem odd in the case of $f(x) = x^3$ because there are no other variables to worry about. But in expressions like st^3 that involve variables other than x, it is necessary to specify just what the variable of the function is. This is the same reason that we write "$f(x) = x^3$" rather than just "$f = x^3$."

You may wonder why we sneaked in the words "with respect to x." All this means is that the variable of the function is x, and not any other variable.✱ Because we use the phrase "the derivative with respect to x" often, we use the following abbreviation.

Differential Notation; Differentiation

$\dfrac{d}{dx}$ means "the derivative with respect to x."

Thus, $\dfrac{d}{dx}[f(x)]$ is the same thing as $f'(x)$, the derivative of $f(x)$ with respect to x. If y is a function of x, then the derivative of y with respect to x is

$$\frac{d}{dx}(y) \qquad \text{or, more compactly,} \qquad \frac{dy}{dx}$$

To **differentiate** a function $f(x)$ with respect to x means to take its derivative with respect to x.

Quick Examples

In Words	Formula
1. The derivative with respect to x of x^3 is $3x^2$.	$\dfrac{d}{dx}(x^3) = 3x^2$
2. The derivative with respect to t of $\dfrac{1}{t}$ is $-\dfrac{1}{t^2}$.	$\dfrac{d}{dt}\left(\dfrac{1}{t}\right) = -\dfrac{1}{t^2}$
3. If $y = x^4$, then $\dfrac{dy}{dx} = 4x^3$.	
4. If $u = \dfrac{1}{t^2}$, then $\dfrac{du}{dt} = -\dfrac{2}{t^3}$.	

Notes

1. $\dfrac{dy}{dx}$ is Leibniz' notation for the derivative we discussed in Section 3.5. (See the discussion before Example 3 there.)

2. Leibniz notation illustrates units nicely: units of $\dfrac{dy}{dx}$ are units of y per unit of x. ∎

The Rules for Sums and Constant Multiples

We can now find the derivatives of more complicated functions, such as polynomials, using the following rules:

Theorem 4.2 Derivatives of Sums, Differences, and Constant Multiples

If $f(x)$ and $g(x)$ are any two differentiable functions, and if c is any constant, then the functions $f(x) + g(x)$ and $cf(x)$ are differentiable, and

$$[f(x) \pm g(x)]' = f'(x) \pm g'(x) \qquad \text{Sum Rule}$$

$$[cf(x)]' = cf'(x). \qquad \text{Constant Multiple Rule}$$

In Words:

- The derivative of a sum is the sum of the derivatives, and the derivative of a difference is the difference of the derivatives.
- The derivative of c times a function is c times the derivative of the function.

Differential Notation:

$$\frac{d}{dx}[f(x) \pm g(x)] = \frac{d}{dx}f(x) \pm \frac{d}{dx}g(x)$$

$$\frac{d}{dx}[cf(x)] = c\frac{d}{dx}f(x)$$

Quick Examples

1. $\dfrac{d}{dx}[x^2 - x^4] = \dfrac{d}{dx}[x^2] - \dfrac{d}{dx}[x^4] = 2x - 4x^3$

2. $\dfrac{d}{dx}[7x^3] = 7\dfrac{d}{dx}[x^3] = 7(3x^2) = 21x^3$

   In other words, we multiply the coefficient (7) by the exponent (3), and then decrease the exponent by 1.

3. $\dfrac{d}{dx}[12x] = 12\dfrac{d}{dx}[x] = 12(1) = 12$

   In other words, the derivative of a constant times x is that constant.

4. $\dfrac{d}{dx}[-x^{0.5}] = \dfrac{d}{dx}[(-1)x^{0.5}] = (-1)\dfrac{d}{dx}[x^{0.5}] = (-1)(0.5)x^{-0.5}$
   $= -0.5x^{-0.5}$

5. $\dfrac{d}{dx}[12] = \dfrac{d}{dx}[12(1)] = 12\dfrac{d}{dx}[1] = 12(0) = 0.$

   In other words, the derivative of a constant is zero.

6. If my company earns twice as much (annual) revenue as yours and the derivative of your revenue function is the curve on the left, then the derivative of my revenue function is the curve on the right.

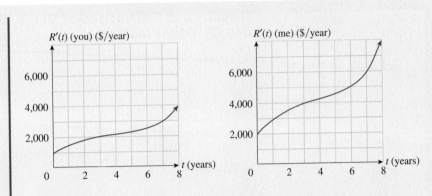

7. Suppose that a company's revenue R and cost C are changing with time. Then so is the profit, $P(t) = R(t) - C(t)$, and the rate of change of the profit is

$$P'(t) = R'(t) - C'(t).$$

In words: *The derivative of the profit is the derivative of revenue minus the derivative of cost.*

Proof of the Sum Rule

By the definition of the derivative of a function,

$$\frac{d}{dx}[f(x) + g(x)] = \lim_{h \to 0} \frac{[f(x + h) + g(x + h)] - [f(x) + g(x)]}{h}$$

$$= \lim_{h \to 0} \frac{[f(x + h) - f(x)] + [g(x + h) - g(x)]}{h}$$

$$= \lim_{h \to 0} \left[\frac{f(x + h) - f(x)}{h} + \frac{g(x + h) - g(x)}{h} \right]$$

$$= \lim_{h \to 0} \frac{f(x + h) - f(x)}{h} + \lim_{h \to 0} \frac{g(x + h) - g(x)}{h}$$

$$= \frac{d}{dx}[f(x)] + \frac{d}{dx}[g(x)].$$

The next-to-last step uses a property of limits: the limit of a sum is the sum of the limits. Think about why this should be true. The last step uses the definition of the derivative again (and the fact that the functions are differentiable).

The proof of the rule for constant multiples is similar.

EXAMPLE 2 Combining the Sum and Constant Multiple Rules, and Dealing with *x* in the Denominator

Find the derivatives of the following:

a. $f(x) = 3x^2 + 2x - 4$

b. $f(x) = \dfrac{2x}{3} - \dfrac{6}{x} + \dfrac{2}{3x^{0.2}} - \dfrac{x^4}{2}$

Solution

a. $\dfrac{d}{dx}(3x^2 + 2x - 4) = \dfrac{d}{dx}(3x^2) + \dfrac{d}{dx}(2x - 4)$ Rule for sums

$\qquad\qquad\qquad\qquad = \dfrac{d}{dx}(3x^2) + \dfrac{d}{dx}(2x) - \dfrac{d}{dx}(4)$ Rule for differences

$\qquad\qquad\qquad\qquad = 3(2x) + 2(1) - 0$ See Quick Example 2.

$\qquad\qquad\qquad\qquad = 6x + 2$

b. Notice that f has x and powers of x in the denominator. We deal with these terms the same way we did in Example 1, by rewriting them in exponent form (that is, in the form constant $\times$ power of x):

$$f(x) = \frac{2x}{3} - \frac{6}{x} + \frac{2}{3x^{0.2}} - \frac{x^4}{2} \qquad \text{Rational form}$$

$$= \frac{2}{3}x - 6x^{-1} + \frac{2}{3}x^{-0.2} - \frac{1}{2}x^4 \qquad \text{Exponent form}$$

We are now ready to take the derivative:

$$f'(x) = \frac{2}{3}(1) - 6(-1)x^{-2} + \frac{2}{3}(-0.2)x^{-1.2} - \frac{1}{2}(4x^3)$$

$$= \frac{2}{3} + 6x^{-2} - \frac{0.4}{3}x^{-1.2} - 2x^3 \qquad \text{Exponent form}$$

$$= \frac{2}{3} + \frac{6}{x^2} - \frac{0.4}{3x^{1.2}} - 2x^3 \qquad \text{Rational form}$$

Notice that in Example 2(a) we had three terms in the expression for $f(x)$, not just two. By applying the rule for sums and differences twice, we saw that the derivative of a sum or difference of three terms is the sum or difference of the derivatives of the terms. (One of those terms had zero derivative, so the final answer had only two terms.) In fact, the derivative of a sum or difference of any number of terms is the sum or difference of the derivatives of the terms. Put another way, to take the derivative of a sum or difference of any number of terms, we take derivatives term by term.

Note Nothing forces us to use only x as the independent variable when taking derivatives (although it is traditional to give x preference). For instance, part (a) in Example 2 can be rewritten as

$$\frac{d}{dt}(3t^2 + 2t - 4) = 6t + 2 \qquad \frac{d}{dt} \text{ means "derivative with respect to } t."$$

or

$$\frac{d}{du}(3u^2 + 2u - 4) = 6u + 2. \qquad \frac{d}{du} \text{ means "derivative with respect to } u." \qquad \blacksquare$$

In the previous examples, we saw instances of the following important facts. (Think about these graphically to see why they must be true.)

The Derivative of a Constant Times *x* and the Derivative of a Constant

If c is any constant, then:

Rule

$$\frac{d}{dx}(cx) = c$$

$$\frac{d}{dx}(c) = 0$$

Quick Examples

$$\frac{d}{dx}(6x) = 6 \qquad\qquad \frac{d}{dx}(-x) = -1$$

$$\frac{d}{dx}(5) = 0 \qquad\qquad \frac{d}{dx}(\pi) = 0$$

In Example 5 of Section 3.6 we saw that $f(x) = |x|$ fails to be differentiable at $x = 0$. In the next example we use the power rule and find more functions not differentiable at a point.

EXAMPLE 3 Functions Not Differentiable at a Point

Find the natural domains of the derivatives of $f(x) = x^{1/3}$ and $g(x) = x^{2/3}$, and $h(x) = |x|$.

Solution Let's first look at the functions f and g. By the power rule,

$$f'(x) = \frac{1}{3}x^{-2/3} = \frac{1}{3x^{2/3}}$$

and

$$g'(x) = \frac{2}{3}x^{-1/3} = \frac{2}{3x^{1/3}}.$$

$f'(x)$ and $g'(x)$ are defined only for nonzero values of x, and their natural domains consist of all real numbers except 0. Thus, the derivatives f' and g' do not exist at $x = 0$. In other words, f and g are not differentiable at $x = 0$. If we look at Figure 1, we notice why these functions fail to be differentiable at $x = 0$: The graph of f has a vertical tangent line at 0. Because a vertical line has undefined slope, the derivative is undefined at that point. The graph of g comes to a sharp point (called a **cusp**) at 0, so it is not meaningful to speak about a tangent line at that point; therefore, the derivative of g is not defined there. (Actually, there is a reasonable candidate for the tangent line at $x = 0$, but it is the vertical line again.)

We can also detect this nondifferentiability by computing some difference quotients numerically. In the case of $f(x) = x^{1/3}$, we get the following table:

h	± 1	± 0.1	± 0.01	± 0.001	± 0.0001
$\dfrac{f(0 + h) - f(0)}{h}$	1	4.6416	21.544	100	464.16

suggesting that the difference quotients $[f(0 + h) - f(0)]/h$ grow large without bound rather than approach any fixed number as h approaches 0. (Can you see how the behavior of the difference quotients in the table is reflected in the graph?)

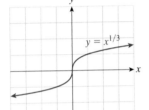

$f(x) = x^{1/3}$

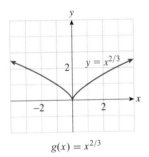

$g(x) = x^{2/3}$

Figure 1

using Technology

If you try to graph the function $f(x) = x^{2/3}$ using the format

$$X^{\wedge}(2/3)$$

you may get only the right-hand portion of Figure 1 because graphing utilities are (often) not programmed to raise negative numbers to fractional exponents. (However, many will handle $X^{\wedge}(1/3)$ correctly, as a special case they recognize.) To avoid this difficulty, you can take advantage of the identity

$$x^{2/3} = (x^2)^{1/3}$$

so that it is always a nonnegative number that is being raised to a fractional exponent. Thus, use the format

$$(X^2)^{\wedge}(1/3)$$

to obtain both portions of the graph.

Now we return to the function $h(x) = |x|$ discussed in Example 5 of Section 3.6. We saw there that $|x|$ is not differentiable at $x = 0$. What about values of x *other than* 0? For such values, we can write:

$$|x| = \begin{cases} -x & \text{if } x < 0 \\ x & \text{if } x > 0 \end{cases}$$

Hence, by the power rule (think of x as x^1):

$$f'(x) = \begin{cases} -1 & \text{if } x < 0 \\ 1 & \text{if } x > 0 \end{cases}$$

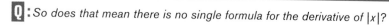

Q: *So does that mean there is no single formula for the derivative of* $|x|$?

A: Actually, there *is* a convenient formula. Consider the ratio

$$\frac{|x|}{x}.$$

If x is positive, then $|x| = x$, so $|x|/x = x/x = 1$. On the other hand, if x is negative then $|x| = -x$, so $|x|/x = -x/x = -1$. In other words,

$$\frac{|x|}{x} = \begin{cases} -1 & \text{if } x < 0 \\ 1 & \text{if } x > 0 \end{cases},$$

which is exactly the formula we obtained for $f'(x)$. In other words:

Derivative of $|x|$

$$\frac{d}{dx}|x| = \frac{|x|}{x}$$

Note that the derivative does not exist when $x = 0$.

Quick Example

$$\frac{d}{dx}[3|x| + x] = 3\frac{|x|}{x} + 1$$

APPLICATION

The next Example is similar to Example 3 in Section 3.4, but this time we analyze the curve using the derivative.

EXAMPLE 4 **Gold Price**

You are a commodities trader and you monitor the price of gold on the New York Spot Market very closely during an active morning. Suppose you find that the price of an ounce of gold can be approximated by the function

$$G(t) = -8t^2 + 144t + 150 \text{ dollars} \quad (7.5 \leq t \leq 10.5)$$

where t is time in hours. (See Figure 2. $t = 8$ represents 8:00 AM.)

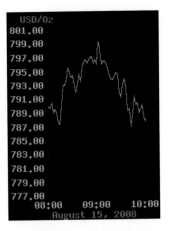

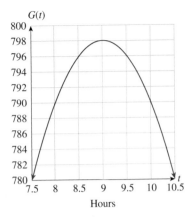

Source: www.kitco.com (August 15, 2008) $G(t) = -8t^2 + 144t + 150$

Figure 2

a. According to the model, how fast was the price of gold changing at 10:00 AM?

b. According to the model, the price of gold

   (A) increased at a faster and faster rate
   (B) increased at a slower and slower rate
   (C) decreased at a faster and faster rate
   (D) decreased at a slower and slower rate

between 9:30 and 10:30 AM.

Solution

a. Differentiating the given function with respect to t gives

$$G'(t) = -16t + 144.$$

Because 10:00 AM corresponds to $t = 10$, we obtain

$$G'(10) = -16(10) + 144 = -16.$$

The units of the derivative are dollars per hour, so we conclude that, at 10:00 AM, the price of gold was dropping at a rate of $16 per hour.

b. From the graph, we can see that, between 9:30 and 10:30 AM (the interval [9.5, 10.5]), the price of gold was decreasing. Also from the graph, we see that the slope of the tangent becomes more and more negative as t increases, so the price of gold is decreasing at a faster and faster rate (choice (C)).

We can also see this algebraically from the derivative, $G'(t) = -16t + 144$: For values of t larger than 9, $G'(t)$ is negative; that is, the rate of change of G is negative, so the price of gold is decreasing. Further, as t increases, $G'(t)$ becomes more and more negative, so the price of gold is decreasing at a faster and faster rate, confirming that choice (C) is the correct one.

An Application to Limits: L'Hospital's Rule

The limits that caused us some trouble in Sections 3.1–3.3 are those of the form $\lim_{x \to a} f(x)$ in which substituting $x = a$ gave us an indeterminate form, such as

$$\lim_{x \to 2} \frac{x^3 - 8}{x - 2} \qquad \text{Substituting } x = 2 \text{ yields } \tfrac{0}{0}.$$

$$\lim_{x \to +\infty} \frac{2x - 4}{x - 1} \qquad \text{Substituting } x = +\infty \text{ yields } \tfrac{\infty}{\infty}.$$

L'Hospital's rule gives us an alternate way of computing limits such as these without the need to do any preliminary simplification. It also allows us to compute some limits for which algebraic simplification does not work.*

* NOTE Guillaume François Antoine, Marquis de l'Hospital (1661–1704) wrote the first textbook on calculus, *Analyse des infiniment petits pour l'intelligence des lignes courbes*, in 1692. The rule now known as l'Hospital's Rule appeared first in this book.

Theorem 4.3 L'Hospital's Rule

If f and g are two differentiable functions such that substituting $x = a$ in the expression $\dfrac{f(x)}{g(x)}$ gives the indeterminate form $\dfrac{0}{0}$ or $\dfrac{\infty}{\infty}$, then

$$\lim_{x \to a} \frac{f(x)}{g(x)} = \lim_{x \to a} \frac{f'(x)}{g'(x)}$$

That is, we can replace $f(x)$ and $g(x)$ with their *derivatives* and try again to take the limit.

Quick Examples

1. Substituting $x = 2$ in $\dfrac{x^3 - 8}{x - 2}$ yields $\dfrac{0}{0}$. Therefore, l'Hospital's rule applies and

$$\lim_{x \to 2} \frac{x^3 - 8}{x - 2} = \lim_{x \to 2} \frac{3x^2}{1} = \frac{3(2)^2}{1} = 12.$$

2. Substituting $x = +\infty$ in $\dfrac{2x - 4}{x - 1}$ yields $\dfrac{\infty}{\infty}$. Therefore, l'Hospital's rule applies and

$$\lim_{x \to +\infty} \frac{2x - 4}{x - 1} = \lim_{x \to +\infty} \frac{2}{1} = 2.$$

* NOTE A proof of l'Hospital's rule can be found in most advanced calculus textbooks.

The proof of l'Hospital's rule is beyond the scope of this text.*

EXAMPLE 5 Applying L'Hospital's Rule

Check whether l'Hospital's rule applies to each of the following limits. If it does, use it to evaluate the limit. Otherwise, use some other method to evaluate the limit.

a. $\displaystyle\lim_{x \to 1} \frac{x^2 - 2x + 1}{4x^3 - 3x^2 - 6x + 5}$
    b. $\displaystyle\lim_{x \to +\infty} \frac{2x^2 - 4x}{5x^3 - 3x + 5}$

c. $\lim\limits_{x \to 1} \dfrac{x - 1}{x^3 - 3x^2 + 3x - 1}$ **d.** $\lim\limits_{x \to 1} \dfrac{x}{x^3 - 3x^2 + 3x - 1}$

Solution

a. Setting $x = 1$ yields

$$\frac{1 - 2 + 1}{4 - 3 - 6 + 5} = \frac{0}{0}.$$

Therefore, l'Hospital's rule applies and

$$\lim_{x \to 1} \frac{x^2 - 2x + 1}{4x^3 - 3x^2 - 6x + 5} = \lim_{x \to 1} \frac{2x - 2}{12x^2 - 6x - 6}.$$

We are left with a closed-form function. However, we cannot substitute $x = 1$ to find the limit because the function $(2x - 2)/(12x^2 - 6x - 6)$ is still not defined at $x = 1$. In fact, if we set $x = 1$, we again get $0/0$. Thus, l'Hospital's rule applies again, and

$$\lim_{x \to 1} \frac{2x - 2}{12x^2 - 6x - 6} = \lim_{x \to 1} \frac{2}{24x - 6}.$$

Once again we have a closed-form function, but this time it is defined when $x = 1$, giving

$$\frac{2}{24 - 6} = \frac{1}{9}.$$

Thus,

$$\lim_{x \to 1} \frac{x^2 - 2x + 1}{4x^3 - 3x^2 - 6x + 5} = \frac{1}{9}.$$

b. Setting $x = +\infty$ yields $\dfrac{\infty}{\infty}$, so

$$\lim_{x \to +\infty} \frac{2x^2 - 4x}{5x^3 - 3x + 5} = \lim_{x \to +\infty} \frac{4x - 4}{15x^2 - 3}.$$

Setting $x = +\infty$ again yields $\dfrac{\infty}{\infty}$, so we can apply the rule again to obtain

$$\lim_{x \to +\infty} \frac{4x - 4}{15x^2 - 3} = \lim_{x \to +\infty} \frac{4}{30x}.$$

Note that we cannot apply l'Hospital's rule a third time because setting $x = +\infty$ yields the *determinate* form $4/\infty = 0$ (see the discussion at the end of Section 3.3). Thus, the limit is 0.

c. Setting $x = 1$ yields $0/0$ so, by l'Hospital's rule,

$$\lim_{x \to 1} \frac{x - 1}{x^3 - 3x^2 + 3x - 1} = \lim_{x \to 1} \frac{1}{3x^2 - 6x + 3}.$$

We are left with a closed-form function that is still not defined at $x = 1$. Further, l'Hospital's rule no longer applies because putting $x = 1$ yields the determinate form $1/0$. To investigate this limit, we refer to the discussion at the end of Section 3.3 and find

$$\lim_{x \to 1} \frac{1}{3x^2 - 6x + 3} = \lim_{x \to 1} \frac{1}{3(x - 1)^2} = +\infty. \qquad \frac{1}{0^+} = +\infty$$

d. Setting $x = 1$ in the expression yields the determinate form $1/0$, so l'Hospital's rule does not apply here. Using the methods of Section 3.3 again, we find that the limit does not exist.

FAQs

Using the Rules and Recognizing When a Function is Not Differentiable

Q: I would *like* to say that the derivative of $5x^2 - 8x + 4$ is just $10x - 8$ without having to go through all that stuff about derivatives of sums and constant multiples. Can I simply forget about all the rules and write down the answer?

A: We developed the rules for sums and constant multiples precisely for that reason: so that we could simply write down a derivative without having to think about it too hard. So, you are perfectly justified in simply writing down the derivative without going through the rules, but bear in mind that what you are really doing is applying the power rule, the rule for sums, and the rule for multiples over and over.

Q: Is there a way of telling from its formula whether a function f is not differentiable at a point?

A: Here are some indicators to look for in the formula for f:

- The absolute value of some expression; f may not be differentiable at points where that expression is zero.

  Example: $f(x) = 3x^2 - |x - 4|$ is not differentiable at $x = 4$.

- A fractional power smaller than 1 of some expression; f may not be differentiable at points where that expression is zero.

  Example: $f(x) = (x^2 - 16)^{2/3}$ is not differentiable at $x = \pm 4$.

4.1 EXERCISES

▼ more advanced   ◆ challenging
⊤ indicates exercises that should be solved using technology

*In Exercises 1–10, use the shortcut rules to **mentally** calculate the derivative of the given function.* HINT [See Examples 1 and 2.]

1. $f(x) = x^5$ 　　　　**2.** $f(x) = x^4$

3. $f(x) = 2x^{-2}$ 　　　**4.** $f(x) = 3x^{-1}$

5. $f(x) = -x^{0.25}$ 　　**6.** $f(x) = -x^{-0.5}$

7. $f(x) = 2x^4 + 3x^3 - 1$ 　**8.** $f(x) = -x^3 - 3x^2 - 1$

9. $f(x) = -x + \dfrac{1}{x} + 1$ 　**10.** $f(x) = \dfrac{1}{x} + \dfrac{1}{x^2}$

In Exercises 11–16, obtain the derivative dy/dx and state the rules that you use. HINT [See Example 2.]

11. $y = 10$ 　　　　　**12.** $y = x^3$

13. $y = x^2 + x$ 　　　**14.** $y = x - 5$

15. $y = 4x^3 + 2x - 1$ 　**16.** $y = 4x^{-1} - 2x - 10$

In Exercises 17–40, find the derivative of each function.
HINT [See Examples 1 and 2.]

17. $f(x) = x^2 - 3x + 5$ 　**18.** $f(x) = 3x^3 - 2x^2 + x$

19. $f(x) = x + x^{0.5}$ 　　**20.** $f(x) = x^{0.5} + 2x^{-0.5}$

21. $g(x) = x^{-2} - 3x^{-1} - 2$ 　**22.** $g(x) = 2x^{-1} + 4x^{-2}$

23. $g(x) = \dfrac{1}{x} - \dfrac{1}{x^2}$ 　　**24.** $g(x) = \dfrac{1}{x^2} + \dfrac{1}{x^3}$

25. $h(x) = \dfrac{2}{x^{0.4}}$ 　　　**26.** $h(x) = -\dfrac{1}{2x^{0.2}}$

27. $h(x) = \dfrac{1}{x^2} + \dfrac{2}{x^3}$ 　　**28.** $h(x) = \dfrac{2}{x} - \dfrac{2}{x^3} + \dfrac{1}{x^4}$

29. $r(x) = \dfrac{2}{3x} - \dfrac{1}{2x^{0.1}}$ 　**30.** $r(x) = \dfrac{4}{3x^2} + \dfrac{1}{x^{3.2}}$

31. $r(x) = \dfrac{2x}{3} - \dfrac{x^{0.1}}{2} + \dfrac{4}{3x^{1.1}} - 2$

32. $r(x) = \dfrac{4x^2}{3} + \dfrac{x^{3.2}}{6} - \dfrac{2}{3x^2} + 4$

33. $t(x) = |x| + \dfrac{1}{x}$ 　　**34.** $t(x) = 3|x| - \sqrt{x}$

35. $s(x) = \sqrt{x} + \dfrac{1}{\sqrt{x}}$ 　　**36.** $s(x) = x + \dfrac{7}{\sqrt{x}}$

HINT [For Exercises 37–40, first expand the given function.]

37. ▼ $s(x) = x\left(x^2 - \dfrac{1}{x}\right)$ **38.** ▼ $s(x) = x^{-1}\left(x - \dfrac{2}{x}\right)$

39. ▼ $t(x) = \dfrac{x^2 - 2x^3}{x}$ **40.** ▼ $t(x) = \dfrac{2x + x^2}{x}$

In Exercises 41–46, evaluate the given expression.

41. $\dfrac{d}{dx}(2x^{1.3} - x^{-1.2})$ **42.** $\dfrac{d}{dx}(2x^{4.3} + x^{0.6})$

43. ▼ $\dfrac{d}{dx}[1.2(x - |x|)]$ **44.** ▼ $\dfrac{d}{dx}[4(x^2 + 3|x|)]$

45. ▼ $\dfrac{d}{dt}(at^3 - 4at)$;   (a constant)

46. ▼ $\dfrac{d}{dt}(at^2 + bt + c)$;   (a, b, c constant)

In Exercises 47–52, find the indicated derivative.

47. $y = \dfrac{x^{10.3}}{2} + 99x^{-1}$; $\dfrac{dy}{dx}$ **48.** $y = \dfrac{x^{1.2}}{3} - \dfrac{x^{0.9}}{2}$; $\dfrac{dy}{dx}$

49. $s = 2.3 + \dfrac{2.1}{t^{1.1}} - \dfrac{t^{0.6}}{2}$; $\dfrac{ds}{dt}$ **50.** $s = \dfrac{2}{t^{1.1}} + t^{-1.2}$; $\dfrac{ds}{dt}$

51. ▼ $V = \dfrac{4}{3}\pi r^3$; $\dfrac{dV}{dr}$ **52.** ▼ $A = 4\pi r^2$; $\dfrac{dA}{dr}$

In Exercises 53–58, find the slope of the tangent to the graph of the given function at the indicated point. HINT [Recall that the slope of the tangent to the graph of f at x = a is f'(a).]

53. $f(x) = x^3$; $(-1, -1)$ **54.** $g(x) = x^4$; $(-2, 16)$

55. $f(x) = 1 - 2x$; $(2, -3)$ **56.** $f(x) = \dfrac{x}{3} - 1$; $(-3, -2)$

57. $g(t) = \dfrac{1}{t^5}$; $(1, 1)$ **58.** $s(t) = \dfrac{1}{t^3}$; $\left(-2, -\dfrac{1}{8}\right)$

In Exercises 59–64, find the equation of the tangent line to the graph of the given function at the point with the indicated x-coordinate. In each case, sketch the curve together with the appropriate tangent line.

59. ▼ $f(x) = x^3$; $x = -1$ **60.** ▼ $f(x) = x^2$; $x = 0$

61. ▼ $f(x) = x + \dfrac{1}{x}$; $x = 2$ **62.** ▼ $f(x) = \dfrac{1}{x^2}$; $x = 1$

63. ▼ $f(x) = \sqrt{x}$; $x = 4$ **64.** ▼ $f(x) = 2x + 4$; $x = -1$

In Exercises 65–70, find all values of x (if any) where the tangent line to the graph of the given equation is horizontal. HINT [The tangent line is horizontal when its slope is zero.]

65. ▼ $y = 2x^2 + 3x - 1$ **66.** ▼ $y = -3x^2 - x$

67. ▼ $y = 2x + 8$ **68.** ▼ $y = -x + 1$

69. ▼ $y = x + \dfrac{1}{x}$ **70.** ▼ $y = x - \sqrt{x}$

71. ◆ Write out the proof that $\dfrac{d}{dx}(x^4) = 4x^3$.

72. ◆ Write out the proof that $\dfrac{d}{dx}(x^5) = 5x^4$.

🖥 In Exercises 73–76, use technology to graph the derivative of the given function for the given range of values of x. Then use your graph to estimate all values of x (if any) where **(a)** the given function is not differentiable, and **(b)** the tangent line to the graph of the given function is horizontal. Round answers to one decimal place.

73. ▼ $h(x) = |x - 3|$; $-5 \le x \le 5$

74. ▼ $h(x) = 2x + (x - 3)^{1/3}$; $-5 \le x \le 5$

75. ▼ $f(x) = x - 5(x - 1)^{2/5}$; $-4 \le x \le 6$

76. ▼ $f(x) = |2x + 5| - x^2$; $-4 \le x \le 4$

🖥 In Exercises 77–80, investigate the differentiability of the given function at the given points numerically (that is, use a table of values). If f'(a) exists, give its approximate value. HINT [See Example 3.]

77. $f(x) = x^{1/3}$ **a.** $a = 1$ **b.** $a = 0$

78. $f(x) = x + |1 - x|$ **a.** $a = 1$ **b.** $a = 0$

79. ▼ $f(x) = [x(1 - x)]^{1/3}$ **a.** $a = 1$ **b.** $a = 0$

80. ▼ $f(x) = (1 - x)^{2/3}$ **a.** $a = -1$ **b.** $a = 1$

In Exercises 81–92 say whether l'Hospital's rule applies. If is does, use it to evaluate the given limit. If not, use some other method.

81. $\lim\limits_{x \to 1} \dfrac{x^2 - 2x + 1}{x^2 - x}$ **82.** $\lim\limits_{x \to -1} \dfrac{x^2 + 3x + 2}{x^2 + x}$

83. $\lim\limits_{x \to 2} \dfrac{x^3 - 8}{x - 2}$ **84.** $\lim\limits_{x \to 0} \dfrac{x^3 + 8}{x^2 + 3x + 2}$

85. $\lim\limits_{x \to 1} \dfrac{x^2 + 3x + 2}{x^2 + x}$ **86.** $\lim\limits_{x \to -2} \dfrac{x^3 + 8}{x^2 + 3x + 2}$

87. $\lim\limits_{x \to -\infty} \dfrac{3x^2 + 10x - 1}{2x^2 - 5x}$ **88.** $\lim\limits_{x \to -\infty} \dfrac{6x^2 + 5x + 100}{3x^2 - 9}$

89. $\lim\limits_{x \to -\infty} \dfrac{10x^2 + 300x + 1}{5x + 2}$ **90.** $\lim\limits_{x \to -\infty} \dfrac{2x^4 + 20x^3}{1000x^3 + 6}$

91. $\lim\limits_{x \to -\infty} \dfrac{x^3 - 100}{2x^2 + 500}$ **92.** $\lim\limits_{x \to -\infty} \dfrac{x^2 + 30x}{2x^6 + 10x}$

APPLICATIONS

93. *Crude Oil Prices* The price per barrel of crude oil in constant 2008 dollars can be approximated by

$$P(t) = 0.45t^2 - 12t + 105 \text{ dollars}   (0 \le t \le 28)$$

where t is time in years since the start of 1980.[1] Find $P'(t)$ and $P'(20)$. What does the answer tell you about the price of crude oil? HINT [See Example 2.]

94. **Median Home Price** The median home price in the United States over the period 2004–2009 can be approximated by

$$P(t) = -5t^2 + 75t - 30 \text{ thousand dollars} \quad (4 \le t \le 9)$$

where t is time in years since the start of 2000.[2] Find $P'(t)$ and $P'(6)$. What does the answer tell you about home prices? HINT [See Example 2.]

95. **College Basketball: Men** The number of NCAA men's college basketball teams in the United States can be modeled by:

$$n(t) = -0.56t^2 + 14t + 930 \quad (0 \le t \le 8)$$

where t is time in years since 2000.[3]

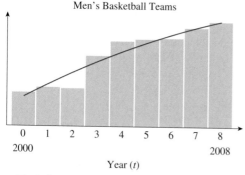

Men's Basketball Teams

Year (t)

a. Find $n'(t)$. HINT [See Example 2.]
b. How fast (to the nearest whole number) was the number of men's college basketball teams increasing in 2006?
c. According to the model, did the rate of increase of the number of teams increase or decrease with time? Explain. HINT [See Example 4.]

96. **College Basketball: Women** The number of NCAA women's college basketball teams in the United States can be modeled by:

$$n(t) = -0.98t^2 + 32t + 1,850 \quad (0 \le t \le 8)$$

where t is time in years since 2000.[4]

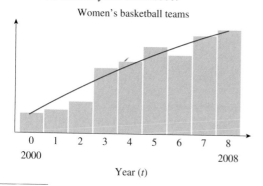

Women's basketball teams

Year (t)

a. Find $n'(t)$. HINT [See Example 2.]
b. How fast (to the nearest whole number) was the number of women's college basketball teams increasing in 2005?
c. According to the model, did the rate of increase of the number of teams increase or decrease with time? Explain. HINT [See Example 4.]

97. **Food Versus Education** The following equation shows the approximate relationship between the percentage y of total personal consumption spent on food and the corresponding percentage x spent on education.[5]

$$y = \frac{35}{x^{0.35}} \text{ percentage points} \quad (6.5 \le x \le 17.5)$$

According to the model, spending on food is decreasing at a rate of _____ percentage points per one percentage point increase in spending on education when 10% of total consumption is spent on education. (Answer should be rounded to two significant digits.) HINT [See Example 2(b).]

98. **Food Versus Recreation** The following equation shows the approximate relationship between the percentage y of total personal consumption spent on food and the corresponding percentage x spent on recreation.[6]

$$y = \frac{33}{x^{0.63}} \text{ percentage points} \quad (2.5 \le x \le 4.5)$$

According to the model, spending on food is decreasing at a rate of _____ percentage points per one percentage point increase in spending on recreation when 3% of total consumption is spent on recreation. (Answer should be rounded to two significant digits.) HINT [See Example 2(b).]

99. **Velocity** If a stone is dropped from a height of 400 feet, its height s after t seconds is given by $s(t) = 400 - 16t^2$, with s in feet.

a. Compute $s'(t)$ and hence find its velocity at times $t = 0$, 1, 2, 3, and 4 seconds.
b. When does it reach the ground, and how fast is it traveling when it hits the ground? HINT [It reaches the ground when $s(t) = 0$.]

100. **Velocity** If a stone is thrown down at 120 ft/s from a height of 1,000 feet, its height s after t seconds is given by $s(t) = 1,000 - 120t - 16t^2$, with s in feet.

a. Compute $s'(t)$ and hence find its velocity at times $t = 0$, 1, 2, 3, and 4 seconds.
b. When does it reach the ground, and how fast is it traveling when it hits the ground? HINT [It reaches the ground when $s(t) = 0$.]

[1] Source for data: www.inflationdata.com.
[2] Source for data: www.investmenttools.com.
[3] 2007 and 2008 figures are estimates. Source: The 2008 Statistical Abstract, www.census.gov/.
[4] Ibid.
[5] Model based on historical and projected data from 1908–2010. Sources: Historical data, Bureau of Economic Analysis; projected data, Bureau of Labor Statistics/*New York Times*, December 1, 2003, p. C2.
[6] Ibid.

101. *iPhone Sales* iPhone sales from the 2nd quarter in 2007 through the 2nd quarter in 2008 can be approximated by

$$S(t) = -390t^2 + 3,300t - 4,800 \text{ thousand phones}$$
$$(2 \le t \le 6)$$

in quarter t. ($t = 1$ represents the start of the first quarter of 2007.)[7]

iPhone sales (thousands)

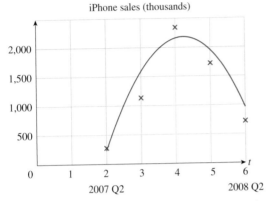

2007 Q2   2008 Q2

a. Compute $S'(t)$. How fast were iPhone sales changing in the first quarter of 2008 ($t = 5$)? (Be careful to give correct units of measurement.)

b. According to the model, iPhone sales

    (A) increased at a faster and faster rate
    (B) increased at a slower and slower rate
    (C) decreased at a faster and faster rate
    (D) decreased at a slower and slower rate

    during the first two quarters shown (the interval $[2, 4]$). Justify your answer in two ways: geometrically, reasoning entirely from the graph; and algebraically, reasoning from the derivative of S. HINT [See Example 4.]

102. *Facebook Membership* The number of **Facebook** members from the start of 2006 to mid-2008 can be approximated by

$$S(t) = 15t^2 - 76t + 101 \text{ million members} \quad (2 \le t \le 4.5)$$

in year t ($t = 0$ represents the start of 2004).[8]

Facebook membership (millions)

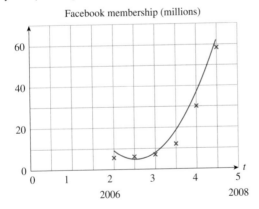

2006   2008

a. Compute $S'(t)$. According to the model, how fast was **Facebook** membership changing at the start of 2008 ($t = 4$)? (Be careful to give correct units of measurement.)

b. According to the model, **Facebook** membership

    (A) increased at a faster and faster rate
    (B) increased at a slower and slower rate
    (C) decreased at a faster and faster rate
    (D) decreased at a slower and slower rate

    during 2007 (the interval $[3, 4]$). Justify your answer in two ways: geometrically, reasoning entirely from the graph; and algebraically, reasoning from the derivative of S. HINT [See Example 4.]

103. *Ecology* Increasing numbers of manatees ("sea sirens") have been killed by boats off the Florida coast. The following graph shows the relationship between the number of boats registered in Florida and the number of manatees killed each year.

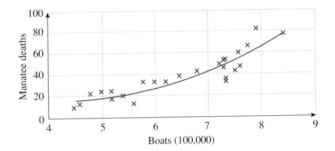

Boats (100,000)

The regression curve shown is given by

$$f(x) = 3.55x^2 - 30.2x + 81 \quad (4.5 \le x \le 8.5)$$

where x is the number of boats (hundreds of thousands) registered in Florida in a particular year and $f(x)$ is the number of manatees killed by boats in Florida that year.[9]

a. Compute $f'(x)$. What are the units of measurement of $f'(x)$?

b. Is $f'(x)$ increasing or decreasing with increasing x? Interpret the answer. HINT [See Example 4.]

c. Compute and interpret $f'(8)$.

104. *SAT Scores by Income* The graph on the next page shows U.S. verbal SAT scores as a function of parents' income level.[10]

---

[7] The model is the authors'. Source for data: Apple financial statements, www.apple.com.

[8] The model is the authors'. Sources for data: www.facebook.com/, http://insidehighered.com (Some data are interpolated.)

[9] Regression model is based on data from 1976 to 2000. Sources for data: Florida Department of Highway Safety & Motor Vehicles, Florida Marine Institute/*New York Times*, February 12, 2002, p. F4.

[10] Based on 1994 data. Source: The College Board/*New York Times*, March 5, 1995, p. E16.

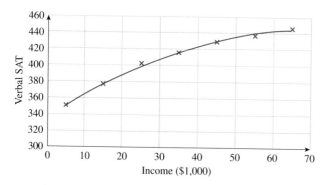

Income ($1,000)

The regression curve shown is given by

$$f(x) = -0.021x^2 + 3.0x + 336 \quad (5 \le x \le 65)$$

where $f(x)$ is the average SAT verbal score of a student whose parents earn x thousand dollars per year.[11]

a. Compute $f'(x)$. What are the units of measurement of $f'(x)$?

b. Is $f'(x)$ increasing or decreasing with increasing x? Interpret the answer. HINT [See Example 4.]

c. Compute and interpret $f'(30)$.

105. ISP Market Share The following graph shows approximate market shares, in percentage points, of Microsoft's MSN Internet service provider, and the combined shares of MSN, Comcast, Earthlink, and AOL for the period 1999–2004.[12]

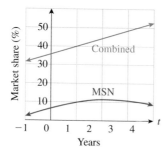

Years

Here, t is time in years since June 2000. Let $c(t)$ be the combined market share at time t, and let $m(t)$ be MSN's share at time t.

a. What does the function $c(t) - m(t)$ measure? What does $c'(t) - m'(t)$ measure?

b. Based on the graphs shown, $c(t) - m(t)$ is

(A) increasing
(B) decreasing
(C) increasing, then decreasing
(D) decreasing, then increasing

on the interval [3, 4].

c. Based on the graphs shown, $c'(t) - m'(t)$ is

(A) positive
(B) negative
(C) positive, then negative
(D) negative, then positive

on the interval [3, 4].

d. The two market shares are approximated by

MSN: $m(t) = -0.83t^2 + 3.8t + 6.8 \quad (-1 \le t \le 4)$
Combined: $c(t) = 4.2t + 36 \quad (-1 \le t \le 4)$

Compute $c'(2) - m'(2)$. Interpret your answer.

106. ▼ ISP Revenue The following graph shows the approximate total revenue, in millions of dollars, of Microsoft's MSN Internet service provider, as well as the portion of the revenue due to advertising for the period June 2001–January 2004.[13]

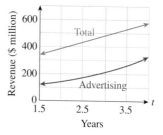

Years

Here, t is time in years since January 2000. Let $s(t)$ be the total revenue at time t, and let $a(t)$ be revenue due to advertising at time t.

a. What does the function $s(t) - a(t)$ measure? What does $s'(t) - a'(t)$ measure?

b. Based on the graphs shown, $s(t) - a(t)$ is

(A) increasing
(B) decreasing
(C) increasing, then decreasing
(D) decreasing, then increasing

on the interval [2, 4].

c. Based on the graphs shown, $s'(t) - a'(t)$ is

(A) positive
(B) negative
(C) positive, then negative
(D) negative, then positive

on the interval [2, 4].

d. The two revenue curves are approximated by

Advertising: $a(t) = 20t^2 - 27t + 120 \quad (1.5 \le t \le 4)$
Total: $s(t) = 96t + 190 \quad (1.5 \le t \le 4)$

Compute $a'(2), s'(2)$, and hence $s'(2) - a'(2)$. Interpret your answer.

[11] Regression model is based on 1994 data. Source: The College Board/ *New York Times*, March 5, 1995, p. E16.

[12] The curves are regression models. Source for data: Solomon Research, Morgan Stanley/*New York Times*, July 19, 2004.

[13] Ibid.

COMMUNICATION AND REASONING EXERCISES

107. What instructions would you give to a fellow student who wanted to accurately graph the tangent line to the curve $y = 3x^2$ at the point $(-1, 3)$?

108. What instructions would you give to a fellow student who wanted to accurately graph a line at right angles to the curve $y = 4/x$ at the point where $x = 0.5$?

109. Consider $f(x) = x^2$ and $g(x) = 2x^2$. How do the slopes of the tangent lines of f and g at the same x compare?

110. Consider $f(x) = x^3$ and $g(x) = x^3 + 3$. How do the slopes of the tangent lines of f and g compare?

111. Suppose $g(x) = -f(x)$. How do the derivatives of f and g compare?

112. Suppose $g(x) = f(x) - 50$. How do the derivatives of f and g compare?

113. Following is an excerpt from your best friend's graded homework:

$$3x^4 + 11x^5 = 12x^3 + 55x^4 \quad \text{✗ WRONG} \quad -8$$

Why was it marked wrong? How would you correct it?

114. Following is an excerpt from your second best friend's graded homework:

$$f(x) = \frac{3}{4x^2}; f'(x) = \frac{3}{8x} \quad \text{✗ WRONG} \quad -10$$

Why was it marked wrong? How would you correct it?

115. Following is an excerpt from your worst enemy's graded homework:

$$f(x) = 4x^2; f'(x) = (0)(2x) = 0 \quad \text{✗ WRONG} \quad -6$$

Why was it marked wrong? How would you correct it?

116. Following is an excerpt from your second worst enemy's graded homework:

$$f(x) = \frac{3}{4x}; f'(x) = \frac{0}{4} = 0 \quad \text{✗ WRONG} \quad -10$$

Why was it marked wrong? How would you correct it?

117. One of the questions in your last calculus test was "**Question 1(a)** Give the definition of the derivative of a function f." Following is your answer and the grade you received:

$$nx^{n-1} \quad \text{✗ WRONG} \quad -10$$

Why was it marked wrong? What is the correct answer?

118. ▼ How would you respond to an acquaintance who says, "I finally understand what the derivative is: It is nx^{n-1}! Why weren't we taught that in the first place instead of the difficult way using limits?"

119. ▼ Sketch the graph of a function whose derivative is undefined at exactly two points but which has a tangent line at all but one point.

120. ▼ Sketch the graph of a function that has a tangent line at each of its points, but whose derivative is undefined at exactly two points.

4.2 A First Application: Marginal Analysis

In Chapter 1, we considered linear *cost functions* of the form $C(x) = mx + b$, where C is the total cost, x is the number of items, and m and b are constants. The slope m is the *marginal cost*. It measures the *cost of one more item*. Notice that the derivative of $C(x) = mx + b$ is $C'(x) = m$. In other words, for a linear cost function, *the marginal cost is the derivative of the cost function.*

In general, we make the following definition.

Marginal Cost

A **cost function** specifies the total cost C as a function of the number of items x. In other words, $C(x)$ is the total cost of x items. The **marginal cost function** is the derivative $C'(x)$ of the cost function $C(x)$. It measures the rate of change of cost with respect to x.

Units

The units of marginal cost are units of cost (dollars, say) per item.

✳ NOTE See Example 1.

Interpretation

We interpret $C'(x)$ as the approximate cost of one more item.✳

Quick Example

If $C(x) = 400x + 1{,}000$ dollars, then the marginal cost function is $C'(x) = \$400$ per item (a constant).

✳ NOTE You might well ask where on Earth this formula came from. There are two approaches to obtaining cost functions in real life: analytical and empirical. The analytical approach is to calculate the cost function from scratch. For example, in the above situation, we might have fixed costs of $150,000, plus a production cost of $20 per CD player. The term $0.0001x^2$ may reflect a cost saving for high levels of production, such as a bulk discount in the cost of electronic components. In the empirical approach, we first obtain the cost at several different production levels by direct observation. This gives several points on the (as yet unknown) cost versus production level graph. Then find the equation of the curve that best fits these points, usually using regression.

EXAMPLE 1   Marginal Cost

Suppose that the cost in dollars to manufacture portable CD players is given by

$$C(x) = 150{,}000 + 20x - 0.0001x^2$$

where x is the number of CD players manufactured.✳ Find the marginal cost function $C'(x)$ and use it to estimate the cost of manufacturing the 50,001st CD player.

Solution Since

$$C(x) = 150{,}000 + 20x - 0.0001x^2$$

the marginal cost function is

$$C'(x) = 20 - 0.0002x.$$

The units of $C'(x)$ are units of C (dollars) per unit of x (CD players). Thus, $C'(x)$ is measured in dollars per CD player.

The cost of the 50,001st CD player is the amount by which the total cost would rise if we increased production from 50,000 CD players to 50,001. Thus, we need to know the rate at which the total cost rises as we increase production. This rate of change is measured by the derivative, or marginal cost, which we just computed. At $x = 50{,}000$, we get

$$C'(50{,}000) = 20 - 0.0002(50{,}000) = \$10 \text{ per CD player.}$$

In other words, we estimate that the 50,001st CD player will cost approximately $10.

➡ **Before we go on...** In Example 1, the marginal cost is really only an *approximation* to the cost of the 50,001st CD player:

$$C'(50{,}000) \approx \frac{C(50{,}001) - C(50{,}000)}{1} \qquad \text{Set } h = 1 \text{ in the definition of the derivative.}$$
$$= C(50{,}001) - C(50{,}000)$$
$$= \text{cost of the 50,001st CD player}$$

The exact cost of the 50,001st CD player is

$$C(50,001) - C(50,000) = [150,000 + 20(50,001) - 0.0001(50,001)^2]$$
$$- [150,000 + 20(50,000) - 0.0001(50,000)^2]$$
$$= \$9.9999$$

So, the marginal cost is a good approximation to the actual cost.

Graphically, we are using the tangent line to approximate the cost function near a production level of 50,000. Figure 3 shows the graph of the cost function together with the tangent line at $x = 50,000$. Notice that the tangent line is essentially indistinguishable from the graph of the function for some distance on either side of 50,000.

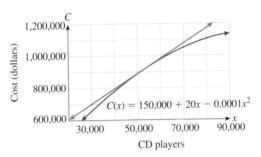

Figure 3

Notes

1. In general, the difference quotient $[C(x + h) - C(x)]/h$ gives the **average cost per item** to produce h more items at a current production level of x items. (Why?)

2. Notice that $C'(x)$ is much easier to calculate than $[C(x + h) - C(x)]/h$. (Try it.)

We can extend the idea of marginal cost to include other functions, like revenue and profit:

Marginal Revenue and Profit

A **revenue** or **profit function** specifies the total revenue R or profit P as a function of the number of items x. The derivatives, $R'(x)$ and $P'(x)$ of these functions are called the **marginal revenue** and **marginal profit** functions. They measure the rate of change of revenue and profit with respect to x.

Units
The units of marginal revenue and profit are the same as those of marginal cost: dollars (or euros, pesos, etc.) per item.

Interpretation
We interpret $R'(x)$ and $P'(x)$ as the approximate revenue and profit from the sale of one more item.

EXAMPLE 2 Marginal Revenue and Profit

You operate an *iPod* customizing service (a typical customized iPod might have a custom color case with blinking lights and a personalized logo). The cost to refurbish x iPods in a month is calculated to be

$$C(x) = 0.25x^2 + 40x + 1,000 \text{ dollars.}$$

You charge customers $80 per iPod for the work.

a. Calculate the marginal revenue and profit functions. Interpret the results.

b. Compute the revenue and profit, and also the marginal revenue and profit, if you have refurbished 20 units this month. Interpret the results.

c. For which value of x is the marginal profit zero? Interpret your answer.

Solution

a. We first calculate the revenue and profit functions:

$$R(x) = 80x \qquad \text{Revenue} = \text{Price} \times \text{Quantity}$$
$$P(x) = R(x) - C(x) \qquad \text{Profit} = \text{Revenue} - \text{Cost}$$
$$= 80x - (0.25x^2 + 40x + 1,000)$$
$$P(x) = -0.25x^2 + 40x - 1,000.$$

The marginal revenue and profit functions are then the derivatives:

$$\text{Marginal revenue} = R'(x) = 80$$
$$\text{Marginal profit} = P'(x) = -0.5x + 40.$$

Interpretation: $R'(x)$ gives the approximate revenue from the refurbishing of one more item, and $P'(x)$ gives the approximate profit from the refurbishing of one more item. Thus, if x iPods have been refurbished in a month, you will earn a revenue of $80 and make a profit of approximately $(-0.5x + 40)$ if you refurbish one more that month.

Notice that the marginal revenue is a constant, so you earn the same revenue ($80) for each iPod you refurbish. However, the marginal profit, $(-0.5x + 40)$, decreases as x increases, so your additional profit is about 50¢ less for each additional iPod you refurbish.

b. From part (a), the revenue, profit, marginal revenue, and marginal profit functions are

$$R(x) = 80x$$
$$P(x) = -0.25x^2 + 40x - 1,000$$
$$R'(x) = 80$$
$$P'(x) = -0.5x + 40$$

Because you have refurbished $x = 20$ iPods this month, $x = 20$, so

$$R(20) = 80(20) = \$1,600 \qquad \text{Total revenue from 20 iPods}$$
$$P(20) = -0.25(20)^2 + 40(20) - 1,000 = -\$300 \qquad \text{Total profit from 20 iPods}$$
$$R'(20) = \$80 \text{ per unit} \qquad \text{Approximate revenue from the 21st iPod}$$

$$P'(20) = -0.5(20) + 40 = \$30 \text{ per unit} \qquad \text{Approximate profit from the 21st iPod}$$

Interpretation: If you refurbish 20 iPods in a month, you will earn a total revenue of $160 and a profit of –$300 (indicating a loss of $300). Refurbishing one more iPod that month will earn you an additional revenue of $80 and an additional profit of about $30.

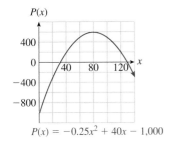

$P(x) = -0.25x^2 + 40x - 1{,}000$

Figure 4

c. The marginal profit is zero when $P'(x) = 0$:

$$-0.5x + 40 = 0$$

$$x = \frac{40}{0.5} = 80 \text{ iPods}$$

Thus, if you refurbish 80 iPods in a month, refurbishing one more will get you (approximately) zero additional profit. To understand this further, let us take a look at the graph of the profit function, shown in Figure 4. Notice that the graph is a parabola (the profit function is quadratic) with vertex at the point $x = 80$, where $P'(x) = 0$, so the profit is a maximum at this value of x.

➡ **Before we go on...** In general, setting $P'(x) = 0$ and solving for x will always give the exact values of x for which the profit peaks as in Figure 4, assuming there is such a value. We recommend that you graph the profit function to check whether the profit is indeed a maximum at such a point. ■

EXAMPLE 3 Marginal Product

A consultant determines that Precision Manufacturers' annual profit (in dollars) is given by

$$P(n) = -200{,}000 + 400{,}000n - 4{,}600n^2 - 10n^3 \qquad (10 \le n \le 50)$$

where n is the number of assembly-line workers it employs.

a. Compute $P'(n)$. $P'(n)$ is called the **marginal product** at the employment level of n assembly-line workers. What are its units?

b. Calculate $P(20)$ and $P'(20)$, and interpret the results.

c. Precision Manufacturers currently employs 20 assembly-line workers and is considering laying off some of them. What advice would you give the company's management?

Solution

a. Taking the derivative gives

$$P'(n) = 400{,}000 - 9{,}200n - 30n^2.$$

The units of $P'(n)$ are profit (in dollars) per worker.

b. Substituting into the formula for $P(n)$, we get

$$P(20) = -200{,}000 + 400{,}000(20) - 4{,}600(20)^2 - 10(20)^3 = \$5{,}880{,}000.$$

Thus, Precision Manufacturer will make an annual profit of $5,880,000 if it employs 20 assembly-line workers. On the other hand,

$$P'(20) = 400{,}000 - 9{,}200(20) - 30(20)^2 = \$204{,}000/\text{worker}.$$

Thus, at an employment level of 20 assembly-line workers, annual profit is increasing at a rate of $204,000 per additional worker. In other words, if the company were to employ one more assembly-line worker, its annual profit would increase by approximately $204,000.

c. Because the marginal product is positive, profits will increase if the company increases the number of workers and will decrease if it decreases the number of workers, so your advice would be to hire additional assembly-line workers. Downsizing their assembly-line workforce would reduce their annual profits.

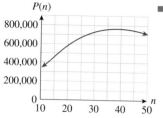

Figure 5

➡ **Before we go on...** In Example 3, it would be interesting for Precision Manufacturers to ascertain how many additional assembly-line workers they should hire to obtain the *maximum* annual profit. Taking our cue from Example 2, we suspect that such a value of n would correspond to a point where $P'(n) = 0$. Figure 5 shows the graph of P, and on it we see that the highest point of the graph is indeed a point where the tangent line is horizontal; that is, $P'(n) = 0$, and occurs somewhere between $n = 35$ and 40. To compute this value of n more accurately, set $P'(n) = 0$ and solve for n:

$$P'(n) = 400{,}000 - 9{,}200n - 30n^2 = 0 \quad \text{or} \quad 40{,}000 - 920n - 3n^2 = 0.$$

We can now obtain n using the quadratic formula:

$$n = \frac{-b \pm \sqrt{b^2 - 4ac}}{2a} = \frac{920 \pm \sqrt{920^2 - 4(-3)(40{,}000)}}{2(-3)}$$

$$= \frac{920 \pm \sqrt{1{,}326{,}400}}{-6} \approx -345.3 \text{ or } 38.6.$$

The only meaningful solution is the positive one, $n \approx 38.6$ workers, and we conclude that the company should employ between 38 and 39 assembly-line workers for a maximum profit. To see which gives the larger profit, 38 or 39, we check:

$$P(38) = \$7{,}808{,}880$$

while

$$P(39) = \$7{,}810{,}210.$$

This tells us that the company should employ 39 assembly-line workers for a maximum profit. Thus, instead of laying off any of its 20 assembly-line workers, the company should hire 19 additional assembly line workers for a total of 39. ■

Average Cost

EXAMPLE 4 Average Cost

Suppose the cost in dollars to manufacture portable CD players is given by

$$C(x) = 150{,}000 + 20x - 0.0001x^2$$

where x is the number of CD players manufactured. (This is the cost equation we saw in Example 1.)

a. Find the average cost per CD player if 50,000 CD players are manufactured.

b. Find a formula for the average cost per CD player if x CD players are manufactured. This function of x is called the **average cost function, $\bar{C}(x)$**.

Solution

a. The total cost of manufacturing 50,000 CD players is given by

$$C(50{,}000) = 150{,}000 + 20(50{,}000) - 0.0001(50{,}000)^2$$
$$= \$900{,}000.$$

Because 50,000 CD players cost a total of $900,000 to manufacture, the average cost of manufacturing one CD player is this total cost divided by 50,000:

$$\bar{C}(50,000) = \frac{900,000}{50,000} = \$18.00 \text{ per CD player.}$$

Thus, if 50,000 CD players are manufactured, each CD player costs the manufacturer an average of $18.00 to manufacture.

b. If we replace 50,000 by x, we get the general formula for the average cost of manufacturing x CD players:

$$\bar{C}(x) = \frac{C(x)}{x}$$

$$= \frac{1}{x}(150,000 + 20x - 0.0001x^2)$$

$$= \frac{150,000}{x} + 20 - 0.0001x. \qquad \text{Average cost function}$$

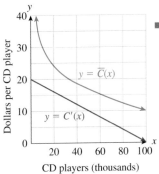

Dollars per CD player

$y = \bar{C}(x)$

$y = C'(x)$

CD players (thousands)

Figure 6

➡ **Before we go on...** Average cost and marginal cost convey different but related information. The average cost $\bar{C}(50,000) = \$18$ that we calculated in Example 4 is the cost per item of manufacturing the first 50,000 CD players, whereas the marginal cost $C'(50,000) = \$10$ that we calculated in Example 1 gives the (approximate) cost of manufacturing the *next* CD player. Thus, according to our calculations, the first 50,000 CD players cost an average of $18 to manufacture, but it costs only about $10 to manufacture the next one. Note that the marginal cost at a production level of 50,000 CD players is lower than the average cost. This means that the average cost to manufacture CDs is going down with increasing volume. (Think about why.)

Figure 6 shows the graphs of average and marginal cost. Notice how the decreasing marginal cost seems to pull the average cost down with it. ■

To summarize:

Average Cost

Given a cost function C, the **average cost** of the first x items is given by
$$\bar{C}(x) = \frac{C(x)}{x}.$$
The average cost is distinct from the **marginal cost** $C'(x)$, which tells us the approximate cost of the *next* item.

Quick Example

For the cost function $C(x) = 20x + 100$ dollars

Marginal Cost $= C'(x) = \$20$ per additional item.

Average Cost $= \bar{C}(x) = \dfrac{C(x)}{x} = \dfrac{20x + 100}{x} = \$(20 + 100/x)$ per item.

4.2 EXERCISES

▼ more advanced   ◆ challenging
🔲 indicates exercises that should be solved using technology

In Exercises 1–4, for each cost function, find the marginal cost at the given production level x, and state the units of measurement. (All costs are in dollars.) HINT [See Example 1.]

1. $C(x) = 10,000 + 5x - 0.0001x^2$; $x = 1,000$

2. $C(x) = 20,000 + 7x - 0.00005x^2$; $x = 10,000$

3. $C(x) = 15,000 + 100x + \dfrac{1,000}{x}$; $x = 100$

4. $C(x) = 20,000 + 50x + \dfrac{10,000}{x}$; $x = 100$

In Exercises 5 and 6, find the marginal cost, marginal revenue, and marginal profit functions, and find all values of x for which the marginal profit is zero. Interpret your answer. HINT [See Example 2.]

5. $C(x) = 4x$; $R(x) = 8x - 0.001x^2$

6. $C(x) = 5x^2$; $R(x) = x^3 + 7x + 10$

7. ▼ A certain cost function has the following graph:

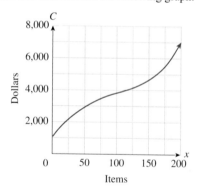

a. The associated marginal cost is

   (A) increasing, then decreasing
   (B) decreasing, then increasing
   (C) always increasing
   (D) always decreasing

b. The marginal cost is least at approximately

   (A) $x = 0$ **(B)** $x = 50$ **(C)** $x = 100$ **(D)** $x = 150$

c. The cost of 50 items is

   (A) approximately $20, and increasing at a rate of about $3,000 per item
   (B) approximately $0.50, and increasing at a rate of about $3,000 per item
   (C) approximately $3,000, and increasing at a rate of about $20 per item
   (D) approximately $3,000, and increasing at a rate of about $0.50 per item

8. ▼ A certain cost function has the following graph:

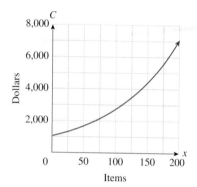

a. The associated marginal cost is

   (A) increasing, then decreasing
   (B) decreasing, then increasing
   (C) always increasing
   (D) always decreasing

b. When $x = 100$, the marginal cost is

   (A) greater than the average cost
   (B) less than the average cost
   (C) approximately equal to the average cost

c. The cost of 150 items is

   (A) approximately $4,400, and increasing at a rate of about $40 per item
   (B) approximately $40, and increasing at a rate of about $4,400 per item
   (C) approximately $4,400, and increasing at a rate of about $1 per item
   (D) approximately $1, and increasing at a rate of about $4,400 per item

APPLICATIONS

9. *Advertising Costs* The cost, in thousands of dollars, of airing x television commercials during a Super Bowl game is given by[14]

$$C(x) = 150 + 2,250x - 0.02x^2.$$

a. Find the marginal cost function and use it to estimate how fast the cost is increasing when $x = 4$. Compare this with the exact cost of airing the fifth commercial. HINT [See Example 1.]

b. Find the average cost function $\bar{C}$, and evaluate $\bar{C}(4)$. What does the answer tell you? HINT [See Example 4.]

---

[14] CBS charged an average of $2.25 million per 30-second television spot during the 2004 Super Bowl game. This explains the coefficient of x in the cost function. Source: Advertising Age Research, www.AdAge.com/.

10. *Marginal Cost and Average Cost* The cost of producing x teddy bears per day at the Cuddly Companion Co. is calculated by their marketing staff to be given by the formula

$$C(x) = 100 + 40x - 0.001x^2.$$

a. Find the marginal cost function and use it to estimate how fast the cost is going up at a production level of 100 teddy bears. Compare this with the exact cost of producing the 101st teddy bear. HINT [See Example 1.]

b. Find the average cost function $\bar{C}$, and evaluate $\bar{C}(100)$. What does the answer tell you? HINT [See Example 4.]

11. *Marginal Revenue and Profit* Your college newspaper, *The Collegiate Investigator*, sells for 90¢ per copy. The cost of producing x copies of an edition is given by

$$C(x) = 70 + 0.10x + 0.001x^2 \text{ dollars.}$$

a. Calculate the marginal revenue and profit functions. HINT [See Example 2.]

b. Compute the revenue and profit, and also the marginal revenue and profit, if you have produced and sold 500 copies of the latest edition. Interpret the results.

c. For which value of x is the marginal profit zero? Interpret your answer.

12. *Marginal Revenue and Profit* The Audubon Society at Enormous State University (ESU) is planning its annual fund-raising "Eatathon." The society will charge students $1.10 per serving of pasta. The society estimates that the total cost of producing x servings of pasta at the event will be

$$C(x) = 350 + 0.10x + 0.002x^2 \text{ dollars.}$$

a. Calculate the marginal revenue and profit functions. HINT [See Example 2.]

b. Compute the revenue and profit, and also the marginal revenue and profit, if you have produced and sold 200 servings of pasta. Interpret the results.

c. For which value of x is the marginal profit zero? Interpret your answer.

13. *Marginal Profit* Suppose $P(x)$ represents the profit on the sale of x DVDs. If $P(1,000) = 3,000$ and $P'(1,000) = -3$, what do these values tell you about the profit?

14. *Marginal Loss* An automobile retailer calculates that its loss on the sale of type M cars is given by $L(50) = 5,000$ and $L'(50) = -200$, where $L(x)$ represents the loss on the sale of x type M cars. What do these values tell you about losses?

15. *Marginal Profit* Your monthly profit (in dollars) from selling magazines is given by

$$P = 5x + \sqrt{x}$$

where x is the number of magazines you sell in a month. If you are currently selling $x = 50$ magazines per month, find your profit and your marginal profit. Interpret your answers.

16. *Marginal Profit* Your monthly profit (in dollars) from your newspaper route is given by

$$P = 2n - \sqrt{n}$$

where n is the number of subscribers on your route. If you currently have 100 subscribers, find your profit and your marginal profit. Interpret your answers.

17. ▼ *Marginal Revenue: Pricing Tuna* Assume that the demand function for tuna in a small coastal town is given by

$$p = \frac{20,000}{q^{1.5}} \qquad (200 \le q \le 800)$$

where p is the price (in dollars) per pound of tuna, and q is the number of pounds of tuna that can be sold at the price p in one month.

a. Calculate the price that the town's fishery should charge for tuna in order to produce a demand of 400 pounds of tuna per month.

b. Calculate the monthly revenue R as a function of the number of pounds of tuna q.

c. Calculate the revenue and marginal revenue (derivative of the revenue with respect to q) at a demand level of 400 pounds per month, and interpret the results.

d. If the town fishery's monthly tuna catch amounted to 400 pounds of tuna, and the price is at the level in part (a), would you recommend that the fishery raise or lower the price of tuna in order to increase its revenue?

18. ▼ *Marginal Revenue: Pricing Tuna* Repeat Exercise 17, assuming a demand equation of

$$p = \frac{60}{q^{0.5}} \qquad (200 \le q \le 800).$$

19. *Marginal Product* A car wash firm calculates that its daily profit (in dollars) depends on the number n of workers it employs according to the formula

$$P = 400n - 0.5n^2.$$

Calculate the marginal product at an employment level of 50 workers, and interpret the result. HINT [See Example 3.]

20. *Marginal Product* Repeat the preceding exercise using the formula

$$P = -100n + 25n^2 - 0.005n^4.$$

HINT [See Example 3.]

21. *Average and Marginal Cost* The daily cost to manufacture generic trinkets for gullible tourists is given by the cost function

$$C(x) = -0.001x^2 + 0.3x + 500 \text{ dollars}$$

where x is the number of trinkets.

a. As x increases, the marginal cost
(A) increases (B) decreases (C) increases, then decreases (D) decreases, then increases

b. As x increases, the average cost
   (A) increases   (B) decreases   (C) increases, then decreases   (D) decreases, then increases
c. The marginal cost is
   (A) greater than   (B) equal to   (C) less than the average cost when $x = 100$. HINT [See Example 4.]

22. Average and Marginal Cost Repeat Exercise 21, using the following cost function for imitation oil paintings (x is the number of "oil paintings" manufactured):

$$C(x) = 0.1x^2 - 3.5x + 500 \text{ dollars.}$$

HINT [See Example 4.]

23. Advertising Cost Your company is planning to air a number of television commercials during the ABC Television Network's presentation of the Academy Awards. ABC is charging your company $1.6 million per 30-second spot.[15] Additional fixed costs (development and personnel costs) amount to $500,000, and the network has agreed to provide a discount of $10,000\sqrt{x}$ for x television spots.

a. Write down the cost function C, marginal cost function C', and average cost function $\bar{C}$.
b. Compute $C'(3)$ and $\bar{C}(3)$. (Round all answers to three significant digits.) Use these two answers to say whether the average cost is increasing or decreasing as x increases.

24. Housing Costs The cost C of building a house is related to the number k of carpenters used and the number x of electricians used by the formula[16]

$$C = 15,000 + 50k^2 + 60x^2.$$

a. Assuming that 10 carpenters are currently being used, find the cost function C, marginal cost function C', and average cost function $\bar{C}$, all as functions of x.
b. Use the functions you obtained in part (a) to compute $C'(15)$ and $\bar{C}(15)$. Use these two answers to say whether the average cost is increasing or decreasing as the number of electricians increases.

25. ▼ Emission Control The cost of controlling emissions at a firm rises rapidly as the amount of emissions reduced increases. Here is a possible model:

$$C(q) = 4,000 + 100q^2$$

where q is the reduction in emissions (in pounds of pollutant per day) and C is the daily cost (in dollars) of this reduction.

a. If a firm is currently reducing its emissions by 10 pounds each day, what is the marginal cost of reducing emissions further?
b. Government clean-air subsidies to the firm are based on the formula

$$S(q) = 500q$$

where q is again the reduction in emissions (in pounds per day) and S is the subsidy (in dollars). At what reduction level does the marginal cost surpass the marginal subsidy?
c. Calculate the net cost function, $N(q) = C(q) - S(q)$, given the cost function and subsidy above, and find the value of q that gives the lowest net cost. What is this lowest net cost? Compare your answer to that for part (b) and comment on what you find.

26. ▼ Taxation Schemes Here is a curious proposal for taxation rates based on income:

$$T(i) = 0.001i^{0.5}$$

where i represents total annual income in dollars and $T(i)$ is the income tax rate as a percentage of total annual income. (Thus, for example, an income of $50,000 per year would be taxed at about 22%, while an income of double that amount would be taxed at about 32%.)[17]

a. Calculate the after-tax (net) income $N(i)$ an individual can expect to earn as a function of income i.
b. Calculate an individual's marginal after-tax income at income levels of $100,000 and $500,000.
c. At what income does an individual's marginal after-tax income become negative? What is the after-tax income at that level, and what happens at higher income levels?
d. What do you suspect is the most anyone can earn after taxes? (See NOTE at the bottom of this page.)

27. ▼ Fuel Economy Your Porsche's gas mileage (in miles per gallon) is given as a function $M(x)$ of speed x in miles per hour. It is found that

$$M'(x) = \frac{3,600x^{-2} - 1}{(3,600x^{-1} + x)^2}.$$

Estimate $M'(10)$, $M'(60)$, and $M'(70)$. What do the answers tell you about your car?

28. ▼ Marginal Revenue The estimated marginal revenue for sales of ESU soccer team T-shirts is given by

$$R'(p) = \frac{(8 - 2p)e^{-p^2 + 8p}}{10,000,000}$$

---

[15] ABC charged an average of $1.6 million for a 30-second spot during the 2005 Academy Awards presentation. Source: CNN/Reuters, www.cnn.com, February 9, 2005.

[16] Based on an exercise in *Introduction to Mathematical Economics* by A. L. Ostrosky, Jr., and J. V. Koch (Waveland Press, Prospect Heights, Illinois, 1979).

[17] This model has the following interesting feature: An income of $1 million per year would be taxed at 100%, leaving the individual penniless!

where p is the price (in dollars) that the soccer players charge for each shirt. Estimate $R'(3)$, $R'(4)$, and $R'(5)$. What do the answers tell you?

29. ◆ **Marginal Cost** *(from the GRE Economics Test)* In a multi-plant firm in which the different plants have different and continuous cost schedules, if costs of production for a given output level are to be minimized, which of the following is essential?

   (A) Marginal costs must equal marginal revenue.
   (B) Average variable costs must be the same in all plants.
   (C) Marginal costs must be the same in all plants.
   (D) Total costs must be the same in all plants.
   (E) Output per worker per hour must be the same in all plants.

30. ◆ **Study Time** *(from the GRE economics test)* A student has a fixed number of hours to devote to study and is certain of the relationship between hours of study and the final grade for each course. Grades are given on a numerical scale (0 to 100), and each course is counted equally in computing the grade average. In order to maximize his or her grade average, the student should allocate these hours to different courses so that

   (A) the grade in each course is the same.
   (B) the marginal product of an hour's study (in terms of final grade) in each course is zero.
   (C) the marginal product of an hour's study (in terms of final grade) in each course is equal, although not necessarily equal to zero.
   (D) the average product of an hour's study (in terms of final grade) in each course is equal.
   (E) the number of hours spent in study for each course is equal.

31. ◆ **Marginal Product** *(from the GRE Economics Test)* Assume that the marginal product of an additional senior professor is 50% higher than the marginal product of an additional junior professor and that junior professors are paid one-half the amount that senior professors receive. With a fixed overall budget, a university that wishes to maximize its quantity of output from professors should do which of the following?

   (A) Hire equal numbers of senior professors and junior professors.
   (B) Hire more senior professors and junior professors.
   (C) Hire more senior professors and discharge junior professors.
   (D) Discharge senior professors and hire more junior professors.
   (E) Discharge all senior professors and half of the junior professors.

32. ◆ **Marginal Product** *(based on a question from the GRE Economics Test)* Assume that the marginal product of an additional senior professor is twice the marginal product of an additional junior professor and that junior professors are paid two-thirds the amount that senior professors receive. With a fixed overall budget, a university that wishes to maximize its quantity of output from professors should do which of the following?

   (A) Hire equal numbers of senior professors and junior professors.
   (B) Hire more senior professors and junior professors.
   (C) Hire more senior professors and discharge junior professors.
   (D) Discharge senior professors and hire more junior professors.
   (E) Discharge all senior professors and half of the junior professors.

COMMUNICATION AND REASONING EXERCISES

33. The marginal cost of producing the 1,001st item is

   (A) equal to
   (B) approximately equal to
   (C) always slightly greater than

   the actual cost of producing the 1,001st item.

34. For the cost function $C(x) = mx + b$, the marginal cost of producing the 1,001st item is,

   (A) equal to
   (B) approximately equal to
   (C) always slightly greater than

   the actual cost of producing the 1,001st item.

35. What is a cost function? Carefully explain the difference between *average cost* and *marginal cost* in terms of (a) their mathematical definition, (b) graphs, and (c) interpretation.

36. The cost function for your grand piano manufacturing plant has the property that $\bar{C}(1,000) = \$3,000$ per unit and $C'(1,000) = \$2,500$ per unit. Will the average cost increase or decrease if your company manufactures a slightly larger number of pianos? Explain your reasoning.

37. If the average cost to manufacture one grand piano increases as the production level increases, which is greater, the marginal cost or the average cost?

38. If your analysis of a manufacturing company yielded positive marginal profit but negative profit at the company's current production levels, what would you advise the company to do?

39. ▽ If the marginal cost is decreasing, is the average cost necessarily decreasing? Explain.

40. ▽ If the average cost is decreasing, is the marginal cost necessarily decreasing? Explain.

41. ◆ If a company's marginal average cost is zero at the current production level, positive for a slightly higher production level, and negative for a slightly lower production level, what should you advise the company to do?

42. ◆ The **acceleration** of cost is defined as the derivative of the marginal cost function: that is, the derivative of the derivative—or *second derivative*—of the cost function. What are the units of acceleration of cost, and how does one interpret this measure?

4.3 The Product and Quotient Rules

We know how to find the derivatives of functions that are sums of powers, such as polynomials. In general, if a function is a sum or difference of functions whose derivatives we know, then we know how to find its derivative. But what about *products and quotients* of functions whose derivatives we know? For instance, how do we calculate the derivative of something like $x^2/(x + 1)$? The derivative of $x^2/(x + 1)$ is not, as one might suspect, $2x/1 = 2x$. That calculation is based on an assumption that the derivative of a quotient is the quotient of the derivatives. But it is easy to see that this assumption is false: For instance, the derivative of $1/x$ is not $0/1 = 0$, but $-1/x^2$. Similarly, the derivative of a product is not the product of the derivatives: For instance, the derivative of $x = 1 \cdot x$ is not $0 \cdot 1 = 0$, but 1.

To identify the correct method of computing the derivatives of products and quotients, let's look at a simple example. We know that the daily revenue resulting from the sale of q items per day at a price of p dollars per item is given by the product, $R = pq$ dollars. Suppose you are currently selling wall posters on campus. At this time your daily sales are 50 posters, and sales are increasing at a rate of 4 per day. Furthermore, you are currently charging $10 per poster, and you are also raising the price at a rate of $2 per day. Let's use this information to estimate how fast your daily revenue is increasing. In other words, let us estimate the rate of change, dR/dt, of the revenue R.

There are two contributions to the rate of change of daily revenue: the increase in daily sales and the increase in the unit price. We have

$\dfrac{dR}{dt}$ due to increasing price: $2 per day $\times$ 50 posters $= \$100$ per day

$\dfrac{dR}{dt}$ due to increasing sales: $10 per poster $\times$ 4 posters per day $= \$40$ per day

Thus, we estimate the daily revenue to be increasing at a rate of $100 + $40 = 140 per day. Let us translate what we have said into symbols:

$\dfrac{dR}{dt}$ due to increasing price: $\dfrac{dp}{dt} \times q$

$\dfrac{dR}{dt}$ due to increasing sales: $p \times \dfrac{dq}{dt}$

Thus, the rate of change of revenue is given by

$$\frac{dR}{dt} = \frac{dp}{dt}q + p\frac{dq}{dt}.$$

Because $R = pq$, we have discovered the following rule for differentiating a product:

$$\frac{d}{dt}(pq) = \frac{dp}{dt}q + p\frac{dq}{dt}$$ The derivative of a product is the derivative of the first times the second, plus the first times the derivative of the second.

This rule and a similar rule for differentiating quotients are given next, and also a discussion of how these results are proved rigorously.

Product Rule

If $f(x)$ and $g(x)$ are differentiable functions of x, then so is their product $f(x)g(x)$, and

$$\frac{d}{dx}[f(x)g(x)] = f'(x)g(x) + f(x)g'(x).$$

Product Rule in Words

The derivative of a product is the derivative of the first times the second, plus the first times the derivative of the second.

Quick Example

$f(x) = x^2$ and $g(x) = 3x - 1$ are both differentiable functions of x, and so their product $x^2(3x - 1)$ is differentiable, and

$$\frac{d}{dx}[x^2(3x - 1)] = 2x \cdot (3x - 1) + x^2 \cdot (3).$$

Derivative of first   Second   First   Derivative of second

Quotient Rule

If $f(x)$ and $g(x)$ are differentiable functions of x, then so is their quotient $f(x)/g(x)$ (provided $g(x) \neq 0$), and

$$\frac{d}{dx}\left(\frac{f(x)}{g(x)}\right) = \frac{f'(x)g(x) - f(x)g'(x)}{[g(x)]^2}.$$

Quotient Rule in Words

The derivative of a quotient is the derivative of the top times the bottom, minus the top times the derivative of the bottom, all over the bottom squared.

Quick Example

$f(x) = x^3$ and $g(x) = x^2 + 1$ are both differentiable functions of x, and so their quotient $x^3/(x^2 + 1)$ is differentiable, and

Derivative of top   Bottom   Top   Derivative of bottom

$$\frac{d}{dx}\left(\frac{x^3}{x^2 + 1}\right) = \frac{3x^2(x^2 + 1) - x^3 \cdot 2x}{(x^2 + 1)^2}$$

Bottom squared

Notes

1. Don't try to remember the rules by the symbols we have used, but remember them in words. (The slogans are easy to remember, even if the terms are not precise.)

2. One more time: *The derivative of a product is* NOT *the product of the derivatives, and the derivative of a quotient is* NOT *the quotient of the derivatives.* To find the derivative of a product, you must use the product rule, and to find the derivative of a quotient, you must use the quotient rule.*

✱ **NOTE** Leibniz made this mistake at first, too, so you would be in good company if you forgot to use the product or quotient rule.

Q: *Wait a minute! The expression $2x^3$ is a product, and we already know that its derivative is $6x^2$. Where did we use the product rule?*

A: To differentiate functions such as $2x^3$, we have used the rule from Section 3.4:

The derivative of c times a function is c times the derivative of the function.

However, the product rule gives us the same result:

$$\underset{\substack{\uparrow \\ \text{Derivative of first}}}{\frac{d}{dx}(2x^3) = (0)(x^3)} + \underset{\substack{\uparrow \quad \uparrow \\ \text{First Derivative of second}}}{(2)(3x^2)} = 6x^2 \qquad \text{Product rule}$$

$$\frac{d}{dx}(2x^3) = (2)(3x^2) = 6x^2 \qquad \text{Derivative of a constant times a function}$$

We do not recommend that you use the product rule to differentiate functions such as $2x^3$; continue to use the simpler rule when one of the factors is a constant.

Derivation of the Product Rule

Before we look at more examples of using the product and quotient rules, let's see why the product rule is true. To calculate the derivative of the product $f(x)g(x)$ of two differentiable functions, we go back to the definition of the derivative:

$$\frac{d}{dx}[f(x)g(x)] = \lim_{h \to 0} \frac{f(x+h)g(x+h) - f(x)g(x)}{h}.$$

* NOTE Adding an appropriate form of zero is an age-old mathematical ploy.

We now rewrite this expression so that we can evaluate the limit: Notice that the numerator reflects a simultaneous change in f [from $f(x)$ to $f(x+h)$] and g [from $g(x)$ to $g(x+h)$]. To separate the two effects, we add and subtract a quantity in the numerator that reflects a change in only one of the functions:

$$\frac{d}{dx}[f(x)g(x)] = \lim_{h \to 0} \frac{f(x+h)g(x+h) - f(x)g(x)}{h}$$

$$= \lim_{h \to 0} \frac{f(x+h)g(x+h) - f(x)g(x+h) + f(x)g(x+h) - f(x)g(x)}{h} \qquad \text{We subtracted and added the quantity* } f(x)g(x+h).$$

$$= \lim_{h \to 0} \frac{[f(x+h) - f(x)]\,g(x+h) + f(x)[g(x+h) - g(x)]}{h} \qquad \text{Common factors}$$

$$= \lim_{h \to 0} \left(\frac{f(x+h) - f(x)}{h}\right) g(x+h) + \lim_{h \to 0} f(x) \left(\frac{g(x+h) - g(x)}{h}\right) \qquad \text{Limit of sum}$$

$$= \lim_{h \to 0} \left(\frac{f(x+h) - f(x)}{h}\right) \lim_{h \to 0} g(x+h) + \lim_{h \to 0} f(x) \lim_{h \to 0} \left(\frac{g(x+h) - g(x)}{h}\right) \qquad \text{Limit of product}$$

Web Site
www.AppliedCalc.org
For a proof of the fact that, if g is differentiable, it must be continuous, go to the Web site and follow the path

Everything for Calculus

→ Chapter 4

→ Continuity and
   Differentiability

Now we already know the following four limits:

$$\lim_{h \to 0} \frac{f(x+h) - f(x)}{h} = f'(x) \qquad \text{Definition of derivative of } f; f \text{ is differentiable.}$$

$$\lim_{h \to 0} \frac{g(x+h) - g(x)}{h} = g'(x) \qquad \text{Definition of derivative of } g; g \text{ is differentiable.}$$

$$\lim_{h \to 0} g(x+h) = g(x) \qquad \text{If } g \text{ is differentiable, it must be continuous.}$$

$$\lim_{h \to 0} f(x) = f(x) \qquad \text{Limit of a constant}$$

Web Site

www.AppliedCalc.org

The quotient rule can be proved in a very similar way. Go to the Web site and follow the path

Everything for Calculus

→ Chapter 4

→ Proof of Quotient Rule

Putting these limits into the one we're calculating, we get

$$\frac{d}{dx}[f(x)g(x)] = f'(x)g(x) + f(x)g'(x)$$

which is the product rule.

EXAMPLE 5   Using the Product Rule

Compute the following derivatives.

a. $\dfrac{d}{dx}[(x^{3.2} + 1)(1 - x)]$ Simplify the answer.

b. $\dfrac{d}{dx}[(x + 1)(x^2 + 1)(x^3 + 1)]$ Do not expand the answer.

Solution

a. We can do the calculation in two ways.

$$\underset{\substack{\uparrow \\ \text{Derivative of first}}}{} \quad \underset{\substack{\uparrow \\ \text{Second}}}{} \quad \underset{\substack{\uparrow \\ \text{First}}}{} \quad \underset{\substack{\uparrow \\ \text{Derivative} \\ \text{of second}}}{}$$

Using the
Product Rule: $\dfrac{d}{dx}[(x^{3.2} + 1)(1 - x)] = (3.2x^{2.2})(1 - x) + (x^{3.2} + 1)(-1)$

$$= 3.2x^{2.2} - 3.2x^{3.2} - x^{3.2} - 1 \quad \text{Expand the}$$
$$= -4.2x^{3.2} + 3.2x^{2.2} - 1 \quad \text{answer.}$$

Not Using the Product Rule: First, expand the given expression.

$$(x^{3.2} + 1)(1 - x) = -x^{4.2} + x^{3.2} - x + 1$$

Thus,

$$\frac{d}{dx}[(x^{3.2} + 1)(1 - x)] = \frac{d}{dx}(-x^{4.2} + x^{3.2} - x + 1)$$
$$= -4.2x^{3.2} + 3.2x^{2.2} - 1$$

In this example the product rule saves us little or no work, but in later sections we shall see examples that can be done in no other way. Learn how to use the product rule now!

b. Here we have a product of *three* functions, not just two. We can find the derivative by using the product rule twice:

$$\frac{d}{dx}[(x + 1)(x^2 + 1)(x^3 + 1)]$$
$$= \frac{d}{dx}(x + 1) \cdot [(x^2 + 1)(x^3 + 1)] + (x + 1) \cdot \frac{d}{dx}[(x^2 + 1)(x^3 + 1)]$$
$$= (1)(x^2 + 1)(x^3 + 1) + (x + 1)[(2x)(x^3 + 1) + (x^2 + 1)(3x^2)]$$
$$= (1)(x^2 + 1)(x^3 + 1) + (x + 1)(2x)(x^3 + 1) + (x + 1)(x^2 + 1)(3x^2)$$

We can see here a more general product rule:

$$(fgh)' = f'gh + fg'h + fgh'$$

Notice that every factor has a chance to contribute to the rate of change of the product. There are similar formulas for products of four or more functions.

EXAMPLE 6 Using the Quotient Rule

Compute the derivatives **a.** $\dfrac{d}{dx}\left[\dfrac{1 - 3.2x^{-0.1}}{x + 1}\right]$ **b.** $\dfrac{d}{dx}\left[\dfrac{(x + 1)(x + 2)}{x - 1}\right]$

Solution

a.

$$\underbrace{\dfrac{d}{dx}\left[\dfrac{1 - 3.2x^{-0.1}}{x + 1}\right]}_{} = \dfrac{\overset{\text{Derivative of top}}{(0.32x^{-1.1})}\overset{\text{Bottom}}{(x + 1)} - \overset{\text{Top}}{(1 - 3.2x^{-0.1})}\overset{\text{Derivative of bottom}}{(1)}}{\underset{\text{Bottom squared}}{(x + 1)^2}}$$

$$= \dfrac{0.32x^{-0.1} + 0.32x^{-1.1} - 1 + 3.2x^{-0.1}}{(x + 1)^2} \qquad \text{Expand the numerator.}$$

$$= \dfrac{3.52x^{-0.1} + 0.32x^{-1.1} - 1}{(x + 1)^2}$$

b. Here we have both a product and a quotient. Which rule do we use, the product or the quotient rule? Here is a way to decide. Think about how we would calculate, step by step, the value of $(x + 1)(x + 2)/(x - 1)$ for a specific value of x—say $x = 11$. Here is how we would probably do it:

1. Calculate $(x + 1)(x + 2) = (11 + 1)(11 + 2) = 156$.
2. Calculate $x - 1 = 11 - 1 = 10$.
3. Divide 156 by 10 to get 15.6.

Now ask: *What was the last operation we performed?* The last operation we performed was division, so we can regard the whole expression as a *quotient*—that is, as $(x + 1)(x + 2)$ *divided by* $(x - 1)$. Therefore, we should use the quotient rule.

The first thing the quotient rule tells us to do is to take the derivative of the numerator. Now, the numerator is a product, so we must use the product rule to take its derivative. Here is the calculation:

$$\dfrac{d}{dx}\left[\dfrac{(x + 1)(x + 2)}{x - 1}\right] = \dfrac{\overbrace{[(1)(x + 2) + (x + 1)(1)]}^{\text{Derivative of top}}\overbrace{(x - 1)}^{\text{Bottom}} - \overbrace{[(x + 1)(x + 2)]}^{\text{Top}}\overbrace{(1)}^{\substack{\text{Derivative} \\ \text{of bottom}}}}{\underset{\text{Bottom squared}}{(x - 1)^2}}$$

$$= \dfrac{(2x + 3)(x - 1) - (x + 1)(x + 2)}{(x - 1)^2}$$

$$= \dfrac{x^2 - 2x - 5}{(x - 1)^2}$$

What is important is to determine the *order of operations* and, in particular, to determine the last operation to be performed. Pretending to do an actual calculation reminds us of the order of operations; we call this technique the **calculation thought experiment**.

➡ **Before we go on...** We used the quotient rule in Example 6 because the function was a quotient; we used the product rule to calculate the derivative of the numerator because the numerator was a product. Get used to this: Differentiation rules usually must be used in combination.

Here is another way we could have done this problem: Our calculation thought experiment could have taken the following form.

1. Calculate $(x + 1)/(x - 1) = (11 + 1)/(11 - 1) = 1.2$.

2. Calculate $x + 2 = 11 + 2 = 13$.

3. Multiply 1.2 by 13 to get 15.6.

We would have then regarded the expression as a *product*—the product of the factors $(x + 1)/(x - 1)$ and $(x + 2)$—and used the product rule instead. We can't escape the quotient rule, however: We need to use it to take the derivative of the first factor, $(x + 1)/(x - 1)$. Try this approach for practice and check that you get the same answer. ∎

Calculation Thought Experiment

The **calculation thought experiment** is a technique to determine whether to treat an algebraic expression as a product, quotient, sum, or difference. Given an expression, consider the steps you would use in computing its value. If the last operation is multiplication, treat the expression as a product; if the last operation is division, treat the expression as a quotient; and so on.

Quick Examples

1. $(3x^2 - 4)(2x + 1)$ can be computed by first calculating the expressions in parentheses and then multiplying. Because the last step is multiplication, we can treat the expression as a product.

2. $\dfrac{2x - 1}{x}$ can be computed by first calculating the numerator and denominator and then dividing one by the other. Because the last step is division, we can treat the expression as a quotient.

3. $x^2 + (4x - 1)(x + 2)$ can be computed by first calculating x^2, then calculating the product $(4x - 1)(x + 2)$, and finally adding the two answers. Thus, we can treat the expression as a sum.

4. $(3x^2 - 1)^5$ can be computed by first calculating the expression in parentheses and then raising the answer to the fifth power. Thus, we can treat the expression as a power. (We shall see how to differentiate powers of expressions in Section 4.4.)

5. The expression $(x + 1)(x + 2)/(x - 1)$ can be treated as either a quotient or a product: We can write it as a quotient: $\dfrac{(x + 1)(x + 2)}{x - 1}$ or as a product: $(x + 1)\left(\dfrac{x + 2}{x - 1}\right)$. (See Example 6(b).)

EXAMPLE 7 Using the Calculation Thought Experiment

Find $\dfrac{d}{dx}\left[6x^2 + 5\left(\dfrac{x}{x-1}\right)\right]$.

Solution The calculation thought experiment tells us that the expression we are asked to differentiate can be treated as a *sum*. Because the derivative of a sum is the sum of the derivatives, we get

$$\frac{d}{dx}\left[6x^2 + 5\left(\frac{x}{x-1}\right)\right] = \frac{d}{dx}(6x^2) + \frac{d}{dx}\left[5\left(\frac{x}{x-1}\right)\right].$$

In other words, we must take the derivatives of $6x^2$ and $5\left(\dfrac{x}{x-1}\right)$ separately and then add the answers. The derivative of $6x^2$ is $12x$. There are two ways of taking the derivative of $5\left(\dfrac{x}{x-1}\right)$: We could either first multiply the expression $\left(\dfrac{x}{x-1}\right)$ by 5 to get $\left(\dfrac{5x}{x-1}\right)$ and then take its derivative using the quotient rule, or we could pull the 5 out, as we do next.

$$\frac{d}{dx}\left(6x^2 + 5\left(\frac{x}{x-1}\right)\right) = \frac{d}{dx}(6x^2) + \frac{d}{dx}\left[5\left(\frac{x}{x-1}\right)\right] \qquad \text{Derivative of sum}$$

$$= 12x + 5\frac{d}{dx}\left(\frac{x}{x-1}\right) \qquad \text{Constant} \times \text{Function}$$

$$= 12x + 5\left(\frac{(1)(x-1) - (x)(1)}{(x-1)^2}\right) \qquad \text{Quotient rule}$$

$$= 12x + 5\left(\frac{-1}{(x-1)^2}\right)$$

$$= 12x - \frac{5}{(x-1)^2}$$

APPLICATIONS

In the next example, we return to a scenario similar to the one discussed at the start of this section.

EXAMPLE 8 Applying the Product and Quotient Rules: Revenue and Average Cost

Sales of your newly launched miniature wall posters for college dorms, *iMiniPosters*, are really taking off. (Those old-fashioned large wall posters no longer fit in today's "downsized" college dorm rooms.) Monthly sales to students at the start of this year were 1,500 iMiniPosters, and since that time, sales have been increasing by 300 posters each month, even though the price you charge has also been going up.

a. The price you charge for iMiniPosters is given by:

$$p(t) = 10 + 0.05t^2 \text{ dollars per poster,}$$

where t is time in months since the start of January of this year. Find a formula for the monthly revenue, and then compute its rate of change at the beginning of March.

b. The number of students who purchase iMiniPosters in a month is given by

$$n(t) = 800 + 0.2t,$$

where t is as in part (a). Find a formula for the average number of posters each student buys, and hence estimate the rate at which this number was growing at the beginning of March.

Solution

a. To compute monthly revenue as a function of time t, we use

$$R(t) = p(t)q(t). \qquad \text{Revenue} = \text{Price} \times \text{Quantity}$$

We already have a formula for $p(t)$. The function $q(t)$ measures sales, which were 1,500 posters/month at time $t = 0$, and rising by 300 per month:

$$q(t) = 1{,}500 + 300t.$$

Therefore, the formula for revenue is

$$R(t) = p(t)q(t)$$
$$R(t) = (10 + 0.05t^2)(1{,}500 + 300t).$$

Rather than expand this expression, we shall leave it as a product so that we can use the product rule in computing its rate of change:

$$R'(t) = p'(t)q(t) + p(t)q'(t)$$
$$= [0.10t][1{,}500 + 300t] + [10 + 0.05t^2][300].$$

Because the beginning of March corresponds to $t = 2$, we have

$$R'(2) = [0.10(2)][1{,}500 + 300(2)] + [10 + 0.05(2)^2][300]$$
$$= (0.2)(2{,}100) + (10.2)(300) = \$3{,}480 \text{ per month.}$$

Therefore, your monthly revenue was increasing at a rate of $3,480 per month at the beginning of March.

b. The average number of posters sold to each student is

$$k(t) = \frac{\text{Number of posters}}{\text{Number of students}}$$

$$k(t) = \frac{q(t)}{n(t)} = \frac{1{,}500 + 300t}{800 + 0.2t}.$$

The rate of change of $k(t)$ is computed with the quotient rule:

$$k'(t) = \frac{q'(t)n(t) - q(t)n'(t)}{n(t)^2}$$

$$= \frac{(300)(800 + 0.2t) - (1{,}500 + 300t)(0.2)}{(800 + 0.2t)^2}$$

so that

$$k'(2) = \frac{(300)[800 + 0.2(2)] - [1{,}500 + 300(2)](0.2)}{[800 + 0.2(2)]^2}$$

$$= \frac{(300)(800.4) - (2{,}100)(0.2)}{800.4^2} \approx 0.37 \text{ posters/student per month.}$$

Therefore, the average number of posters sold to each student was increasing at a rate of about 0.37 posters/student per month.

4.3 EXERCISES

▼ more advanced   ◆ challenging
Ⓣ indicates exercises that should be solved using technology

In Exercises 1–12:

a. Calculate the derivative of the given function without using either the product or quotient rule.

b. Use the product or quotient rule to find the derivative. Check that you obtain the same answer. HINT [See Quick Examples on page 314.]

1. $f(x) = 3x$ **2.** $f(x) = 2x^2$

3. $g(x) = x \cdot x^2$ **4.** $g(x) = x \cdot x$

5. $h(x) = x(x + 3)$ **6.** $h(x) = x(1 + 2x)$

7. $r(x) = 100x^{2.1}$ **8.** $r(x) = 0.2x^{-1}$ **9.** $s(x) = \dfrac{2}{x}$

10. $t(x) = \dfrac{x}{3}$ **11.** $u(x) = \dfrac{x^2}{3}$ **12.** $s(x) = \dfrac{3}{x^2}$

Calculate $\dfrac{dy}{dx}$ in Exercises 13–20. Simplify your answer.
HINT [See Example 5.]

13. $y = 3x(4x^2 - 1)$ **14.** $y = 3x^2(2x + 1)$

15. $y = x^3(1 - x^2)$ **16.** $y = x^5(1 - x)$

17. $y = (2x + 3)^2$ **18.** $y = (4x - 1)^2$

19. $x\sqrt{x}$ **20.** $x^2\sqrt{x}$

Calculate $\dfrac{dy}{dx}$ in Exercises 21–50. You need not expand your answers.

21. $y = (x + 1)(x^2 - 1)$

22. $y = (4x^2 + x)(x - x^2)$

23. $y = (2x^{0.5} + 4x - 5)(x - x^{-1})$

24. $y = (x^{0.7} - 4x - 5)(x^{-1} + x^{-2})$

25. $y = (2x^2 - 4x + 1)^2$

26. $y = (2x^{0.5} - x^2)^2$

27. $y = \left(\dfrac{x}{3.2} + \dfrac{3.2}{x}\right)(x^2 + 1)$

28. $y = \left(\dfrac{x^{2.1}}{7} + \dfrac{2}{x^{2.1}}\right)(7x - 1)$

29. $x^2(2x + 3)(7x + 2)$ HINT [See Example 5b.]

30. $x(x^2 - 3)(2x^2 + 1)$ HINT [See Example 5b.]

31. $(5.3x - 1)(1 - x^{2.1})(x^{-2.3} - 3.4)$

32. $(1.1x + 4)(x^{2.1} - x)(3.4 - x^{-2.1})$

33. ▼$y = (\sqrt{x} + 1)\left(\sqrt{x} + \dfrac{1}{x^2}\right)$

34. ▼$y = (4x^2 - \sqrt{x})\left(\sqrt{x} - \dfrac{2}{x^2}\right)$

35. $y = \dfrac{2x + 4}{3x - 1}$ HINT [See Example 6.]

36. $y = \dfrac{3x - 9}{2x + 4}$ HINT [See Example 6.]

37. $y = \dfrac{2x^2 + 4x + 1}{3x - 1}$ **38.** $y = \dfrac{3x^2 - 9x + 11}{2x + 4}$

39. $y = \dfrac{x^2 - 4x + 1}{x^2 + x + 1}$ **40.** $y = \dfrac{x^2 + 9x - 1}{x^2 + 2x - 1}$

41. $y = \dfrac{x^{0.23} - 5.7x}{1 - x^{-2.9}}$ **42.** $y = \dfrac{8.43x^{-0.1} - 0.5x^{-1}}{3.2 + x^{2.9}}$

43. ▼$y = \dfrac{\sqrt{x} + 1}{\sqrt{x} - 1}$ **44.** ▼$y = \dfrac{\sqrt{x} - 1}{\sqrt{x} + 1}$

45. ▼$y = \dfrac{\left(\dfrac{1}{x} + \dfrac{1}{x^2}\right)}{x + x^2}$ **46.** ▼$y = \dfrac{\left(1 - \dfrac{1}{x^2}\right)}{x^2 - 1}$

47. $y = \dfrac{(x + 3)(x + 1)}{3x - 1}$ HINT [See Example 6b.]

48. $y = \dfrac{x}{(x - 5)(x - 4)}$ HINT [See Example 6b.]

49. $y = \dfrac{(x + 3)(x + 1)(x + 2)}{3x - 1}$

50. $y = \dfrac{3x - 1}{(x - 5)(x - 4)(x - 1)}$

In Exercises 51–56, compute the derivatives.

51. $\dfrac{d}{dx}[(x^2 + x)(x^2 - x)]$

52. $\dfrac{d}{dx}[(x^2 + x^3)(x + 1)]$

53. $\dfrac{d}{dx}[(x^3 + 2x)(x^2 - x)]\Big|_{x=2}$

54. $\dfrac{d}{dx}[(x^2 + x)(x^2 - x)]\Big|_{x=1}$

55. $\dfrac{d}{dt}[(t^2 - t^{0.5})(t^{0.5} + t^{-0.5})]\Big|_{t=1}$

56. $\dfrac{d}{dt}[(t^2 + t^{0.5})(t^{0.5} - t^{-0.5})]\Big|_{t=1}$

In Exercises 57–64 use the calculation thought experiment to say whether the expression is written as a sum, difference, scalar multiple, product, or quotient. Then use the appropriate rules to find its derivative. HINT [See Quick Examples on page 318 and Example 7.]

57. $y = x^4 - (x^2 + 120)(4x - 1)$

58. $y = x^4 - \dfrac{x^2 + 120}{4x - 1}$

59. $y = x + 1 + 2\left(\dfrac{x}{x+1}\right)$

60. $y = (x+2) - 4(x^2 - x)\left(x + \dfrac{1}{x}\right)$

(Do not simplify the answer.)

61. $y = (x+2)\left(\dfrac{x}{x+1}\right)$

(Do not simplify the answer.)

62. $y = \dfrac{(x+2)x}{x+1}$

(Do not simplify the answer.)

63. $y = (x+1)(x-2) - 2\left(\dfrac{x}{x+1}\right)$

64. $y = \dfrac{x+2}{x+1} + (x+1)(x-2)$

In Exercises 65–70, find the equation of the line tangent to the graph of the given function at the point with the indicated x-coordinate.

65. $f(x) = (x^2 + 1)(x^3 + x); \; x = 1$

66. $f(x) = (x^{0.5} + 1)(x^2 + x); \; x = 1$

67. $f(x) = \dfrac{x+1}{x+2}; \; x = 0$ **68.** $f(x) = \dfrac{\sqrt{x}+1}{\sqrt{x}+2}; \; x = 4$

69. $f(x) = \dfrac{x^2+1}{x}; \; x = -1$ **70.** $f(x) = \dfrac{x}{x^2+1}; \; x = 1$

APPLICATIONS

71. *Revenue* The monthly sales of **Sunny Electronics'** new sound system are given by $q(t) = 2{,}000t - 100t^2$ units per month, t months after its introduction. The price Sunny charges is $p(t) = 1{,}000 - t^2$ dollars per sound system, t months after introduction. Find the rate of change of monthly sales, the rate of change of the price, and the rate of change of monthly revenue five months after the introduction of the sound system. Interpret your answers. HINT [See Example 8(a).]

72. *Revenue* The monthly sales of **Sunny Electronics'** new *iSun* walkman is given by $q(t) = 2{,}000t - 100t^2$ units per month, t months after its introduction. The price Sunny charges is $p(t) = 100 - t^2$ dollars per *iSun*, t months after introduction. Find the rate of change of monthly sales, the rate of change of the price, and the rate of change of monthly revenue six months after the introduction of the *iSun*. Interpret your answers. HINT [See Example 8(a).]

73. *Saudi Oil Revenues* The spot price of crude oil during the period 2000–2005 can be approximated by

$$P(t) = 5t + 25 \text{ dollars per barrel} \quad (0 \le t \le 5)$$

in year t, where $t = 0$ represents 2000. Saudi Arabia's crude oil production over the same period can be approximated by

$$Q(t) = 0.082t^2 - 0.22t + 8.2 \text{ million barrels per day.}[18]$$
$$(0 \le t \le 5)$$

Use these models to estimate Saudi Arabia's daily oil revenue and also its rate of change in 2001. (Round your answers to the nearest \$1 million.)

74. *Russian Oil Revenues* Russia's crude oil production during the period 2000–2005 can be approximated by

$$Q(t) = -0.066t^2 + 0.96t + 6.1 \text{ million barrels per day}[19]$$
$$(0 \le t \le 5)$$

in year t, where $t = 0$ represents 2000. Use the model for the spot price in Exercise 73 to estimate Russia's daily oil revenue and also its rate of change in 2001.

75. *Revenue* Dorothy Wagner is currently selling 20 "I ♥ Calculus" T-shirts per day, but sales are dropping at a rate of 3 per day. She is currently charging \$7 per T-shirt, but to compensate for dwindling sales, she is increasing the unit price by \$1 per day. How fast, and in what direction is her daily revenue currently changing?

76. *Pricing Policy* Let us turn Exercise 75 around a little: Dorothy Wagner is currently selling 20 "I ♥ Calculus" T-shirts per day, but sales are dropping at a rate of 3 per day. She is currently charging \$7 per T-shirt, and she wishes to increase her daily revenue by \$10 per day. At what rate should she increase the unit price to accomplish this (assuming that the price increase does not affect sales)?

77. *Bus Travel* Thoroughbred Bus Company finds that its monthly costs for one particular year were given by $C(t) = 10{,}000 + t^2$ dollars after t months. After t months the company had $P(t) = 1{,}000 + t^2$ passengers per month. How fast is its cost per passenger changing after 6 months? HINT [See Example 8(b).]

78. *Bus Travel* Thoroughbred Bus Company finds that its monthly costs for one particular year were given by $C(t) = 100 + t^2$ dollars after t months. After t months, the company had $P(t) = 1{,}000 + t^2$ passengers per month. How fast is its cost per passenger changing after 6 months? HINT [See Example 8(b).]

79. *Fuel Economy* Your muscle car's gas mileage (in miles per gallon) is given as a function $M(x)$ of speed x in mph, where

$$M(x) = \dfrac{3{,}000}{x + 3{,}600x^{-1}}.$$

Calculate $M'(x)$, and then $M'(10)$, $M'(60)$, and $M'(70)$. What do the answers tell you about your car?

---

[18] Source for data: EIA/Saudi British Bank (www.sabb.com). 2004 figures are based on mid-year data, and 2005 data are estimates.

[19] Source for data: Energy Information Administration (www.eia.doe.gov), Pravda (http://english.pravda.ru). 2004 figures are based on mid-year data, and 2005 data are estimates.

80. *Fuel Economy* Your used Chevy's gas mileage (in miles per gallon) is given as a function $M(x)$ of speed x in mph, where

$$M(x) = \frac{4,000}{x + 3,025x^{-1}}.$$

Calculate $M'(x)$ and hence determine *the sign* of each of the following: $M'(40)$, $M'(55)$, and $M'(60)$. Interpret your results.

81. ▼*Oil Imports from Mexico* Daily oil production in Mexico and daily U.S. oil imports from Mexico during 2005–2009 can be approximated by

$$P(t) = 3.9 - 0.10t \text{ million barrels } (5 \leq t \leq 9)$$
$$I(t) = 2.1 - 0.11t \text{ million barrels } (5 \leq t \leq 9)$$

where t is time in years since the start of 2000.[20]

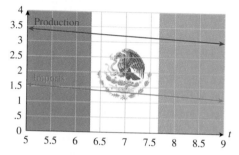

a. What are represented by the functions $P(t) - I(t)$ and $I(t)/P(t)$?

b. Compute $\dfrac{d}{dt}\left[\dfrac{I(t)}{P(t)}\right]\Big|_{t=8}$ to two significant digits. What does the answer tell you about oil imports from Mexico?

82. ▼*Oil Imports from Mexico* Daily oil production in Mexico and daily U.S. oil imports from Mexico during 2000–2004 can be approximated by

$$P(t) = 3.0 + 0.13t \text{ million barrels } (0 \leq t \leq 4)$$
$$I(t) = 1.4 + 0.06t \text{ million barrels } (0 \leq t \leq 4)$$

where t is time in years since the start of 2000.[21]

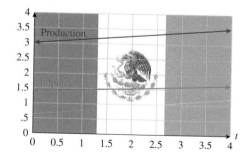

a. What are represented by the functions $P(t) - I(t)$ and $I(t)/P(t)$?

b. Compute $\dfrac{d}{dt}\left[\dfrac{I(t)}{P(t)}\right]\Big|_{t=3}$ to two significant digits. What does the answer tell you about oil imports from Mexico?

83. ▼*Military Spending* The annual cost per active-duty armed service member in the United States increased from $80,000 in 1995 to a projected $120,000 in 2007. In 1995, there were 1.5 million armed service personnel, and this number was projected to decrease to 1.4 million in 2003.[22] Use linear models for annual cost and personnel to estimate, to the nearest $10 million, the rate of change of total military personnel costs in 2002.

84. ▼*Military Spending in the 1990s* The annual cost per active-duty armed service member in the United States increased from $80,000 in 1995 to $90,000 in 2000. In 1990, there were 2 million armed service personnel and this number decreased to 1.5 million in 2000.[23] Use linear models for annual cost and personnel to estimate, to the nearest $10 million, the rate of change of total military personnel costs in 1995.

85. ▼*Biology—Reproduction* The Verhulst model for population growth specifies the reproductive rate of an organism as a function of the total population according to the following formula:

$$R(p) = \frac{r}{1 + kp}$$

where p is the total population in thousands of organisms, r and k are constants that depend on the particular circumstances and the organism being studied, and $R(p)$ is the reproduction rate in thousands of organisms per hour.[24] If $k = 0.125$ and $r = 45$, find $R'(p)$ and then $R'(4)$. Interpret the result.

86. ▼*Biology—Reproduction* Another model, the predator satiation model for population growth, specifies that the reproductive rate of an organism as a function of the total population varies according to the following formula:

$$R(p) = \frac{rp}{1 + kp}$$

where p is the total population in thousands of organisms, r and k are constants that depend on the particular circumstances and the organism being studied, and $R(p)$ is the reproduction rate in new organisms per hour.[25] Given that $k = 0.2$ and $r = 0.08$, find $R'(p)$ and $R'(2)$. Interpret the result.

[22] Annual costs are adjusted for inflation. Sources: Department of Defense, Stephen Daggett, military analyst, Congressional Research Service/*New York Times*, April 19, 2002, p. A21.

[23] Ibid.

[24] Source: *Mathematics in Medicine and the Life Sciences* by F. C. Hoppensteadt and C. S. Peskin (Springer-Verlag, New York, 1992) pp. 20–22.

[25] Ibid.

[20] Source for data: Energy Information Administration (www.eia.doe.gov)/Pemex.

[21] Ibid.

87. ▼*Embryo Development* Bird embryos consume oxygen from the time the egg is laid through the time the chick hatches. For a typical galliform bird egg, the oxygen consumption (in milliliters) t days after the egg was laid can be approximated by[26]

$$C(t) = -0.016t^4 + 1.1t^3 - 11t^2 + 3.6t.   (15 \le t \le 30)$$

(An egg will usually hatch at around $t = 28$.) Suppose that at time $t = 0$ you have a collection of 30 newly laid eggs and that the number of eggs decreases linearly to zero at time $t = 30$ days. How fast is the total oxygen consumption of your collection of embryos changing after 25 days? (Round your answers to two significant digits.) Comment on the result. HINT [Total oxygen consumption = Oxygen consumption per egg × Number of eggs.]

88. ▼*Embryo Development* Turkey embryos consume oxygen from the time the egg is laid through the time the chick hatches. For a brush turkey, the oxygen consumption (in milliliters) t days after the egg was laid can be approximated by[27]

$$C(t) = -0.0071t^4 + 0.95t^3 - 22t^2 + 95t.   (25 \le t \le 50)$$

(An egg will typically hatch at around $t = 50$.) Suppose that at time $t = 0$ you have a collection of 100 newly laid eggs and that the number of eggs decreases linearly to zero at time $t = 50$ days. How fast is the total oxygen consumption of your collection of embryos changing after 40 days? (Round your answer to two significant digits.) Interpret the result. HINT [Total oxygen consumption = Oxygen consumption per egg × Number of eggs.]

COMMUNICATION AND REASONING EXERCISES

89. If f and g are functions of time, and at time $t = 3$, f equals 5 and is rising at a rate of 2 units per second, and g equals 4 and is rising at a rate of 5 units per second, then the product fg equals _____ and is rising at a rate of _____ units per second.

90. If f and g are functions of time, and at time $t = 2$, f equals 3 and is rising at a rate of 4 units per second, and g equals 5 and is rising at a rate of 6 units per second, then fg equals _____ and is rising at a rate of _____ units per second.

91. If f and g are functions of time, and at time $t = 3$, f equals 5 and is rising at a rate of 2 units per second, and g equals 4 and is rising at a rate of 5 units per second, then f/g equals _____ and is changing at a rate of _____ units per second.

92. If f and g are functions of time, and at time $t = 2$, f equals 3 and is rising at a rate of 4 units per second, and g equals 5 and is rising at a rate of 6 units per second, then f/g equals _____ and is changing at a rate of _____ units per second.

93. You have come across the following in a newspaper article: "Revenues of HAL Home Heating Oil Inc. are rising by $4.2 million per year. This is due to an annual increase of 70¢ per gallon in the price HAL charges for heating oil and an increase in sales of 6 million gallons of oil per year." Comment on this analysis.

94. Your friend says that because average cost is obtained by dividing the cost function by the number of units x, it follows that the derivative of average cost is the same as marginal cost because the derivative of x is 1. Comment on this analysis.

95. ▼Find a demand function $q(p)$ such that, at a price per item of $p = \$100$, revenue will rise if the price per item is increased.

96. ▼What must be true about a demand function $q(p)$ so that, at a price per item of $p = \$100$, revenue will decrease if the price per item is increased?

97. ▼You and I are both selling a steady 20 T-shirts per day. The price I am getting for my T-shirts is increasing twice as fast as yours, but your T-shirts are currently selling for twice the price of mine. Whose revenue is increasing faster: yours, mine, or neither? Explain.

98. ▼You and I are both selling T-shirts for a steady $20 per shirt. Sales of my T-shirts are increasing at twice the rate of yours, but you are currently selling twice as many as I am. Whose revenue is increasing faster: yours, mine, or neither? Explain.

99. ◆*Marginal Product* (from the GRE Economics Test) Which of the following statements about average product and marginal product is correct?

(A) If average product is decreasing, marginal product must be less than average product.

(B) If average product is increasing, marginal product must be increasing.

(C) If marginal product is decreasing, average product must be less than marginal product.

(D) If marginal product is increasing, average product must be decreasing.

(E) If marginal product is constant over some range, average product must be constant over that range.

100. ◆*Marginal Cost* (based on a question from the GRE Economics Test) Which of the following statements about average cost and marginal cost is correct?

(A) If average cost is increasing, marginal cost must be increasing.

(B) If average cost is increasing, marginal cost must be decreasing.

(C) If average cost is increasing, marginal cost must be more than average cost.

(D) If marginal cost is increasing, average cost must be increasing.

(E) If marginal cost is increasing, average cost must be larger than marginal cost.

---

[26] The model is derived from graphical data published in the article "The Brush Turkey" by Roger S. Seymour, *Scientific American*, December, 1991, pp. 108–114.

[27] Ibid.

4.4 The Chain Rule

We can now find the derivatives of expressions involving powers of x combined using addition, subtraction, multiplication, and division, but we still cannot take the derivative of an expression like $(3x + 1)^{0.5}$. For this we need one more rule. The function $h(x) = (3x + 1)^{0.5}$ is not a sum, difference, product, or quotient. To find out what it is, we can use the calculation thought experiment and think about the last operation we would perform in calculating $h(x)$.

1. Calculate $3x + 1$.

2. Take the 0.5 power (square root) of the answer.

The last operation is "take the 0.5 power." We do not yet have a rule for finding the derivative of the 0.5 power of a quantity other than x.

There is a way to build $h(x) = (3x + 1)^{0.5}$ out of two simpler functions: $u(x) = 3x + 1$ (the function that corresponds to the first step in the calculation above) and $f(x) = x^{0.5}$ (the function that corresponds to the second step):

$$h(x) = (3x + 1)^{0.5}$$
$$= [u(x)]^{0.5} \qquad u(x) = 3x + 1$$
$$= f(u(x)) \qquad f(x) = x^{0.5}$$

We say that h is the **composite** of f and u. We read $f(u(x))$ as "f of u of x."

To compute $h(1)$, say, we first compute $3 \cdot 1 + 1 = 4$ and then take the square root of 4, giving $h(1) = 2$. To compute $f(u(1))$ we follow exactly the same steps: First compute $u(1) = 4$ and then $f(u(1)) = f(4) = 2$. We always compute $f(u(x))$ numerically from the inside out: Given x, first compute $u(x)$ and then $f(u(x))$.

Now, f and u are functions *whose derivatives we know.* The *chain rule* allows us to use our knowledge of the derivatives of f and u to find the derivative of $f(u(x))$. For the purposes of stating the rule, let us avoid some of the nested parentheses by abbreviating $u(x)$ as u. Thus, we write $f(u)$ instead of $f(u(x))$ and remember that u is a function of x.

Chain Rule

If f is a differentiable function of u and u is a differentiable function of x, then the composite $f(u)$ is a differentiable function of x, and

$$\frac{d}{dx}[f(u)] = f'(u)\frac{du}{dx} \qquad \text{Chain Rule}$$

In words *The derivative of f(quantity) is the derivative of f, evaluated at that quantity, times the derivative of the quantity.*

Quick Examples

1. Take $f(u) = u^2$. Then

$$\frac{d}{dx}[u^2] = 2u\frac{du}{dx} \qquad \text{Because } f'(u) = 2u$$

The derivative of a quantity squared is two times the quantity, times the derivative of the quantity.

2. Take $f(u) = u^{0.5}$. Then

$$\frac{d}{dx}[u^{0.5}] = 0.5u^{-0.5}\frac{du}{dx} \qquad \text{Because } f'(u) = 0.5u^{-0.5}$$

The derivative of a quantity raised to the 0.5 is 0.5 times the quantity raised to the −0.5, times the derivative of the quantity.

As the quick examples illustrate, for every power of a function u whose derivative we know, we now get a "generalized" differentiation rule. The following table gives more examples.

Original Rule	Generalized Rule	In Words
$\dfrac{d}{dx}[x^2] = 2x$	$\dfrac{d}{dx}[u^2] = 2u\dfrac{du}{dx}$	The derivative of a quantity squared is twice the quantity, times the derivative of the quantity.
$\dfrac{d}{dx}[x^3] = 3x^2$	$\dfrac{d}{dx}[u^3] = 3u^2\dfrac{du}{dx}$	The derivative of a quantity cubed is 3 times the quantity squared, times the derivative of the quantity.
$\dfrac{d}{dx}\left(\dfrac{1}{x}\right) = -\dfrac{1}{x^2}$	$\dfrac{d}{dx}\left(\dfrac{1}{u}\right) = -\dfrac{1}{u^2}\dfrac{du}{dx}$	The derivative of 1 over a quantity is negative 1 over the quantity squared, times the derivative of the quantity.
Power Rule	**Generalized Power Rule**	**In Words**
$\dfrac{d}{dx}[x^n] = nx^{n-1}$	$\dfrac{d}{dx}[u^n] = nu^{n-1}\dfrac{du}{dx}$	The derivative of a quantity raised to the n is n times the quantity raised to the n − 1, times the derivative of the quantity.

To motivate the chain rule, let us see why it is true in the special case when $f(u) = u^3$, where the chain rule tells us that

$$\frac{d}{dx}[u^3] = 3u^2\frac{du}{dx} \qquad \text{Generalized Power Rule with } n = 3$$

But we could have done this using the product rule instead:

$$\frac{d}{dx}[u^3] = \frac{d}{dx}[u \cdot u \cdot u] = \frac{du}{dx}u \cdot u + u\frac{du}{dx}u + u \cdot u\frac{du}{dx} = 3u^2\frac{du}{dx}$$

Web Site
www.AppliedCalc.org
Everything for Calculus
→ Chapter 4
→ Proof of Chain Rule

which gives us the same result. A similar argument works for $f(u) = u^n$ where $n = 2, 3, 4, \ldots$ We can then use the quotient rule and the chain rule for positive powers to verify the generalized power rule for *negative* powers as well. For the case of a general differentiable function f, the proof of the chain rule is beyond the scope of this book, but you can find one on the Web site by the path shown in the margin.

EXAMPLE 1 Using the Chain Rule

Compute the following derivatives.

a. $\dfrac{d}{dx}[(2x^2 + x)^3]$ **b.** $\dfrac{d}{dx}[(x^3 + x)^{100}]$ **c.** $\dfrac{d}{dx}\sqrt{3x + 1}$

Solution

a. Using the calculation thought experiment, we see that the last operation we would perform in calculating $(2x^2 + x)^3$ is that of *cubing*. Thus we think of $(2x^2 + x)^3$ as *a quantity cubed*. There are two similar methods we can use to calculate its derivative.

Method 1: Using the formula We think of $(2x^2 + x)^3$ as u^3, where $u = 2x^2 + x$. By the formula,

$$\frac{d}{dx}[u^3] = 3u^2\frac{du}{dx} \qquad \text{Generalized Power Rule}$$

Now substitute for u:

$$\frac{d}{dx}[(2x^2 + x)^3] = 3(2x^2 + x)^2\frac{d}{dx}(2x^2 + x)$$

$$= 3(2x^2 + x)^2(4x + 1)$$

Method 2: Using the verbal form If we prefer to use the verbal form, we get:

The derivative of $(2x^2 + x)$ cubed is three times $(2x^2 + x)$ squared, times the derivative of $(2x^2 + x)$.

In symbols,

$$\frac{d}{dx}[(2x^2 + x)^3] = 3(2x^2 + x)^2(4x + 1),$$

as we obtained above.

b. First, the calculation thought experiment: If we were computing $(x^3 + x)^{100}$, the last operation we would perform is *raising a quantity to the power* 100. Thus we are dealing with *a quantity raised to the power* 100, and so we must again use the generalized power rule. According to the verbal form of the generalized power rule, the derivative of a quantity raised to the power 100 is 100 times that quantity to the power 99, times the derivative of that quantity. In symbols,

$$\frac{d}{dx}[(x^3 + x)^{100}] = 100(x^3 + x)^{99}(3x^2 + 1).$$

c. We first rewrite the expression $\sqrt{3x + 1}$ as $(3x + 1)^{0.5}$ and then use the generalized power rule as in parts (a) and (b):

The derivative of a quantity raised to the 0.5 is 0.5 times the quantity raised to the −0.5, times the derivative of the quantity.

Thus,

$$\frac{d}{dx}[(3x + 1)^{0.5}] = 0.5(3x + 1)^{-0.5} \cdot 3 = 1.5(3x + 1)^{-0.5}.$$

➡ **Before we go on...** The following are examples of common errors in solving Example 1(b):

$$``\frac{d}{dx}[(x^3 + x)^{100}] = 100(3x^2 + 1)^{99}\text{''} \qquad ✗ \quad WRONG!$$

$$``\frac{d}{dx}[(x^3 + x)^{100}] = 100(x^3 + x)^{99}\text{''} \qquad ✗ \quad WRONG!$$

Remember that the generalized power rule says that the derivative of a quantity to the power 100 is 100 times *that same quantity* raised to the power 99, *times the derivative of that quantity.* ∎

Q: *It seems that there are now two formulas for the derivative of an nth power:*

1. $\dfrac{d}{dx}[x^n] = nx^{n-1}$

2. $\dfrac{d}{dx}[u^n] = nu^{n-1}\dfrac{du}{dx}$

Which one do I use?

A: Formula 1 is the original power rule, which applies only to a power of x. For instance, it applies to x^{10}, but it does not apply to $(2x+1)^{10}$ because the quantity that is being raised to a power is not x. Formula 2 applies to a power of any *function of x*, such as $(2x+1)^{10}$. It can even be used in place of the original power rule. For example, if we take $u = x$ in Formula 2, we obtain

$$\frac{d}{dx}[x^n] = nx^{n-1}\frac{dx}{dx}$$

$$= nx^{n-1} \qquad \text{The derivative of } x \text{ with respect to } x \text{ is 1.}$$

Thus, the generalized power rule really *is* a generalization of the original power rule, as its name suggests.

EXAMPLE 2 More Examples Using the Chain Rule

Find: **a.** $\dfrac{d}{dx}[(2x^5 + x^2 - 20)^{-2/3}]$ **b.** $\dfrac{d}{dx}\left[\dfrac{1}{\sqrt{x+2}}\right]$ **c.** $\dfrac{d}{dx}\left[\dfrac{1}{x^2+x}\right]$

Solution Each of the given functions is, or can be rewritten as, a power of a function whose derivative we know. Thus, we can use the method of Example 1.

a. $\dfrac{d}{dx}[(2x^5 + x^2 - 20)^{-2/3}] = -\dfrac{2}{3}(2x^5 + x^2 - 20)^{-5/3}(10x^4 + 2x)$

b. $\dfrac{d}{dx}\left[\dfrac{1}{\sqrt{x+2}}\right] = \dfrac{d}{dx}(x+2)^{-1/2} = -\dfrac{1}{2}(x+2)^{-3/2} \cdot 1 = -\dfrac{1}{2(x+2)^{3/2}}$

c. $\dfrac{d}{dx}\left[\dfrac{1}{x^2+x}\right] = \dfrac{d}{dx}(x^2+x)^{-1} = -(x^2+x)^{-2}(2x+1) = -\dfrac{2x+1}{(x^2+x)^2}$

➡ **Before we go on...** In Example 2(c), we could have used the quotient rule instead of the generalized power rule. We can think of the quantity $1/(x^2 + x)$ in two different ways using the calculation thought experiment:

1. As 1 divided by something—in other words, as a quotient

2. As something raised to the -1 power

Of course, we get the same derivative using either approach. ■

We now look at some more complicated examples.

EXAMPLE 3 Harder Examples Using the Chain Rule

Find $\dfrac{dy}{dx}$ in each case.   **a.** $y = [(x+1)^{-2.5} + 3x]^{-3}$ **b.** $y = (x+10)^3 \sqrt{1-x^2}$

Solution

a. The calculation thought experiment tells us that the last operation we would perform in calculating y is raising the quantity $[(x+1)^{-2.5} + 3x]$ to the power -3. Thus, we use the generalized power rule.

$$\frac{dy}{dx} = -3[(x+1)^{-2.5} + 3x]^{-4} \frac{d}{dx}[(x+1)^{-2.5} + 3x]$$

We are not yet done; we must still find the derivative of $(x+1)^{-2.5} + 3x$. Finding the derivative of a complicated function in several steps helps to keep the problem manageable. Continuing, we have

$$\frac{dy}{dx} = -3[(x+1)^{-2.5} + 3x]^{-4} \frac{d}{dx}[(x+1)^{-2.5} + 3x]$$

$$= -3[(x+1)^{-2.5} + 3x]^{-4} \left[\frac{d}{dx}[(x+1)^{-2.5}] + \frac{d}{dx}(3x) \right] \quad \text{Derivative of a sum}$$

Now we have two derivatives left to calculate. The second of these we know to be 3, and the first is the derivative of a quantity raised to the -2.5 power. Thus

$$\frac{dy}{dx} = -3[(x+1)^{-2.5} + 3x]^{-4}[-2.5(x+1)^{-3.5} \cdot 1 + 3].$$

b. The expression $(x+10)^3 \sqrt{1-x^2}$ is a product, so we use the product rule:

$$\frac{d}{dx}[(x+10)^3 \sqrt{1-x^2}] = \left(\frac{d}{dx}[(x+10)^3] \right) \sqrt{1-x^2} + (x+10)^3 \left(\frac{d}{dx} \sqrt{1-x^2} \right)$$

$$= 3(x+10)^2 \sqrt{1-x^2} + (x+10)^3 \frac{1}{2\sqrt{1-x^2}}(-2x)$$

$$= 3(x+10)^2 \sqrt{1-x^2} - \frac{x(x+10)^3}{\sqrt{1-x^2}}$$

APPLICATIONS

The next example is a new treatment of Example 3 from Section 4.2.

EXAMPLE 4 Marginal Product

Precision Manufacturers is informed by a consultant that its annual profit is given by

$$P = -200{,}000 + 4{,}000q - 0.46q^2 - 0.00001q^3$$

where q is the number of surgical lasers it sells each year. The consultant also informs Precision that the number of surgical lasers it can manufacture each year depends on the number n of assembly line workers it employs according to the equation

$$q = 100n \qquad \text{Each worker contributes 100 lasers per year.}$$

Use the chain rule to find the marginal product $\dfrac{dP}{dn}$.

Solution We could calculate the marginal product by substituting the expression for q in the expression for P to obtain P as a function of n (as given in Example 3 from Section 4.2) and then finding dP/dn. Alternatively—and this will simplify the calculation—we can use the chain rule. To see how the chain rule applies, notice that P is a function of q, where q in turn is given as a function of n. By the chain rule,

$$\frac{dP}{dn} = P'(q)\frac{dq}{dn} \qquad \text{Chain Rule}$$

$$= \frac{dP}{dq}\frac{dq}{dn} \qquad \text{Notice how the "quantities" } dq \text{ appear to cancel.}$$

Now we compute

$$\frac{dP}{dq} = 4{,}000 - 0.92q - 0.00003q^2$$

and $\dfrac{dq}{dn} = 100.$

Substituting into the equation for $\dfrac{dP}{dn}$ gives

$$\frac{dP}{dn} = (4{,}000 - 0.92q - 0.00003q^2)(100)$$

$$= 400{,}000 - 92q - 0.003q^2$$

Notice that the answer has q as a variable. We can express dP/dn as a function of n by substituting $100n$ for q:

$$\frac{dP}{dn} = 400{,}000 - 92(100n) - 0.003(100n)^2$$

$$= 400{,}000 - 9{,}200n - 30n^2$$

The equation

$$\frac{dP}{dn} = \frac{dP}{dq}\frac{dq}{dn}$$

in the example above is an appealing way of writing the chain rule because it suggests that the "quantities" dq cancel. In general, we can write the chain rule as follows.

Chain Rule in Differential Notation

If y is a differentiable function of u, and u is a differentiable function of x, then

$$\frac{dy}{dx} = \frac{dy}{du}\frac{du}{dx}$$

Notice how the units cancel:

$$\frac{\text{Units of } y}{\text{Units of } x} = \frac{\text{Units of } y}{\text{Units of } u}\frac{\text{Units of } u}{\text{Units of } x}$$

Quick Examples

1. If $y = u^3$, where $u = 4x + 1$, then

$$\frac{dy}{dx} = \frac{dy}{du}\frac{du}{dx} = 3u^2 \cdot 4 = 12u^2 = 12(4x + 1)^2.$$

2. If $q = 43p^2$ where p (and hence q also) is a differentiable function of t, then

$$\frac{dq}{dt} = \frac{dq}{dp}\frac{dp}{dt}$$

$$= 86p\frac{dp}{dt}. \qquad p \text{ is not specified, so we leave } dp/dt \text{ as is.}$$

You can see one of the reasons we still use Leibniz differential notation: The chain rule looks like a simple "cancellation" of du terms.

EXAMPLE 5 Marginal Revenue

Suppose a company's weekly revenue R is given as a function of the unit price p, and p in turn is given as a function of weekly sales q (by means of a demand equation). If

$$\left.\frac{dR}{dp}\right|_{q=1,000} = \$40 \text{ per } \$1 \text{ increase in price}$$

and

$$\left.\frac{dp}{dq}\right|_{q=1,000} = -\$20 \text{ per additional item sold per week}$$

find the marginal revenue when sales are 1,000 items per week.

Solution The marginal revenue is $\dfrac{dR}{dq}$. By the chain rule, we have

$$\frac{dR}{dq} = \frac{dR}{dp}\frac{dp}{dq} \qquad \text{Units: Revenue per item}$$
$$= \text{Revenue per } \$1 \text{ price increase} \times \text{price increase per additional item}$$

Because we are interested in the marginal revenue at a demand level of 1,000 items per week, we have

$$\left.\frac{dR}{dq}\right|_{q=1,000} = (40)(-20) = -\$800 \text{ per additional item sold.}$$

Thus, if the price is lowered to increase the demand from 1,000 to 1,001 items per week, the weekly revenue will drop by approximately $800.

Look again at the way the terms "du" appeared to cancel in the differential formula $\dfrac{dy}{dx} = \dfrac{dy}{du}\dfrac{du}{dx}$. In fact, the chain rule tells us more:

＊ **NOTE** The notion of "thinking of *x* as a function of *y*" will be made more precise in Section 4.4.

Manipulating Derivatives in Differential Notation

1. Suppose y is a function of x. Then, thinking of x as a function of y (as, for instance, when we can solve for x)＊ one has

$$\frac{dx}{dy} = \frac{1}{\left(\dfrac{dy}{dx}\right)}, \quad \text{provided } \frac{dy}{dx} \neq 0. \qquad \text{Notice again how } \frac{dy}{dx} \text{ behaves like a fraction.}$$

Quick Example

In the demand equation $q = -0.2p - 8$, we have $\dfrac{dq}{dp} = -0.2$. Therefore,

$$\frac{dp}{dq} = \frac{1}{\left(\dfrac{dq}{dp}\right)} = \frac{1}{-0.2} = -5.$$

2. Suppose x and y are functions of t. Then, thinking of y as a function of x (as, for instance, when we can solve for t as a function of x, and hence obtain y as a function of x) one has

$$\frac{dy}{dx} = \frac{dy/dt}{dx/dt}. \qquad \text{The terms } dt \text{ appear to cancel.}$$

Quick Example

If $x = 3 - 0.2t$ and $y = 6 + 6t$, then

$$\frac{dy}{dx} = \frac{dy/dt}{dx/dt} = \frac{6}{-0.2} = -30.$$

To see why the above formulas work, notice that the second formula,

$$\frac{dy}{dx} = \frac{\left(\dfrac{dy}{dt}\right)}{\left(\dfrac{dx}{dt}\right)}$$

can be written as

$$\frac{dy}{dx}\frac{dx}{dt} = \frac{dy}{dt}, \qquad \text{Multiply both sides by } \frac{dx}{dt}.$$

which is just the differential form of the chain rule. For the first formula, use the second formula with y playing the role of t:

$$\frac{dy}{dx} = \frac{dy/dy}{dx/dy}$$

$$= \frac{1}{dx/dy}. \qquad \frac{dy}{dy} = \frac{d}{dy}[y] = 1$$

FAQs

Using the Chain Rule

Q: *How do I decide whether or not to use the chain rule when taking a derivative?*

A: Use the calculation thought experiment (Section 4.3): Given an expression, consider the steps you would use in computing its value.

- If the last step is *raising a quantity to a power*, as in $\left(\dfrac{x^2 - 1}{x + 4}\right)^4$, then the first step to use is the chain rule (in the form of the generalized power rule):

$$\frac{d}{dx}\left(\frac{x^2 - 1}{x + 4}\right)^4 = 4\left(\frac{x^2 - 1}{x + 4}\right)^3 \frac{d}{dx}\left(\frac{x^2 - 1}{x + 4}\right).$$

Then use the appropriate rules to finish the computation. You may need to again use the calculation thought experiment to decide on the next step (here the quotient rule):

$$= 4\left(\frac{x^2 - 1}{x + 4}\right)^3 \frac{(2x)(x + 4) - (x^2 - 1)(1)}{(x + 4)^2}.$$

- If the last step is *division*, as in $\dfrac{(x^2 - 1)}{(3x + 4)^4}$, then the first step to use is the quotient rule:

$$\frac{d}{dx}\frac{(x^2 - 1)}{(3x + 4)^4} = \frac{(2x)(3x + 4)^4 - (x^2 - 1)\dfrac{d}{dx}(3x + 4)^4}{(3x + 4)^8}.$$

Then use the appropriate rules to finish the computation (here the chain rule):

$$= \frac{(2x)(3x + 4)^4 - (x^2 - 1)4(3x + 4)^3(3)}{(3x + 4)^8}.$$

- If the last step is *multiplication, addition, subtraction, or multiplication by a constant,* then the first rule to use is the product rule, or the rule for sums, differences, or constant multiples as appropriate.

Q: *Every time I compute a derivative, I leave something out. How do I make sure I am really done when taking the derivative of a complicated-looking expression?*

A: Until you are an expert at taking derivatives, the key is to use one rule at a time and write out each step, rather than trying to compute the derivative in a single step.

To illustrate this, try computing the derivative of $(x + 10)^3\sqrt{1 - x^2}$ in Example 3(b) in two ways: First try to compute it in a single step, and then compute it by writing out each step as shown in the example. How do your results compare? For more practice, try Exercises 83 and 84 following.

4.4 EXERCISES

▼ more advanced   ◆ challenging
T indicates exercises that should be solved using technology

Calculate the derivatives of the functions in Exercises 1–46.
HINT [See Example 1.]

1. $f(x) = (2x + 1)^2$

2. $f(x) = (3x - 1)^2$

3. $f(x) = (x - 1)^{-1}$

4. $f(x) = (2x - 1)^{-2}$

5. $f(x) = (2 - x)^{-2}$

6. $f(x) = (1 - x)^{-1}$

7. $f(x) = (2x + 1)^{0.5}$

8. $f(x) = (-x + 2)^{1.5}$

9. $f(x) = (4x - 1)^{-1}$

10. $f(x) = (x + 7)^{-2}$

11. $f(x) = \dfrac{1}{3x - 1}$

12. $f(x) = \dfrac{1}{(x + 1)^2}$

13. $f(x) = (x^2 + 2x)^4$

14. $f(x) = (x^3 - x)^3$

15. $f(x) = (2x^2 - 2)^{-1}$

16. $f(x) = (2x^3 + x)^{-2}$

17. $g(x) = (x^2 - 3x - 1)^{-5}$

18. $g(x) = (2x^2 + x + 1)^{-3}$

19. $h(x) = \dfrac{1}{(x^2 + 1)^3}$

20. $h(x) = \dfrac{1}{(x^2 + x + 1)^2}$

HINT [See Example 2.]   HINT [See Example 2.]

21. $r(x) = (0.1x^2 - 4.2x + 9.5)^{1.5}$

22. $r(x) = (0.1x - 4.2x^{-1})^{0.5}$

23. $r(s) = (s^2 - s^{0.5})^4$

24. $r(s) = (2s + s^{0.5})^{-1}$

25. $f(x) = \sqrt{1 - x^2}$

26. $f(x) = \sqrt{x + x^2}$

27. $h(x) = 2[(x + 1)(x^2 - 1)]^{-1/2}$ HINT [See Example 3.]

28. $h(x) = 3[(2x - 1)(x - 1)]^{-1/3}$ HINT [See Example 3.]

29. $h(x) = (3.1x - 2)^2 - \dfrac{1}{(3.1x - 2)^2}$

30. $h(x) = \left[3.1x^2 - 2 - \dfrac{1}{3.1x - 2}\right]^2$

31. $f(x) = [(6.4x - 1)^2 + (5.4x - 2)^3]^2$

32. $f(x) = (6.4x - 3)^{-2} + (4.3x - 1)^{-2}$

33. $f(x) = (x^2 - 3x)^{-2}(1 - x^2)^{0.5}$

34. $f(x) = (3x^2 + x)(1 - x^2)^{0.5}$

35. $s(x) = \left(\dfrac{2x + 4}{3x - 1}\right)^2$

36. $s(x) = \left(\dfrac{3x - 9}{2x + 4}\right)^3$

37. $g(z) = \left(\dfrac{z}{1 + z^2}\right)^3$

38. $g(z) = \left(\dfrac{z^2}{1 + z}\right)^2$

39. $f(x) = [(1 + 2x)^4 - (1 - x)^2]^3$

40. $f(x) = [(3x - 1)^2 + (1 - x)^5]^2$

41. $t(x) = [2 + (x + 1)^{-0.1}]^{4.3}$

42. $t(x) = [(x + 1)^{0.1} - 4x]^{-5.1}$

43. ▼ $r(x) = \left(\sqrt{2x + 1} - x^2\right)^{-1}$

44. ▼ $r(x) = \left(\sqrt{x + 1} + \sqrt{x}\right)^3$

45. ▼ $f(x) = (1 + (1 + (1 + 2x)^3)^3)^3$

46. ▼ $f(x) = 2x + (2x + (2x + 1)^3)^3$

Find the indicated derivatives in Exercises 47–54. In each case, the independent variable is a (unspecified) function of t.
HINT [See Quick Example 2 on page 331.]

47. $y = x^{100} + 99x^{-1}$. Find $\dfrac{dy}{dt}$.

48. $y = x^{0.5}(1 + x)$. Find $\dfrac{dy}{dt}$.

49. $s = \dfrac{1}{r^3} + r^{0.5}$. Find $\dfrac{ds}{dt}$.

50. $s = r + r^{-1}$. Find $\dfrac{ds}{dt}$.

51. $V = \dfrac{4}{3}\pi r^3$. Find $\dfrac{dV}{dt}$.

52. $A = 4\pi r^2$. Find $\dfrac{dA}{dt}$.

53. ▼ $y = x^3 + \dfrac{1}{x}$, $x = 2$ when $t = 1$, $\left.\dfrac{dx}{dt}\right|_{t=1} = -1$

Find $\left.\dfrac{dy}{dt}\right|_{t=1}$.

54. ▼ $y = \sqrt{x} + \dfrac{1}{\sqrt{x}}$, $x = 9$ when $t = 1$, $\left.\dfrac{dx}{dt}\right|_{t=1} = -1$

Find $\left.\dfrac{dy}{dt}\right|_{t=1}$.

In Exercises 55–60, compute the indicated derivative using the chain rule. HINT [See Quick Examples on page 332.]

55. $y = 3x - 2$; $\dfrac{dx}{dy}$

56. $y = 8x + 4$; $\dfrac{dx}{dy}$

57. $x = 2 + 3t$, $y = -5t$; $\dfrac{dy}{dx}$

58. $x = 1 - t/2$, $y = 4t - 1$; $\dfrac{dy}{dx}$

59. $y = 3x^2 - 2x$; $\left.\dfrac{dx}{dy}\right|_{x=1}$

60. $y = 3x - \dfrac{2}{x}$; $\left.\dfrac{dx}{dy}\right|_{x=2}$

APPLICATIONS

61. **Marginal Product** Paramount Electronics has an annual profit given by

$$P = -100,000 + 5,000q - 0.25q^2$$

where q is the number of laptop computers it sells each year. The number of laptop computers it can make and sell each year depends on the number n of electrical engineers Paramount employs, according to the equation

$$q = 30n + 0.01n^2.$$

Use the chain rule to find $\left.\dfrac{dP}{dn}\right|_{n=10}$ and interpret the result. HINT [See Example 3.]

62. Marginal Product Refer back to Exercise 61. The average profit $\bar{P}$ per computer is given by dividing the total profit P by q:

$$\bar{P} = -\frac{100{,}000}{q} + 5{,}000 - 0.25q.$$

Determine the **marginal average product**, $d\bar{P}/dn$ at an employee level of 10 engineers. Interpret the result. HINT [See Example 3.]

63. Food Versus Education The percentage y (of total personal consumption) an individual spends on food is approximately

$$y = 35x^{-0.25} \text{ percentage points} \quad (6.5 \leq x \leq 17.5)$$

where x is the percentage the individual spends on education.[28] An individual finds that she is spending

$$x = 7 + 0.2t$$

percent of her personal consumption on education, where t is time in months since January 1. Use direct substitution to express the percentage y as a function of time t (do not simplify the expression) and then use the chain rule to estimate how fast the percentage she spends on food is changing on November 1. Be sure to specify the units.

64. Food Versus Recreation The percentage y (of total personal consumption) an individual spends on food is approximately

$$y = 33x^{-0.63} \text{ percentage points} \quad (2.5 \leq x \leq 4.5)$$

where x is the percentage the individual spends on recreation.[29] A college student finds that he is spending

$$x = 3.5 + 0.1t$$

percent of his personal consumption on recreation, where t is time in months since January 1. Use direct substitution to express the percentage y as a function of time t (do not simplify the expression) and then use the chain rule to estimate how fast the percentage he spends on food is changing on November 1. Be sure to specify the units.

65. Marginal Revenue The weekly revenue from the sale of rubies at **Royal Ruby Retailers (RRR)** is increasing at a rate of $40 per $1 increase in price, and the price is decreasing at a rate of $0.75 per additional ruby sold. What is the marginal revenue? (Be sure to state the units of measurement.) Interpret the result. HINT [See Example 5.]

66. Marginal Revenue The weekly revenue from the sale of emeralds at **Eduardo's Emerald Emporium (EEE)** is decreasing at a rate of €500 per €1 increase in price, and the price is decreasing at a rate of €0.45 per additional emerald sold.

What is the marginal revenue? (Be sure to state the units of measurement.) Interpret the result. HINT [See Example 5.]

67. Crime Statistics The murder rate in large cities (over 1 million residents) can be related to that in smaller cities (500,000–1,000,000 residents) by the following linear model:[30]

$$y = 1.5x - 1.9 \quad (15 \leq x \leq 25)$$

where y is the murder rate (in murders per 100,000 residents each year) in large cities and x is the murder rate in smaller cities. During the period 1991–1998, the murder rate in small cities was decreasing at an average rate of 2 murders per 100,000 residents each year. Use the chain rule to estimate how fast the murder rate was changing in larger cities during that period. (Show how you used the chain rule in your answer.)

68. Crime Statistics Following is a quadratic model relating the murder rates described in the preceding exercise:

$$y = 0.1x^2 - 3x + 39 \quad (15 \leq x \leq 25)$$

In 1996, the murder rate in smaller cities was approximately 22 murders per 100,000 residents each year and was decreasing at a rate of approximately 2.5 murders per 100,000 residents each year. Use the chain rule to estimate how fast the murder rate was changing for large cities. (Show how you used the chain rule in your answer.)

69. Existing Home Sales The following graph shows the approximate value of home prices and existing home sales in 2006–2010 as a percentage change from 2003, together with quadratic approximations.[31]

Home prices and sales of existing homes

The quadratic approximations are given by

Home Prices: $\quad P(t) = t^2 - 10t + 41 \quad (0 \leq t \leq 4)$

Existing Home Sales: $\quad S(t) = 1.5t^2 - 11t \quad (0 \leq t \leq 4)$

where t is time in years since the start of 2006. Use the chain rule to estimate $\left.\dfrac{dS}{dP}\right|_{t=2}$. What does the answer tell you about home sales and prices? HINT [See Quick Example 2 on page 332.]

[28] Model based on historical and projected data from 1908–2010. Sources: Historical data, Bureau of Economic Analysis; projected data, Bureau of Labor Statistics/*New York Times*, December 1, 2003, p. C2.
[29] Ibid.

[30] The model is a linear regression model. Source for data: Federal Bureau of Investigation, Supplementary Homicide Reports/*New York Times*, May 29, 2000, p. A12.
[31] Sources: Standard & Poors/Bloomberg Financial Markets/*New York Times*, September 29, 2007, p. C3. Projection is the authors'.

70. *Existing Home Sales* The following graph shows the approximate value of home prices and existing home sales in 2004–2007 as a percentage change from 2003, together with quadratic approximations.[32]

Home prices and sales of existing homes

The quadratic approximations are given by

Home Prices: $P(t) = -6t^2 + 27t + 10$ $(0 \le t \le 3)$

Existing Home Sales: $S(t) = -4t^2 + 4t + 11$ $(0 \le t \le 3)$

where t is time in years since the start of 2004. Use the chain rule to estimate $\left.\dfrac{dS}{dP}\right|_{t=2}$. What does the answer tell you about home sales and prices? HINT [See Quick Example 2 on page 332.]

71. ▼ *Pollution* An offshore oil well is leaking oil and creating a circular oil slick. If the radius of the slick is growing at a rate of 2 miles/hour, find the rate at which the area is increasing when the radius is 3 miles. (The area of a disc of radius r is $A = \pi r^2$.) HINT [See Quick Example 2 on page 332.]

72. ▼ *Mold* A mold culture in a dorm refrigerator is circular and growing. The radius is growing at a rate of 0.3 cm/day. How fast is the area growing when the culture is 4 centimeters in radius? (The area of a disc of radius r is $A = \pi r^2$.) HINT [See Quick Example 2 on page 332.]

73. ▼ *Budget Overruns* The Pentagon is planning to build a new, spherical satellite. As is typical in these cases, the specifications keep changing, so that the size of the satellite keeps growing. In fact, the radius of the planned satellite is growing 0.5 feet per week. Its cost will be $1,000 per cubic foot. At the point when the plans call for a satellite 10 feet in radius, how fast is the cost growing? (The volume of a solid sphere of radius r is $V = \frac{4}{3}\pi r^3$.)

74. ▼ *Soap Bubbles* The soap bubble I am blowing has a radius that is growing at a rate of 4 cm/s. How fast is the surface area growing when the radius is 10 cm? (The surface area of a sphere of radius r is $S = 4\pi r^2$.)

75. ▣ ▼ *Revenue Growth* The demand for the Cyberpunk II arcade video game is modeled by the logistic curve

$$q(t) = \frac{10,000}{1 + 0.5e^{-0.4t}}$$

where $q(t)$ is the total number of units sold t months after its introduction.

a. Use technology to estimate $q'(4)$.
b. Assume that the manufacturers of Cyberpunk II sell each unit for $800. What is the company's marginal revenue dR/dq?
c. Use the chain rule to estimate the rate at which revenue is growing 4 months after the introduction of the video game.

76. ▣ ▼ *Information Highway* The amount of information transmitted each month in the early years of the Internet (1988 to 1994) can be modeled by the equation

$$q(t) = \frac{2e^{0.69t}}{3 + 1.5e^{-0.4t}} \qquad (0 \le t \le 6)$$

where q is the amount of information transmitted each month in billions of data packets and t is the number of years since the start of 1988.[33]

a. Use technology to estimate $q'(2)$.
b. Assume that it costs $5 to transmit a million packets of data. What is the marginal cost $C'(q)$?
c. How fast was the cost increasing at the start of 1990?

Money Stock *Exercises 77–80 are based on the following demand function for money (taken from a question on the GRE Economics Test):*

$$M_d = 2 \times y^{0.6} \times r^{-0.3} \times p$$

where

$M_d =$ *demand for nominal money balances (money stock)*
$y =$ *real income*
$r =$ *an index of interest rates*
$p =$ *an index of prices*

*These exercises also use the idea of **percentage rate of growth:***

$$\text{Percentage Rate of Growth of } M = \frac{\text{Rate of Growth of } M}{M}$$

$$= \frac{dM/dt}{M}$$

77. ◆ (from the GRE Economics Test) If the interest rate and price level are to remain constant while real income grows at 5 percent per year, the money stock must grow at what percent per year?

78. ◆ (from the GRE Economics Test) If real income and price level are to remain constant while the interest rate grows at 5 percent per year, the money stock must change by what percent per year?

79. ◆ (from the GRE Economics Test) If the interest rate is to remain constant while real income grows at 5 percent per year

[32] Sources: Standard & Poors /Bloomberg Financial Markets/*New York Times*, September 29, 2007, p. C3. Projection is the authors'.

[33] This is the authors' model, based on figures published in *New York Times*, Nov. 3, 1993.

and the price level rises at 5 percent per year, the money stock must grow at what percent per year?

80. ◆ (from the GRE Economics Test) If real income grows by 5 percent per year, the interest rate grows by 2 percent per year, and the price level drops by 3 percent per year, the money stock must change by what percent per year?

COMMUNICATION AND REASONING EXERCISES

81. Complete the following: The derivative of 1 over a glob is -1 over . . . .

82. Complete the following: The derivative of the square root of a glob is 1 over . . . .

83. Say why the following was marked wrong and give the correct answer.

$$\frac{d}{dx}[(3x^3 - x)^3] = 3(9x^2 - 1)^2 \qquad ✗ \quad WRONG!$$

84. Say why the following was marked wrong and give the correct answer.

$$\frac{d}{dx}\left[\left(\frac{3x^2 - 1}{2x - 2}\right)^3\right] = 3\left(\frac{3x^2 - 1}{2x - 2}\right)^2\left(\frac{6x}{2}\right) \qquad ✗ \quad WRONG!$$

85. Name two major errors in the following graded test question and give the correct answer.

$$\frac{d}{dx}\left[\left(\frac{3x^2 - 1}{2x - 2}\right)^3\right] = 3\left(\frac{6x}{2}\right)^2 \qquad ✗ \quad WRONG!\ SEE\ ME!$$

86. Name two major errors in the following graded test question and give the correct answer.

$$\frac{d}{dx}[(3x^3 - x)(2x + 1)]^4 = 4[(9x^2 - 1)(2)]^3 \qquad ✗ \quad WRONG!\ SEE\ ME!$$

87. ▼ Formulate a simple procedure for deciding whether to apply first the chain rule, the product rule, or the quotient rule when finding the derivative of a function.

88. ▼ Give an example of a function f with the property that calculating $f'(x)$ requires use of the following rules in the given order: (1) the chain rule, (2) the quotient rule, and (3) the chain rule.

89. ◆ Give an example of a function f with the property that calculating $f'(x)$ requires use of the chain rule five times in succession.

90. ◆ What can you say about composites of linear functions?

4.5 Derivatives of Logarithmic and Exponential Functions

At this point, we know how to take the derivative of any algebraic expression in x (involving powers, radicals, and so on). We now turn to the derivatives of logarithmic and exponential functions.

Derivative of the Natural Logarithm

$$\frac{d}{dx}[\ln x] = \frac{1}{x} \qquad \text{Recall that } \ln x = \log_e x.$$

Quick Examples

1. $\dfrac{d}{dx}[3 \ln x] = 3 \cdot \dfrac{1}{x} = \dfrac{3}{x}$ Derivative of a constant times a function

2. $\dfrac{d}{dx}[x \ln x] = 1 \cdot \ln x + x \cdot \dfrac{1}{x}$ Product rule, because $x \ln x$ is a product

   $= \ln x + 1.$

The above simple formula works only for the natural logarithm (the logarithm with base e). For logarithms with bases other than e, we have the following:

Derivative of the Logarithm with Base b

$$\frac{d}{dx}[\log_b x] = \frac{1}{x \ln b}$$

Notice that, if $b = e$, we get the same formula as previously.

Quick Examples

1. $\dfrac{d}{dx}[\log_3 x] = \dfrac{1}{x \ln 3} \approx \dfrac{1}{1.0986x}$

2. $\dfrac{d}{dx}[\log_2(x^4)] = \dfrac{d}{dx}(4 \log_2 x)$ We used the logarithm identity $\log_b(x^r) = r \log_b x$.

$$= 4 \cdot \frac{1}{x \ln 2} \approx \frac{4}{0.6931x}$$

Derivation of the formulas $\dfrac{d}{dx}[\ln x] = \dfrac{1}{x}$ and $\dfrac{d}{dx}[\log_b x] = \dfrac{1}{x \ln b}$

To compute $\dfrac{d}{dx}[\ln x]$, we need to use the definition of the derivative. We also use properties of the logarithm to help evaluate the limit.

$$\frac{d}{dx}[\ln x] = \lim_{h \to 0} \frac{\ln(x+h) - \ln x}{h}$$ Definition of the derivative

$$= \lim_{h \to 0} \frac{1}{h}[\ln(x+h) - \ln x]$$ Algebra

$$= \lim_{h \to 0} \frac{1}{h} \ln\left(\frac{x+h}{x}\right)$$ Properties of the logarithm

$$= \lim_{h \to 0} \frac{1}{h} \ln\left(1 + \frac{h}{x}\right)$$ Algebra

$$= \lim_{h \to 0} \ln\left(1 + \frac{h}{x}\right)^{1/h}$$ Properties of the logarithm

which we rewrite as

$$\lim_{h \to 0} \ln\left[\left(1 + \frac{1}{(x/h)}\right)^{x/h}\right]^{1/x}.$$

As $h \to 0^+$, the quantity x/h is getting large and positive, and so the quantity in brackets is approaching e (see the definition of e in Section 2.2), which leaves us with

$$\ln[e]^{1/x} = \frac{1}{x} \ln e = \frac{1}{x}$$

which is the derivative we are after.[*] What about the limit as $h \to 0^-$? We will glide over that case and leave it for the interested reader to pursue.[†]

The rule for the derivative of $\log_b x$ follows from the fact that $\log_b x = \ln x / \ln b$.

If we were to take the derivative of the natural logarithm of a *quantity* (a function of x), rather than just x, we would need to use the chain rule:

Derivatives of Logarithms of Functions

Original Rule	*Generalized Rule*	*In Words*
$\dfrac{d}{dx}[\ln x] = \dfrac{1}{x}$	$\dfrac{d}{dx}[\ln u] = \dfrac{1}{u}\dfrac{du}{dx}$	*The derivative of the natural logarithm of a quantity is 1 over that quantity, times the derivative of that quantity.*
$\dfrac{d}{dx}[\log_b x] = \dfrac{1}{x \ln b}$	$\dfrac{d}{dx}[\log_b u] = \dfrac{1}{u \ln b}\dfrac{du}{dx}$	*The derivative of the log to base b of a quantity is 1 over the product of $\ln b$ and that quantity, times the derivative of that quantity.*

Quick Examples

1. $\dfrac{d}{dx}\ln[x^2 + 1] = \dfrac{1}{x^2 + 1}\dfrac{d}{dx}(x^2 + 1)$ $u = x^2 + 1$ (See the margin note.[§])

$$= \frac{1}{x^2 + 1}(2x) = \frac{2x}{x^2 + 1}$$

2. $\dfrac{d}{dx}\log_2[x^3 + x] = \dfrac{1}{(x^3 + x)\ln 2}\dfrac{d}{dx}(x^3 + x)$ $u = x^3 + x$

$$= \frac{1}{(x^3 + x)\ln 2}(3x^2 + 1) = \frac{3x^2 + 1}{(x^3 + x)\ln 2}$$

EXAMPLE 1 Derivative of Logarithmic Function

Find $\dfrac{d}{dx}[\ln\sqrt{x + 1}]$.

Solution The calculation thought experiment tells us that we have the natural logarithm of a quantity, so

$$\frac{d}{dx}[\ln\sqrt{x+1}] = \frac{1}{\sqrt{x+1}}\frac{d}{dx}\sqrt{x+1} \qquad \frac{d}{dx}\ln u = \frac{1}{u}\frac{du}{dx}$$

$$= \frac{1}{\sqrt{x+1}} \cdot \frac{1}{2\sqrt{x+1}} \qquad \frac{d}{dx}\sqrt{u} = \frac{1}{2\sqrt{u}}\frac{du}{dx}$$

$$= \frac{1}{2(x+1)}.$$

➡ **Before we go on...** What happened to the square root in Example 1? As with many problems involving logarithms, we could have done this one differently and with less bother if we had simplified the expression $\ln\sqrt{x+1}$ using the properties of logarithms *before* differentiating. Doing this, we get

$$\ln\sqrt{x+1} = \ln(x+1)^{1/2} = \frac{1}{2}\ln(x+1). \qquad \text{Simplify the logarithm first.}$$

Thus,

$$\frac{d}{dx}[\ln\sqrt{x+1}] = \frac{d}{dx}\left[\frac{1}{2}\ln(x+1)\right]$$

$$= \frac{1}{2}\left(\frac{1}{x+1}\right) \cdot 1 = \frac{1}{2(x+1)},$$

the same answer as above. ■

EXAMPLE 2 Derivative of a Logarithmic Function

Find $\dfrac{d}{dx}[\ln[(1+x)(2-x)]]$.

Solution This time, we simplify the expression $\ln[(1+x)(2-x)]$ before taking the derivative.

$$\ln[(1+x)(2-x)] = \ln(1+x) + \ln(2-x) \qquad \text{Simplify the logarithm first.}$$

Thus,

$$\frac{d}{dx}[\ln[(1+x)(2-x)]] = \frac{d}{dx}[\ln(1+x)] + \frac{d}{dx}\ln(2-x)]$$

$$= \frac{1}{1+x} - \frac{1}{2-x} \qquad \text{Because } \frac{d}{dx}\ln(2-x) = -\frac{1}{2-x}$$

$$= \frac{1-2x}{(1+x)(2-x)}.$$

➡️ **Before we go on...** For practice, try doing Example 2 without simplifying first. What other differentiation rule do you need to use? ■

EXAMPLE 3 **Logarithm of an Absolute Value**

Find $\dfrac{d}{dx}[\ln|x|]$.

Solution Before we start, we note that $\ln x$ is defined only for positive values of x, so its domain is the set of positive real numbers. The domain of $\ln|x|$, on the other hand, is the set of *all* nonzero real numbers. For example, $\ln|-2| = \ln 2 \approx 0.6931$. For this reason, $\ln|x|$ often turns out to be more useful than the ordinary logarithm function.

Now we'll get to work. The calculation thought experiment tells us that $\ln|x|$ is the natural logarithm of a quantity, so we use the chain rule:

$$\frac{d}{dx}[\ln|x|] = \frac{1}{|x|}\frac{d}{dx}|x| \qquad u = |x|$$

$$= \frac{1}{|x|}\frac{|x|}{x} \qquad \text{Recall that } \frac{d}{dx}|x| = \frac{|x|}{x}.$$

$$= \frac{1}{x}.$$

➡️ **Before we go on...** Figure 7(a) shows the graphs of $y = \ln|x|$ and $y = 1/x$. Figure 7(b) shows the graphs of $y = \ln|x|$ and $y = 1/|x|$. You should be able to see from these graphs why the derivative of $\ln|x|$ is $1/x$ and not $1/|x|$.

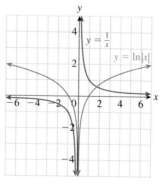

Figure 7(a)

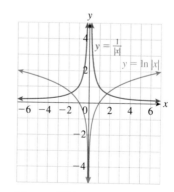

Figure 7(b)

■

This last example, in conjunction with the chain rule, gives us the following formulas.

Derivative of Logarithms of Absolute Values

Original Rule	Generalized Rule	In Words
$\dfrac{d}{dx}[\ln |x|] = \dfrac{1}{x}$	$\dfrac{d}{dx}[\ln |u|] = \dfrac{1}{u}\dfrac{du}{dx}$	The derivative of the natural logarithm of the absolute value of a quantity is 1 over that quantity, times the derivative of that quantity.
$\dfrac{d}{dx}[\log_b |x|] = \dfrac{1}{x \ln b}$	$\dfrac{d}{dx}[\log_b |u|] = \dfrac{1}{u \ln b}\dfrac{du}{dx}$	The derivative of the log to base b of the absolute value of a quantity is 1 over the product of ln b and that quantity, times the derivative of that quantity.

Note: Compare the above formulas with those on page 339. They tell us that we can simply ignore the absolute values in $\ln |u|$ or $\log_b |u|$ when taking the derivative.

Quick Examples

1. $\dfrac{d}{dx}[\ln|x^2 + 1|] = \dfrac{1}{x^2 + 1}\dfrac{d}{dx}(x^2 + 1)$ $u = x^2 + 1$

   $= \dfrac{1}{x^2 + 1}(2x) = \dfrac{2x}{x^2 + 1}$

2. $\dfrac{d}{dx}[\log_2|x^3 + x|] = \dfrac{1}{(x^3 + x)\ln 2}\dfrac{d}{dx}(x^3 + x)$ $u = x^3 + x$

   $= \dfrac{1}{(x^3 + x)\ln 2}(3x^2 + 1) = \dfrac{3x^2 + 1}{(x^3 + x)\ln 2}$

We now turn to the derivatives of *exponential* functions—that is, functions of the form $f(x) = b^x$. We begin by showing how *not* to differentiate them.

Caution The derivative of b^x is *not* $x b^{x-1}$. The power rule applies only to *constant* exponents. In this case the exponent is decidedly *not* constant, and so the power rule does not apply.

The following shows the correct way of differentiating b^x, beginning with a special case.

Derivative of e^x

$$\frac{d}{dx}[e^x] = e^x$$

Quick Examples

1. $\dfrac{d}{dx}[3e^x] = 3\dfrac{d}{dx}[e^x] = 3e^x$

2. $\dfrac{d}{dx}\left[\dfrac{e^x}{x}\right] = \dfrac{e^x x - e^x(1)}{x^2}$ Quotient rule

   $= \dfrac{e^x(x-1)}{x^2}$

---

* **NOTE** There is another—very simple—function that is its own derivative. What is it?

Thus, e^x has the amazing property that its derivative is itself!* For bases other than e, we have the following generalization:

Derivative of b^x

If b is any positive number, then

$$\frac{d}{dx}[b^x] = b^x \ln b.$$

Note that if $b = e$, we obtain the previous formula.

Quick Example

$\dfrac{d}{dx}[3^x] = 3^x \ln 3$

Derivation of the formula $\dfrac{d}{dx}[e^x] = e^x$

* **NOTE** This shortcut is an example of a technique called *logarithmic differentiation*, which is occasionally useful. We will see it again in the next section.

To find the derivative of e^x we use a shortcut.* Write $g(x) = e^x$. Then

$$\ln g(x) = x.$$

Take the derivative of both sides of this equation to get

$$\frac{g'(x)}{g(x)} = 1$$

or

$$g'(x) = g(x) = e^x.$$

In other words, the exponential function with base e is its own derivative. The rule for exponential functions with other bases follows from the equality $b^x = e^{x \ln b}$ (why?) and the chain rule. (Try it.)

If we were to take the derivative of e raised to a *quantity*, not just x, we would need to use the chain rule, as follows.

Derivatives of Exponentials of Functions

Original Rule	*Generalized Rule*	*In Words*
$\dfrac{d}{dx}[e^x] = e^x$	$\dfrac{d}{dx}[e^u] = e^u \dfrac{du}{dx}$	*The derivative of e raised to a quantity is e raised to that quantity, times the derivative of that quantity.*
$\dfrac{d}{dx}[b^x] = b^x \ln b$	$\dfrac{d}{dx}[b^u] = b^u \ln b \dfrac{du}{dx}$	*The derivative of b raised to a quantity is b raised to that quantity, times $\ln b$, times the derivative of that quantity.*

Quick Examples

✱ NOTE The calculation thought experiment tells us that we have e raised to a quantity.

1. $\dfrac{d}{dx}\left[e^{x^2+1}\right] = e^{x^2+1}\dfrac{d}{dx}\left[x^2+1\right]$ $u = x^2 + 1$ (See margin note.✱)

$\qquad\qquad = e^{x^2+1}(2x) = 2x\,e^{x^2+1}$

2. $\dfrac{d}{dx}[2^{3x}] = 2^{3x}\ln 2\dfrac{d}{dx}[3x]$ $u = 3x$

$\qquad\qquad = 2^{3x}(\ln 2)(3) = (3\ln 2)2^{3x}$

3. $\dfrac{d}{dt}[30e^{1.02t}] = 30e^{1.02t}(1.02) = 30.6e^{1.02t}$ $u = 1.02t$

4. If \$1,000 is invested in an account earning 5% per year compounded continuously, then the rate of change of the account balance after t years is

$$\dfrac{d}{dt}[1,000e^{0.05t}] = 1,000(0.05)e^{0.05t} = 50e^{0.05t} \text{ dollars/year.}$$

APPLICATIONS

EXAMPLE 4 Epidemics

In the early stages of the AIDS epidemic during the 1980s, the number of cases in the United States was increasing by about 50% every 6 months. By the start of 1983, there were approximately 1,600 AIDS cases in the United States.* Had this trend continued, how many new cases per year would have been occurring by the start of 1993?

---

*Data based on regression of 1982–1986 figures. Source for data: Centers for Disease Control and Prevention. HIV/AIDS Surveillance Report, 2000;12 (No. 2).

Solution To find the answer, we must first model this exponential growth using the methods of Chapter 2. Referring to Example 4 in Section 2.2, we find that t years after the start of 1983 the number of cases is

$$A = 1,600(2.25^t).$$

We are asking for the number of new cases each year. In other words, we want the rate of change, dA/dt:

$$\frac{dA}{dt} = 1,600(2.25)^t \ln 2.25 \text{ cases per year.}$$

At the start of 1993, $t = 10$, so the number of new cases per year is

$$\left.\frac{dA}{dt}\right|_{r=10} = 1,600(2.25)^{10} \ln 2.25 \approx 4,300,000 \text{ cases per year.}$$

➡ **Before we go on...** In Example 4, the figure for the number of new cases per year is so large because we assumed that exponential growth—the 50% increase every six months—would continue. A more realistic model for the spread of a disease is the logistic model. (See Section 2.4, as well as the next example.) ∎

Photononstop/Superstock

EXAMPLE 5 **Sales Growth**

The sales of the Cyberpunk II video game can be modeled by the logistic curve

$$q(t) = \frac{10,000}{1 + 0.5e^{-0.4t}}$$

where $q(t)$ is the total number of units sold t months after its introduction. How fast is the game selling 2 years after its introduction?

Solution We are asked for $q'(24)$. We can find the derivative of $q(t)$ using the quotient rule, or we can first write

$$q(t) = 10,000(1 + 0.5e^{-0.4t})^{-1}$$

and then use the generalized power rule:

$$q'(t) = -10,000(1 + 0.5e^{-0.4t})^{-2}(0.5e^{-0.4t})(-0.4)$$
$$= \frac{2,000e^{-0.4t}}{(1 + 0.5e^{-0.4t})^2}.$$

Thus,

$$q'(24) = \frac{2,000e^{-0.4(24)}}{(1 + 0.5e^{-0.4(24)})^2} \approx 0.135 \text{ units per month.}$$

So, after 2 years, sales are quite slow.

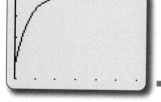

Figure 8

➡ **Before we go on...** We can check the answer in Example 5 graphically. If we plot the total sales curve for $0 \le t \le 30$ and $6,000 \le q \le 10,000$, on a TI-83/84 Plus, for example, we get the graph shown in Figure 8. Notice that total sales level off at about

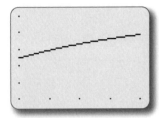

✳ NOTE We can also say
this using limits:
$$\lim_{t \to +\infty} q(t) = 10{,}000.$$

10,000 units.✳ We computed $q'(24)$, which is the slope of the curve at the point with t-coordinate 24. If we zoom in to the portion of the curve near $t = 24$, we obtain the graph shown in Figure 9, with $23 \le t \le 25$ and $9{,}999 \le q \le 10{,}000$. The curve is almost linear in this range. If we use the two endpoints of this segment of the curve, $(23, 9{,}999.4948)$ and $(25, 9{,}999.7730)$, we can approximate the derivative as

$$\frac{9{,}999.7730 - 9{,}999.4948}{25 - 23} = 0.1391$$

which is accurate to two decimal places. ■

Figure 9

4.5 EXERCISES

▼ more advanced   ◆ challenging
🔳 indicates exercises that should be solved using technology

Find the derivatives of the functions in Exercises 1–76. HINT [See Quick Examples on page 339.]

1. $f(x) = \ln(x - 1)$

2. $f(x) = \ln(x + 3)$

3. $f(x) = \log_2 x$

4. $f(x) = \log_3 x$

5. $g(x) = \ln|x^2 + 3|$

6. $g(x) = \ln|2x - 4|$

7. $h(x) = e^{x+3}$

8. $h(x) = e^{x^2}$

HINT [See Quick Examples on page 344.]

HINT [See Quick Examples on page 344.]

9. $f(x) = e^{-x}$

10. $f(x) = e^{1-x}$

11. $g(x) = 4^x$

12. $g(x) = 5^x$

13. $h(x) = 2^{x^2-1}$

14. $h(x) = 3^{x^2-x}$

15. $f(x) = x \ln x$

16. $f(x) = 3 \ln x$

17. $f(x) = (x^2 + 1) \ln x$

18. $f(x) = (4x^2 - x) \ln x$

19. $f(x) = (x^2 + 1)^5 \ln x$

20. $f(x) = (x + 1)^{0.5} \ln x$

21. $g(x) = \ln|3x - 1|$

22. $g(x) = \ln|5 - 9x|$

23. $g(x) = \ln|2x^2 + 1|$

24. $g(x) = \ln|x^2 - x|$

25. $g(x) = \ln(x^2 - 2.1x^{0.3})$

26. $g(x) = \ln(x - 3.1x^{-1})$

27. $h(x) = \ln[(-2x + 1)(x + 1)]$

28. $h(x) = \ln[(3x + 1)(-x + 1)]$

29. $h(x) = \ln\left(\dfrac{3x + 1}{4x - 2}\right)$

30. $h(x) = \ln\left(\dfrac{9x}{4x - 2}\right)$

31. $r(x) = \ln\left|\dfrac{(x + 1)(x - 3)}{-2x - 9}\right|$

32. $r(x) = \ln\left|\dfrac{-x + 1}{(3x - 4)(x - 9)}\right|$

33. $s(x) = \ln(4x - 2)^{1.3}$

34. $s(x) = \ln(x - 8)^{-2}$

35. $s(x) = \ln\left|\dfrac{(x + 1)^2}{(3x - 4)^3(x - 9)}\right|$

36. $s(x) = \ln\left|\dfrac{(x + 1)^2(x - 3)^4}{2x + 9}\right|$

37. $h(x) = \log_2(x + 1)$

38. $h(x) = \log_3(x^2 + x)$

39. $r(t) = \log_3(t + 1/t)$

40. $r(t) = \log_3\left(t + \sqrt{t}\right)$

41. $f(x) = (\ln|x|)^2$

42. $f(x) = \dfrac{1}{\ln|x|}$

43. $r(x) = \ln(x^2) - [\ln(x - 1)]^2$

44. $r(x) = (\ln(x^2))^2$

45. $f(x) = xe^x$

46. $f(x) = 2e^x - x^2 e^x$

47. $r(x) = \ln(x + 1) + 3x^3 e^x$

48. $r(x) = \ln|x + e^x|$

49. $f(x) = e^x \ln|x|$

50. $f(x) = e^x \log_2|x|$

51. $f(x) = e^{2x+1}$

52. $f(x) = e^{4x-5}$

53. $h(x) = e^{x^2-x+1}$

54. $h(x) = e^{2x^2-x+1/x}$

55. $s(x) = x^2 e^{2x-1}$

56. $s(x) = \dfrac{e^{4x-1}}{x^3 - 1}$

57. $r(x) = (e^{2x-1})^2$

58. $r(x) = (e^{2x^2})^3$

59. $t(x) = 3^{2x-4}$

60. $t(x) = 4^{-x+5}$

61. $v(x) = 3^{2x+1} + e^{3x+1}$

62. $v(x) = e^{2x} 4^{2x}$

63. $u(x) = \dfrac{3^{x^2}}{x^2 + 1}$

64. $u(x) = (x^2 + 1)4^{x^2-1}$

65. $g(x) = \dfrac{e^x + e^{-x}}{e^x - e^{-x}}$

66. $g(x) = \dfrac{1}{e^x + e^{-x}}$

67. ▼ $g(x) = e^{3x-1} e^{x-2} e^x$

68. ▼ $g(x) = e^{-x+3} e^{2x-1} e^{-x+11}$

69. ▼ $f(x) = \dfrac{1}{x \ln x}$

70. ▼ $f(x) = \dfrac{e^{-x}}{xe^x}$

71. ▼ $f(x) = [\ln(e^x)]^2 - \ln[(e^x)^2]$

72. ▼ $f(x) = e^{\ln x} - e^{2\ln(x^2)}$

73. ▼ $f(x) = \ln|\ln x|$

74. ▼ $f(x) = \ln|\ln|\ln x||$

75. ▼ $s(x) = \ln\sqrt{\ln x}$

76. ▼ $s(x) = \sqrt{\ln(\ln x)}$

Find the equations of the straight lines described in Exercises 77–82. Use graphing technology to check your answers by plotting the given curve together with the tangent line.

77. Tangent to $y = e^x \log_2 x$ at the point $(1, 0)$

78. Tangent to $y = e^x + e^{-x}$ at the point $(0, 2)$

79. Tangent to $y = \ln\sqrt{2x + 1}$ at the point where $x = 0$

80. Tangent to $y = \ln\sqrt{2x^2 + 1}$ at the point where $x = 1$

81. At right angles to $y = e^{x^2}$ at the point where $x = 1$

82. At right angles to $y = \log_2(3x + 1)$ at the point where $x = 1$

APPLICATIONS

83. *Research and Development: Industry* The total spent on research and development by industry in the United States during 1995–2007 can be approximated by

$$S(t) = 57.5 \ln t + 31 \text{ billion dollars} \quad (5 \le t \le 19)$$

where t is the year since 1990.[34] What was the total spent in 2000 ($t = 10$) and how fast was it increasing? HINT [See Quick Examples on page 337.]

84. *Research and Development: Federal* The total spent on research and development by the federal government in the United States during 1995–2007 can be approximated by

$$S(t) = 7.4 \ln t + 3 \text{ billion dollars} \quad (5 \le t \le 19)$$

where t is the year since 1990.[35] What was the total spent in 2005 ($t = 15$) and how fast was it increasing? HINT [See Quick Examples on page 337.]

85. *Research and Development: Industry* The function $S(t)$ in Exercise 83 can also be written (approximately) as

$$S(t) = 57.5 \ln (1.71t + 17.1) \text{ billion dollars}$$
$$(-5 \le t \le 9)$$

where this time t is the year since 2000. Use this alternative formula to estimate the amount spent in 2000 and its rate of change, and check your answers by comparing it with those in Exercise 83.

86. *Research and Development: Federal* The function $S(t)$ in Exercise 84 can also be written (approximately) as

$$S(t) = 7.4 \ln (1.5t + 15) \text{ billion dollars}$$
$$(-5 \le t \le 9)$$

where this time t is the year since 2000. Use this alternative formula to estimate the amount spent in 2005 and its rate of change, and check your answers by comparing it with those in Exercise 84.

87. ▼*Carbon Dating* The age in years of a specimen that originally contained 10g of carbon 14 is given by

$$y = \log_{0.999879}(0.1x)$$

where x is the amount of carbon 14 it currently contains. Compute $\dfrac{dy}{dx}\Big|_{x=5}$ and interpret your answer. HINT [For the calculation, see Quick Examples on page 339.]

88. ▼*Iodine Dating* The age in years of a specimen that originally contained 10g of iodine 131 is given by

$$y = \log_{0.999567}(0.1x)$$

where x is the amount of iodine 131 it currently contains. Compute $\dfrac{dy}{dx}\Big|_{x=8}$ and interpret your answer. HINT [For the calculation, see Quick Examples on page 339.]

89. *New York City Housing Costs: Downtown* The average price of a two-bedroom apartment in downtown New York City during the real estate boom from 1994 to 2004 can be approximated by

$$p(t) = 0.33e^{0.16t} \text{ million dollars} \quad (0 \le t \le 10)$$

where t is time in years ($t = 0$ represents 1994).[36] What was the average price of a two-bedroom apartment in downtown New York City in 2003, and how fast was it increasing? (Round your answers to two significant digits.) HINT [See Quick Example 3 on page 344.]

90. *New York City Housing Costs: Uptown* The average price of a two-bedroom apartment in uptown New York City during the real estate boom from 1994 to 2004 can be approximated by

$$p(t) = 0.14e^{0.10t} \text{ million dollars} \quad (0 \le t \le 10)$$

where t is time in years ($t = 0$ represents 1994).[37] What was the average price of a two-bedroom apartment in uptown New York City in 2002, and how fast was it increasing? (Round your answers to two significant digits.) HINT [See Quick Example 3 on page 344.]

91. *Big Brother* The following chart shows the total number of wiretaps authorized each year by U.S. state and federal courts from 1990 to 2007 ($t = 0$ represents 1990):[38]

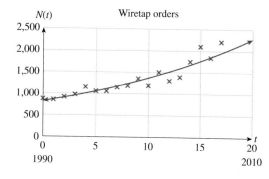

These data can be approximated with the model (shown on the graph)

$$N(t) = 820e^{0.051t}. \quad (0 \le t \le 17)$$

---

[34] Spending is in constant 2000 dollars. Source for data through 2006: National Science Foundation, Division of Science Resources Statistics, National Patterns of R&D Resources (www.nsf.gov/statistics) August 2008.

[35] Federal funding excluding grants to industry and nonprofit organizations. Spending is in constant 2000 dollars. Source for data through 2006: National Science Foundation, Division of Science Resources Statistics, National Patterns of R&D Resources (www.nsf.gov/statistics) August 2008.

[36] Model is based on a exponential regression. Source for data: Miller Samuel/*New York Times*, March 28, 2004, p. RE 11.

[37] Ibid.

[38] Source for data: 2007 Wiretap Report, Administrative Office of the United States Courts (www.uscourts.gov/wiretap07/2007WTText.pdf).

a. Find $N(15)$ and $N'(15)$. Be sure to state the units of measurement. To how many significant digits should we round the answers? Why?

b. The number of people whose communications are intercepted averages around 100 per wiretap order.[39] What does the answer to part (a) tell you about the number of people whose communications were intercepted?[40]

c. According to the model, the number of wiretaps orders each year (choose one):

(A) increased at a linear rate
(B) decreased at a quadratic rate
(C) increased at an exponential rate
(D) increased at a logarithmic rate

over the period shown.

92. *Big Brother* The following chart shows the number of wiretaps authorized each year by U.S. state courts from 1990 to 2007 ($t = 0$ represents 1990):[41]

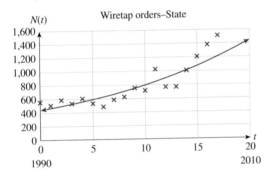

Wiretap orders–State

These data can be approximated with the model (shown on the graph)

$$N(t) = 440e^{0.06t}. \quad (0 \le t \le 17)$$

a. Find $N(10)$ and $N'(10)$. Be sure to state the units of measurement. To how many significant digits should we round the answers? Why?

b. The number of people whose communications are intercepted averages around 100 per wiretap order.[42] What does the answer to part (a) tell you about the number of people whose communications were intercepted?[43]

c. According to the model, the number of wiretaps orders each year (choose one)

(A) increased at a linear rate
(B) decreased at a quadratic rate

(C) increased at an exponential rate
(D) increased at a logarithmic rate

over the period shown.

93. *Investments* If $10,000 is invested in a savings account offering 4% per year, compounded continuously, how fast is the balance growing after 3 years?

94. *Investments* If $20,000 is invested in a savings account offering 3.5% per year, compounded continuously, how fast is the balance growing after 3 years?

95. *Investments* If $10,000 is invested in a savings account offering 4% per year, compounded semiannually, how fast is the balance growing after 3 years?

96. *Investments* If $20,000 is invested in a savings account offering 3.5% per year, compounded semiannually, how fast is the balance growing after 3 years?

97. *SARS* In the early stages of the deadly SARS (Severe Acute Respiratory Syndrome) epidemic in 2003, the number of cases was increasing by about 18% each day.[44] On March 17, 2003 (the first day for which statistics were reported by the World Health Organization) there were 167 cases. Find an exponential model that predicts the number of people infected t days after March 17, 2003, and use it to estimate how fast the epidemic was spreading on March 31, 2003. (Round your answer to the nearest whole number of new cases per day.) HINT [See Example 4.]

98. *SARS* A few weeks into the deadly SARS (Severe Acute Respiratory Syndrome) epidemic in 2003, the number of cases was increasing by about 4% each day.[45] On April 1, 2003 there were 1,804 cases. Find an exponential model that predicts the number $A(t)$ of people infected t days after April 1, 2003, and use it to estimate how fast the epidemic was spreading on April 30, 2003. (Round your answer to the nearest whole number of new cases per day.) HINT [See Example 4.]

99. ▼ *SAT Scores by Income* The following chart shows United State verbal SAT scores as a function of parents' income level:[46]

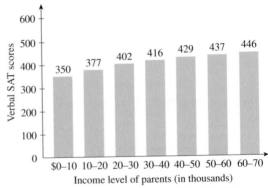

a. The data can best be modeled by which of the following?

(A) $S(x) = 470 - 136e^{-0.0000264x}$
(B) $S(x) = 136e^{-0.0000264x}$

[39] Source for data: 2007 Wiretap Report, Administrative Office of the United States Courts (www.uscourts.gov/wiretap07/2007WTText.pdf).

[40] Assume there is no significant overlap between the people whose communications are intercepted in different wiretap orders.

[41] Source for data: 2007 Wiretap Report, Administrative Office of the United States Courts (www.uscourts.gov/wiretap07/2007WTText.pdf).

[42] Ibid.

[43] Assume there is no significant overlap between the people whose communications are intercepted in different wiretap orders.

[44] World Health Organization (www.who.int).

[45] Ibid.

[46] Source: The College Board/*New York Times*, March 5, 1995, p. E16.

(C) $S(x) = 355(1.000004^x)$
(D) $S(x) = 470 - 355(1.000004^x)$

($S(x)$ is the average verbal SAT score of students whose parents earn $x per year.)

b. Use $S'(x)$ to predict how a student's verbal SAT score is affected by a $1,000 increase in parents' income for a student whose parents earn $45,000.

c. Does $S'(x)$ increase or decrease as x increases? Interpret your answer.

100. ▼ *SAT Scores by Income* The following chart shows U.S. average math SAT scores as a function of parents' income level:[47]

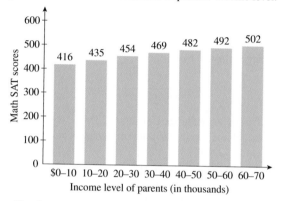

Income level of parents (in thousands)

a. The data can best be modeled by which of the following?

(A) $S(x) = 535 - 415(1.000003^x)$
(B) $S(x) = 535 - 136e^{0.0000213x}$
(C) $S(x) = 535 - 136e^{-0.0000213x}$
(D) $S(x) = 415(1.000003^x)$

($S(x)$ is the average math SAT score of students whose parents earn $x per year.)

b. Use $S'(x)$ to predict how a student's math SAT score is affected by a $1,000 increase in parents' income for a student whose parents earn $45,000.

c. Does $S'(x)$ increase or decrease as x increases? Interpret your answer.

101. ▼ *Demographics: Average Age and Fertility* The following graph shows a plot of average age of a population versus fertility rate (the average number of children each woman has in her lifetime) in the United States and Europe over the period 1950–2005.[48]

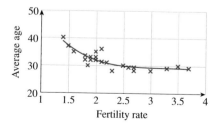

Fertility rate

The equation of the accompanying curve is

$$a = 28.5 + 120(0.172)^x \quad (1.4 \le x \le 3.7)$$

where a is the average age (in years) of the population and x is the fertility rate.

a. Compute $a'(2)$. What does the answer tell you about average age and fertility rates?

b. Use the answer to part (a) to estimate how much the fertility rate would need to increase from a level of 2 children per woman to lower the average age of a population by about 1 year.

102. ▼ *Demographics: Average Age and Fertility* The following graph shows a plot of average age of a population versus fertility rate (the average number of children each woman has in her lifetime) in Europe over the period 1950–2005.[49]

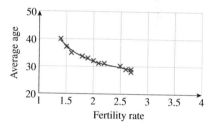

Fertility rate

The equation of the accompanying curve is

$$g = 27.6 + 128(0.181)^x \quad (1.4 \le x \le 3.7)$$

where g is the average age (in years) of the population and x is the fertility rate.

a. Compute $g'(2.5)$. What does the answer tell you about average age and fertility rates?

b. Referring to the model that combines the data for Europe and the United States in Exercise 101, which population's average age is affected more by a changing fertility rate at the level of 2.5 children per woman?

103. *Epidemics* A flu epidemic described in Example 1 in Section 2.4 approximately followed the curve

$$P = \frac{150}{1 + 15,000e^{-0.35t}} \text{ million people}$$

where P is the number of people infected and t is the number of weeks after the start of the epidemic. How fast is the epidemic growing (that is, how many new cases are there each week) after 20 weeks? After 30 weeks? After 40 weeks? (Round your answers to two significant digits.) HINT [See Example 5.]

104. *Epidemics* Another epidemic follows the curve

$$P = \frac{200}{1 + 20,000e^{-0.549t}} \text{ million people}$$

[47] Source: The College Board/*New York Times*, March 5, 1995, p. E16.

[48] The separate data for Europe and the United States are collected in the same graph. 2005 figures are estimates. Source: United Nations World Population Division/*New York Times*, June 29, 2003, p. 3.

[49] All European countries including the Russian Federation. 2005 figures are estimates. Source: United Nations World Population Division/*New York Times*, June 29, 2003, p. 3.

where t is in years. How fast is the epidemic growing after 10 years? After 20 years? After 30 years? (Round your answers to two significant digits.) HINT [See Example 5.]

105. **Subprime Mortgages** The percentage of mortgages issued in the United States that are subprime (normally classified as risky) can be approximated by

$$A(t) = \frac{15.0}{1 + 8.6e^{-0.59t}} \text{ percent} \quad (0 \le t \le 8)$$

t years after the start of 2000.[50]

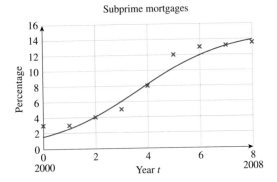

Subprime mortgages

How fast, to the nearest 0.1 percent, was the percentage increasing at the start of 2003? How would you check that the answer is approximately correct by looking at the graph?

106. **Subprime Mortgage Debt** The approximate value of subprime (normally classified as risky) mortgage debt outstanding in the United States can be approximated by

$$A(t) = \frac{1{,}350}{1 + 4.2e^{-0.53t}} \text{ \$ billion} \quad (0 \le t \le 8)$$

t years after the start of 2000.[51]

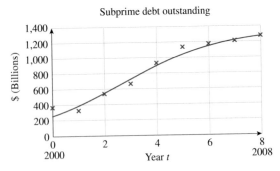

Subprime debt outstanding

How fast, to the nearest \$1 billion, was the subprime mortgage debt increasing at the start of 2005? How would you

check that the answer is approximately correct by looking at the graph?

107. **Subprime Mortgages** (Compare Exercise 105.) The percentage of mortgages issued in the United States that are subprime (normally classified as risky) can be approximated by

$$A(t) = \frac{15.0}{1 + 8.6(1.8)^{-t}} \text{ percent} \quad (0 \le t \le 8)$$

t years after the start of 2000.[52] How fast, to the nearest 0.1 percent, was the percentage increasing at the start of 2003?

108. **Subprime Mortgage Debt** (Compare Exercise 106.) The approximate value of subprime (normally classified as risky) mortgage debt outstanding in the United States can be approximated by

$$A(t) = \frac{1{,}350}{1 + 4.2(1.7)^{-t}} \text{ \$ billion} \quad (0 \le t \le 8)$$

t years after the start of 2000.[53] How fast, to the nearest \$1 billion, was the subprime mortgage debt increasing at the start of 2005?

109. ▼ **Population Growth** The population of Lower Anchovia was 4,000,000 at the start of 2010 and was doubling every 10 years. How fast was it growing per year at the start of 2010? (Round your answer to three significant digits.) HINT [Use the method of Example 2 in Section 2.2 to obtain an exponential model for the population.]

110. ▼ **Population Growth** The population of Upper Anchovia was 3,000,000 at the start of 2011 and doubling every 7 years. How fast was it growing per year at the start of 2011? (Round your answer to three significant digits.) HINT [Use the method of Example 2 in Section 2.2 to obtain an exponential model for the population.]

111. ▼ **Radioactive Decay** Plutonium 239 has a half-life of 24,400 years. How fast is a lump of 10 grams decaying after 100 years?

112. ▼ **Radioactive Decay** Carbon 14 has a half-life of 5,730 years. How fast is a lump of 20 grams decaying after 100 years?

113. ▮ ▼ **Diffusion of New Technology** Numeric control is a technology whereby the operation of machines is controlled by numerical instructions on disks, tapes, or cards. In a study, E. Mansfield and associates[54] modeled the growth of this technology using the equation

$$p(t) = \frac{0.80}{1 + e^{4.46 - 0.477t}}$$

[50] 2009 figure is an estimate. Sources: Mortgage Bankers Association, UBS.

[51] 2008–2009 figures are estimates. Source: www.data360.org/dataset.aspx? Data_Set_Id=9549.

[52] 2009 figure is an estimate. Sources: Mortgage Bankers Association, UBS.

[53] 2008–2009 figures are estimates. Source: www.data360.org/dataset.aspx? Data_Set_Id=9549.

[54] Source: "The Diffusion of a Major Manufacturing Innovation," in *Research and Innovation in the Modern Corporation* (W.W. Norton and Company, Inc., New York, 1971, pp. 186-205).

where $p(t)$ is the fraction of firms using numeric control in year t.

a. Graph this function for $0 \le t \le 20$ and estimate $p'(10)$ graphically. Interpret the result.

b. Use your graph to estimate $\lim_{t \to +\infty} p(t)$ and interpret the result.

c. Compute $p'(t)$, graph it, and again find $p'(10)$.

d. Use your graph to estimate $\lim_{t \to +\infty} p'(t)$ and interpret the result.

114. 🔲 ▼ *Diffusion of New Technology* Repeat Exercise 113 using the revised formula

$$p(t) = \frac{0.90e^{-0.1t}}{1 + e^{4.50 - 0.477t}}$$

which takes into account that in the long run this new technology will eventually become outmoded and will be replaced by a newer technology. Draw your graphs using the range $0 \le t \le 40$.

115. ◆*Cell Phone Revenues* The number of cell phone subscribers in China for the period 2000–2005 was projected to follow the equation[55]

$$N(t) = 39t + 68 \text{ million subscribers}$$

in year t ($t = 0$ represents 2000). The average annual revenue per cell phone user was \$350 in 2000. Assuming that, due to competition, the revenue per cell phone user decreases continuously at an annual rate of 10%, give a formula for the annual revenue in year t. Hence, project the annual revenue and its rate of change in 2002. Round all answers to the nearest billion dollars or billion dollars per year.

116. ◆*Cell Phone Revenues* The annual revenue for cell phone use in China for the period 2000–2005 was projected to follow the equation[56]

$$R(t) = 14t + 24 \text{ billion dollars}$$

in year t ($t = 0$ represents 2000). At the same time, there were approximately 68 million subscribers in 2000. Assuming that the number of subscribers increases continuously at an annual rate of 10%, give a formula for the annual revenue per subscriber in year t. Hence, project to the nearest dollar the annual revenue per subscriber and its rate of change in 2002. (Be careful with units!)

---

[55] Based on a regression of projected figures (coefficients are rounded). Source: Intrinsic Technology/*New York Times*, Nov. 24, 2000, p. C1.

[56] Not allowing for discounting due to increased competition. Source: Ibid.

COMMUNICATION AND REASONING EXERCISES

117. Complete the following: The derivative of e raised to a glob is . . . .

118. Complete the following: The derivative of the natural logarithm of a glob is . . . .

119. Complete the following: The derivative of 2 raised to a glob is . . . .

120. Complete the following: The derivative of the base 2 logarithm of a glob is . . . .

121. What is wrong with the following?

$$\frac{d}{dx} \ln|3x + 1| = \frac{3}{|3x + 1|} \qquad ✗ \quad WRONG!$$

122. What is wrong with the following?

$$\frac{d}{dx} 2^{2x} = (2)2^{2x} \qquad ✗ \quad WRONG!$$

123. What is wrong with the following?

$$\frac{d}{dx} 3^{2x} = (2x)3^{2x-1} \qquad ✗ \quad WRONG!$$

124. What is wrong with the following?

$$\frac{d}{dx} \ln(3x^2 - 1) = \frac{1}{6x} \qquad ✗ \quad WRONG!$$

125. ▼ The number N of music downloads on campus is growing exponentially with time. Can $N'(t)$ grow linearly with time? Explain.

126. ▼ The number N of graphing calculators sold on campus is decaying exponentially with time. Can $N'(t)$ grow with time? Explain.

*The **percentage rate of change** or **fractional rate of change** of a function is defined to be the ratio $f'(x)/f(x)$. (It is customary to express this as a percentage when speaking about percentage rate of change.)*

127. ◆Show that the fractional rate of change of the exponential function e^{kx} is equal to k, which is often called its **fractional growth rate**.

128. ◆Show that the fractional rate of change of $f(x)$ is the rate of change of $\ln(f(x))$.

129. ◆Let $A(t)$ represent a quantity growing exponentially. Show that the percentage rate of change, $A'(t)/A(t)$, is constant.

130. ◆Let $A(t)$ be the amount of money in an account that pays interest which is compounded some number of times per year. Show that the percentage rate of growth, $A'(t)/A(t)$, is constant. What might this constant represent?

4.6 Implicit Differentiation

Consider the equation $y^5 + y + x = 0$, whose graph is shown in Figure 10.

How did we obtain this graph? We did not solve for y as a function of x; that is impossible. In fact, we solved for x in terms of y to find points to plot. Nonetheless, the graph in Figure 10 is the graph of a function because it passes the vertical line test: Every vertical line crosses the graph no more than once, so for each value of x there is no more than one corresponding value of y. Because we cannot solve for y explicitly in terms of x, we say that the equation $y^5 + y + x = 0$ determines y as an **implicit function** of x.

Now, suppose we want to find the slope of the tangent line to this curve at, say, the point $(2, -1)$ (which, you should check, is a point on the curve). In the following example we find, surprisingly, that it is possible to obtain a formula for dy/dx without having to first solve the equation for y.

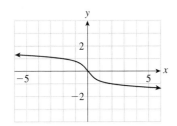

Figure 10

EXAMPLE 1 Implicit Differentiation

Find $\dfrac{dy}{dx}$, given that $y^5 + y + x = 0$.

Solution We use the chain rule and a little cleverness. Think of y as a function of x and take the derivative with respect to x of both sides of the equation:

$$y^5 + y + x = 0 \qquad \text{Original equation}$$

$$\frac{d}{dx}[y^5 + y + x] = \frac{d}{dx}[0] \qquad \text{Derivative with respect to } x \text{ of both sides}$$

$$\frac{d}{dx}[y^5] + \frac{d}{dx}[y] + \frac{d}{dx}[x] = 0 \qquad \text{Derivative rules}$$

Now we must be careful. The derivative *with respect to x* of y^5 is *not* $5y^4$. Rather, because y is a function of x, we must use the chain rule, which tells us that

$$\frac{d}{dx}[y^5] = 5y^4 \frac{dy}{dx}.$$

Thus, we get

$$5y^4 \frac{dy}{dx} + \frac{dy}{dx} + 1 = 0.$$

We want to find dy/dx, so we *solve for it*:

$$(5y^4 + 1)\frac{dy}{dx} = -1 \qquad \text{Isolate } dy/dx \text{ on one side.}$$

$$\frac{dy}{dx} = -\frac{1}{5y^4 + 1} \qquad \text{Divide both sides by } 5y^4 + 1.$$

➡ **Before we go on...** Note that we should not expect to obtain dy/dx as an explicit function of x if y was not an explicit function of x to begin with. For example, the formula we found in Example 1 for dy/dx is not a function of x because there is a y in it. However, the result is still useful because we can evaluate the derivative at any point on the graph. For instance, at the point $(2, -1)$ on the graph, we get

$$\frac{dy}{dx} = -\frac{1}{5y^4 + 1} = -\frac{1}{5(-1)^4 + 1} = -\frac{1}{6}.$$

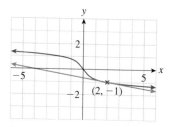

Figure 11

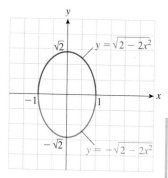

Figure 12

Thus, the slope of the tangent line to the curve $y^5 + y + x = 0$ at the point $(2, -1)$ is $-1/6$. Figure 11 shows the graph and this tangent line. ∎

This procedure we just used—differentiating an equation to find dy/dx without first solving the equation for y—is called **implicit differentiation.**

In Example 1 we were given an equation in x and y that determined y as an (implicit) function of x, even though we could not solve for y. But an equation in x and y need not always determine y as a function of x. Consider, for example, the equation

$$2x^2 + y^2 = 2.$$

Solving for y yields $y = \pm\sqrt{2 - 2x^2}$. The $\pm$ sign reminds us that for some values of x there are two corresponding values for y. We can graph this equation by superimposing the graphs of

$$y = \sqrt{2 - 2x^2} \quad \text{and} \quad y = -\sqrt{2 - 2x^2}.$$

The graph, an *ellipse*, is shown in Figure 12.

The graph of $y = \sqrt{2 - 2x^2}$ constitutes the top half of the ellipse, and the graph of $y = -\sqrt{2 - 2x^2}$ constitutes the bottom half.

EXAMPLE 2 Slope of Tangent Line

Refer to Figure 12. Find the slope of the tangent line to the ellipse $2x^2 + y^2 = 2$ at the point $(1/\sqrt{2}, 1)$.

Solution Because $(1/\sqrt{2}, 1)$ is on the top half of the ellipse in Figure 12, we *could* differentiate the function $y = \sqrt{2 - 2x^2}$, to obtain the result, but it is actually easier to apply implicit differentiation to the original equation.

$$2x^2 + y^2 = 2 \qquad \text{Original equation}$$

$$\frac{d}{dx}[2x^2 + y^2] = \frac{d}{dx}[2] \qquad \text{Derivative with respect to } x \text{ of both sides}$$

$$4x + 2y\frac{dy}{dx} = 0$$

$$2y\frac{dy}{dx} = -4x \qquad \text{Solve for } dy/dx.$$

$$\frac{dy}{dx} = -\frac{4x}{2y} = -\frac{2x}{y}$$

To find the slope at $(1/\sqrt{2}, 1)$ we now substitute for x and y:

$$\frac{dy}{dx}\bigg|_{(1/\sqrt{2},1)} -\frac{2/\sqrt{2}}{1} = -\sqrt{2}.$$

Thus, the slope of the tangent to the ellipse at the point $(1/\sqrt{2}, 1)$ is $-\sqrt{2} \approx -1.414$.

EXAMPLE 3 Tangent Line for an Implicit Function

Find the equation of the tangent line to the curve $\ln y = xy$ at the point where $y = 1$.

Solution First, we use implicit differentiation to find dy/dx:

$$\frac{d}{dx}[\ln y] = \frac{d}{dx}[xy] \qquad \text{Take } d/dx \text{ of both sides.}$$

$$\frac{1}{y}\frac{dy}{dx} = (1)y + x\frac{dy}{dx}. \qquad \text{Chain rule on left, product rule on right}$$

To solve for dy/dx, we bring all the terms containing dy/dx to the left-hand side and all terms not containing it to the right-hand side:

$$\frac{1}{y}\frac{dy}{dx} - x\frac{dy}{dx} = y \qquad\qquad \text{Bring the terms with } dy/dx \text{ to the left.}$$

$$\frac{dy}{dx}\left(\frac{1}{y} - x\right) = y \qquad\qquad \text{Factor out } dy/dx.$$

$$\frac{dy}{dx}\left(\frac{1 - xy}{y}\right) = y$$

$$\frac{dy}{dx} = y\left(\frac{y}{1 - xy}\right) = \frac{y^2}{1 - xy}. \qquad \text{Solve for } dy/dx.$$

The derivative gives the slope of the tangent line, so we want to evaluate the derivative at the point where $y = 1$. However, the formula for dy/dx requires values for both x and y. We get the value of x by substituting $y = 1$ in the original equation:

$$\ln y = xy$$

$$\ln(1) = x \cdot 1$$

But $\ln(1) = 0$, and so $x = 0$ for this point. Thus,

$$\frac{dy}{dx}\bigg|_{(0,1)} = \frac{1^2}{1 - (0)(1)} = 1.$$

Therefore, the tangent line is the line through $(x, y) = (0, 1)$ with slope 1, which is

$$y = x + 1.$$

➡ **Before we go on...** Example 3 presents an instance of an implicit function in which it is simply not possible to solve for y. Try it. ■

Sometimes, it is easiest to differentiate a complicated function of x by first taking the logarithm and then using implicit differentiation—a technique called **logarithmic differentiation**.

EXAMPLE 4 Logarithmic Differentiation

Find $\dfrac{d}{dx}\left[\dfrac{(x + 1)^{10}(x^2 + 1)^{11}}{(x^3 + 1)^{12}}\right]$ without using the product or quotient rules.

Solution Write

$$y = \frac{(x + 1)^{10}(x^2 + 1)^{11}}{(x^3 + 1)^{12}}$$

and then take the natural logarithm of both sides:

$$\ln y = \ln\left[\frac{(x + 1)^{10}(x^2 + 1)^{11}}{(x^3 + 1)^{12}}\right].$$

We can use properties of the logarithm to simplify the right-hand side:

$$\ln y = \ln(x + 1)^{10} + \ln(x^2 + 1)^{11} - \ln(x^3 + 1)^{12}$$

$$= 10\ln(x + 1) + 11\ln(x^2 + 1) - 12\ln(x^3 + 1).$$

Now we can find $\dfrac{dy}{dx}$ using implicit differentiation:

$$\frac{1}{y}\frac{dy}{dx} = \frac{10}{x+1} + \frac{22x}{x^2+1} - \frac{36x^2}{x^3+1}$$ Take d/dx of both sides.

$$\frac{dy}{dx} = y\left(\frac{10}{x+1} + \frac{22x}{x^2+1} - \frac{36x^2}{x^3+1}\right)$$ Solve for dy/dx.

$$= \frac{(x+1)^{10}(x^2+1)^{11}}{(x^3+1)^{12}}\left(\frac{10}{x+1} + \frac{22x}{x^2+1} - \frac{36x^2}{x^3+1}\right).$$ Substitute for y.

➡ **Before we go on...** Redo Example 4 using the product and quotient rules (and the chain rule) instead of logarithmic differentiation and compare the answers. Compare also the amount of work involved in both methods. ■

APPLICATION

Productivity usually depends on both labor and capital. Suppose, for example, you are managing a surfboard manufacturing company. You can measure its productivity by counting the number of surfboards the company makes each year. As a measure of labor, you can use the number of employees, and as a measure of capital you can use its operating budget. The so-called *Cobb-Douglas* model uses a function of the form:

$$P = Kx^a y^{1-a}$$ Cobb-Douglas model for productivity

where P stands for the number of surfboards made each year, x is the number of employees, and y is the operating budget. The numbers K and a are constants that depend on the particular situation studied, with a between 0 and 1.

EXAMPLE 5 **Cobb-Douglas Production Function**

The surfboard company you own has the Cobb-Douglas production function

$$P = x^{0.3}y^{0.7}$$

where P is the number of surfboards it produces per year, x is the number of employees, and y is the daily operating budget (in dollars). Assume that the production level P is constant.

a. Find $\dfrac{dy}{dx}$.

b. Evaluate this derivative at $x = 30$ and $y = 10,000$, and interpret the answer.

Solution

a. We are given the equation $P = x^{0.3}y^{0.7}$, in which P is constant. We find $\dfrac{dy}{dx}$ by implicit differentiation

$$0 = \frac{d}{dx}[x^{0.3}y^{0.7}]$$ d/dx of both sides

$$0 = 0.3x^{-0.7}y^{0.7} + x^{0.3}(0.7)y^{-0.3}\frac{dy}{dx}$$ Product and chain rules

David Samuel Robbins/CORBIS

$$-0.7x^{0.3}y^{-0.3}\frac{dy}{dx} = 0.3x^{-0.7}y^{0.7} \qquad \text{Bring term with } dy/dx \text{ to left.}$$

$$\frac{dy}{dx} = -\frac{0.3x^{-0.7}y^{0.7}}{0.7x^{0.3}y^{-0.3}} \qquad \text{Solve for } dy/dx.$$

$$= -\frac{3y}{7x}. \qquad \text{Simplify.}$$

b. Evaluating this derivative at $x = 30$ and $y = 10{,}000$ gives

$$\left.\frac{dy}{dx}\right|_{x=30,\ y=10{,}000} = -\frac{3(10{,}000)}{7(30)} \approx -143.$$

To interpret this result, first look at the units of the derivative: We recall that the units of dy/dx are units of y per unit of x. Because y is the daily budget, its units are dollars; because x is the number of employees, its units are employees. Thus,

$$\left.\frac{dy}{dx}\right|_{x=30,\ y=10{,}000} \approx -\$143 \text{ per employee.}$$

Next, recall that dy/dx measures the rate of change of y as x changes. Because the answer is negative, the daily budget to maintain production at the fixed level is decreasing by approximately \$143 per additional employee at an employment level of 30 employees and a daily operating budget of \$10,000. In other words, increasing the workforce by one worker will result in a savings of approximately \$143 per day. Roughly speaking, *a new employee is worth \$143 per day* at the current levels of employment and production.

4.6 EXERCISES

▼ more advanced   ◆ challenging
🅣 indicates exercises that should be solved using technology

In Exercises 1–10, find dy/dx, using implicit differentiation. In each case, compare your answer with the result obtained by first solving for y as a function of x and then taking the derivative.
HINT [See Example 1.]

1. $2x + 3y = 7$

2. $4x - 5y = 9$

3. $x^2 - 2y = 6$

4. $3y + x^2 = 5$

5. $2x + 3y = xy$

6. $x - y = xy$

7. $e^x y = 1$

8. $e^x y - y = 2$

9. $y \ln x + y = 2$

10. $\dfrac{\ln x}{y} = 2 - x$

In Exercises 11–30, find the indicated derivative using implicit differentiation. HINT [See Example 1.]

11. $x^2 + y^2 = 5;\ \dfrac{dy}{dx}$

12. $2x^2 - y^2 = 4;\ \dfrac{dy}{dx}$

13. $x^2 y - y^2 = 4;\ \dfrac{dy}{dx}$

14. $xy^2 - y = x;\ \dfrac{dy}{dx}$

15. $3xy - \dfrac{y}{3} = \dfrac{2}{x};\ \dfrac{dy}{dx}$

16. $\dfrac{xy}{2} - y^2 = 3;\ \dfrac{dy}{dx}$

17. $x^2 - 3y^2 = 8;\ \dfrac{dx}{dy}$

18. $(xy)^2 + y^2 = 8;\ \dfrac{dx}{dy}$

19. $p^2 - pq = 5p^2 q^2;\ \dfrac{dp}{dq}$

20. $q^2 - pq = 5p^2 q^2;\ \dfrac{dp}{dq}$

21. $xe^y - ye^x = 1;\ \dfrac{dy}{dx}$

22. $x^2 e^y - y^2 = e^x;\ \dfrac{dy}{dx}$

23. ▼ $e^{st} = s^2;\ \dfrac{ds}{dt}$

24. ▼ $e^{s^2 t} - st = 1;\ \dfrac{ds}{dt}$

25. ▼ $\dfrac{e^x}{y^2} = 1 + e^y;\ \dfrac{dy}{dx}$

26. ▼ $\dfrac{x}{e^y} + xy = 9y;\ \dfrac{dy}{dx}$

27. ▼ $\ln(y^2 - y) + x = y;\ \dfrac{dy}{dx}$

28. ▼ $\ln(xy) - x \ln y = y;\ \dfrac{dy}{dx}$

29. ▼ $\ln(xy + y^2) = e^y;\ \dfrac{dy}{dx}$

30. ▼ $\ln(1 + e^{xy}) = y;\ \dfrac{dy}{dx}$

5

Further Applications of the Derivative

Case Study Production Lot Size Management

Your publishing company is planning the production of its latest best seller, which it predicts will sell 100,000 copies each month over the coming year. The book will be printed in several batches of the same number, evenly spaced throughout the year. Each print run has a setup cost of $5,000, a single book costs $1 to produce, and monthly storage costs for books awaiting shipment average 1¢ per book. **To meet the anticipated demand at minimum total cost to your company, how many printing runs should you plan?**

SUNNYphotography.com/Alamy

Web Site

At the Web site you will find:

- Section by section tutorials, including game tutorials with randomized quizzes

- A detailed chapter summary

- A true/false quiz

- Additional review exercises

- Graphers, Excel tutorials, and other resources

- The following extra topic:

  Linear Approximation and Error Estimation

Introduction

In this chapter we begin to see the power of calculus as an optimization tool. In Chapter 2 we saw how to price an item in order to get the largest revenue when the demand function is linear. Using calculus, we can handle nonlinear functions, which are much more general. In Section 5.1 we show how calculus can be used to solve the problem of finding the values of a variable that lead to a maximum or minimum value of a given function. In Section 5.2 we show how this helps us in various real-world applications.

Another theme in this chapter is that calculus can help us to draw and understand the graph of a function. By the time you have completed the material in Section 5.1, you will be able to locate and sketch some of the important features of a graph, such as where it rises and where it falls. In Section 5.3 we look at the *second derivative,* the derivative of the derivative function, and what it tells us about how the graph *curves.* In Section 5.4 we put a number of ideas together that help to explain what you see in a graph (drawn, for example, using graphing technology) and to locate its most important points.

We also include sections on related rates and elasticity of demand. The first of these (Section 5.5) examines further the concept of the derivative as a rate of change. The second (Section 5.6) returns to the problem of optimizing revenue based on the demand equation, looking at it in a new way that leads to an important idea in economics—elasticity.

algebra Review

For this chapter, you should be familiar with the algebra reviewed in **Chapter 0**, **sections 5 and 6**.

5.1 **Maxima and Minima**

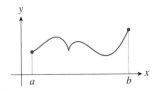

Figure 1

Figure 1 shows the graph of a function f whose domain is the closed interval $[a, b]$. A mathematician sees lots of interesting things going on here. There are hills and valleys, and even a small chasm (called a *cusp*) near the center. For many purposes, the important features of this curve are the highs and lows. Suppose, for example, you know that the price of the stock of a certain company will follow this graph during the course of a week. Although you would certainly make a handsome profit if you bought at time a and sold at time b, your best strategy would be to follow the old adage to "buy low and sell high," buying at all the lows and selling at all the highs.

Figure 2 shows the graph once again with the highs and lows marked. Mathematicians have names for these points: the highs (at the x-values p, r, and b) are referred to as **relative maxima**, and the lows (at the x-values a, q, and s) are referred to as **relative minima**. Collectively, these highs and lows are referred to as **relative extrema**. (A point of language: The singular forms of the plurals *minima, maxima,* and *extrema* are *minimum, maximum,* and *extremum.*)

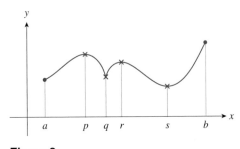

Figure 2

Why do we refer to these points as relative extrema? Take a look at the point corresponding to $x = r$. It is the highest point of the graph *compared to other points nearby.*

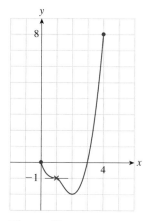

Figure 10

✱ **NOTE** Why "first" derivative test? To distinguish it from a test based on the **second derivative** of a function, which we shall discuss in Section 5.3.

Q : *How can we be sure that the graph in Example 1 doesn't look like Figure 10?*

A : If it did, there would be another critical point somewhere between $x = 1$ and $x = 4$. But we already know that there aren't any other critical points. The table we made listed all of the possible extrema; there can be no more.

First Derivative Test

The **first derivative test**✱ gives another, very systematic, way of checking whether a critical point is a relative maximum or minimum. To motivate the first derivative test, consider again the critical point $x = 1$ in Example 1. If we look at some values of $f'(x)$ to the left and right of the critical point, we obtain the information shown in the following table:

	Point to the Left	Critical Point	Point to the Right
x	0	1	2
$f'(x) = 2x - 2$	-2	0	2
Direction of Graph	↘	→	↗

At $x = 0$ (to the left of the critical point) we see that $f'(0) = -2 < 0$, so the graph has negative slope and f is decreasing. We note this with the downward pointing arrow. At $x = 2$ (to the right of the critical point), we find $f'(2) = 2 > 0$, so the graph has positive slope and f is increasing. In fact, because $f'(x) = 0$ only at $x = 1$, we know that $f'(x) < 0$ for all x in $[0, 1)$, and we can say that f is decreasing on the interval $[0, 1]$. Similarly, f is increasing on $[1, 4]$.

So, starting at $x = 0$, the graph of f goes down until we reach $x = 1$ and then it goes back up, telling us that $x = 1$ must be a relative minimum. Notice how the relative minimum is suggested by the arrows to the left and right.

First Derivative Test for Relative Extrema

Suppose that c is a critical point of the continuous function f, and that its derivative is defined for x close to, and on both sides of, $x = c$. Then, determine the sign of the derivative to the left and right of $x = c$.

1. If $f'(x)$ is positive to the left of $x = c$ and negative to the right, then f has a relative maximum at $x = c$.

2. If $f'(x)$ is negative to the left of $x = c$ and positive to the right, then f has a relative minimum at $x = c$.

3. If $f'(x)$ has the same sign on both sides of $x = c$, then f has neither a relative maximum nor a relative minimum at $x = c$.

Quick Examples

1. In Example 1 above, we saw that $f(x) = x^2 - 2x$ has a critical point at $x = 1$ with $f'(x)$ negative to the left of $x = 1$ and positive to the right (see the table). Therefore, f has a relative minimum at $x = 1$.

2. Here is a graph showing a function f with a singular point at $x = 1$:

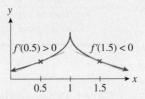

The graph gives us the information shown in the table:

	Point to the Left	Critical Point	Point to the Right
x	0.5	1	1.5
$f'(x)$	+	Undefined	−
Direction of Graph	↗		↘

Since $f'(x)$ is positive to the left of $x = 1$ and negative to the right, we see that f has a relative maximum at $x = 1$. (Notice again how this is suggested by the direction of the arrows.)

EXAMPLE 2 Unbounded Interval

Find all extrema of $f(x) = 3x^4 - 4x^3$ on $[-1, \infty)$.

Solution We first calculate $f'(x) = 12x^3 - 12x^2$.

Stationary points We solve the equation $f'(x) = 0$, which is

$$12x^3 - 12x^2 = 0 \text{ or}$$
$$12x^2(x - 1) = 0.$$

There are two solutions, $x = 0$ and $x = 1$, and both are in the domain. These are our candidates for the x-coordinates of stationary relative extrema.

Singular points There are no points where $f'(x)$ is not defined, so there are no singular points.

Endpoints The domain is $[-1, \infty)$, so there is one endpoint, at $x = -1$.

We record these points in a table with the corresponding y-coordinates:

x	-1	0	1
$f(x) = 3x^4 - 4x^3$	7	0	-1

We will illustrate three methods we can use to determine which are minima, which are maxima, and which are neither:

1. Plot these points and sketch the graph by hand.

2. Use the First Derivative Test.

3. Use technology to help us.

Use the method you find most convenient.

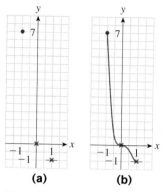

(a)   **(b)**

Figure 11

Figure 12

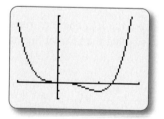

Figure 13

Using a Hand Plot: If we plot these points by hand, we obtain Figure 11(a), which suggests Figure 11(b).

We can't be sure what happens to the right of $x = 1$. Does the curve go up, or does it go down? To find out, let's plot a "test point" to the right of $x = 1$. Choosing $x = 2$, we obtain $y = 3(2)^4 - 4(2)^3 = 16$, so $(2, 16)$ is another point on the graph. Thus, it must turn upward to the right of $x = 1$, as shown in Figure 12.

From the graph, we find that f has the following extrema:

A relative (endpoint) maximum at $(-1, 7)$

An absolute (stationary) minimum at $(1, -1)$

Using the First Derivative Test: List the critical and endpoints in a table, and add additional points as necessary so that each critical point has a noncritical point on either side. Then compute the derivative at each of these points, and draw an arrow to indicate the direction of the graph.

	End Point	Critical Point		Critical Point	
x	-1	0	0.5	1	2
$f'(x) = 12x^3 - 12x^2$	-24	0	-1.5	0	48
Direction of Graph	↘	→	↘	→	↗

Notice that the arrows now suggest the shape of the curve in Figure 12. The first derivative test tells us that the function has a relative maximum at $x = -1$, neither a maximum nor a minimum at $x = 0$, and a relative minimum at $x = 1$. Deciding which of these extrema are absolute and which are relative requires us to compute y-coordinates and plot the corresponding points on the graph by hand, as we did in the first method.

using Technology

If we use technology to show the graph, we should choose the viewing window so that it contains the three interesting points we found: $x = -1$, $x = 0$, and $x = 1$. Again, we can't be sure yet what happens to the right of $x = 1$; does the graph go up or down from that point? If we set the viewing window to an interval of $[-1, 2]$ for x and $[-2, 8]$ for y, we will leave enough room to the right of $x = 1$ and below $y = -1$ to see what the graph will do. The result will be something like Figure 13.

Now we can tell what happens to the right of $x = 1$: the function increases. We know that it cannot later decrease again because if it did, there would have to be another critical point where it turns around, and we found that there are no other critical points. ◼

➡ **Before we go on...** Notice that the stationary point at $x = 0$ in Example 2 is neither a relative maximum nor a relative minimum. It is simply a place where the graph of f flattens out for a moment before it continues to fall. Notice also that f has no absolute maximum because $f(x)$ increases without bound as x gets large. ◼

EXAMPLE 3 Singular Point

Find all extrema of $f(t) = t^{2/3}$ on $[-1, 1]$.

Solution First, $f'(t) = \dfrac{2}{3}t^{-1/3}$.

Stationary points We need to solve

$$\frac{2}{3}t^{-1/3} = 0.$$

We can rewrite this equation without the negative exponent:

$$\frac{2}{3t^{1/3}} = 0.$$

Now, the only way that a fraction can equal 0 is if the numerator is 0, so this fraction can never equal 0. Thus, there are no stationary points.

Singular points The derivative

$$f'(t) = \frac{2}{3t^{1/3}}$$

is not defined for $t = 0$. However, f itself *is* defined at $t = 0$, so 0 is in the domain. Thus, f has a singular point at $t = 0$.

Endpoints There are two endpoints, -1 and 1.

We now put these three points in a table with the corresponding y-coordinates:

t	-1	0	1
$f(t)$	1	0	1

Using a Hand Plot: The derivative, $f'(t) = 2/(3t^{1/3})$, is not defined at the singular point $t = 0$. To help us sketch the graph, let's use limits to investigate what happens to the derivative as we approach 0 from either side:

$$\lim_{t \to 0^-} f'(t) = \lim_{t \to 0^-} \frac{2}{3t^{1/3}} = -\infty$$

$$\lim_{t \to 0^+} f'(t) = \lim_{t \to 0^+} \frac{2}{3t^{1/3}} = +\infty.$$

Thus, the graph decreases very steeply, approaching $t = 0$ from the left, and then rises very steeply as it leaves to the right. It would make sense to say that the tangent line at $x = 0$ is vertical, as seen in Figure 14.

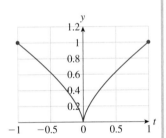

Figure 14

From this graph, we find the following extrema for f:

An absolute (endpoint) maximum at $(-1, 1)$
An absolute (singular) minimum at $(0, 0)$
An absolute (endpoint) maximum at $(1, 1)$.

Notice that the absolute maximum value of f is achieved at two values of t: $t = -1$ and $t = 1$.

First Derivative Test: Here is the corresponding table for the first derivative test.

t	-1	0	1
$f'(t) = \dfrac{2}{3t^{1/3}}$	$-\dfrac{2}{3}$	Undefined	$\dfrac{2}{3}$
Direction of Graph	↘	↕	↗

(We drew a vertical arrow at $t = 0$ to indicate a vertical tangent.) Again, notice how the arrows suggest the shape of the curve in Figure 14, and the first derivative test confirms that we have a relative minimum at $x = 0$.

using Technology

Because there is only one critical point, at $t = 0$, it is clear from this table that f must decrease from $t = -1$ to $t = 0$ and then increase from $t = 0$ to $t = 1$. To graph f using technology, choose a viewing window with an interval of $[-1, 1]$ for t and $[0, 1]$ for y. The result will be something like Figure 14.✳ ∎

In Examples 1 and 3, we could have found the absolute maxima and minima without doing any graphing. In Example 1, after finding the critical points and endpoints, we created the following table:

x	0	1	4
$f(x)$	0	−1	8

From this table we can see that f must decrease from its value of 0 at $x = 0$ to −1 at $x = 1$, and then increase to 8 at $x = 4$. The value of 8 must be the largest value it takes on, and the value of −1 must be the smallest, on the interval $[0, 4]$. Similarly, in Example 3 we created the following table:

t	−1	0	1
$f(t)$	1	0	1

From this table we can see that the largest value of f on the interval $[-1, 1]$ is 1 and the smallest value is 0. We are taking advantage of the following fact, the proof of which uses some deep and beautiful mathematics (alas, beyond the scope of this book):

Extreme Value Theorem

If f is *continuous* on a *closed interval* $[a, b]$, then it will have an absolute maximum and an absolute minimum value on that interval. Each absolute extremum must occur at either an endpoint or a critical point. Therefore, the absolute maximum is the largest value in a table of the values of f at the endpoints and critical points, and the absolute minimum is the smallest value.

Quick Example

The function $f(x) = 3x - x^3$ on the interval $[0, 2]$ has one critical point at $x = 1$. The values of f at the critical point and the endpoints of the interval are given in the following table:

	Endpoint	Critical point	Endpoint
x	0	1	2
$f(x)$	0	2	−2

From this table we can say that the absolute maximum value of f on $[0, 2]$ is 2, which occurs at $x = 1$, and the absolute minimum value of f is −2, which occurs at $x = 2$.

As we can see in Example 2 and the following examples, if the domain is not a closed interval then f may not have an absolute maximum and minimum, and a table of values as above is of little help in determining whether it does.

EXAMPLE 4 **Domain Not a Closed Interval**

Find all extrema of $f(x) = x + \dfrac{1}{x}$.

Solution Because no domain is specified, we take the domain to be as large as possible. The function is not defined at $x = 0$ but is at all other points, so we take its domain to be $(-\infty, 0) \cup (0, +\infty)$. We calculate

$$f'(x) = 1 - \frac{1}{x^2}.$$

Stationary Points Setting $f'(x) = 0$, we solve

$$1 - \frac{1}{x^2} = 0$$

to find $x = \pm 1$. Calculating the corresponding values of f, we get the two stationary points $(1, 2)$ and $(-1, -2)$.

Singular Points The only value of x for which $f'(x)$ is not defined is $x = 0$, but then f is not defined there either, so there are no singular points in the domain.

Endpoints The domain, $(-\infty, 0) \cup (0, +\infty)$, has no endpoints.

From this scant information, it is hard to tell what f does. If we are sketching the graph by hand, or using the first derivative test, we will need to plot additional "test points" to the left and right of the stationary points $x = \pm 1$.

 using Technology

For the technology approach, let's choose a viewing window with an interval of $[-3, 3]$ for x and $[-4, 4]$ for y, which should leave plenty of room to see how f behaves near the stationary points. The result is something like Figure 15.

From this graph we can see that f has:

A relative (stationary) maximum at $(-1, -2)$

A relative (stationary) minimum at $(1, 2)$

Curiously, the relative maximum is lower than the relative minimum! Notice also that, because of the break in the graph at $x = 0$, the graph did not need to rise to get from $(-1, -2)$ to $(1, 2)$. ∎

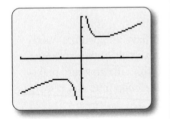

Figure 15

So far we have been solving the equation $f'(x) = 0$ to obtain our candidates for stationary extrema. However, it is often not easy—or even possible—to solve equations analytically. In the next example, we show a way around this problem by using graphing technology.

EXAMPLE 5 ▯ **Finding Approximate Extrema Using Technology**

Graph the function $f(x) = (x - 1)^{2/3} - \dfrac{x^2}{2}$ with domain $[-2, +\infty)$. Also graph its derivative and hence locate and classify all extrema of f, with coordinates accurate to two decimal places.

Solution In Example 4 of Section 3.5, we saw how to draw the graphs of f and f' using technology. Note that the technology formula to use for the graph of f is

```
((x-1)^2)^(1/3)-0.5*x^2
```

instead of

```
(x-1)^(2/3)-0.5*x^2.
```

(Why?)

    Figure 16 shows the resulting graphs of f and f'.

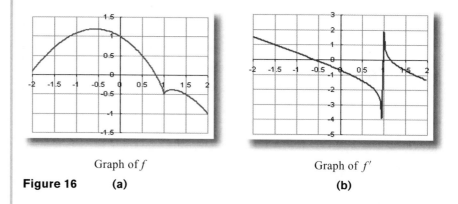

| Graph of f | Graph of f' |

Figure 16   **(a)**   **(b)**

If we extend Xmax beyond $x = 2$, we find that the graph continues downward, apparently without any further interesting behavior.

    Stationary Points The graph of f shows two stationary points, both maxima, at around $x = -0.6$ and $x = 1.2$. Notice that the graph of f' is zero at precisely these points. Moreover, it is easier to locate these values accurately on the graph of f' because it is easier to pinpoint where a graph crosses the x-axis than to locate a stationary point. Zooming in to the stationary point at $x \approx -0.6$ results in Figure 17.

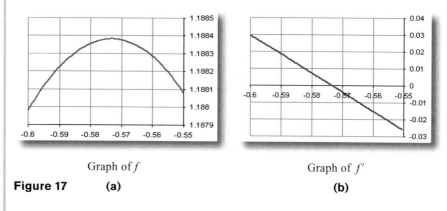

| Graph of f | Graph of f' |

Figure 17   **(a)**   **(b)**

From the graph of f, we can see that the stationary point is somewhere between -0.58 and -0.57. The graph of f' shows more clearly that the zero of f', hence the stationary point of f lies somewhat closer to -0.57 than to -0.58. Thus, the stationary point occurs at $x \approx -0.57$, rounded to two decimal places.

    In a similar way, we find the second stationary point at $x \approx 1.18$.

Singular Points Going back to Figure 16, we notice what appears to be a cusp (singular point) at the relative minimum around $x = 1$, and this is confirmed by a glance at the graph of f', which seems to take a sudden jump at that value. Zooming in closer suggests that the singular point occurs at exactly $x = 1$. In fact, we can calculate

$$f'(x) = \frac{2}{3(x-1)^{1/3}} - x.$$

From this formula we see clearly that $f'(x)$ is defined everywhere except at $x = 1$.

Endpoints The only endpoint in the domain is $x = -2$, which gives a relative minimum.

Thus, we have found the following approximate extrema for f:

A relative (endpoint) minimum at $(-2, 0.08)$

An absolute (stationary) maximum at $(-0.57, 1.19)$

A relative (singular) minimum at $(1, -0.5)$

A relative (stationary) maximum at $(1.18, -0.38)$.

5.1 **EXERCISES**

In Exercises 1–12, locate and classify all extrema in each graph. (By classifying the extrema, we mean listing whether each extremum is a relative or absolute maximum or minimum.) Also, locate any stationary points or singular points that are not relative extrema. HINT [See Figure 7.]

1.
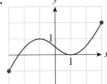

2.
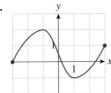

3.
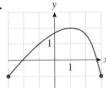

4.
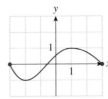

5.
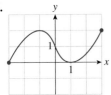

6.
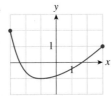

7.
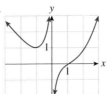

8.
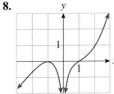

9.
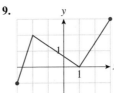

10.
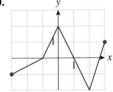

11.
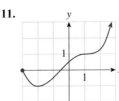

12.
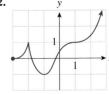

Find the exact location of all the relative and absolute extrema of each function in Exercises 13–44. HINT [See Example 1.]

13. $f(x) = x^2 - 4x + 1$ with domain $[0, 3]$

14. $f(x) = 2x^2 - 2x + 3$ with domain $[0, 3]$

15. $g(x) = x^3 - 12x$ with domain $[-4, 4]$

16. $g(x) = 2x^3 - 6x + 3$ with domain $[-2, 2]$

17. $f(t) = t^3 + t$ with domain $[-2, 2]$

18. $f(t) = -2t^3 - 3t$ with domain $[-1, 1]$

19. $h(t) = 2t^3 + 3t^2$ with domain $[-2, +\infty)$ HINT [See Example 2.]

20. $h(t) = t^3 - 3t^2$ with domain $[-1, +\infty)$ HINT [See Example 2.]

21. $f(x) = x^4 - 4x^3$ with domain $[-1, +\infty)$

22. $f(x) = 3x^4 - 2x^3$ with domain $[-1, +\infty)$

23. $g(t) = \dfrac{1}{4}t^4 - \dfrac{2}{3}t^3 + \dfrac{1}{2}t^2$ with domain $(-\infty, +\infty)$

24. $g(t) = 3t^4 - 16t^3 + 24t^2 + 1$ with domain $(-\infty, +\infty)$

25. $h(x) = (x - 1)^{2/3}$ with domain $[0, 2]$ HINT [See Example 3.]

26. $h(x) = (x + 1)^{2/5}$ with domain $[-2, 0]$ HINT [See Example 3.]

27. $k(x) = \dfrac{2x}{3} + (x + 1)^{2/3}$ with domain $(-\infty, 0]$

28. $k(x) = \dfrac{2x}{5} - (x - 1)^{2/5}$ with domain $[0, +\infty)$

29. ▼ $f(t) = \dfrac{t^2 + 1}{t^2 - 1}; -2 \le t \le 2, t \ne \pm 1$

30. ▼ $f(t) = \dfrac{t^2 - 1}{t^2 + 1}$ with domain $[-2, 2]$

31. ▼ $f(x) = \sqrt{x}(x - 1); x \ge 0$

32. ▼ $f(x) = \sqrt{x}(x + 1); x \ge 0$

33. ▼ $g(x) = x^2 - 4\sqrt{x}$

34. ▼ $g(x) = \dfrac{1}{x} - \dfrac{1}{x^2}$

35. ▼ $g(x) = \dfrac{x^3}{x^2 + 3}$

36. ▼ $g(x) = \dfrac{x^3}{x^2 - 3}$

37. ▼ $f(x) = x - \ln x$ with domain $(0, +\infty)$

38. ▼ $f(x) = x - \ln x^2$ with domain $(0, +\infty)$

39. ▼ $g(t) = e^t - t$ with domain $[-1, 1]$

40. ▼ $g(t) = e^{-t^2}$ with domain $(-\infty, +\infty)$

41. ▼ $f(x) = \dfrac{2x^2 - 24}{x + 4}$

42. ▼ $f(x) = \dfrac{x - 4}{x^2 + 20}$

43. ▼ $f(x) = xe^{1-x^2}$

44. ▼ $f(x) = x \ln x$ with domain $(0, +\infty)$

In Exercises 45–48, use graphing technology and the method in Example 5 to find the x-coordinates of the critical points, accurate to two decimal places. Find all relative and absolute maxima and minima. HINT [See Example 5.]

45. ▣ $y = x^2 + \dfrac{1}{x - 2}$ with domain $(-3, 2) \cup (2, 6)$

46. ▣ $y = x^2 - 10(x - 1)^{2/3}$ with domain $(-4, 4)$

47. ▣ $f(x) = (x - 5)^2(x + 4)(x - 2)$ with domain $[-5, 6]$

48. ▣ $f(x) = (x + 3)^2(x - 2)^2$ with domain $[-5, 5]$

In Exercises 49–56, the graph of the derivative of a function f is shown. Determine the x-coordinates of all stationary and singular points of f, and classify each as a relative maximum, relative minimum, or neither. (Assume that f(x) is defined and continuous everywhere in $[-3, 3]$.) HINT [See Example 5.]

49. ▼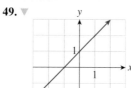

50. ▼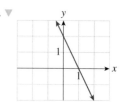

51. ▼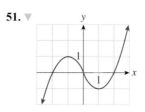

52. ▼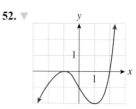

53. ▼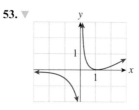

54. ▼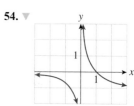

55. ▼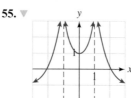

56. ▼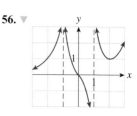

COMMUNICATION AND REASONING EXERCISES

57. Draw the graph of a function f with domain the set of all real numbers, such that f is not linear and has no relative extrema.

58. Draw the graph of a function g with domain the set of all real numbers, such that g has a relative maximum and minimum but no absolute extrema.

59. Draw the graph of a function that has stationary and singular points but no relative extrema.

60. Draw the graph of a function that has relative, not absolute, maxima and minima, but has no stationary or singular points.

61. If a stationary point is not a relative maximum, then must it be a relative minimum? Explain your answer.

62. If one endpoint is a relative maximum, must the other be a relative minimum? Explain your answer.

63. ▼ We said that if f is continuous on a closed interval $[a, b]$, then it will have an absolute maximum and an absolute minimum. Draw the graph of a function with domain $[0, 1]$ having an absolute maximum but no absolute minimum.

64. ▼ Refer to Exercise 63. Draw the graph of a function with domain $[0, 1]$ having no absolute extrema.

65. ⒤ ▼ Must endpoints always be extrema? Consider the following function (based on the trigonometric sine function—see Chapter 9 for a discussion of its properties):

$$f(x) = \begin{cases} x \sin\left(\dfrac{1}{x}\right) & \text{if } x > 0 \\ 0 & \text{if } x = 0 \end{cases}.$$

Technology formula:
`x*sin(1/x)`

Graph this function using the technology formula above for $0 \le x \le h$, choosing smaller and smaller values of h, and decide whether f has a either a relative maximum or relative

minimum at the endpoint $x = 0$. Explain your answer. (Note: Very few graphers can draw this curve accurately; the grapher that comes with Mac computers is probably among the best, while the TI-83/84 Plus is probably among the worst.)

66. ⒤ ▼ Refer to the preceding exercise, and consider the function

$$f(x) = \begin{cases} x^2 \sin\left(\dfrac{1}{x}\right) & \text{if } x \neq 0 \\ 0 & \text{if } x = 0 \end{cases}.$$

Technology formula:
`x^2*sin(1/x)`

Graph this function using the technology formula above for $0 \le x \le h$, choosing smaller and smaller values of h, and decide **(a)** whether $x = 0$ is a stationary point, and **(b)** whether f has either a relative maximum or a relative minimum at $x = 0$. [For part (a), use technology to estimate the derivative at $x = 0$.] Explain your answers.

5.2 Applications of Maxima and Minima

In many applications we would like to find the largest or smallest possible value of some quantity—for instance, the greatest possible profit or the lowest cost. We call this the *optimal* (best) value. In this section we consider several such examples and use calculus to find the optimal value in each.

In all applications the first step is to translate a written description into a mathematical problem. In the problems we look at in this section, there are *unknowns* that we are asked to find, there is an expression involving those unknowns that must be made as large or as small as possible—the **objective function**—and there may be **constraints**— equations or inequalities relating the variables.*

＊NOTE If you have studied linear programming, you will notice a similarity here, but unlike the situation in linear programming, neither the objective function nor the constraints need be linear.

EXAMPLE 1 Minimizing Average Cost

Gymnast Clothing manufactures expensive hockey jerseys for sale to college bookstores in runs of up to 500. Its cost (in dollars) for a run of x hockey jerseys is

$$C(x) = 2{,}000 + 10x + 0.2x^2.$$

How many jerseys should Gymnast produce per run in order to minimize average cost?*

＊NOTE Why don't we seek to minimize total cost? The answer would be uninteresting; to minimize total cost, we would make *no* jerseys at all. Minimizing the average cost is a more practical objective.

Solution Here is the procedure we will follow to solve problems like this.

1. *Identify the unknown(s).* There is one unknown: x, the number of hockey jerseys Gymnast should produce per run. (We know this because the question is, How many jerseys . . . ?)

2. *Identify the objective function.* The objective function is the quantity that must be made as small (in this case) as possible. In this example it is the average cost, which is given by

$$\bar{C}(x) = \frac{C(x)}{x} = \frac{2{,}000 + 10x + 0.2x^2}{x}$$

$$= \frac{2{,}000}{x} + 10 + 0.2x \text{ dollars/jersey.}$$

3. *Identify the constraints (if any).* At most 500 jerseys can be manufactured in a run. Also, $\bar{C}(0)$ is not defined. Thus, x is constrained by

$$0 < x \le 500.$$

Put another way, the domain of the objective function $\bar{C}(x)$ is $(0, 500]$.

4. *State and solve the resulting optimization problem.* Our optimization problem is:

$$\text{Minimize } \bar{C}(x) = \frac{2{,}000}{x} + 10 + 0.2x \qquad \text{Objective function}$$

$$\text{subject to } 0 < x \le 500. \qquad \text{Constraint}$$

We now solve this problem as in Section 5.1. We first calculate

$$\bar{C}'(x) = -\frac{2{,}000}{x^2} + 0.2.$$

We solve $\bar{C}'(x) = 0$ to find $x = \pm 100$. We reject $x = -100$ because -100 is not in the domain of $\bar{C}$ (and makes no sense), so we have one stationary point, at $x = 100$. There, the average cost is $\bar{C}(100) = \$50$ per jersey.

The only point at which the formula for $\bar{C}'$ is not defined is $x = 0$, but that is not in the domain of $\bar{C}$, so we have no singular points. We have one endpoint in the domain, at $x = 500$. There, the average cost is $\bar{C}(500) = \$114$.

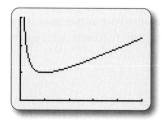

Figure 18

---

using Technology

Let's plot $\bar{C}$ in a viewing window with the intervals $[0, 500]$ for x and $[0, 150]$ for y, which will show the whole domain and the two interesting points we've found so far. The result is Figure 18.

From the graph of $\bar{C}$, we can see that the stationary point at $x = 100$ gives the absolute minimum. We can therefore say that Gymnast Clothing should produce 100 jerseys per run, for a lowest possible average cost of $50 per jersey. ∎

EXAMPLE 2 Maximizing Area

Slim wants to build a rectangular enclosure for his pet rabbit, Killer, against the side of his house, as shown in Figure 19. He has bought 100 feet of fencing. What are the dimensions of the largest area that he can enclose?

Figure 19

Solution

1. *Identify the unknown(s).* To identify the unknown(s), we look at the question: What are the *dimensions* of the largest area he can enclose? Thus, the unknowns are the dimensions of the fence. We call these x and y, as shown in Figure 20.

2. *Identify the objective function.* We look for what it is that we are trying to maximize (or minimize). The phrase "largest area" tells us that our object is to *maximize the area*, which is the product of length and width, so our objective function is

$$A = xy, \text{ where } A \text{ is the area of the enclosure.}$$

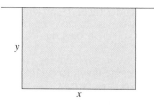

Figure 20

3. ***Identify the constraints (if any).*** What stops Slim from making the area as large as he wants? He has only 100 feet of fencing to work with. Looking again at Figure 20, we see that the sum of the lengths of the three sides must equal 100, so

$$x + 2y = 100.$$

One more point: Because x and y represent the lengths of the sides of the enclosure, neither can be a negative number.

4. ***State and solve the resulting optimization problem.*** Our mathematical problem is:

> Maximize $A = xy$ Objective function
>
> subject to $x + 2y = 100$, $x \geq 0$, and $y \geq 0$.   Constraints

We know how to find maxima and minima of a function of one variable, but A appears to depend on two variables. We can remedy this by using a constraint to express one variable in terms of the other. Let's take the constraint $x + 2y = 100$ and solve for x in terms of y:

$$x = 100 - 2y.$$

Substituting into the objective function gives

$$A = xy = (100 - 2y)y = 100y - 2y^2$$

and we have eliminated x from the objective function. What about the inequalities? One says that $x \geq 0$, but we want to eliminate x from this as well. We substitute for x again, getting

$$100 - 2y \geq 0.$$

Solving this inequality for y gives $y \leq 50$. The second inequality says that $y \geq 0$. Now, we can restate our problem with x eliminated:

> Maximize $A(y) = 100y - 2y^2$ subject to $0 \leq y \leq 50$.

We now proceed with our usual method of solving such problems. We calculate $A'(y) = 100 - 4y$. Solving $100 - 4y = 0$, we get one stationary point at $y = 25$. There, $A(25) = 1{,}250$. There are no points at which $A'(y)$ is not defined, so there are no singular points. We have two endpoints, at $y = 0$ and $y = 50$. The corresponding areas are $A(0) = 0$ and $A(50) = 0$. We record the three points we found in a table:

y	0	25	50
$A(y)$	0	1,250	0

It's clear now how A must behave: It increases from 0 at $y = 0$ to 1,250 at $y = 25$ and then decreases back to 0 at $y = 50$. Thus, the largest possible value of A is 1,250 square feet, which occurs when $y = 25$. To completely answer the question that was asked, we need to know the corresponding value of x. We have $x = 100 - 2y$, so $x = 50$ when $y = 25$. Thus, Slim should build his enclosure 50 feet across and 25 feet deep (with the "missing" 50-foot side being formed by part of the house).

➡ **Before we go on...** Notice that the problem in Example 2 came down to finding the absolute maximum value of A on the closed and bounded interval [0, 50]. As we noted in the preceding section, the table of values of A at its critical points and the endpoints of the interval gives us enough information to find the absolute maximum. ∎

Let's stop for a moment and summarize the steps we've taken in these two examples.

Solving an Optimization Problem

1. **Identify the unknown(s), possibly with the aid of a diagram.** These are usually the quantities asked for in the problem.
2. **Identify the objective function.** This is the quantity you are asked to maximize or minimize. You should name it explicitly, as in "Let S = surface area."
3. **Identify the constraint(s).** These can be equations relating variables or inequalities expressing limitations on the values of variables.
4. **State the optimization problem.** This will have the form "Maximize [minimize] the objective function subject to the constraint(s)."
5. **Eliminate extra variables.** If the objective function depends on several variables, solve the constraint equations to express all variables in terms of one particular variable. Substitute these expressions into the objective function to rewrite it as a function of a single variable. Substitute the expressions into any inequality constraints to help determine the domain of the objective function.
6. **Find the absolute maximum (or minimum) of the objective function.** Use the techniques of the preceding section.

Now for some further examples.

EXAMPLE 3 Maximizing Revenue

Cozy Carriage Company builds baby strollers. Using market research, the company estimates that if it sets the price of a stroller at p dollars, then it can sell $q = 300{,}000 - 10p^2$ strollers per year. What price will bring in the greatest annual revenue?

Solution The question we are asked identifies our main unknown, the price p. However, there is another quantity that we do not know, q, the number of strollers the company will sell per year. The question also identifies the objective function, revenue, which is

$$R = pq.$$

Including the equality constraint given to us, that $q = 300{,}000 - 10p^2$, and the "reality" inequality constraints $p \geq 0$ and $q \geq 0$, we can write our problem as

Maximize $R = pq$ subject to $q = 300{,}000 - 10p^2$, $p \geq 0$, and $q \geq 0$.

We are given q in terms of p, so let's substitute to eliminate q:

$$R = pq = p(300{,}000 - 10p^2) = 300{,}000p - 10p^3$$

Substituting in the inequality $q \geq 0$, we get

$$300{,}000 - 10p^2 \geq 0.$$

Thus, $p^2 \leq 30{,}000$, which gives $-100\sqrt{3} \leq p \leq 100\sqrt{3}$. When we combine this with $p \geq 0$, we get the following restatement of our problem:

Maximize $R(p) = 300{,}000p - 10p^3$ such that $0 \leq p \leq 100\sqrt{3}$.

We solve this problem in much the same way we did the preceding one. We calculate $R'(p) = 300{,}000 - 30p^2$. Setting $300{,}000 - 30p^2 = 0$, we find one stationary point at $p = 100$. There are no singular points and we have the endpoints $p = 0$ and $p = 100\sqrt{3}$. Putting these points in a table and computing the corresponding values of R, we get the following:

p	0	100	$100\sqrt{3}$
$R(p)$	0	20,000,000	0

Thus, Cozy Carriage should price its strollers at $100 each, which will bring in the largest possible revenue of $20,000,000.

Figure 21

EXAMPLE 4 Optimizing Resources

The Metal Can Company has an order to make cylindrical cans with a volume of 250 cubic centimeters. What should be the dimensions of the cans in order to use the least amount of metal in their production?

Solution We are asked to find the dimensions of the cans. It is traditional to take as the dimensions of a cylinder the height h and the radius of the base r, as in Figure 21.

We are also asked to minimize the amount of metal used in the can, which is the area of the surface of the cylinder. We can look up the formula or figure it out ourselves: Imagine removing the circular top and bottom and then cutting vertically and flattening out the hollow cylinder to get a rectangle, as shown in Figure 22.

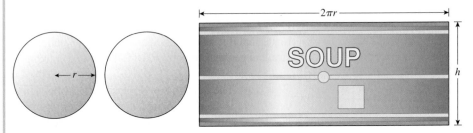

Figure 22

Our objective function is the (total) surface area S of the can. The area of each disc is πr^2, while the area of the rectangular piece is $2\pi r h$. Thus, our objective function is

$$S = 2\pi r^2 + 2\pi r h.$$

As usual, there is a constraint: The volume must be exactly 250 cubic centimeters. The formula for the volume of a cylinder is $V = \pi r^2 h$, so

$$\pi r^2 h = 250.$$

It is easiest to solve this constraint for h in terms of r:

$$h = \frac{250}{\pi r^2}.$$

Substituting in the objective function, we get

$$S = 2\pi r^2 + 2\pi r \frac{250}{\pi r^2} = 2\pi r^2 + \frac{500}{r}.$$

Now r cannot be negative or 0, but it can become very large (a very wide but very short can could have the right volume). We therefore take the domain of $S(r)$ to be $(0, +\infty)$, so our mathematical problem is as follows:

$$\text{Minimize } S(r) = 2\pi r^2 + \frac{500}{r} \text{ subject to } r > 0.$$

Now we calculate

$$S'(r) = 4\pi r - \frac{500}{r^2}.$$

To find stationary points, we set this equal to 0 and solve:

$$4\pi r - \frac{500}{r^2} = 0$$

$$4\pi r = \frac{500}{r^2}$$

$$4\pi r^3 = 500$$

$$r^3 = \frac{125}{\pi}.$$

So

$$r = \sqrt[3]{\frac{125}{\pi}} = \frac{5}{\sqrt[3]{\pi}} \approx 3.41.$$

The corresponding surface area is approximately $S(3.41) \approx 220$. There are no singular points or endpoints in the domain.

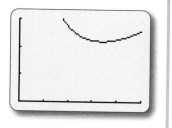

Figure 23

▦ using Technology

To see how S behaves near the one stationary point, let's graph it in a viewing window with interval $[0, 5]$ for r and $[0, 300]$ for S. The result is Figure 23.

From the graph we can clearly see that the smallest surface area occurs at the stationary point at $r \approx 3.41$. The height of the can will be

$$h = \frac{250}{\pi r^2} \approx 6.83.$$ ◼

Thus, the can that uses the least amount of metal has a height of approximately 6.83 centimeters and a radius of approximately 3.41 centimeters. Such a can will use approximately 220 square centimeters of metal.

➡ **Before we go on...** We obtained the value of r in Example 4 by solving the equation

$$4\pi r = \frac{500}{r^2}.$$

This time, let us do things differently: Divide both sides by 4π to obtain

$$r = \frac{500}{4\pi r^2} = \frac{125}{\pi r^2}$$

and compare what we got with the expression for h:

$$h = \frac{250}{\pi r^2}$$

which we see is exactly twice the expression for r. Put another way, the height is exactly equal to the diameter so that the can looks square when viewed from the side. Have you ever seen cans with that shape? Why do you think most cans do not have this shape? ∎

EXAMPLE 5 Allocation of Labor

The Gym Sock Company manufactures cotton athletic socks. Production is partially automated through the use of robots. Daily operating costs amount to $50 per laborer and $30 per robot. The number of pairs of socks the company can manufacture in a day is given by a Cobb-Douglas* production formula

$$q = 50n^{0.6}r^{0.4}$$

* NOTE Cobb-Douglas production formulas were discussed in Section 4.6.

where q is the number of pairs of socks that can be manufactured by n laborers and r robots. Assuming that the company wishes to produce 1,000 pairs of socks per day at a minimum cost, how many laborers and how many robots should it use?

Solution The unknowns are the number of laborers n and the number of robots r. The objective is to minimize the daily cost:

$$C = 50n + 30r.$$

The constraints are given by the daily quota

$$1{,}000 = 50n^{0.6}r^{0.4}$$

and the fact that n and r are nonnegative. We solve the constraint equation for one of the variables; let's solve for n:

$$n^{0.6} = \frac{1{,}000}{50r^{0.4}} = \frac{20}{r^{0.4}}.$$

Taking the $1/0.6$ power of both sides gives

$$n = \left(\frac{20}{r^{0.4}}\right)^{1/0.6} = \frac{20^{1/0.6}}{r^{0.4/0.6}} = \frac{20^{5/3}}{r^{2/3}} \approx \frac{147.36}{r^{2/3}}.$$

Substituting in the objective equation gives us the cost as a function of r:

$$C(r) \approx 50\left(\frac{147.36}{r^{2/3}}\right) + 30r$$

$$= 7{,}368r^{-2/3} + 30r.$$

The only remaining constraint on r is that $r > 0$. To find the minimum value of $C(r)$, we first take the derivative:

$$C'(r) \approx -4{,}912r^{-5/3} + 30.$$

Setting this equal to zero, we solve for r:

$$r^{-5/3} \approx 0.006107$$

$$r \approx (0.006107)^{-3/5} \approx 21.3.$$

The corresponding cost is $C(21.3) \approx \$1{,}600$. There are no singular points or endpoints in the domain of C.

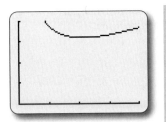

Figure 24

using Technology

To see how C behaves near its stationary point, let's draw its graph in a viewing window with an interval of $[0, 40]$ for r and $[0, 2,000]$ for C. The result is Figure 24.

From the graph we can see that C does have its minimum at the stationary point. The corresponding value of n is

$$n \approx \frac{147.36}{r^{2/3}} \approx 19.2.$$

At this point, our solution appears to be this: Use (approximately) 19.2 laborers and (approximately) 21.3 robots to meet the manufacturing quota at a minimum cost. However, we are not interested in fractions of robots or people, so we need to find integer solutions for n and r. If we round these numbers, we get the solution $(n, r) = (19, 21)$. However, a quick calculation shows that

$$q = 50(19)^{0.6}(21)^{0.4} \approx 989 \text{ pairs of socks},$$

which fails to meet the quota of 1,000. Thus, we need to round at least one of the quantities n and r *upward* in order to meet the quota. The three possibilities, with corresponding values of q and C, are as follows:

$$(n, r) = (20, 21), \text{ with } q \approx 1,020 \text{ and } C = \$1,630$$
$$(n, r) = (19, 22), \text{ with } q \approx 1,007 \text{ and } C = \$1,610$$
$$(n, r) = (20, 22), \text{ with } q \approx 1,039 \text{ and } C = \$1,660.$$

Of these, the solution that meets the quota at a minimum cost is $(n, r) = (19, 22)$. Thus, the Gym Sock Co. should use 19 laborers and 22 robots, at a cost of $50 \times 19 + 30 \times 22 = \$1,610$, to manufacture $50 \times 19^{0.6} \times 22^{0.4} \approx 1,007$ pairs of socks.

5.2 EXERCISES

▼ more advanced   ◆ challenging
T indicates exercises that should be solved using technology

Solve the optimization problems in Exercises 1–8. HINT [See Example 2.]

1. Maximize $P = xy$ with $x + y = 10$.

2. Maximize $P = xy$ with $x + 2y = 40$.

3. Minimize $S = x + y$ with $xy = 9$ and both x and $y > 0$.

4. Minimize $S = x + 2y$ with $xy = 2$ and both x and $y > 0$.

5. Minimize $F = x^2 + y^2$ with $x + 2y = 10$.

6. Minimize $F = x^2 + y^2$ with $xy^2 = 16$.

7. Maximize $P = xyz$ with $x + y = 30$ and $y + z = 30$, and x, y, and $z \geq 0$.

8. Maximize $P = xyz$ with $x + z = 12$ and $y + z = 12$, and x, y, and $z \geq 0$.

9. For a rectangle with perimeter 20 to have the largest area, what dimensions should it have?

10. For a rectangle with area 100 to have the smallest perimeter, what dimensions should it have?

APPLICATIONS

11. *Average Cost: iPods* Assume that it costs **Apple** approximately

$$C(x) = 22,500 + 100x + 0.01x^2$$

dollars to manufacture x 30-gigabyte video iPods in a day.[1] How many iPods should be manufactured in order to minimize average cost? What is the resulting average cost of an iPod? (Give your answer to the nearest dollar.) HINT [See Example 1.]

12. *Average Cost: Xboxes* Assume that it costs **Microsoft** approximately

$$C(x) = 14,400 + 550x + 0.01x^2$$

---

[1] Not the actual cost equation; the authors do not know Apple's actual cost equation. The marginal cost in the model given is in rough agreement with the actual marginal cost for reasonable values of x. Source for cost data: *Manufacturing & Technology News*, July 31, 2007 Volume 14, No. 14 (www.manufacturingnews.com).

dollars to manufacture x Xbox 360s in a day.[2] How many Xboxes should be manufactured in order to minimize average cost? What is the resulting average cost of an Xbox? (Give your answer to the nearest dollar.) HINT [See Example 1.]

13. Pollution Control The cost of controlling emissions at a firm rises rapidly as the amount of emissions reduced increases. Here is a possible model:

$$C(q) = 4{,}000 + 100q^2$$

where q is the reduction in emissions (in pounds of pollutant per day) and C is the daily cost to the firm (in dollars) of this reduction. What level of reduction corresponds to the lowest average cost per pound of pollutant, and what would be the resulting average cost to the nearest dollar?

14. Pollution Control Repeat the preceding exercise using the following cost function:

$$C(q) = 2{,}000 + 200q^2.$$

15. Pollution Control (Compare Exercise 13.) The cost of controlling emissions at a firm is given by

$$C(q) = 4{,}000 + 100q^2$$

where q is the reduction in emissions (in pounds of pollutant per day) and C is the daily cost to the firm (in dollars) of this reduction. Government clean-air subsidies amount to $500 per pound of pollutant removed. How many pounds of pollutant should the firm remove each day in order to minimize *net* cost (cost minus subsidy)?

16. Pollution Control (Compare Exercise 14.) Repeat the preceding exercise, using the following cost function:

$$C(q) = 2{,}000 + 200q^2$$

with government subsidies amounting to $100 per pound of pollutant removed per day.

17. Fences I would like to create a rectangular vegetable patch. The fencing for the east and west sides costs $4 per foot, and the fencing for the north and south sides costs only $2 per foot. I have a budget of $80 for the project. What are the dimensions of the vegetable patch with the largest area I can enclose? HINT [See Example 2.]

18. Fences I would like to create a rectangular orchid garden that abuts my house so that the house itself forms the northern boundary. The fencing for the southern boundary costs $4 per foot, and the fencing for the east and west sides costs $2 per foot. If I have a budget of $80 for the project, what are the dimensions of the garden with the largest area I can enclose? HINT [See Example 2.]

_____

[2] Not the actual cost equation; the authors do not know Microsoft's actual cost equation. The marginal cost in the model given is in rough agreement with the actual marginal cost for reasonable values of x. Source for estimate of marginal cost: iSuppli (www.isuppli.com).

19. Fences You are building a right-angled triangular flower garden along a stream as shown in the figure.

The fencing of the left border costs $5 per foot, while the fencing of the lower border costs $1 per foot. (No fencing is required along the river.) You want to spend $100 and enclose as much area as possible. What are the dimensions of your garden, and what area does it enclose? [The area of a right-triangle is given by $A = xy/2$.]

20. Fences Repeat Exercise 19, this time assuming that the fencing of the left border costs $8 per foot, while the fencing of the lower border costs $2 per foot, and that you can spend $400.

21. ▼ Fences (Compare Exercise 17.) For tax reasons, I need to create a rectangular vegetable patch with an area of exactly 242 sq. ft. The fencing for the east and west sides costs $4 per foot, and the fencing for the north and south sides costs only $2 per foot. What are the dimensions of the vegetable patch with the least expensive fence? HINT [Compare Exercise 3.]

22. ▼ Fences (Compare Exercise 18.) For reasons too complicated to explain, I need to create a rectangular orchid garden with an area of exactly 324 sq. ft. abutting my house so that the house itself forms the northern boundary. The fencing for the southern boundary costs $4 per foot, and the fencing for the east and west sides costs $2 per foot. What are the dimensions of the orchid garden with the least expensive fence? HINT [Compare Exercise 4.]

23. Revenue Hercules Films is deciding on the price of the video release of its film *Son of Frankenstein*. Its marketing people estimate that at a price of p dollars, it can sell a total of $q = 200{,}000 - 10{,}000p$ copies. What price will bring in the greatest revenue? HINT [See Example 3.]

24. Profit Hercules Films is also deciding on the price of the video release of its film *Bride of the Son of Frankenstein*. Again, marketing estimates that at a price of p dollars, it can sell $q = 200{,}000 - 10{,}000p$ copies, but each copy costs $4 to make. What price will give the greatest *profit*?

25. Revenue: Cell Phones Worldwide quarterly sales of **Nokia** cell phones were approximately $q = -p + 156$ million phones when the wholesale price was $p. At what wholesale price should **Nokia** have sold its phones to maximize its quarterly revenue? What would have been the resulting revenue?[3]

26. **Revenue: Cell Phones** Worldwide annual sales of all cell phones were approximately $-10p + 1,600$ million phones when the wholesale price was $p. At what wholesale price should cell phones have been sold to maximize annual revenue? What would have been the resulting revenue?[4]

27. **Revenue: Monorail Service** The demand, in rides per day, for monorail service in Las Vegas in 2005 can be approximated by $q = -4,500p + 41,500$ when the fare was $p. What price should have been charged to maximize total revenue?[5]

28. **Demand for Monorail Service, Mars** The demand, in rides per day, for monorail service in the three urbynes (or districts) of Utarek, Mars, can be approximated by $q = -2p + 24$ million riders when the fare is $\bar{\bar{Z}}p$. What price should be charged to maximize total revenue?[6]

29. ▼ **Revenue** Assume that the demand for tuna in a small coastal town is given by

$$p = \frac{500,000}{q^{1.5}}$$

where q is the number of pounds of tuna that can be sold in a month at p dollars per pound. Assume that the town's fishery wishes to sell at least 5,000 pounds of tuna per month.

a. How much should the town's fishery charge for tuna in order to maximize monthly revenue? HINT [See Example 3, and don't neglect endpoints.]

b. How much tuna will it sell per month at that price?

c. What will be its resulting revenue?

30. ▼ **Revenue** Economist Henry Schultz devised the following demand function for corn:

$$p = \frac{6,570,000}{q^{1.3}}$$

where q is the number of bushels of corn that could be sold at p dollars per bushel in one year.[7] Assume that at least 10,000 bushels of corn per year must be sold.

a. How much should farmers charge per bushel of corn to maximize annual revenue? HINT [See Example 3, and don't neglect endpoints.]

b. How much corn can farmers sell per year at that price?

c. What will be the farmers' resulting revenue?

31. ▼ **Revenue** The wholesale price for chicken in the United States fell from 25¢ per pound to 14¢ per pound, while per capita chicken consumption rose from 22 pounds per year to 27.5 pounds per year.[8] Assuming that the demand for chicken depends linearly on the price, what wholesale price for chicken maximizes revenues for poultry farmers, and what does that revenue amount to?

32. ▼ **Revenue** Your underground used-book business is booming. Your policy is to sell all used versions of *Calculus and You* at the same price (regardless of condition). When you set the price at $10, sales amounted to 120 volumes during the first week of classes. The following semester, you set the price at $30 and sold not a single book. Assuming that the demand for books depends linearly on the price, what price gives you the maximum revenue, and what does that revenue amount to?

33. **Profit: Cell Phones** (Compare Exercise 25.) Worldwide quarterly sales of **Nokia** cell phones were approximately $q = -p + 156$ million phones when the wholesale price was $p. Assuming that it cost **Nokia** $40 to manufacture each cell phone, at what wholesale price should **Nokia** have sold its phones to maximize its quarterly profit? What would have been the resulting profit?[9] (The actual wholesale price was $105 in the fourth quarter of 2004.) HINT [See Example 3, and recall that Profit = Revenue − Cost.]

34. **Profit: Cell Phones** (Compare Exercise 26.) Worldwide annual sales of all cell phones were approximately $-10p + 1,600$ million phones when the wholesale price was $p. Assuming that it costs $30 to manufacture each cell phone, at what wholesale price should cell phones have been sold to maximize annual profit? What would have been the resulting profit?[10] HINT [See Example 3, and recall that Profit = Revenue − Cost.]

35. ▼ **Profit** The demand equation for your company's virtual reality video headsets is

$$p = \frac{1,000}{q^{0.3}}$$

where q is the total number of headsets that your company can sell in a week at a price of p dollars. The total manufacturing and shipping cost amounts to $100 per headset.

a. What is the greatest profit your company can make in a week, and how many headsets will your company sell at this level of profit? (Give answers to the nearest whole number.)

b. How much, to the nearest $1, should your company charge per headset for the maximum profit?

---

[3] Demand equation based on second- and fourth-quarter sales. Source: Embedded.com/Company reports December, 2004.

[4] Demand equation based on estimated 2004 sales and projected 2008 sales. Source: I-Stat/NDR, December 2004.

[5] Source for ridership data: *New York Times*, February 10, 2007, p. A9.

[6] $\bar{\bar{Z}}$ designates Zonars, the official currency in Mars. See www.marsnext.com for details of the Mars colony, its commerce, and its culture.

[7] Based on data for the period 1915–1929. Source: Henry Schultz, *The Theory and Measurement of Demand*, (as cited in *Introduction to Mathematical Economics* by A. L. Ostrosky, Jr., and J. V. Koch, Waveland Press, Prospect Heights, Illinois, 1979).

[8] Data are provided for the years 1951–1958. Source: U.S. Department of Agriculture, *Agricultural Statistics*.

[9] Source: Embedded.com/Company reports, December 2004.

[10] Wholesale price projections are the authors'. Source for sales prediction: I-Stat/NDR, December 2004.

36. ▼ *Profit* Due to sales by a competing company, your company's sales of virtual reality video headsets have dropped, and your financial consultant revises the demand equation to

$$p = \frac{800}{q^{0.35}}$$

where q is the total number of headsets that your company can sell in a week at a price of p dollars. The total manufacturing and shipping cost still amounts to $100 per headset.

   a. What is the greatest profit your company can make in a week, and how many headsets will your company sell at this level of profit? (Give answers to the nearest whole number.)
   b. How much, to the nearest $1, should your company charge per headset for the maximum profit?

37. *Paint Cans* A company manufactures cylindrical paint cans with open tops with a volume of 27,000 cubic centimeters. What should be the dimensions of the cans in order to use the least amount of metal in their production? HINT [See Example 4.]

38. *Metal Drums* A company manufactures cylindrical metal drums with open tops with a volume of 1 cubic meter. What should be the dimensions of the drum in order to use the least amount of metal in their production? HINT [See Example 4.]

39. *Tin Cans* A company manufactures cylindrical tin cans with closed tops with a volume of 250 cubic centimeters. The metal used to manufacture the cans costs $0.01 per square cm for the sides and $0.02 per square cm for the (thicker) top and bottom. What should be the dimensions of the cans in order to minimize the cost of metal in their production? What is the ratio height/radius? HINT [See Example 4.]

40. *Metal Drums* A company manufactures cylindrical metal drums with open tops with a volume of 2 cubic meters. The metal used to manufacture the cans costs $2 per square meter for the sides and $3 per square meter for the (thicker) bottom. What should be the dimensions of the drums in order to minimize the cost of metal in their production? What is the ratio height/radius? HINT [See Example 4.]

41. ▼ *Box Design* Chocolate Box Company is going to make open-topped boxes out of 6×16-inch rectangles of cardboard by cutting squares out of the corners and folding up the sides. What is the largest volume box it can make this way?

42. ▼ *Box Design* Vanilla Box Company is going to make open-topped boxes out of 12×12-inch rectangles of cardboard by cutting squares out of the corners and folding up the sides. What is the largest volume box it can make this way?

43. ▼ *Box Design* A packaging company is going to make closed boxes, with square bases, that hold 125 cubic centimeters. What are the dimensions of the box that can be built with the least material?

44. ▼ *Box Design* A packaging company is going to make open-topped boxes, with square bases, that hold 108 cubic centimeters. What are the dimensions of the box that can be built with the least material?

45. ▼ *Luggage Dimensions* **American Airlines** requires that the total outside dimensions (length + width + height) of a checked bag not exceed 62 inches.[11] Suppose you want to check a bag whose height equals its width. What is the largest volume bag of this shape that you can check on an **American** flight?

46. ▼ *Luggage Dimensions* **American Airlines** requires that the total outside dimensions (length + width + height) of a carry-on bag not exceed 45 inches.[12] Suppose you want to carry on a bag whose length is twice its height. What is the largest volume bag of this shape that you can carry on an **American** flight?

47. ▼ *Luggage Dimensions* Fly-by-Night Airlines has a peculiar rule about luggage: The length and width of a bag must add up to at most 45 inches, and the width and height must also add up to 45 inches. What are the dimensions of the bag with the largest volume that Fly-by-Night will accept?

48. ▼ *Luggage Dimensions* Fair Weather Airlines has a similar rule. It will accept only bags for which the sum of the length and width is at most 36 inches, while the sum of length, height, and twice the width is at most 72 inches. What are the dimensions of the bag with the largest volume that Fair Weather will accept?

49. ▼ *Package Dimensions* The **U.S. Postal Service (USPS)** will accept packages only if the length plus girth is no more than 108 inches.[13] (See the figure.)

Girth   Length

Assuming that the front face of the package (as shown in the figure) is square, what is the largest volume package that the **USPS** will accept?

50. ▼ *Package Dimensions* **United Parcel Service (UPS)** will accept only packages with a length of no more than 108 inches and length plus girth of no more than 165 inches.[14] (See figure for the preceding exercise.) Assuming that the front face of the package (as shown in the figure) is square, what is the largest volume package that **UPS** will accept?

51. ▼ *Cell Phone Revenues* The number of cell phone subscribers in China in the years 2000–2005 was projected to follow the equation $N(t) = 39t + 68$ million subscribers in year t ($t = 0$ represents January 2000). The average annual revenue per cell phone user was $350 in 2000.[15] If we assume

---

[11] According to information on its Web site (www.aa.com/).
[12] Ibid.
[13] The requirement for packages sent other than Parcel Post, as of September 2008 (www.usps.com/).
[14] The requirement as of September 2008 (www.ups.com/).
[15] Based on a regression of projected figures (coefficients are rounded). Source: Intrinsic Technology/*New York Times*, Nov. 24, 2000, p. C1.

that due to competition the revenue per cell phone user decreases continuously at an annual rate of 30%, we can model the annual revenue as

$$R(t) = 350(39t + 68)e^{-0.3t} \text{ million dollars.}$$

Determine **a.** when to the nearest 0.1 year the revenue was projected to peak and **b.** the revenue, to the nearest $1 million, at that time.

52. ▼ *Cell Phone Revenues* (Refer to Exercise 51.) If we assume instead that the revenue per cell phone user decreases continuously at an annual rate of 20%, we obtain the revenue model

$$R(t) = 350(39t + 68)e^{-0.2t} \text{ million dollars.}$$

Determine **a.** when to the nearest 0.1 year the revenue was projected to peak and **b.** the revenue, to the nearest $1 million, at that time.

53. ▼ *Research and Development* Spending on research and development by drug companies in the United States t years after 1970 can be modeled by

$$S(t) = 2.5e^{0.08t} \text{ billion dollars.} \quad (0 \le t \le 31)$$

The number of new drugs approved by the Federal Drug Administration (FDA) over the same period can be modeled by

$$D(t) = 10 + t \text{ drugs per year.}^{16} \quad (0 \le t \le 31)$$

When was the function $D(t)/S(t)$ at a maximum? What is the maximum value of $D(t)/S(t)$? What does the answer tell you about the cost of developing new drugs?

54. ▼ *Research and Development* (Refer to Exercise 53.) If the number of new drugs approved by the FDA had been $10 + 2t$ new drugs each year, when would the function $D(t)/S(t)$ have reached a maximum? What does the answer tell you about the cost of developing new drugs?

55. ▼ *Asset Appreciation* As the financial consultant to a classic auto dealership, you estimate that the total value (in dollars) of its collection of 1959 Chevrolets and Fords is given by the formula

$$v = 300{,}000 + 1{,}000t^2 \quad (t \ge 5)$$

where t is the number of years from now. You anticipate a continuous inflation rate of 5% per year, so that the discounted (present) value of an item that will be worth $\$v$ in t years' time is

$$p = ve^{-0.05t}.$$

When would you advise the dealership to sell the vehicles to maximize their discounted value?

56. ▼ *Plantation Management* The value of a fir tree in your plantation increases with the age of the tree according to the formula

$$v = \frac{20t}{1 + 0.05t}$$

where t is the age of the tree in years. Given a continuous inflation rate of 5% per year, the discounted (present) value of a newly planted seedling is

$$p = ve^{-0.05t}.$$

At what age (to the nearest year) should you harvest your trees in order to ensure the greatest possible discounted value?

57. ▼ *Marketing Strategy* FeatureRich Software Company has a dilemma. Its new program, Doors-X 10.27, is almost ready to go on the market. However, the longer the company works on it, the better it can make the program and the more it can charge for it. The company's marketing analysts estimate that if it delays t days, it can set the price at $100 + 2t$ dollars. On the other hand, the longer it delays, the more market share they will lose to their main competitor (see the next exercise) so that if it delays t days it will be able to sell $400{,}000 - 2{,}500t$ copies of the program. How many days should FeatureRich delay the release in order to get the greatest revenue?

58. ▼ *Marketing Strategy* FeatureRich Software's main competitor (see previous exercise) is Moon Systems, and Moon is in a similar predicament. Its product, Walls-Y 11.4, could be sold now for $200, but for each day Moon delays, it could increase the price by $4. On the other hand, it could sell 300,000 copies now, but each day it waits will cut sales by 1,500. How many days should Moon delay the release in order to get the greatest revenue?

59. ▼ *Average Profit* The FeatureRich Software Company sells its graphing program, Dogwood, with a volume discount. If a customer buys x copies, then he or she pays[17] $\$500\sqrt{x}$. It cost the company $10,000 to develop the program and $2 to manufacture each copy. If a single customer were to buy all the copies of Dogwood, how many copies would the customer have to buy for FeatureRich Software's average profit per copy to be maximized? How are average profit and marginal profit related at this number of copies?

60. ▼ *Average Profit* Repeat the preceding exercise with the charge to the customer $\$600\sqrt{x}$ and the cost to develop the program $9,000.

61. *Resource Allocation* Your company manufactures automobile alternators, and production is partially automated through the use of robots. Daily operating costs amount to $100 per laborer and $16 per robot. In order to meet production deadlines, the company calculates that the numbers of laborers and robots must satisfy the constraint

$$xy = 10{,}000$$

---

[16] The exponential model for R&D is based on the 1970 and 2001 spending in constant 2001 dollars, while the linear model for new drugs approved is based on the 6-year moving average from data from 1970–2000. Source for data: Pharmaceutical Research and Manufacturers of America, FDA/*New York Times*, April 19, 2002, p. C1.

[17] This is similar to the way site licenses have been structured for the program Maple®.

where x is the number of laborers and y is the number of robots. Assuming that the company wishes to meet production deadlines at a minimum cost, how many laborers and how many robots should it use? HINT [See Example 5.]

62. *Resource Allocation* Your company is the largest sock manufacturer in the solar system, and production is automated through the use of androids and robots. Daily operating costs amount to ₴200 per android and ₴8 per robot.[18] In order to meet production deadlines, the company calculates that the numbers of androids and robots must satisfy the constraint

$$xy = 1,000,000$$

where x is the number of androids and y is the number of robots. Assuming that the company wishes to meet production deadlines at a minimum cost, how many androids and how many robots should it use? HINT [See Example 5.]

63. ▼ *Resource Allocation* Your automobile assembly plant has a Cobb-Douglas production function given by

$$q = x^{0.4}y^{0.6}$$

where q is the number of automobiles it produces per year, x is the number of employees, and y is the daily operating budget (in dollars). Annual operating costs amount to an average of $20,000 per employee plus the operating budget of $365y$. Assume that you wish to produce 1,000 automobiles per year at a minimum cost. How many employees should you hire? HINT [See Example 5.]

64. ▼ *Resource Allocation* Repeat the preceding exercise using the production formula

$$q = x^{0.5}y^{0.5}.$$

HINT [See Example 5.]

65. ▼ *Incarceration Rate* The incarceration rate (the number of persons in prison per 100,000 residents) in the United States can be approximated by

$$N(t) = 0.04t^3 - 2t^2 + 40t + 460 \quad (0 \le t \le 18)$$

(t is the year since 1990).[19] When, to the nearest year, was the incarceration rate increasing most rapidly? When was it increasing least rapidly? HINT [You are being asked to find the extreme values of the rate of change of the incarceration rate.]

66. ▼ *Prison Population* The prison population in the United States can be approximated by

$$N(t) = 0.02t^3 - 2t^2 + 100t + 1,100 \text{ thousand people}$$
$$(0 \le t \le 18)$$

(t is the year since 1990).[20] When, to the nearest year, was the prison population increasing most rapidly? When was it increasing least rapidly? HINT [You are being asked to find the extreme values of the rate of change of the prison population.]

67. ▼ *Embryo Development* The oxygen consumption of a bird embryo increases from the time the egg is laid through the time the chick hatches. In a typical galliform bird, the oxygen consumption can be approximated by

$$c(t) = -0.065t^3 + 3.4t^2 - 22t + 3.6 \text{ milliliters per day}$$
$$(8 \le t \le 30)$$

where t is the time (in days) since the egg was laid.[21] (An egg will typically hatch at around $t = 28$.) When, to the nearest day, is $c'(t)$ a maximum? What does the answer tell you?

68. ▼ *Embryo Development* The oxygen consumption of a turkey embryo increases from the time the egg is laid through the time the chick hatches. In a brush turkey, the oxygen consumption can be approximated by

$$c(t) = -0.028t^3 + 2.9t^2 - 44t + 95 \text{ milliliters per day}$$
$$(20 \le t \le 50)$$

where t is the time (in days) since the egg was laid.[22] (An egg will typically hatch at around $t = 50$.) When, to the nearest day, is $c'(t)$ a maximum? What does the answer tell you?

69. ▢ ▼ *Subprime Mortgages* The percentage of U.S.-issued mortgages that are subprime can be approximated by

$$A(t) = \frac{15.0}{1 + 8.6(1.8)^{-t}} \text{ percent} \quad (0 \le t \le 8)$$

t years after the start of 2000.[23] Graph the *derivative* of $A(t)$ and determine the year during which this derivative had an absolute maximum and also its value at that point. What does the answer tell you?

70. ▢ ▼ *Subprime Mortgage Debt* The approximate value of subprime (normally classified as risky) mortgage debt outstanding in the United States can be approximated by

$$A(t) = \frac{1,350}{1 + 4.2(1.7)^{-t}} \text{ billion dollars} \quad (0 \le t \le 8)$$

t years after the start of 2000.[24] Graph the *derivative* of $A(t)$ and determine the year during which this derivative had an absolute maximum and also its value at that point. What does the answer tell you?

71. ▢ ▼ *Asset Appreciation* You manage a small antique company that owns a collection of Louis XVI jewelry boxes. Their value v is increasing according to the formula

$$v = \frac{10,000}{1 + 500e^{-0.5t}}$$

---

[18] ₴ are Standard Solar Units of currency.

[19] Source for data: Sourcebook of Criminal Justice Statistics Online (www.albany.edu/sourcebook).

[20] Ibid.

[21] The model approximates graphical data published in the article "The Brush Turkey" by Roger S. Seymour, *Scientific American,* December, 1991, pp. 108–114.

[22] Ibid.

[23] Sources: Mortgage Bankers Association, UBS.

[24] Source: www.data360.org/dataset.aspx?Data_Set_Id=9549.

where t is the number of years from now. You anticipate an inflation rate of 5% per year, so that the present value of an item that will be worth $\$v$ in t years' time is given by

$$p = v(1.05)^{-t}.$$

When (to the nearest year) should you sell the jewelry boxes to maximize their present value? How much (to the nearest constant dollar) will they be worth at that time?

72. [T] ▼ *Harvesting Forests* The following equation models the approximate volume in cubic feet of a typical Douglas fir tree of age t years.[25]

$$V = \frac{22,514}{1 + 22,514t^{-2.55}}$$

The lumber will be sold at $10 per cubic foot, and you do not expect the price of lumber to appreciate in the foreseeable future. On the other hand, you anticipate a general inflation rate of 5% per year, so that the present value of an item that will be worth $\$v$ in t years' time is given by

$$p = v(1.05)^{-t}.$$

At what age (to the nearest year) should you harvest a Douglas fir tree in order to maximize its present value? How much (to the nearest constant dollar) will a Douglas fir tree be worth at that time?

73. ◆ *Agriculture* The fruit yield per tree in an orchard containing 50 trees is 100 pounds per tree each year. Due to crowding, the yield decreases by 1 pound per season for every additional tree planted. How may additional trees should be planted for a maximum total annual yield?

74. ◆ *Agriculture* Two years ago your orange orchard contained 50 trees and the total yield was 75 bags of oranges. Last year you removed ten of the trees and noticed that the total yield increased to 80 bags. Assuming that the yield per tree depends linearly on the number of trees in the orchard, what should you do this year to maximize your total yield?

75. ◆ *Revenue* (based on a question on the GRE Economics Test[26]) If total revenue (TR) is specified by $TR = a + bQ - cQ^2$, where Q is quantity of output and a, b, and c are positive parameters, then TR is maximized for this firm when it produces Q equal to:

(A) $b/2ac$ **(B)** $b/4c$ **(C)** $(a+b)/c$ **(D)** $b/2c$ **(E)** $c/2b$

76. ◆ *Revenue* (based on a question on the GRE Economics Test) If total demand (Q) is specified by $Q = -aP + b$, where P is unit price and a and b are positive parameters, then

total revenue is maximized for this firm when it charges P equal to:

(A) $b/2a$ **(B)** $b/4a$ **(C)** a/b **(D)** $a/2b$ **(E)** $-b/2a$

COMMUNICATION AND REASONING EXERCISES

77. You are interested in knowing the height of the tallest condominium complex that meets the city zoning requirements that the height H should not exceed eight times the distance D from the road and that it must provide parking for at least 50 cars. The objective function of the associated optimization problem is then:

(A) H **(B)** $H - 8D$ **(C)** D **(D)** $D - 8H$

One of the constraints is:

(A) $8H = D$ **(B)** $8D = H$
(C) $H'(D) = 0$ **(D)** $D'(H) = 0$

78. You are interested in building a condominium complex with a height H of at least 8 times the distance D from the road and parking area of at least 1,000 sq ft. at the cheapest cost C. The objective function of the associated optimization problem is then:

(A) H **(B)** D **(C)** C **(D)** $H + D - C$

One of the constraints is:

(A) $H - 8D = 0$ **(B)** $H + D - C = 0$
(C) $C'(D) = 0$ **(D)** $8H = D$

79. Explain why the following problem is uninteresting: A packaging company wishes to make cardboard boxes with open tops by cutting square pieces from the corners of a square sheet of cardboard and folding up the sides. What is the box with the least surface area it can make this way?

80. Explain why finding the production level that minimizes a cost function is frequently uninteresting. What would a more interesting objective be?

81. Your friend Margo claims that all you have to do to find the absolute maxima and minima in applications is set the derivative equal to zero and solve. "All that other stuff about endpoints and so-on is a waste of time just to make life hard for us," according to Margo. Explain why she is wrong, and find at least one exercise in this exercise set to illustrate your point.

82. You are having a hard time persuading your friend Marco that maximizing revenue is not the same as maximizing profit. "How on earth can you expect to obtain the largest profit if you are not taking in the largest revenue?" Explain why he is wrong, and find at least one exercise in this exercise set to illustrate your point.

83. ▼ If demand q decreases as price p increases, what does the minimum value of dq/dp measure?

84. ▼ Explain how you would solve an optimization problem of the following form. Maximize $P = f(x, y, z)$ subject to $z = g(x, y)$ and $y = h(x)$.

---

[25] The model is the authors' and is based on data in *Environmental and Natural Resource Economics* by Tom Tietenberg, Third Edition, (New York: HarperCollins, 1992), p. 282.

[26] Source: GRE Economics Test, by G. Gallagher, G. E. Pollock, W. J. Simeone, G. Yohe (Piscataway, NJ: Research and Education Association, 1989).

5.3 Higher Order Derivatives: Acceleration and Concavity

The **second derivative** is simply the derivative of the derivative function. To explain why we would be interested in such a thing, we start by discussing one of its interpretations.

Acceleration

Recall that if $s(t)$ represents the position of a car at time t, then its velocity is given by the derivative: $v(t) = s'(t)$. But one rarely drives a car at a constant speed; the velocity itself is changing. The rate at which the velocity is changing is the **acceleration**. Because the derivative measures the rate of change, acceleration is the derivative of velocity: $a(t) = v'(t)$. Because v is the derivative of s, we can express the acceleration in terms of s:

$$a(t) = v'(t) = (s')'(t) = s''(t)$$

That is, a is the derivative of the derivative of s, in other words, the second derivative of s, which we write as s''. (In this context you will often hear the derivative s' referred to as the **first derivative**.)

Second Derivative, Acceleration

If a function f has a derivative that is in turn differentiable, then its **second derivative** is the derivative of the derivative of f, written as f''. If $f''(a)$ exists, we say that f is **twice differentiable at $x = a$.**

Quick Examples

1. If $f(x) = x^3 - x$, then $f'(x) = 3x^2 - 1$, so $f''(x) = 6x$ and $f''(-2) = -12$.
2. If $f(x) = 3x + 1$, then $f'(x) = 3$, so $f''(x) = 0$.
3. If $f(x) = e^x$, then $f'(x) = e^x$, so $f''(x) = e^x$ as well.

The **acceleration** of a moving object is the derivative of its velocity—that is, the second derivative of the position function.

Quick Example

If t is time in hours and the position of a car at time t is $s(t) = t^3 + 2t^2$ miles, then the car's velocity is $v(t) = s'(t) = 3t^2 + 4t$ miles per hour and its acceleration is $a(t) = s''(t) = v'(t) = 6t + 4$ miles per hour per hour.

Differential Notation for the Second Derivative

We have written the second derivative of $f(x)$ as $f''(x)$. We could also use differential notation:

$$f''(x) = \frac{d^2 f}{dx^2}$$

This notation comes from writing the second derivative as the derivative of the derivative in differential notation:

$$f''(x) = \frac{d}{dx}\left[\frac{df}{dx}\right] = \frac{d^2 f}{dx^2}$$

Similarly, if $y = f(x)$, we write $f''(x)$ as $\dfrac{d}{dx}\left[\dfrac{dy}{dx}\right] = \dfrac{d^2y}{dx^2}$. For example, if $y = x^3$, then $\dfrac{d^2y}{dx^2} = 6x$.

An important example of acceleration is the acceleration due to gravity.

EXAMPLE 1 Acceleration Due to Gravity

According to the laws of physics, the height of an object near the surface of the earth falling in a vacuum from an initial rest position 100 feet above the ground under the influence of gravity is approximately

$$s(t) = 100 - 16t^2 \text{ feet}$$

in t seconds. Find its acceleration.

Solution The velocity of the object is

$$v(t) = s'(t) = -32t \text{ ft/s.} \qquad \text{Differential notation: } v = \frac{ds}{dt} = -32t \text{ ft/s.}$$

The reason for the negative sign is that the height of the object is decreasing with time, so its velocity is negative. Hence, the acceleration is

$$a(t) = s''(t) = -32 \text{ ft/s}^2. \qquad \text{Differential notation: } a = \frac{d^2s}{dt^2} = -32 \text{ ft/s}^2.$$

(We write ft/s^2 as an abbreviation for feet/second/second—that is, feet per second per second. It is often read "feet per second squared.") Thus, the *downward* velocity is increasing by 32 ft/s every second. We say that 32 ft/s^2 is the **acceleration due to gravity**. If we ignore air resistance, all falling bodies near the surface of the earth, no matter what their weight, will fall with this acceleration.*

* **NOTE** On other planets the acceleration due to gravity is different. For example, on Jupiter, it is about three times as large as on Earth.

† **NOTE** An interesting aside: Galileo's experiments depended on getting extremely accurate timings. Because the timepieces of his day were very inaccurate, he used the most accurate time measurement he could: He sang and used the beat as his stopwatch.

§ **NOTE** A true story: The point was made again during the Apollo 15 mission to the moon (July 1971) when astronaut David R. Scott dropped a feather and a hammer from the same height. The moon has no atmosphere, so the two hit the surface of the moon simultaneously.

➡ **Before we go on...** In very careful experiments using balls rolling down inclined planes, Galileo made one of his most important discoveries—that the acceleration due to gravity is constant and does not depend on the weight or composition of the object falling.† A famous, though probably apocryphal, story has him dropping cannonballs of different weights off the Leaning Tower of Pisa to prove his point.§ ■

EXAMPLE 2 Acceleration of Sales

For the first 15 months after the introduction of a new video game, the total sales can be modeled by the curve

$$S(t) = 20e^{0.4t} \text{ units sold}$$

where t is the time in months since the game was introduced. After about 25 months total sales follow more closely the curve

$$S(t) = 100,000 - 20e^{17-0.4t}$$

How fast are total sales accelerating after 10 months? How fast are they accelerating after 30 months? What do these numbers mean?

Solution By acceleration we mean the rate of change of the rate of change, which is the second derivative. During the first 15 months, the first derivative of sales is

$$\frac{dS}{dt} = 8e^{0.4t}$$

and so the second derivative is

$$\frac{d^2S}{dt^2} = 3.2e^{0.4t}$$

Thus, after 10 months the acceleration of sales is

$$\frac{d^2S}{dt^2}\bigg|_{t=10} = 3.2e^4 \approx 175 \text{ units/month/month, or units/month}^2$$

We can also compute total sales

$$S(10) = 20e^4 \approx 1{,}092 \text{ units}$$

and the rate of change of sales

$$\frac{dS}{dt}\bigg|_{t=10} = 8e^4 \approx 437 \text{ units/month.}$$

What do these numbers mean? By the end of the tenth month, a total of 1,092 video games have been sold. At that time the game is selling at the rate of 437 units per month. This rate of sales is increasing by 175 units per month per month. More games will be sold each month than the month before.

   To analyze the sales after 30 months is similar, using the formula

$$S(t) = 100{,}000 - 20e^{17-0.4t}.$$

The derivative is

$$\frac{dS}{dt} = 8e^{17-0.4t}$$

and the second derivative is

$$\frac{d^2S}{dt^2} = -3.2e^{17-0.4t}.$$

After 30 months,

$$S(30) = 100{,}000 - 20e^{17-12} \approx 97{,}032 \text{ units}$$

$$\frac{dS}{dt}\bigg|_{t=30} = 8e^{17-12} \approx 1{,}187 \text{ units/month}$$

$$\frac{d^2S}{dt^2}\bigg|_{t=30} = -3.2e^{17-12} \approx -475 \text{ units/month}^2.$$

By the end of the 30th month, 97,032 video games have been sold, the game is selling at a rate of 1,187 units per month, and the rate of sales is *decreasing* by 475 units per month. Fewer games are sold each month than the month before.

Geometric Interpretation of Second Derivative: Concavity

The first derivative of f tells us where the graph of f is rising [where $f'(x) > 0$] and where it is falling [where $f'(x) < 0$]. The second derivative tells in what direction the graph of f *curves* or *bends*. Consider the graphs in Figures 25 and 26.

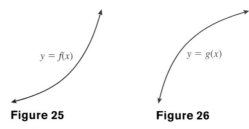

$y = f(x)$ $y = g(x)$

Figure 25   **Figure 26**

Think of a car driving from left to right along each of the roads shown in the two figures. A car driving along the graph of f in Figure 25 will turn to the left (upward); a car driving along the graph of g in Figure 26 will turn to the right (downward). We say that the graph of f is **concave up** and the graph of g is **concave down**. Now think about the derivatives of f and g. The derivative $f'(x)$ starts small but *increases* as the graph gets steeper. Because $f'(x)$ is increasing, its derivative $f''(x)$ must be positive. On the other hand, $g'(x)$ *decreases* as we go to the right. Because $g'(x)$ is decreasing, its derivative $g''(x)$ must be negative. Summarizing, we have the following.

Concavity and the Second Derivative

A curve is **concave up** if its slope is increasing, in which case the second derivative is positive. A curve is **concave down** if its slope is decreasing, in which case the second derivative is negative. A point in the domain of f where the graph of f changes concavity, from concave up to concave down or vice versa, is called a **point of inflection**. At a point of inflection, the second derivative is either zero or undefined.

Locating Points of Inflection

To locate possible points of inflection, list points where $f''(x) = 0$ and also points where $f''(x)$ is not defined.

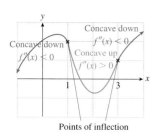

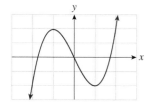

Concave down $f''(x) < 0$

Concave down $f''(x) < 0$

Concave up $f''(x) > 0$

Points of inflection

Figure 27

Figure 28

> ### Quick Examples
>
> 1. The graph of the function f shown in Figure 27 is concave up when $1 < x < 3$, so $f''(x) > 0$ for $1 < x < 3$. It is concave down when $x < 1$ and $x > 3$, so $f''(x) < 0$ when $x < 1$ and $x > 3$. It has points of inflection at $x = 1$ and $x = 3$.
> 2. Consider $f(x) = x^3 - 3x$, whose graph is shown in Figure 28. $f''(x) = 6x$ is negative when $x < 0$ and positive when $x > 0$. The graph of f is concave down when $x < 0$ and concave up when $x > 0$. f has a point of inflection at $x = 0$, where the second derivative is 0.

The following example shows one of the reasons it's useful to look at concavity.

EXAMPLE 3 Inflation

Figure 29 shows the value of the U.S. Consumer Price Index (CPI) from January 2007 through June 2008.*

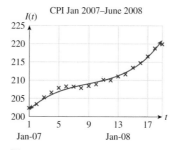

CPI Jan 2007–June 2008

Jan-07   Jan-08

Figure 29

The approximating curve shown on the figure is given by

$$I(t) = 0.0075t^3 - 0.2t^2 + 2.2t + 200 \qquad (1 \le t \le 19)$$

---

* The CPI is compiled by the Bureau of Labor Statistics and is based upon a 1982 value of 100. For instance, a CPI of 200 means the CPI has doubled since 1982. Source: InflationData.com (www.inflationdata.com).

where t is time in months ($t = 1$ represents January 2007). When the CPI is increasing, the U.S. economy is **experiencing inflation**. In terms of the model, this means that the derivative is positive: $I'(t) > 0$. Notice that $I'(t) > 0$ for the entire period shown (the graph is sloping upward), so the U.S. economy experienced inflation for $1 \leq t \leq 19$. We could measure **inflation** by the first derivative $I'(t)$ of the CPI, but we traditionally measure it as a ratio:

$$\text{Inflation rate} = \frac{I'(t)}{I(t)}, \qquad \text{Relative rate of change of the CPI}$$

expressed as a percentage per unit time (per month in this case).

a. Use the model to estimate the inflation rate in January 2008.

b. Was inflation slowing or speeding up in January 2008?

c. When was inflation slowing? When was inflation speeding up? When was inflation slowest?

Solution

a. We need to compute $I'(t)$:

$$I'(t) = 0.0225t^2 - 0.4t + 2.2$$

Thus, the inflation rate in January 2008 was given by

$$\text{Inflation rate} = \frac{I'(13)}{I(13)} = \frac{0.0225(13)^2 - 0.4(13) + 2.2}{0.0075(13)^3 - 0.2(13)^2 + 2.2(13) + 200}$$

$$= \frac{0.8025}{211.2775} \approx 0.00380,$$

or 0.38% per month.*

b. We say that inflation is "slowing" when the CPI is decelerating ($I''(t) < 0$; the index rises at a slower rate). Similarly, inflation is "speeding up" when the CPI is accelerating ($I''(t) > 0$; the index rises at a faster rate). From the formula for $I'(t)$, the second derivative is

$$I''(t) = 0.045t - 0.4$$
$$I''(13) = 0.045(13) - 0.4 = 0.185.$$

Because this quantity is positive, we conclude that inflation was speeding up in January 2008.

c. When inflation is slowing, $I''(t)$ is negative, so the graph of the CPI is concave down. When inflation is speeding up, it is concave up. At the point at which it switches, there is point of inflection (Figure 30).

✳ NOTE The 0.38% monthly inflation rate corresponds to a $12 \times 0.38 = 4.56\%$ annual inflation rate. This result could be obtained directly by changing the units of the t-axis from months to years and then redoing the calculation.

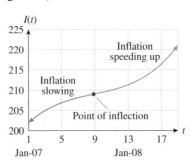

Figure 30

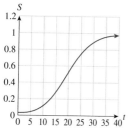

(a) Graph of S

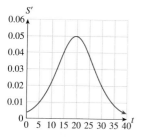

(b) Graph of S'

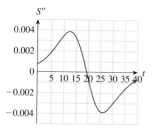

(c) Graph of S''

Figure 31

using Technology

We can use a TI-83/84 Plus or a downloadable Excel sheet at the Web site to graph the second derivative of the function in Example 4:

TI-83/84 Plus

Y₁=1/(1+50*e^(-0.2X))
Y₂=nDeriv(Y₁,X,X)
Y₃=nDeriv(Y₂,X,X)

Web Site

www.AppliedCalc.org

Student Web Site
→ Online Utilities
→ Excel First and Second
  Derivative Graphing Utility

Function:

1/(1+50*exp(-0.2*x))

The point of inflection occurs when $I''(t) = 0$; that is,

$$0.045t - 0.4 = 0$$

$$t = \frac{0.4}{0.45} \approx 8.9.$$

Thus, inflation was slowing when $t < 8.9$ (that is, until the end of August), and speeding up when $t > 8.9$ (after that time). Inflation was slowest at the point when it stopped slowing down and began to speed up, $t \approx 8.9$; notice that the graph has the least slope at that point.

EXAMPLE 4 The Point of Diminishing Returns

After the introduction of a new video game, the total worldwide sales are modeled by the curve

$$S(t) = \frac{1}{1 + 50e^{-0.2t}} \text{ million units sold}$$

where t is the time in months since the game was introduced (compare Example 2). The graphs of $S(t)$, $S'(t)$, and $S''(t)$ are shown in Figure 31. Where is the graph of S concave up, and where is it concave down? Where are any points of inflection? What does this all mean?

Solution Look at the graph of S. We see that the graph of S is concave up in the early months and then becomes concave down later. The point of inflection, where the concavity changes, is somewhere between 15 and 25 months.

Now look at the graph of S''. This graph crosses the t-axis very close to $t = 20$, is positive before that point, and negative after that point. Because positive values of S'' indicate S is concave up and negative values concave down, we conclude that the graph of S is concave up for about the first 20 months; that is, for $0 < t < 20$ and concave down for $20 < t < 40$. The concavity switches at the point of inflection, which occurs at about $t = 20$ (when $S''(t) = 0$; a more accurate answer is $t \approx 19.56$).

What does this all mean? Look at the graph of S', which shows sales per unit time, or monthly sales. From this graph we see that monthly sales are increasing for $t < 20$: more units are being sold each month than the month before. Monthly sales reach a peak of 0.05 million = 50,000 games per month at the point of inflection $t = 20$ and then begin to drop off. Thus, the point of inflection occurs at the time when monthly sales stop increasing and start to fall off; that is, the time when monthly sales peak. The point of inflection is sometimes called the **point of diminishing returns**. Although the total sales figure continues to rise (see the graph of S: game units continue to be sold), the *rate* at which units are sold starts to drop. (See Figure 32.)

Figure 32

The Second Derivative Test for Relative Extrema

The second derivative often gives us a way of knowing whether or not a stationary point is a relative extremum. Figure 33 shows a graph with two stationary points: a relative maximum at $x = a$ and a relative minimum at $x = b$.

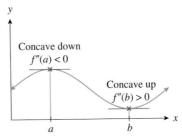

Figure 33

Notice that the curve is *concave down* at the relative maximum ($x = a$), so that $f''(a) < 0$, and *concave up* at the relative minimum ($x = b$), so that $f''(b) > 0$. This suggests the following (compare the First Derivative Test in Section 5.1).

Second Derivative Test for Relative Extrema

Suppose that the function f has a stationary point at $x = c$, and that $f''(c)$ exists. Determine the sign of $f''(c)$.

1. If $f''(c) > 0$ then f has a relative minimum at $x = c$.

2. If $f''(c) < 0$ then f has a relative maximum at $x = c$.

If $f''(c) = 0$ then the test is inconclusive and you need to use one of the methods of Section 5.1 (such as the first derivative test) to determine whether or not f has a relative extremum at $x = c$.

Quick Examples

1. $f(x) = x^2 - 2x$ has $f'(x) = 2x - 2$ and hence a stationary point at $x = 1$. $f''(x) = 2$, and so $f''(1) = 2$, which is positive, so f has a relative minimum at $x = 1$.

2. Let $f(x) = x^3 - 3x^2 - 9x$. Then
$f'(x) = 3x^2 - 6x - 9 = 3(x + 1)(x - 3)$
Stationary points at $x = -1, x = 3$
$f''(x) = 6x - 6$
$f''(-1) = -12$, so there is a relative maximum at $x = -1$
$f''(3) = 12$, so there is a relative minimum at $x = 3$.

3. $f(x) = x^4$ has $f'(x) = 4x^3$ and hence a stationary point at $x = 0$. $f''(x) = 12x^2$ and so $f''(0) = 0$, telling us that the second derivative test is inconclusive. However, we can see from the graph of f or the first derivative test that f has a minimum at $x = 0$.

Higher Order Derivatives

There is no reason to stop at the second derivative; we could once again take the *derivative* of the second derivative to obtain the **third derivative**, f''', and we could take the derivative once again to obtain the **fourth derivative**, written $f^{(4)}$, and then continue to obtain $f^{(5)}$, $f^{(6)}$, and so on (assuming we get a differentiable function at each stage).

Higher Order Derivatives

We define

$$f'''(x) = \frac{d}{dx}[f''(x)]$$

$$f^{(4)}(x) = \frac{d}{dx}[f'''(x)]$$

$$f^{(5)}(x) = \frac{d}{dx}[f^{(4)}(x)],$$

and so on, assuming all these derivatives exist.

Different Notations

$$f'(x), f''(x), f'''(x), f^{(4)}(x), \ldots, f^{(n)}(x), \ldots$$

$$\frac{df}{dx}, \frac{d^2f}{dx^2}, \frac{d^3f}{dx^3}, \frac{d^4f}{dx^4}, \ldots, \frac{d^nf}{dx^n}, \ldots$$

$$\frac{dy}{dx}, \frac{d^2y}{dx^2}, \frac{d^3y}{dx^3}, \frac{d^4y}{dx^4}, \ldots, \frac{d^ny}{dx^n}, \ldots \qquad \text{When } y = f(x)$$

$$y, y', y'', y''', y^{(4)}, \ldots, y^{(n)}, \ldots \qquad \text{When } y = f(x)$$

Quick Examples

1. If $f(x) = x^3 - x$, then $f'(x) = 3x^2 - 1$, $f''(x) = 6x$, $f'''(x) = 6$, $f^{(4)}(x) = f^{(5)}(x) = \cdots = 0$.
2. If $f(x) = e^x$, then $f'(x) = e^x$, $f''(x) = e^x$, $f'''(x) = e^x$, $f^{(4)}(x) = f^{(5)}(x) = \cdots = e^x$.

Q: *We know that the second derivative can be interpreted as acceleration. How do we interpret the third derivative; and the fourth, fifth, and so on?*

A: Think of a car traveling down the road (with position $s(t)$ at time t) in such a way that its acceleration $\dfrac{d^2s}{dt^2}$ is changing with time (for instance, the driver may be slowly increasing pressure on the accelerator, causing the car to accelerate at a greater and greater rate). Then $\dfrac{d^3s}{dt^3}$ is the rate of change of acceleration. $\dfrac{d^4s}{dt^4}$ would then be the *acceleration* of the acceleration, and so on.

Q: *How are these higher order derivatives reflected in the graph of a function f?*

A: Because the concavity is measured by f'', its derivative f''' tells us the rate of change of concavity. Similarly, $f^{(4)}$ would tell us the *acceleration* of concavity, and so on. These properties are very subtle and hard to discern by simply looking at the curve; the higher the order, the more subtle the property. There is a remarkable theorem by Taylor* that tells us that, for a large class of functions (including polynomial, exponential, logarithmic, and trigonometric functions) the values of all orders of derivative $f(a)$, $f'(a)$, $f''(a)$, $f'''(a)$, and so on at the single point $x = a$ are enough to describe the entire graph (even at points very far from $x = a$)! In other words, the smallest piece of a graph near any point a contains sufficient information to "clone" the entire graph!

✳ NOTE Brook Taylor (1685–1731) was an English mathematician.

FAQs

Interpreting Points of Inflection and Using the Second Derivative Test

Q: *It says in Example 4 that monthly sales reach a maximum at the point of inflection (second derivative is zero), but the Second Derivative test says that, for a maximum, the second derivative must be positive. What is going on here?*

A: What is a maximum in Example 4 is the *rate of change of* sales: which is measured in sales per unit time (monthly sales in the example). In other words, it is the *derivative* of the total sales function that is a maximum, so we located the maximum by setting its derivative (which is the *second* derivative of total sales) equal to zero. In general: To find relative (stationary) extrema of the *original* function, set $f'(x)$ equal to zero and solve for x as usual. The second derivative test can then be used to test the stationary point obtained. To find relative (stationary) extrema of the *rate of change of* f, set $f''(x) = 0$ and solve for x.

Q: *I used the second derivative test and it was inconclusive. That means that there is neither a relative maximum nor a relative minimum at $x = a$, right?*

A: Wrong. If (as is often the case) the second derivative is zero at a stationary point, all it means is that the second derivative test itself cannot determine whether the given point is a relative maximum, minimum, or neither. For instance, $f(x) = x^4$ has a stationary minimum at $x = 0$, but the second derivative test is inconclusive. In such cases, one should use another test (such as the first derivative test) to decide if the point is a relative maximum, minimum, or neither.

5.3 **EXERCISES**

▼ more advanced   ◆ challenging
🍦 indicates exercises that should be solved using technology

In Exercises 1–10, calculate $\dfrac{d^2y}{dx^2}$. HINT [See Quick Examples on page 398.]

1. $y = 3x^2 - 6$

2. $y = -x^2 + x$

3. $y = \dfrac{2}{x}$

4. $y = -\dfrac{2}{x^2}$

5. $y = 4x^{0.4} - x$

6. $y = 0.2x^{-0.1}$

7. $y = e^{-(x-1)} - x$

8. $y = e^{-x} + e^x$

9. $y = \dfrac{1}{x} - \ln x$

10. $y = x^{-2} + \ln x$

In Exercises 11–16, the position s of a point (in feet) is given as a function of time t (in seconds). Find (a) its acceleration as a function of t and (b) its acceleration at the specified time. HINT [See Example 1.]

11. $s = 12 + 3t - 16t^2; t = 2$

12. $s = -12 + t - 16t^2; t = 2$

13. $s = \dfrac{1}{t} + \dfrac{1}{t^2}; t = 1$ **14.** $s = \dfrac{1}{t} - \dfrac{1}{t^2}; t = 2$

15. $s = \sqrt{t} + t^2; t = 4$ **16.** $s = 2\sqrt{t} + t^3; t = 1$

In Exercises 17–24, the graph of a function is given. Find the approximate coordinates of all points of inflection of each function (if any). HINT [See Quick Examples on page 401.]

17.
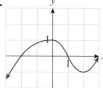

18.
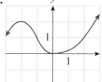

19.
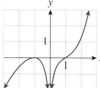

20.
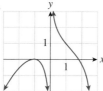

21.
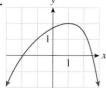

22.
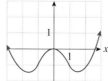

23.
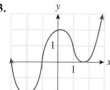

24.
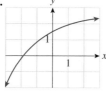

In Exercises 25–28, the graph of the derivative, $f'(x)$, is given. Determine the x-coordinates of all points of inflection of $f(x)$, if any. (Assume that $f(x)$ is defined and continuous everywhere in $[-3, 3]$.) HINT [See the **Before we go on** discussion in Example 4.]

25.
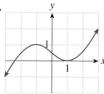

26.
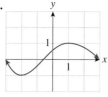

27.
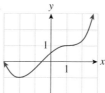

28.
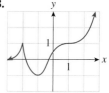

In Exercises 29–32, the graph of the second derivative, $f''(x)$, is given. Determine the x-coordinates of all points of inflection of $f(x)$, if any. (Assume that $f(x)$ is defined and continuous everywhere in $[-3, 3]$.)

29.
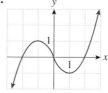

30.
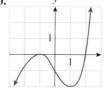

31.
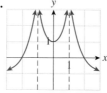

32.
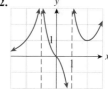

In Exercises 33–44, find the x-coordinates of all critical points of the given function. Determine whether each critical point is a relative maximum, minimum, or neither by first applying the second derivative test, and, if the test fails, by some other method. HINT [See Quick Examples on page 404.]

33. $f(x) = x^2 - 4x + 1$ **34.** $f(x) = 2x^2 - 2x + 3$

35. $g(x) = x^3 - 12x$ **36.** $g(x) = 2x^3 - 6x + 3$

37. $f(t) = t^3 - t$ **38.** $f(t) = -2t^3 + 3t$

39. $f(x) = x^4 - 4x^3$ **40.** $f(x) = 3x^4 - 2x^3$

41. $f(x) = e^{-x^2}$ **42.** $f(x) = e^{2-x^2}$

43. $f(x) = xe^{1-x^2}$ **44.** $f(x) = xe^{-x^2}$

In Exercises 45–54, calculate the derivatives of all orders: $f'(x), f''(x), f'''(x), f^{(4)}(x), \ldots, f^{(n)}(x), \ldots$ HINT [See Quick Examples on page 405.]

45. $f(x) = 4x^2 - x + 1$ **46.** $f(x) = -3x^3 + 4x$

47. $f(x) = -x^4 + 3x^2$ **48.** $f(x) = x^4 + x^3$

49. $f(x) = (2x + 1)^4$ **50.** $f(x) = (-2x + 1)^3$

51. $f(x) = e^{-x}$ **52.** $f(x) = e^{2x}$

53. $f(x) = e^{3x-1}$ **54.** $f(x) = 2e^{-x+3}$

APPLICATIONS

55. *Acceleration on Mars* If a stone is dropped from a height of 40 meters above the Martian surface, its height in meters after t seconds is given by $s = 40 - 1.9t^2$. What is its acceleration? HINT [See Example 1.]

56. Acceleration on the Moon If a stone is thrown up at 10 m per second from a height of 100 meters above the surface of the Moon, its height in meters after t seconds is given by $s = 100 + 10t - 0.8t^2$. What is its acceleration? HINT [See Example 1.]

57. Motion in a Straight Line The position of a particle moving in a straight line is given by $s = t^3 - t^2$ ft after t seconds. Find an expression for its acceleration after a time t. Is its velocity increasing or decreasing when $t = 1$?

58. Motion in a Straight Line The position of a particle moving in a straight line is given by $s = 3e^t - 8t^2$ ft after t seconds. Find an expression for its acceleration after a time t. Is its velocity increasing or decreasing when $t = 1$?

59. Bottled Water Sales Annual sales of bottled water in the United States in the period 2000–2008 can be approximated by

$$R(t) = 12t^2 + 500t + 4{,}700 \text{ million gallons} \quad (0 \le t \le 8)$$

where t is time in years since 2000.[27] Were sales of bottled water accelerating or decelerating in 2004? How quickly? HINT [See Example 2.]

60. Bottled Water Sales Annual U.S. per capita sales of bottled water through the period 2000–2008 can be approximated by

$$Q(t) = 0.04t^2 + 1.5t + 17 \text{ gallons} \quad (0 \le t \le 8)$$

where t is time in years since 2000.[28] Were U.S. per capita sales of bottled water accelerating or decelerating in 2006? How quickly?

61. Embryo Development The daily oxygen consumption of a bird embryo increases from the time the egg is laid through the time the chick hatches. In a typical galliform bird, the oxygen consumption can be approximated by

$$c(t) = -0.065t^3 + 3.4t^2 - 22t + 3.6 \text{ ml} \quad (8 \le t \le 30)$$

where t is the time (in days) since the egg was laid.[29] (An egg will typically hatch at around $t = 28$.) Use the model to estimate the following (give the units of measurement for each answer and round all answers to two significant digits):

a. The daily oxygen consumption 20 days after the egg was laid

b. The rate at which the oxygen consumption is changing 20 days after the egg was laid

c. The rate at which the oxygen consumption is accelerating 20 days after the egg was laid

62. Embryo Development The daily oxygen consumption of a turkey embryo increases from the time the egg is laid through the time the chick hatches. In a brush turkey, the oxygen consumption can be approximated by

$$c(t) = -0.028t^3 + 2.9t^2 - 44t + 95 \text{ ml} \quad (20 \le t \le 50)$$

where t is the time (in days) since the egg was laid.[30] (An egg will typically hatch at around $t = 50$.) Use the model to estimate the following (give the units of measurement for each answer and round all answers to two significant digits):

a. The daily oxygen consumption 40 days after the egg was laid

b. The rate at which the oxygen consumption is changing 40 days after the egg was laid

c. The rate at which the oxygen consumption is accelerating 40 days after the egg was laid

63. Inflation The following graph shows the approximate value of the United States Consumer Price Index (CPI) from December 2006 through July 2007.[31]

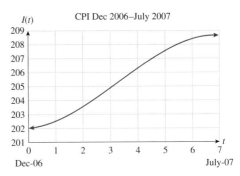

The approximating curve shown on the figure is given by

$$I(t) = -0.04t^3 + 0.4t^2 + 0.1t + 202 \quad (0 \le t \le 7)$$

where t is time in months ($t = 0$ represents December 2006).

a. Use the model to estimate the monthly inflation rate in February 2007 ($t = 2$). [Recall that the inflation *rate* is $I'(t)/I(t)$.]

b. Was inflation slowing or speeding up in February 2007?

c. When was inflation speeding up? When was inflation slowing? HINT [See Example 3.]

64. Inflation The following graph shows the approximate value of the U.S. Consumer Price Index (CPI) from September 2004 through November 2005.[32]

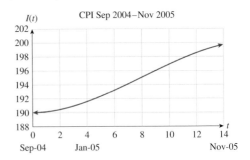

[27] Source for data: Beverage Marketing Corporation (www.bottledwater .org).

[28] Ibid.

[29] The model approximates graphical data published in the article "The Brush Turkey" by Roger S. Seymour, *Scientific American,* December, 1991, pp. 108–114.

[30] Ibid.

[31] The CPI is compiled by the Bureau of Labor Statistics and is based upon a 1982 value of 100. For instance, a CPI of 200 means the CPI has doubled since 1982. Source: InflationData.com (www.inflationdata.com).

[32] Ibid.

The approximating curve shown on the figure is given by

$$I(t) = -0.005t^3 + 0.12t^2 - 0.01t + 190 \quad (0 \le t \le 14)$$

where t is time in months ($t = 0$ represents September 2004).

a. Use the model to estimate the monthly inflation rate in July 2005 ($t = 10$). [Recall that the inflation *rate* is $I'(t)/I(t)$.]

b. Was inflation slowing or speeding up in July 2005?

c. When was inflation speeding up? When was inflation slowing? **HINT** [See Example 3.]

65. *Inflation* The following graph shows the approximate value of the U.S. Consumer Price Index (CPI) from July 2005 through March 2006.[33]

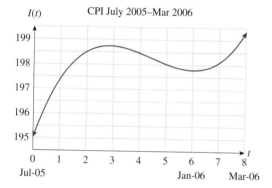

CPI July 2005–Mar 2006

The approximating curve shown on the figure is given by

$$I(t) = 0.06t^3 - 0.8t^2 + 3.1t + 195 \quad (0 \le t \le 8)$$

where t is time in months ($t = 0$ represents July 2005).

a. Use the model to estimate the monthly inflation rates in December 2005 and February 2006 ($t = 5$ and $t = 7$).

b. Was inflation slowing or speeding up in February 2006?

c. When was inflation decreasing? When was inflation increasing?

66. *Inflation* The following graph shows the approximate value of the U.S. Consumer Price Index (CPI) from March 2006 through May 2007.[34]

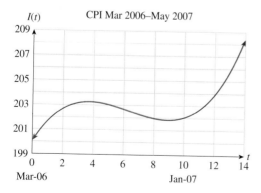

CPI Mar 2006–May 2007

The approximating curve shown on the figure is given by

$$I(t) = 0.02t^3 - 0.38t^2 + 2t + 200 \quad (0 \le t \le 14)$$

where t is time in months ($t = 0$ represents March, 2006).

a. Use the model to estimate the monthly inflation rates in September 2006 and January 2007 ($t = 6$ and $t = 10$).

b. Was inflation slowing or speeding up in January 2007?

c. When was inflation decreasing? When was inflation increasing?

67. *Scientific Research* The percentage of research articles in the prominent journal *Physical Review* that were written by researchers in the United States during the years 1983–2003 can be modeled by

$$P(t) = 25 + \frac{36}{1 + 0.06(0.7)^{-t}}$$

where t is time in years since 1983.[35] The graphs of P, P', and P'' are shown here:

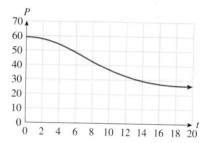

Graph of P

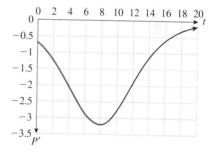

Graph of P'

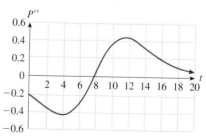

Graph of P''

---

[33] The CPI is compiled by the Bureau of Labor Statistics and is based upon a 1982 value of 100. For instance, a CPI of 200 means the CPI has doubled since 1982. Source: InflationData.com (www.inflationdata.com).

[34] Ibid.

[35] Source: The American Physical Society/*New York Times*, May 3, 2003, p. A1.

Determine, to the nearest whole number, the values of t for which the graph of P is concave up, and where it is concave down, and locate any points of inflection. What does the point of inflection tell you about science articles? HINT [See Example 4.]

68. *Scientific Research* The number of research articles in the prominent journal *Physical Review* that were written by researchers in Europe during the years 1983–2003 can be modeled by

$$P(t) = \frac{7.0}{1 + 5.4(1.2)^{-t}}$$

where t is time in years since 1983.[36] The graphs of P, P', and P'' are shown here:

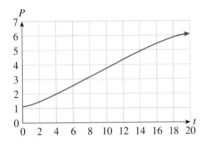

Graph of P

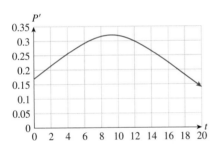

Graph of P'

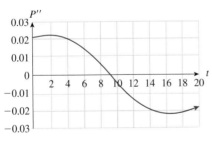

Graph of P''

Determine, to the nearest whole number, the values of t for which the graph of P is concave up, and where it is concave down, and locate any points of inflection. What does the point of inflection tell you about science articles?

[36] Source: The American Physical Society/*New York Times*, May 3, 2003, p. A1.

69. *Embryo Development* Here are sketches of the graphs of c, c', and c'' from Exercise 61:

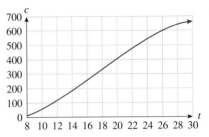

Graph of c

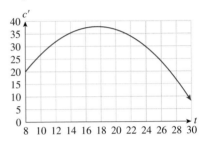

Graph of c'

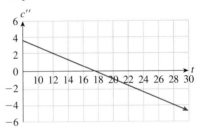

Graph of c''

Multiple choice:

a. The graph of c' **(A)** has a point of inflection **(B)** has no points of inflection in the range shown.

b. At around 18 days after the egg is laid, daily oxygen consumption is: **(A)** at a maximum, **(B)** increasing at a maximum rate, or **(C)** just beginning to decrease.

c. For $t > 18$ days, the oxygen consumption is **(A)** increasing at a decreasing rate, **(B)** decreasing at an increasing rate, or **(C)** increasing at an increasing rate.

70. *Embryo Development* Here are sketches of the graphs of c, c', and c'' from Exercise 62:

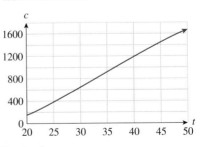

Graph of c

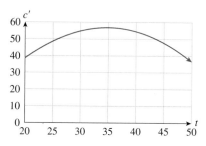

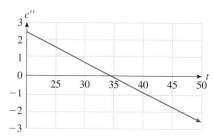

Graph of c'

Graph of c''

Multiple choice:

a. The graph of c: **(A)** has points of inflection, **(B)** has no points of inflection, or **(C)** may or may not have a point of inflection, but the graphs do not provide enough information.

b. At around 35 days after the egg is laid, the rate of change of daily oxygen consumption is: **(A)** at a maximum, **(B)** increasing at a maximum rate, or **(C)** just becoming negative.

c. For $t < 35$ days, the oxygen consumption is: **(A)** increasing at an increasing rate, **(B)** increasing at a decreasing rate, or **(C)** decreasing at an increasing rate.

71. ▣ *Subprime Mortgages* The percentage of U.S.-issued mortgages that are subprime can be approximated by

$$A(t) = \frac{15.0}{1 + 8.6(1.8)^{-t}} \text{ percent} \quad (0 \le t \le 8)$$

t years after the start of 2000.[37] Graph the function as well as its first and second derivatives. Determine, to the nearest whole number, the values of t for which the graph of A is concave up and concave down, and the t-coordinate of any points of inflection. What does the point of inflection tell you about subprime mortgages? HINT [To graph the second derivative, see the note in the margin on page 403.]

72. ▣ *Subprime Mortgage Debt* The approximate value of subprime (normally classified as risky) mortgage debt outstanding in the United States can be approximated by

$$A(t) = \frac{1,350}{1 + 4.2(1.7)^{-t}} \text{ billion dollars} \quad (0 \le t \le 8)$$

t years after the start of 2000.[38] Graph the function as well as its first and second derivatives. Determine, to the nearest whole number, the values of t for which the graph of A is concave up and concave down, and the t-coordinate of any points of inflection. What does the point of inflection tell you about subprime mortgages? HINT [To graph the second derivative, see the note in the margin on page 403.]

73. *Epidemics* The following graph shows the total number n of people (in millions) infected in an epidemic as a function of time t (in years):

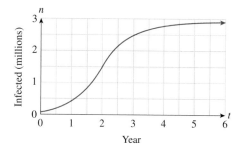

a. When to the nearest year was the rate of new infection largest?

b. When could the Centers for Disease Control and Prevention announce that the rate of new infection was beginning to drop? HINT [See Example 4.]

74. *Sales* The following graph shows the total number of Pomegranate Q4 computers sold since their release (t is in years):

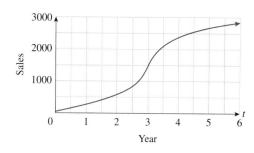

a. When were the computers selling fastest?

b. Explain why this graph might look as it does. HINT [See Example 4.]

---

[37] Sources: Mortgage Bankers Association, UBS.

[38] 2008 figure is an estimate.
Source: www.data360.org/dataset.aspx?Data_Set_Id=9549.

75. *Industrial Output* The following graph shows the yearly industrial output (measured in billions of zonars) of the Republic of Mars over a seven-year period:

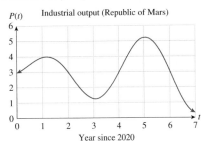

Industrial output (Republic of Mars)

Year since 2020

a. When to the nearest year did the rate of change of yearly industrial output reach a maximum?

b. When to the nearest year did the rate of change of yearly industrial output reach a minimum?

c. When to the nearest year does the graph first change from concave down to concave up? The result tells you that:

   (A) In that year the rate of change of industrial output reached a minimum compared with nearby years.

   (B) In that year the rate of change of industrial output reached a maximum compared with nearby years.

76. *Profits* The following graph shows the yearly profits of Gigantic Conglomerate, Inc. (GCI) from 2020 to 2035:

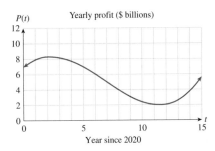

Yearly profit ($ billions)

Year since 2020

a. Approximately when were the profits rising most rapidly?

b. Approximately when were the profits falling most rapidly?

c. Approximately when could GCI's board of directors legitimately tell stockholders that they had "turned the company around"?

77. ▼ ***Education and Crime*** The following graph shows a striking relationship between the total prison population and the average combined SAT score in the United States:

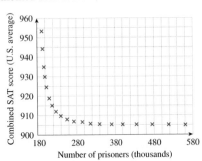

Number of prisoners (thousands)

These data can be accurately modeled by

$$S(n) = 904 + \frac{1{,}326}{(n - 180)^{1.325}}. \quad (192 \le n \le 563)$$

Here, $S(n)$ is the combined U.S. average SAT score at a time when the total U.S. prison population was n thousand.[39]

a. Are there any points of inflection on the graph of S?

b. What does the concavity of the graph of S tell you about prison populations and SAT scores?

78. ▼ ***Education and Crime*** Refer back to the model in the preceding exercise.

a. Are there any points of inflection on the graph of S'?

b. When is S'' a maximum? Interpret your answer in terms of prisoners and SAT scores.

79. ▼ ***Patents*** In 1965, the economist F. M. Scherer modeled the number, n, of patents produced by a firm as a function of the size, s, of the firm (measured in annual sales in millions of dollars). He came up with the following equation based on a study of 448 large firms:[40]

$$n = -3.79 + 144.42s - 23.86s^2 + 1.457s^3.$$

a. Find $\left.\dfrac{d^2n}{ds^2}\right|_{s=3}$. Is the rate at which patents are produced as the size of a firm goes up increasing or decreasing with size when $s = 3$? Comment on Scherer's words, ". . . we find diminishing returns dominating."

b. Find $\left.\dfrac{d^2n}{ds^2}\right|_{s=7}$ and interpret the answer.

c. Find the s-coordinate of any points of inflection and interpret the result.

80. ▼ ***Returns on Investments*** A company finds that the number of new products it develops per year depends on the size of its annual R&D budget, x (in thousands of dollars), according to the formula

$$n(x) = -1 + 8x + 2x^2 - 0.4x^3.$$

a. Find $n''(1)$ and $n''(3)$, and interpret the results.

b. Find the size of the budget that gives the largest rate of return as measured in new products per dollar (again, called the point of diminishing returns).

81. ▣ ▼ ***Oil Imports from Mexico*** Daily oil production in Mexico and daily U.S. oil imports from Mexico during 2005–2009 can be approximated by

$$P(t) = 3.9 - 0.10t \text{ million barrels} \quad (5 \le t \le 9)$$
$$I(t) = 2.1 - 0.11t \text{ million barrels} \quad (5 \le t \le 9)$$

---

[39] The model is the authors' based on data for the years 1967–1989. Sources: *Sourcebook of Criminal Justice Statistics*, 1990, p. 604/ Educational Testing Service.

[40] Source: F. M. Scherer, "Firm Size, Market Structure, Opportunity, and the Output of Patented Inventions," *American Economic Review* 55 (December 1965): pp. 1097–1125.

where t is time in years since the start of 2000.[41]

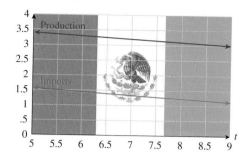

Graph the function $I(t)/P(t)$ and its derivative. Is the graph of $I(t)/P(t)$ concave up or concave down? The concavity of $I(t)/P(t)$ tells you that:

(A) The percentage of oil produced in Mexico that was exported to the United States was decreasing.

(B) The percentage of oil produced in Mexico that was not exported to the United States was increasing.

(C) The percentage of oil produced in Mexico that was exported to the United States was decreasing at a slower rate.

(D) The percentage of oil produced in Mexico that was exported to the United States was decreasing at a faster rate.

82. ▣ ▼ *Oil Imports from Mexico* Repeat Exercise 81 using instead the models for 2000–2004 shown below:

$$P(t) = 3.0 + 0.13t \text{ million barrels} \quad (0 \le t \le 4)$$
$$I(t) = 1.4 + 0.06t \text{ million barrels} \quad (0 \le t \le 4)$$

(t is time in years since the start of 2000).[42]

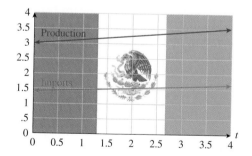

83. ◆ *Logistic Models* Let

$$f(x) = \frac{N}{1 + Ab^{-x}}$$

for constants N, A, and b (A and b positive and $b \ne 1$). Show that f has a single point of inflection at $x = \ln A / \ln b$.

84. ◆ *Logistic Models* Let

$$f(x) = \frac{N}{1 + Ae^{-kx}}$$

for constants N, A, and k (A and k positive). Show that f has a single point of inflection at $x = \ln A / k$.

85. ▣ *Population: Puerto Rico* The population of Puerto Rico in 1950–2025 can be approximated by

$$P(t) = \frac{4{,}500}{1 + 1.1466\,(1.0357)^{-t}} \text{ thousand people} \quad (0 \le t \le 75)$$

(t is the year since 1950).[43] Use the result of Exercise 83 to find the location of the point of inflection in the graph of P. What does the result tell you about the population of Puerto Rico?

86. ▣ *Population: Virgin Islands* The population of the Virgin Islands can be approximated by

$$P(t) = \frac{110}{1 + 2.3596\,(1.0767)^{-t}} \text{ thousand people} \quad (0 \le t \le 75)$$

(t is the year since 1950).[44] Use the result of Exercise 83 to find the location of the point of inflection in the graph of P. What does the result tell you about the population of the Virgin Islands?

87. ▣ ▼ *Asset Appreciation* You manage a small antique store that owns a collection of Louis XVI jewelry boxes. Their value v is increasing according to the formula

$$v = \frac{10{,}000}{1 + 500e^{-0.5t}}$$

where t is the number of years from now. You anticipate an inflation rate of 5% per year, so that the present value of an item that will be worth $\$v$ in t years' time is given by

$$p = v(1.05)^{-t}.$$

What is the greatest rate of increase of the value of your antiques, and when is this rate attained?

88. ▣ ▼ *Harvesting Forests* The following equation models the approximate volume in cubic feet of a typical Douglas fir tree of age t years[45]:

$$V = \frac{22{,}514}{1 + 22{,}514t^{-2.55}}.$$

The lumber will be sold at $10 per cubic foot, and you do not expect the price of lumber to appreciate in the foreseeable future. On the other hand, you anticipate a general inflation

[41] Source for data: Energy Information Administration/Pemex (http://www.eia.doe.gov)

[42] Ibid.

[43] Figures from 2010 on are U.S. census projections. Source for data: The 2008 Statistical Abstract (www.census.gov/).

[44] Ibid.

[45] The model is the authors', and is based on data in *Environmental and Natural Resource Economics* by Tom Tietenberg, Third Edition (New York: HarperCollins, 1992), p. 282.

rate of 5% per year, so that the present value of an item that will be worth v in t years time is given by

$$p = v(1.05)^{-t}.$$

What is the largest rate of increase of the value of a fir tree, and when is this rate attained?

89. □ ▼ *Asset Appreciation* As the financial consultant to a classic auto dealership, you estimate that the total value of its collection of 1959 Chevrolets and Fords is given by the formula

$$v = 300,000 + 1,000t^2$$

where t is the number of years from now. You anticipate a continuous inflation rate of 5% per year, so that the discounted (present) value of an item that will be worth v in t years' time is given by

$$p = ve^{-0.05t}.$$

When is the value of the collection of classic cars increasing most rapidly? When is it decreasing most rapidly?

90. □ ▼ *Plantation Management* The value of a fir tree in your plantation increases with the age of the tree according to the formula

$$v = \frac{20t}{1 + 0.05t}$$

where t is the age of the tree in years. Given a continuous inflation rate of 5% per year, the discounted (present) value of a newly planted seedling is

$$p = ve^{-0.05t}.$$

When is the discounted value of a tree increasing most rapidly? Decreasing most rapidly?

COMMUNICATION AND REASONING EXERCISES

91. Complete the following: If the graph of a function is concave up on its entire domain, then its second derivative is _____ on the domain.

92. Complete the following: If the graph of a function is concave up on its entire domain, then its first derivative is _____ on the domain.

93. Daily sales of Kent's Tents reached a maximum in January 2002 and declined to a minimum in January 2003 before starting to climb again. The graph of daily sales shows a point of inflection at June 2002. What is the significance of the point of inflection?

94. The graph of daily sales of Luddington's Wellington boots is concave down, although sales continue to increase. What properties of the graph of daily sales versus time are reflected in the following behaviors?

   a. a point of inflection next year
   b. a horizontal asymptote

95. ▼ Company A's profits satisfy $P(0) = \$1$ million, $P'(0) = \$1$ million per year, and $P''(0) = -\$1$ million per year per year. Company B's profits satisfy $P(0) = \$1$ million, $P'(0) = -\$1$ million per year, and $P''(0) = \$1$ million per year per year. There are no points of inflection in either company's profit curve. Sketch two pairs of profit curves: one in which Company A ultimately outperforms Company B and another in which Company B ultimately outperforms Company A.

96. ▼ Company C's profits satisfy $P(0) = \$1$ million, $P'(0) = \$1$ million per year, and $P''(0) = -\$1$ million per year per year. Company D's profits satisfy $P(0) = \$0$ million, $P'(0) = \$0$ million per year, and $P''(0) = \$1$ million per year per year. There are no points of inflection in either company's profit curve. Sketch two pairs of profit curves: one in which Company C ultimately outperforms Company D and another in which Company D ultimately outperforms Company C.

97. ▼ Explain geometrically why the derivative of a function has a relative extremum at a point of inflection, if it is defined there. Which points of inflection give rise to relative maxima in the derivative?

98. ▼ If we regard position, s, as a function of time, t, what is the significance of the *third* derivative, $s'''(t)$? Describe an everyday scenario in which this arises.

5.4 Analyzing Graphs

Mathematical curves are beautiful—their subtle form can be imitated by only the best of artists—and calculus gives us the tools we need to probe their secrets. While it is easy to use graphing technology to draw a graph, we must use calculus to understand what we are seeing. Following is a list of some of the most interesting features of the graph of a function.

Features of a Graph

1. *The x- and y-intercepts:* If $y = f(x)$, find the x-intercept(s) by setting $y = 0$ and solving for x; find the y-intercept by setting $x = 0$ and solving for y:

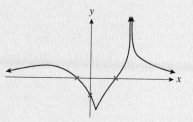

2. *Extrema:* Use the techniques of Section 5.1 to locate the maxima and minima:

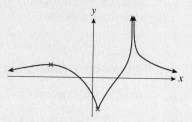

3. *Points of inflection:* Use the techniques of Section 5.2 to locate the points of inflection:

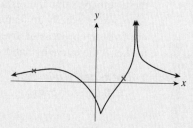

4. *Behavior near points where the function is not defined:* If $f(x)$ is not defined at $x = a$, consider $\lim_{x \to a^-} f(x)$ and $\lim_{x \to a^+} f(x)$ to see how the graph of f behaves as x approaches a:

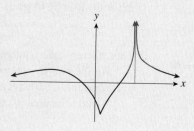

5. *Behavior at infinity:* Consider $\lim_{x\to-\infty} f(x)$ and $\lim_{x\to+\infty} f(x)$ if appropriate, to see how the graph of f behaves far to the left and right:

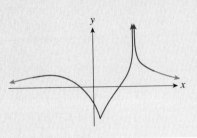

Note It is sometimes difficult or impossible to solve all of the equations that come up in Steps 1, 2, and 3 of the previous analysis. As a consequence, we might not be able to say exactly where the x-intercept, extrema, or points of inflection are. When this happens, we will use graphing technology to assist us in determining accurate numerical approximations. ■

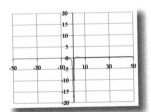

$-50 \le x \le 50, -20 \le y \le 20$

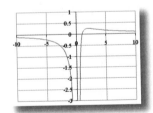

$-10 \le x \le 10, -3 \le y \le 1$

Figure 34

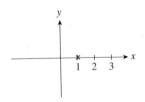

Figure 35

EXAMPLE 1 **Analyzing a Graph**

Analyze the graph of $f(x) = \dfrac{1}{x} - \dfrac{1}{x^2}$.

Solution The graph, as drawn using graphing technology, is shown in Figure 34, using two different viewing windows. (Note that $x = 0$ is not in the domain of f.) The second window in Figure 34 seems to show the features of the graph better than the first. Does the second viewing window include *all* the interesting features of the graph? Or are there perhaps some interesting features to the right of $x = 10$ or to the left of $x = -10$? Also, where exactly do features like maxima, minima, and points of inflection occur? In our five-step process of analyzing the interesting features of the graph, we will be able to sketch the curve by hand, and also answer these questions.

1. *The x- and y-intercepts:* We consider $y = \dfrac{1}{x} - \dfrac{1}{x^2}$. To find the x-intercept(s), we set $y = 0$ and solve for x:

$$0 = \frac{1}{x} - \frac{1}{x^2}$$

$$\frac{1}{x} = \frac{1}{x^2}.$$

Multiplying both sides by x^2 (we know that x cannot be zero, so we are not multiplying both sides by 0) gives

$$x = 1.$$

Thus, there is one x-intercept (which we can see in Figure 34) at $x = 1$.

For the y-intercept, we would substitute $x = 0$ and solve for y. However, we cannot substitute $x = 0$; because $f(0)$ is not defined, the graph does not meet the y-axis.

We add features to our freehand sketch as we go. Figure 35 shows what we have so far.

2. *Relative extrema:* We calculate $f'(x) = -\dfrac{1}{x^2} + \dfrac{2}{x^3}$. To find any stationary points, we set the derivative equal to 0 and solve for x:

$$-\frac{1}{x^2} + \frac{2}{x^3} = 0$$

$$\frac{1}{x^2} = \frac{2}{x^3}$$

$$x = 2.$$

Thus, there is one stationary point, at $x = 2$. We can use a test point to the right to determine that this stationary point is a relative maximum:

x	1 (Intercept)	2	3 (Test point)
$y = \dfrac{1}{x} - \dfrac{1}{x^2}$	0	$\dfrac{1}{4}$	$\dfrac{2}{9}$

The only possible singular point is at $x = 0$ because $f'(0)$ is not defined. However, $f(0)$ is not defined either, so there are no singular points. Figure 36 shows our graph so far.

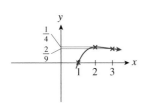

Figure 36

3. *Points of inflection:* We calculate $f''(x) = \dfrac{2}{x^3} - \dfrac{6}{x^4}$. To find points of inflection, we set the second derivative equal to 0 and solve for x:

$$\frac{2}{x^3} - \frac{6}{x^4} = 0$$

$$\frac{2}{x^3} = \frac{6}{x^4}$$

$$2x = 6$$

$$x = 3.$$

Figure 34 confirms that the graph of f changes from being concave down to being concave up at $x = 3$, so this is a point of inflection. $f''(x)$ is not defined at $x = 0$, but that is not in the domain, so there are no other points of inflection. In particular, the graph must be concave down in the whole region $(-\infty, 0)$, as we can see by calculating the second derivative at any one point in that interval: $f''(-1) = -8 < 0$.

Figure 37 shows our graph so far (we extended the curve near $x = 3$ to suggest a point of inflection at $x = 3$).

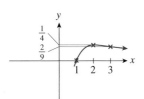

Figure 37

4. *Behavior near points where f is not defined:* The only point where $f(x)$ is not defined is $x = 0$. From the graph, $f(x)$ appears to go to $-\infty$ as x approaches 0 from either side. To calculate these limits, we rewrite $f(x)$:

$$f(x) = \frac{1}{x} - \frac{1}{x^2} = \frac{x - 1}{x^2}$$

Now, if x is close to 0 (on either side), the numerator $x - 1$ is close to -1 and the denominator is a very small but positive number. The quotient is therefore a negative number of very large magnitude. Therefore,

$$\lim_{x \to 0^-} f(x) = -\infty$$

and

$$\lim_{x \to 0^+} f(x) = -\infty.$$

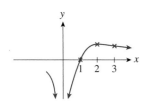

Figure 38

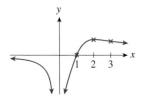

Figure 39

From these limits, we see the following:

(1) Immediately to the *left* of $x = 0$, the graph plunges down toward $-\infty$.

(2) Immediately to the *right* of $x = 0$, the graph also plunges down toward $-\infty$.

Figure 38 shows our graph with these features added. We say that f has a **vertical asymptote** at $x = 0$, meaning that the points on the graph of f get closer and closer to points on a vertical line (the y-axis in this case) further and further from the origin.

5. *Behavior at infinity:* Both $1/x$ and $1/x^2$ go to 0 as x goes to $-\infty$ or $+\infty$; that is,

$$\lim_{x \to -\infty} f(x) = 0$$

and

$$\lim_{x \to +\infty} f(x) = 0.$$

Thus, on the extreme left and right of our picture, the height of the curve levels off toward zero. Figure 39 shows the completed freehand sketch of the graph.

We say that f has a **horizontal asymptote** at $y = 0$. (Notice another thing: We haven't plotted a single point to the left of the y-axis, and yet we have a pretty good idea of what the curve looks like there! Compare the technology-drawn curve in Figure 34.)

In summary, there is one x-intercept at $x = 1$; there is one relative maximum (which, we can now see, is also an absolute maximum) at $x = 2$; there is one point of inflection at $x = 3$, where the graph changes from being concave down to concave up. There is a vertical asymptote at $x = 0$, on both sides of which the graph goes down toward $-\infty$, and a horizontal asymptote at $y = 0$.

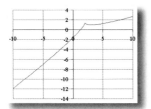

Technology:
2*x/3-((x-2)^2)^(1/3)

Figure 40

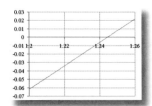

Figure 41

EXAMPLE 2 Analyzing a Graph

Analyze the graph of $f(x) = \dfrac{2x}{3} - (x - 2)^{2/3}$.

Solution Figure 40 shows a technology-generated version of the graph. Note that in the technology formulation $(x - 2)^{2/3}$ is written as $[(x - 2)^2]^{1/3}$ to avoid problems with some graphing calculators and Excel.

Let us now recreate this graph by hand, and in the process identify the features we see in Figure 40.

1. *The x- and y-intercepts:* We consider $y = \dfrac{2x}{3} - (x - 2)^{2/3}$. For the y-intercept, we set $x = 0$ and solve for y:

$$y = \frac{2(0)}{3} - (0 - 2)^{2/3} = -2^{2/3} \approx -1.59.$$

To find the x-intercept(s), we set $y = 0$ and solve for x. However, if we attempt this, we will find ourselves with a cubic equation that is hard to solve. (Try it!) Following the advice in the note on page 416, we use graphing technology to locate the x-intercept we see in Figure 40 by zooming in (Figure 41). From Figure 41, we find $x \approx 1.24$. We shall see in the discussion to follow that there can be no other x-intercepts.

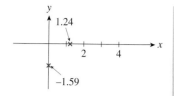

Figure 42

Figure 42 shows our freehand sketch so far.

2. Relative extrema: We calculate

$$f'(x) = \frac{2}{3} - \frac{2}{3}(x-2)^{-1/3}$$

$$= \frac{2}{3} - \frac{2}{3(x-2)^{1/3}}.$$

To find any stationary points, we set the derivative equal to 0 and solve for x:

$$\frac{2}{3} - \frac{2}{3(x-2)^{1/3}} = 0$$

$$(x-2)^{1/3} = 1$$

$$x - 2 = 1^3 = 1$$

$$x = 3.$$

To check for singular points, look for points where $f(x)$ is defined and $f'(x)$ is not defined. The only such point is $x = 2$: $f'(x)$ is not defined at $x = 2$, whereas $f(x)$ is defined there, so we have a singular point at $x = 2$.

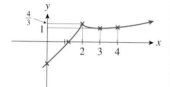

Figure 43

x	2 (Singular point)	3 (Stationary point)	4 (Test point)
$y = \dfrac{2x}{3} - (x-2)^{2/3}$	$\dfrac{4}{3}$	1	1.079

Figure 43 shows our graph so far.

We see that there is a singular relative maximum at $(2, 4/3)$ (we will confirm that the graph eventually gets higher on the right) and a stationary relative minimum at $x = 3$.

3. Points of inflection: We calculate

$$f''(x) = \frac{2}{9(x-2)^{4/3}}.$$

To find points of inflection, we set the second derivative equal to 0 and solve for x. But the equation

$$0 = \frac{2}{9(x-2)^{4/3}}$$

has no solution for x, so there are no points of inflection on the graph.

4. Behavior near points where f is not defined: Because $f(x)$ is defined everywhere, there are no such points to consider. In particular, there are no vertical asymptotes.

5. Behavior at infinity: We estimate the following limits numerically:

$$\lim_{x \to -\infty} \left[\frac{2x}{3} - (x-2)^{2/3} \right] = -\infty$$

and

$$\lim_{x \to +\infty} \left[\frac{2x}{3} - (x-2)^{2/3} \right] = +\infty.$$

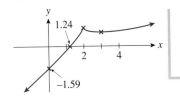

Figure 44

Thus, on the extreme left the curve goes down toward $-\infty$, and on the extreme right the curve rises toward $+\infty$. In particular, there are no horizontal asymptotes. (There can also be no other x-intercepts.)

Figure 44 shows the completed graph.

5.4 EXERCISES

▼ more advanced   ◆ challenging
🅣 indicates exercises that should be solved using technology

In Exercises 1–26, sketch the graph of the given function, indicating (a) x- and y-intercepts, (b) extrema, (c) points of inflection, (d) behavior near points where the function is not defined, and (e) behavior at infinity. Where indicated, technology should be used to approximate the intercepts, coordinates of extrema, and/or points of inflection to one decimal place. Check your sketch using technology. HINT [See Example 1.]

1. $f(x) = x^2 + 2x + 1$

2. $f(x) = -x^2 - 2x - 1$

3. $g(x) = x^3 - 12x$, domain $[-4, 4]$

4. $g(x) = 2x^3 - 6x$, domain $[-4, 4]$

5. $h(x) = 2x^3 - 3x^2 - 36x$ [Use technology for x-intercepts.]

6. $h(x) = -2x^3 - 3x^2 + 36x$ [Use technology for x-intercepts.]

7. $f(x) = 2x^3 + 3x^2 - 12x + 1$ [Use technology for x-intercepts.]

8. $f(x) = 4x^3 + 3x^2 + 2$ [Use technology for x-intercepts.]

9. $k(x) = -3x^4 + 4x^3 + 36x^2 + 10$ [Use technology for x-intercepts.]

10. $k(x) = 3x^4 + 4x^3 - 36x^2 - 10$ [Use technology for x-intercepts.]

11. $g(t) = \dfrac{1}{4}t^4 - \dfrac{2}{3}t^3 + \dfrac{1}{2}t^2$

12. $g(t) = 3t^4 - 16t^3 + 24t^2 + 1$

13. $f(x) = x + \dfrac{1}{x}$

14. $f(x) = x^2 + \dfrac{1}{x^2}$

15. $g(x) = x^3/(x^2 + 3)$

16. $g(x) = x^3/(x^2 - 3)$

17. $f(t) = \dfrac{t^2 + 1}{t^2 - 1}$, domain $[-2, 2]$, $t \neq \pm 1$

18. $f(t) = \dfrac{t^2 - 1}{t^2 + 1}$, domain $[-2, 2]$

19. $k(x) = \dfrac{2x}{3} + (x + 1)^{2/3}$ [Use technology for x-intercepts.

HINT [See Example 2.]

20. $k(x) = \dfrac{2x}{5} - (x - 1)^{2/5}$ [Use technology for x-intercepts.

HINT [See Example 2.]

21. $f(x) = x - \ln x$, domain $(0, +\infty)$

22. $f(x) = x - \ln x^2$, domain $(0, +\infty)$

23. $f(x) = x^2 + \ln x^2$ [Use technology for x-intercepts.]

24. $f(x) = 2x^2 + \ln x$ [Use technology for x-intercepts.]

25. $g(t) = e^t - t$, domain $[-1, 1]$

26. $g(t) = e^{-t^2}$

🅣 In Exercises 27–30, use technology to sketch the graph of the given function, labeling all relative and absolute extrema and points of inflection, and vertical and horizontal asymptotes. The coordinates of the extrema and points of inflection should be accurate to two decimal places. HINT [To locate extrema accurately, plot the first derivative; to locate points of inflection accurately, plot the second derivative.]

27. ▼ $f(x) = x^4 - 2x^3 + x^2 - 2x + 1$

28. ▼ $f(x) = x^4 + x^3 + x^2 + x + 1$

29. ▼ $f(x) = e^x - x^3$

30. ▼ $f(x) = e^x - \dfrac{x^4}{4}$

APPLICATIONS

31. Home Prices The following graph shows the approximate value of the home price index as a percentage change from 2003. The locations of the maximum and the point of inflection are indicated on the graph (t is time in years since the start of 2004).[46]

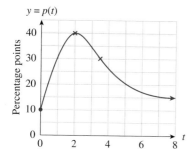

$y = p(t)$

Analyze the graph's important features and interpret each feature in terms of the home price index.

32. Existing Home Sales The following graph shows the approximate value of existing home sales as a percentage change from 2003. The locations of the maximum and the point of inflection are indicated on the graph (t is time in years since the start of 2004).[47]

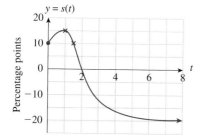

$y = s(t)$

Analyze the graph's important features and interpret each feature in terms of the existing home sales.

33. Consumer Price Index The following graph shows the approximate value of the U.S. Consumer Price Index (CPI) from July 2005 through March 2006.[48]

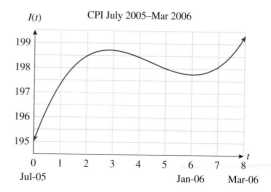

CPI July 2005–Mar 2006

The approximating curve shown on the figure is given by

$$I(t) = 0.06t^3 - 0.8t^2 + 3.1t + 195 \quad (0 \le t \le 8)$$

where t is time in months ($t = 0$ represents July 2005).

a. Locate the intercepts, extrema, and points of inflection of the curve and interpret each feature in terms of the CPI. (Approximate all coordinates to one decimal place.)
HINT [See Example 1.]

b. Recall from Section 5.2 that the inflation rate is defined to be $\dfrac{I'(t)}{I(t)}$. What do the stationary extrema of the curve shown above tell you about the inflation rate?

34. Inflation The following graph shows the approximate value of the U.S. Consumer Price Index (CPI) from March 2006 through May 2007.[49]

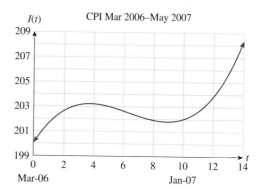

CPI Mar 2006–May 2007

The approximating curve shown on the figure is given by

$$I(t) = 0.02t^3 - 0.38t^2 + 2t + 200 \quad (0 \le t \le 14)$$

where t is time in months ($t = 0$ represents March, 2006).

[46] 2008–2012 data are the authors' projections. Source for data: S&P/Case-Shiller Home Price Index. Source: Standard & Poors/*New York Times*, September 29, 2007, p. C3.

[47] 2008–2012 data are the authors' projections. Source for data: Bloomberg Finiancial Markets/*New York Times*, September 29, 2007, p. C3.

[48] The CPI is compiled by the Bureau of Labor Statistics and is based upon a 1982 value of 100. For instance, a CPI of 200 means the CPI has doubled since 1982. Source: InflationData.com (www.inflationdata.com).

[49] Ibid.

a. Locate the intercepts, extrema, and points of inflection of the curve and interpret each feature in terms of the CPI. (Approximate all coordinates to one decimal place.) HINT [See Example 1.]

b. Recall from Section 5.2 that the inflation rate is defined to be $\dfrac{I'(t)}{I(t)}$. What do the stationary extrema of the curve shown above tell you about the inflation rate?

35. *Motion in a Straight Line* The distance of a UFO from an observer is given by $s = 2t^3 - 3t^2 + 100$ feet after t seconds $(t \geq 0)$. Obtain the extrema, points of inflection, and behavior at infinity. Sketch the curve and interpret these features in terms of the movement of the UFO.

36. *Motion in a Straight Line* The distance of the Mars orbiter from your location in Utarek, Mars is given by $s = 2(t - 1)^3 -3(t - 1)^2 + 100$ km after t seconds $(t \geq 0)$. Obtain the extrema, points of inflection, and behavior at infinity. Sketch the curve and interpret these features in terms of the movement of the Mars orbiter.

37. *Average Cost: iPods* Assume that it costs **Apple** approximately

$$C(x) = 22{,}500 + 100x + 0.01x^2$$

dollars to manufacture x 30-gigabyte video iPods in a day.[50] Obtain the average cost function, sketch its graph, and analyze the graph's important features. Interpret each feature in terms of iPods. HINT [Recall that the average cost function is $\bar{C}(x) = C(x)/x$.]

38. *Average Cost: Xboxes* Assume that it costs **Microsoft** approximately

$$C(x) = 14{,}400 + 550x + 0.01x^2$$

dollars to manufacture x Xbox 360s in a day.[51] Obtain the average cost function, sketch its graph, and analyze the graph's important features. Interpret each feature in terms of Xboxes. HINT [Recall that the average cost function is $\bar{C}(x) = C(x)/x$.]

39. ⊤ ▼ *Subprime Mortgages* The percentage of U.S.-issued mortgages that were subprime can be approximated by

$$A(t) = \frac{15.0}{1 + 8.6(1.8)^{-t}} \text{ percent} \qquad (0 \leq t \leq 8)$$

---

[50] Not the actual cost equation; the authors do not know Apple's actual cost equation. The marginal cost in the model given is in rough agreement with the actual marginal cost for reasonable values of x. Source for cost data: Manufacturing & Technology News, July 31, 2007 Volume 14, No. 14 (www.manufacturingnews.com).

[51] Not the actual cost equation; the authors do not know Microsoft's actual cost equation. The marginal cost in the model given is in rough agreement with the actual marginal cost for reasonable values of x. Source for estimate of marginal cost: iSuppli: (www.isuppli.com/news/xbox/).

t years after the start of 2000.[52] Graph the *derivative $A'(t)$* of $A(t)$ using an extended domain of $0 \leq t \leq 15$. Determine the approximate coordinates of the maximum and determine the behavior of $A'(t)$ at infinity. What do the answers tell you?

40. ⊤ ▼ *Subprime Mortgage Debt* The approximate value of subprime (normally classified as risky) mortgage debt outstanding in the United States can be approximated by

$$A(t) = \frac{1{,}350}{1 + 4.2(1.7)^{-t}} \text{ billion dollars} \qquad (0 \leq t \leq 8)$$

t years after the start of 2000.[53] Graph the *derivative $A'(t)$* of $A(t)$ using an extended domain of $0 \leq t \leq 15$. Determine the approximate coordinates of the maximum and determine the behavior of $A'(t)$ at infinity. What do the answers tell you?

COMMUNICATION AND REASONING EXERCISES

41. A function is *bounded* if its entire graph lies between two horizontal lines. Can a bounded function have vertical asymptotes? Can a bounded function have horizontal asymptotes? Explain.

42. A function is *bounded above* if its entire graph lies below some horizontal line. Can a bounded above function have vertical asymptotes? Can a bounded above function have horizontal asymptotes? Explain.

43. If the graph of a function has a vertical asymptote at $x = a$ in such a way that y increases to $+\infty$ as $x \to a$, what can you say about the graph of its derivative? Explain.

44. If the graph of a function has a horizontal asymptote at $y = a$ in such a way that y decreases to a as $x \to +\infty$, what can you say about the graph of its derivative? Explain.

45. Your friend tells you that he has found a continuous function defined on $(-\infty, +\infty)$ with exactly two critical points, each of which is a relative maximum. Can he be right?

46. Your other friend tells you that she has found a continuous function with two critical points, one a relative minimum and one a relative maximum, and no point of inflection between them. Can she be right?

47. ▼ By thinking about extrema, show that, if $f(x)$ is a polynomial, then between every pair of zeros (x-intercepts) of $f(x)$ there is a zero of $f'(x)$.

48. ▼ If $f(x)$ is a polynomial of degree 2 or higher, show that between every pair of relative extrema of $f(x)$ there is a point of inflection of $f(x)$.

---

[52] 2009 figure is an estimate. Sources: Mortgage Bankers Association, UBS.

[53] 2008–2009 figure are estimates. Source: www.data360.org/dataset.aspx?Data_Set_Id=9549.

5.5 Related Rates

We start by recalling some basic facts about the rate of change of a quantity:

> ## Rate of Change of Q
>
> If Q is a quantity changing over time t, then the derivative dQ/dt is the rate at which Q changes over time.
>
> ### Quick Examples
>
> 1. If A is the area of an expanding circle, then dA/dt is the rate at which the area is increasing.
> 2. *Words:* The radius r of a sphere is currently 3 cm and increasing at a rate of 2 cm/s.
>
>   *Symbols:* $r = 3$ cm and $dr/dt = 2$ cm/s.

In this section we are concerned with what are called **related rates** problems. In such a problem we have two (sometimes more) related quantities, we know the rate at which one is changing, and we wish to find the rate at which another is changing. A typical example is the following.

EXAMPLE 1 The Expanding Circle

The radius of a circle is increasing at a rate of 10 cm/s. How fast is the area increasing at the instant when the radius has reached 5 cm?

Solution We have two related quantities: the radius of the circle, r, and its area, A. The first sentence of the problem tells us that r is increasing at a certain rate. When we see a sentence referring to speed or change, it is very helpful to rephrase the sentence using the phrase "the rate of change of." Here, we can say

> *The rate of change of r is* 10 cm/s.

Because the rate of change is the derivative, we can rewrite this sentence as the equation

$$\frac{dr}{dt} = 10.$$

Similarly, the second sentence of the problem asks how A is changing. We can rewrite that question:

> *What is the rate of change of A when the radius is* 5 cm?

Using mathematical notation, the question is:

> *What is* $\dfrac{dA}{dt}$ *when* $r = 5$?

Thus, knowing one rate of change, dr/dt, we wish to find a related rate of change, dA/dt. To find exactly how these derivatives are related, we need the equation relating the variables, which is

$$A = \pi r^2.$$

To find the relationship between the derivatives, we take the derivative of both sides of this equation *with respect to t*. On the left we get dA/dt. On the right we need to remember that r is a function of t and use the chain rule. We get

$$\frac{dA}{dt} = 2\pi r \frac{dr}{dt}.$$

Now we substitute the given values $r = 5$ and $dr/dt = 10$. This gives

$$\left.\frac{dA}{dt}\right|_{r=5} = 2\pi(5)(10) = 100\pi \approx 314 \text{ cm}^2/\text{s}.$$

Thus, the area is increasing at the rate of $314 \text{ cm}^2/\text{s}$ when the radius is 5 cm.

We can organize our work as follows:

Solving a Related Rates Problem

A. The Problem

1. List the related, changing quantities.
2. Restate the problem in terms of rates of change. Rewrite the problem using mathematical notation for the changing quantities and their derivatives.

B. The Relationship

1. Draw a diagram, if appropriate, showing the changing quantities.
2. Find an equation or equations relating the changing quantities.
3. Take the derivative with respect to time of the equation(s) relating the quantities to get the **derived equation(s)**, which relate the rates of change of the quantities.

C. The Solution

1. Substitute into the derived equation(s) the given values of the quantities and their derivatives.
2. Solve for the derivative required.

We can illustrate the procedure with the "ladder problem" found in almost every calculus textbook.

EXAMPLE 2 The Falling Ladder

Jane is at the top of a 5-foot ladder when it starts to slide down the wall at a rate of 3 feet per minute. Jack is standing on the ground behind her. How fast is the base of the ladder moving when it hits him if Jane is 4 feet from the ground at that instant?

Solution The first sentence talks about (the top of) the ladder sliding down the wall. Thus, one of the changing quantities is the height of the top of the ladder. The question asked refers to the motion of the base of the ladder, so another changing quantity is the distance of the base of the ladder from the wall. Let's record these variables and follow the outline above to obtain the solution.

A. The Problem

1. The changing quantities are

h = height of the top of the ladder
b = distance of the base of the ladder from the wall

2. We rephrase the problem in words, using the phrase "rate of change":

The rate of change of the height of the top of the ladder is -3 feet per minute. What is the rate of change of the distance of the base from the wall when the top of the ladder is 4 feet from the ground?

We can now rewrite the problem mathematically:

$$\frac{dh}{dt} = -3. \text{ Find } \frac{db}{dt} \text{ when } h = 4.$$

B. The Relationship

Figure 45

1. Figure 45 shows the ladder and the variables h and b. Notice that we put in the figure the fixed length, 5, of the ladder, but any changing quantities, like h and b, we leave as variables. We shall not use any specific values for h or b until the very end.

2. From the figure, we can see that h and b are related by the Pythagorean theorem:

$$h^2 + b^2 = 25.$$

3. Taking the derivative with respect to time of the equation above gives us the derived equation:

$$2h\frac{dh}{dt} + 2b\frac{db}{dt} = 0.$$

C. The Solution

1. We substitute the known values $dh/dt = -3$ and $h = 4$ into the derived equation:

$$2(4)(-3) + 2b\frac{db}{dt} = 0.$$

We would like to solve for db/dt, but first we need the value of b, which we can determine from the equation $h^2 + b^2 = 25$, using the value $h = 4$:

$$16 + b^2 = 25$$
$$b^2 = 9$$
$$b = 3.$$

Substituting into the derived equation, we get

$$-24 + 2(3)\frac{db}{dt} = 0.$$

2. Solving for db/dt gives

$$\frac{db}{dt} = \frac{24}{6} = 4.$$

Thus, the base of the ladder is sliding away from the wall at 4 ft/min when it hits Jack.

EXAMPLE 3 **Average Cost**

The cost to manufacture x cell phones in a day is

$$C(x) = 10{,}000 + 20x + \frac{x^2}{10{,}000} \text{ dollars.}$$

The daily production level is currently $x = 5{,}000$ cell phones and is increasing at a rate of 100 units per day. How fast is the average cost changing?

Solution

A. The Problem

1. The changing quantities are the production level x and the average cost, $\bar{C}$.

2. We rephrase the problem as follows:

The daily production level is $x = 5{,}000$ units and the rate of change of x is 100 units/ day. What is the rate of change of the average cost, $\bar{C}$?

In mathematical notation,

$$x = 5{,}000 \text{ and } \frac{dx}{dt} = 100. \text{ Find } \frac{d\bar{C}}{dt}.$$

B. The Relationship

1. In this example the changing quantities cannot easily be depicted geometrically.

2. We are given a formula for the *total* cost. We get the *average* cost by dividing the total cost by x:

$$\bar{C} = \frac{C}{x}.$$

So,

$$\bar{C} = \frac{10{,}000}{x} + 20 + \frac{x}{10{,}000}.$$

3. Taking derivatives with respect to t of both sides, we get the derived equation:

$$\frac{d\bar{C}}{dt} = \left(-\frac{10{,}000}{x^2} + \frac{1}{10{,}000} \right) \frac{dx}{dt}.$$

C. The Solution

Substituting the values from part A into the derived equation, we get

$$\frac{d\bar{C}}{dt} = \left(-\frac{10{,}000}{5{,}000^2} + \frac{1}{10{,}000} \right) 100$$

$$= -0.03 \text{ dollars/day.}$$

Thus, the average cost is decreasing by 3¢ per day.

The scenario in the following example is similar to Example 5 in Section 5.2.

EXAMPLE 4 Allocation of Labor

The Gym Sock Company manufactures cotton athletic socks. Production is partially automated through the use of robots. The number of pairs of socks the company can manufacture in a day is given by a Cobb-Douglas production formula:

$$q = 50n^{0.6}r^{0.4}$$

where q is the number of pairs of socks that can be manufactured by n laborers and r robots. The company currently produces 1,000 pairs of socks each day and employs 20 laborers. It is bringing one new robot on line every month. At what rate are laborers being laid off, assuming that the number of socks produced remains constant?

Solution

A. The Problem

1. The changing quantities are the number of laborers n and the number of robots r.

2. $\dfrac{dr}{dt} = 1$. Find $\dfrac{dn}{dt}$ when $n = 20$.

B. The Relationship

1. No diagram is appropriate here.

2. The equation relating the changing quantities:

$$1,000 = 50n^{0.6}r^{0.4}$$

or

$$20 = n^{0.6}r^{0.4}.$$

(Productivity is constant at 1,000 pairs of socks each day.)

3. The derived equation is

$$0 = 0.6n^{-0.4}\left(\frac{dn}{dt}\right)r^{0.4} + 0.4n^{0.6}r^{-0.6}\left(\frac{dr}{dt}\right)$$

$$= 0.6\left(\frac{r}{n}\right)^{0.4}\left(\frac{dn}{dt}\right) + 0.4\left(\frac{n}{r}\right)^{0.6}\left(\frac{dr}{dt}\right).$$

We solve this equation for dn/dt because we shall want to find dn/dt below and because the equation becomes simpler when we do this:

$$0.6\left(\frac{r}{n}\right)^{0.4}\left(\frac{dn}{dt}\right) = -0.4\left(\frac{n}{r}\right)^{0.6}\left(\frac{dr}{dt}\right)$$

$$\frac{dn}{dt} = -\frac{0.4}{0.6}\left(\frac{n}{r}\right)^{0.6}\left(\frac{n}{r}\right)^{0.4}\left(\frac{dr}{dt}\right)$$

$$= -\frac{2}{3}\left(\frac{n}{r}\right)\left(\frac{dr}{dt}\right).$$

C. The Solution

Substituting the numbers in A into the last equation in B, we get

$$\frac{dn}{dt} = -\frac{2}{3}\left(\frac{20}{r}\right) \quad (1).$$

We need to compute r by substituting the known value of n in the original formula:

$$20 = n^{0.6}r^{0.4}$$
$$20 = 20^{0.6}r^{0.4}$$
$$r^{0.4} = \frac{20}{20^{0.6}} = 20^{0.4}$$
$$r = 20.$$

Thus,

$$\frac{dn}{dt} = -\frac{2}{3}\left(\frac{20}{20}\right)(1) = -\frac{2}{3} \text{ laborers per month.}$$

The company is laying off laborers at a rate of 2/3 per month, or two every three months. We can interpret this result as saying that, at the current level of production and number of laborers, one robot is as productive as 2/3 of a laborer, or 3 robots are as productive as 2 laborers.

5.5 EXERCISES

▼ more advanced   ◆ challenging
⊤ indicates exercises that should be solved using technology

Rewrite the statements and questions in Exercises 1–8 in mathematical notation. HINT [See Quick Examples on page 423.]

1. The population P is currently 10,000 and growing at a rate of 1,000 per year.

2. There are presently 400 cases of Bangkok flu, and the number is growing by 30 new cases every month.

3. The annual revenue of your tie-dye T-shirt operation is currently $7,000 but is decreasing by $700 each year. How fast are annual sales changing?

4. A ladder is sliding down a wall so that the distance between the top of the ladder and the floor is decreasing at a rate of 3 feet per second. How fast is the base of the ladder receding from the wall?

5. The price of shoes is rising $5 per year. How fast is the demand changing?

6. Stock prices are rising $1,000 per year. How fast is the value of your portfolio increasing?

7. The average global temperature is 60°F and rising by 0.1°F per decade. How fast are annual sales of Bermuda shorts increasing?

8. The country's population is now 260,000,000 and is increasing by 1,000,000 people per year. How fast is the annual demand for diapers increasing?

APPLICATIONS

9. *Sun Spots* The area of a circular sun spot is growing at a rate of 1,200 km²/s.

a. How fast is the radius growing at the instant when it equals 10,000 km? HINT [See Example 1.]

b. How fast is the radius growing at the instant when the sun spot has an area of 640,000 km²? HINT [Use the area formula to determine the radius at that instant.]

10. *Puddles* The radius of a circular puddle is growing at a rate of 5 cm/s.

a. How fast is its area growing at the instant when the radius is 10 cm? HINT [See Example 1.]

b. How fast is the area growing at the instant when it equals 36 cm²? HINT [Use the area formula to determine the radius at that instant.]

11. *Balloons* A spherical party balloon is being inflated with helium pumped in at a rate of 3 cubic feet per minute. How fast is the radius growing at the instant when the radius has reached 1 foot? (The volume of a sphere of radius r is $V = \frac{4}{3}\pi r^3$.) HINT [See Example 1.]

12. *More Balloons* A rather flimsy spherical balloon is designed to pop at the instant its radius has reached 10 centimeters. Assuming the balloon is filled with helium at a rate of 10 cubic centimeters per second, calculate how fast the radius is growing at the instant it pops. (The volume of a sphere of radius r is $V = \frac{4}{3}\pi r^3$.) HINT [See Example 1.]

13. **Sliding Ladders** The base of a 50-foot ladder is being pulled away from a wall at a rate of 10 feet per second. How fast is the top of the ladder sliding down the wall at the instant when the base of the ladder is 30 feet from the wall? HINT [See Example 2.]

14. **Sliding Ladders** The top of a 5-foot ladder is sliding down a wall at a rate of 10 feet per second. How fast is the base of the ladder sliding away from the wall at the instant when the top of the ladder is 3 feet from the ground? HINT [See Example 2.]

15. **Average Cost** The average cost function for the weekly manufacture of portable CD players is given by

$$\bar{C}(x) = 150{,}000x^{-1} + 20 + 0.0001x \text{ dollars per player,}$$

where x is the number of CD players manufactured that week. Weekly production is currently 3,000 players and is increasing at a rate of 100 players per week. What is happening to the average cost? HINT [See Example 3.]

16. **Average Cost** Repeat the preceding exercise, using the revised average cost function

$$\bar{C}(x) = 150{,}000x^{-1} + 20 + 0.01x \text{ dollars per player.}$$

HINT [See Example 3.]

17. **Demand** Demand for your tie-dyed T-shirts is given by the formula

$$q = 500 - 100p^{0.5}$$

where q is the number of T-shirts you can sell each month at a price of p dollars. If you currently sell T-shirts for $15 each and you raise your price by $2 per month, how fast will the demand drop? (Round your answer to the nearest whole number.)

18. **Supply** The number of portable CD players you are prepared to supply to a retail outlet every week is given by the formula

$$q = 0.1p^2 + 3p$$

where p is the price it offers you. The retail outlet is currently offering you $40 per CD player. If the price it offers decreases at a rate of $2 per week, how will this affect the number you supply?

19. **Revenue** You can now sell 50 cups of lemonade per week at 30¢ per cup, but demand is dropping at a rate of 5 cups per week each week. Assuming that raising the price does not affect demand, how fast do you have to raise your price if you want to keep your weekly revenue constant? HINT [Revenue = Price × Quantity.]

20. **Revenue** You can now sell 40 cars per month at $20,000 per car, and demand is increasing at a rate of 3 cars per month each month. What is the fastest you could drop your price before your monthly revenue starts to drop? HINT [Revenue = Price × Quantity.]

21. ▼ **Oil Revenues** Daily oil production by **Pemex**, Mexico's national oil company, can be approximated by

$$q(t) = -0.022t^2 + 0.2t + 2.9 \text{ million barrels} \quad (1 \le t \le 9)$$

where t is time in years since the start of 2000.[54]

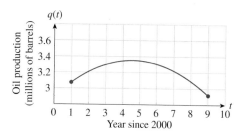

At the start of 2008 the price of oil was $90 per barrel and increasing at a rate of $80 per year.[55] How fast was **Pemex's** oil (daily) revenue changing at that time?

22. ▼ **Oil Expenditures** Daily oil imports to the United States from Mexico can be approximated by

$$q(t) = -0.015t^2 + 0.1t + 1.4 \text{ million barrels} \quad (0 \le t \le 8)$$

where t is time in years since the start of 2000.[56]

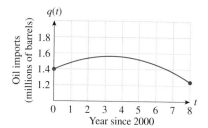

At the start of 2004 the price of oil was $30 per barrel and increasing at a rate of $40 per year.[57] How fast was (daily) oil expenditure for imports from Mexico changing at that time?

23. **Resource Allocation** Your company manufactures automobile alternators, and production is partially automated through the use of robots. In order to meet production deadlines, your company calculates that the numbers of laborers and robots must satisfy the constraint

$$xy = 10{,}000$$

where x is the number of laborers and y is the number of robots. Your company currently uses 400 robots and is increasing robot deployment at a rate of 16 per month. How fast is it laying off laborers? HINT [See Example 4.]

24. **Resource Allocation** Your company is the largest sock manufacturer in the solar system, and production is automated through the use of androids and robots. In order to meet production deadlines, your company calculates that the numbers of androids and robots must satisfy the constraint

$$xy = 1{,}000{,}000$$

[54] Source for data: Energy Information Administration/Pemex (http://www.eia.doe.gov).

[55] Based on NYMEX crude oil futures; average rate of change during January–June, 2008.

[56] Source for data: Energy Information Administration/Pemex (http://www.eia.doe.gov).

[57] Based on NYMEX crude oil futures; average rate of change during 2004–2005.

where x is the number of androids and y is the number of robots. Your company currently uses 5000 androids and is increasing android deployment at a rate of 200 per month. How fast is it scrapping robots? HINT [See Example 4.]

25. **Production** The automobile assembly plant you manage has a Cobb-Douglas production function given by

$$P = 10x^{0.3}y^{0.7}$$

where P is the number of automobiles it produces per year, x is the number of employees, and y is the daily operating budget (in dollars). You maintain a production level of 1,000 automobiles per year. If you currently employ 150 workers and are hiring new workers at a rate of 10 per year, how fast is your daily operating budget changing? HINT [See Example 4.]

26. **Production** Refer back to the Cobb-Douglas production formula in the preceding exercise. Assume that you maintain a constant work force of 200 workers and wish to increase production in order to meet a demand that is increasing by 100 automobiles per year. The current demand is 1000 automobiles per year. How fast should your daily operating budget be increasing? HINT [See Example 4.]

27. **Demand** Assume that the demand equation for tuna in a small coastal town is

$$pq^{1.5} = 50,000$$

where q is the number of pounds of tuna that can be sold in one month at the price of p dollars per pound. The town's fishery finds that the demand for tuna is currently 900 pounds per month and is increasing at a rate of 100 pounds per month each month. How fast is the price changing?

28. **Demand** The demand equation for rubies at Royal Ruby Retailers is

$$q + \frac{4}{3}p = 80$$

where q is the number of rubies RRR can sell per week at p dollars per ruby. RRR finds that the demand for its rubies is currently 20 rubies per week and is dropping at a rate of one ruby per week. How fast is the price changing?

29. ▼ **Ships Sailing Apart** The H.M.S. Dreadnaught is 40 miles north of Montauk and steaming due north at 20 miles/hour, while the U.S.S. Mona Lisa is 50 miles east of Montauk and steaming due east at an even 30 miles/hour. How fast is their distance apart increasing?

30. ▼ **Near Miss** My aunt and I were approaching the same intersection, she from the south and I from the west. She was traveling at a steady speed of 10 miles/hour, while I was approaching the intersection at 60 miles/hour. At a certain instant in time, I was one-tenth of a mile from the intersection, while she was one-twentieth of a mile from it. How fast were we approaching each other at that instant?

31. ▼ **Baseball** A baseball diamond is a square with side 90 ft.

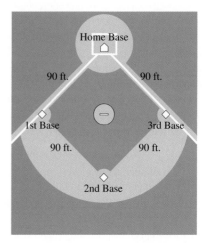

A batter at home base hits the ball and runs toward first base with a speed of 24 ft/s. At what rate is his distance from third base increasing when he is halfway to first base?

32. ▼ **Baseball** Refer to Exercise 31. Another player is running from third base to home at 30 ft/s. How fast is her distance from second base increasing when she is 60 feet from third base?

33. ▼ **Movement along a Graph** A point on the graph of $y = 1/x$ is moving along the curve in such a way that its x-coordinate is increasing at a rate of 4 units per second. What is happening to the y-coordinate at the instant the y-coordinate is equal to 2?

34. ▼ **Motion around a Circle** A point is moving along the circle $x^2 + (y - 1)^2 = 8$ in such a way that its x-coordinate is decreasing at a rate of 1 unit per second. What is happening to the y-coordinate at the instant when the point has reached $(-2, 3)$?

35. ▼ **Education** In 1991, the expected income of an individual depended on his or her educational level according to the following formula:

$$I(n) = 2928.8n^3 - 115,860n^2 + 1,532,900n - 6,760,800.$$
$$(12 \le n \le 15)$$

Here, n is the number of school years completed and $I(n)$ is the individual's expected income.[58] You have completed 13 years of school and are currently a part-time student. Your schedule is such that you will complete the equivalent of one year of college every three years. Assuming that your salary is linked to the above model, how fast is your income going up? (Round your answer to the nearest \$1.)

---

[58] The model is a best-fit cubic based on Table 358, U.S. Department of Education, *Digest of Education Statistics, 1991*, Washington, DC: Government Printing Office, 1991.

36. ▼ *Education* Refer back to the model in the preceding exercise. Assume that someone has completed 14 years of school and that her income is increasing by $10,000 per year. How much schooling per year is this rate of increase equivalent to?

37. ▼ *Employment* An employment research company estimates that the value of a recent MBA graduate to an accounting company is

$$V = 3e^2 + 5g^3$$

where V is the value of the graduate, e is the number of years of prior business experience, and g is the graduate school grade point average. A company that currently employs graduates with a 3.0 average wishes to maintain a constant employee value of $V = 200$, but finds that the grade point average of its new employees is dropping at a rate of 0.2 per year. How fast must the experience of its new employees be growing in order to compensate for the decline in grade point average?

38. ▼ *Grades*[59] A production formula for a student's performance on a difficult English examination is given by

$$g = 4hx - 0.2h^2 - 10x^2$$

where g is the grade the student can expect to obtain, h is the number of hours of study for the examination, and x is the student's grade point average. The instructor finds that students' grade point averages have remained constant at 3.0 over the years, and that students currently spend an average of 15 hours studying for the examination. However, scores on the examination are dropping at a rate of 10 points per year. At what rate is the average study time decreasing?

39. ▼ *Cones* A right circular conical vessel is being filled with green industrial waste at a rate of 100 cubic meters per second. How fast is the level rising after 200π cubic meters have been poured in? The cone has a height of 50 m and a radius of 30 m at its brim. (The volume of a cone of height h and cross-sectional radius r at its brim is given by $V = \frac{1}{3}\pi r^2 h$.)

40. ▼ *More Cones* A circular conical vessel is being filled with ink at a rate of 10 cm³/s. How fast is the level rising after 20 cm³ have been poured in? The cone has height 50 cm and radius 20 cm at its brim. (The volume of a cone of height h and cross-sectional radius r at its brim is given by $V = \frac{1}{3}\pi r^2 h$.)

41. ▼ *Cylinders* The volume of paint in a right cylindrical can is given by $V = 4t^2 - t$ where t is time in seconds and V is the volume in cm³. How fast is the level rising when the height is 2 cm? The can has a height of 4 cm and a radius of 2 cm. HINT [To get h as a function of t, first solve the volume $V = \pi r^2 h$ for h.]

42. ▼ *Cylinders* A cylindrical bucket is being filled with paint at a rate of 6 cm³ per minute. How fast is the level rising when the bucket starts to overflow? The bucket has a radius of 30 cm and a height of 60 cm.

43. ▼ *Computers vs. Income* The demand for personal computers in the home goes up with household income. For a given community, we can approximate the average number of computers in a home as

$$q = 0.3454 \ln x - 3.047 \quad 10{,}000 \le x \le 125{,}000$$

where x is mean household income.[60] Your community has a mean income of $30,000, increasing at a rate of $2,000 per year. How many computers per household are there, and how fast is the number of computers in a home increasing? (Round your answer to four decimal places.)

44. ▼ *Computers vs. Income* Refer back to the model in the preceding exercise. The average number of computers per household in your town is 0.5 and is increasing at a rate of 0.02 computers per household per year. What is the average household income in your town, and how fast is it increasing? (Round your answers to the nearest $10.)

Education and Crime The following graph shows a striking relationship between the total prison population and the average combined SAT score in the U.S.

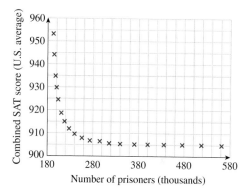

Exercises 45 and 46 are based on the following model for these data:

$$S(n) = 904 + \frac{1{,}326}{(n - 180)^{1.325}}. \quad (192 \le n \le 563)$$

Here, S(n) is the combined average SAT score at a time when the total prison population is n thousand.[61]

45. ▼ In 1985, the U.S. prison population was 475,000 and increasing at a rate of 35,000 per year. What was the average SAT score, and how fast, and in what direction, was it changing? (Round your answers to two decimal places.)

[59] Based on an Exercise in *Introduction to Mathematical Economics* by A.L. Ostrosky Jr. and J.V. Koch (Waveland Press, Illinois, 1979.)

[60] The model is a regression model. Source for data: Income distribution: Computer data: Forrester Research/*The New York Times*, August 8, 1999, p. BU4.

[61] The model is the authors' based on data for the years 1967–1989. Sources: Sourcebook of Criminal Justice Statistics, 1990, p. 604/ Educational Testing Service.

46. ▼ In 1970, the U.S. combined SAT average was 940 and dropping by 10 points per year. What was the U.S. prison population, and how fast, and in what direction, was it changing? (Round your answers to the nearest 100.)

Divorce Rates *A study found that the divorce rate d (given as a percentage) appears to depend on the ratio r of available men to available women.*[62] *This function can be approximated by*

$$d(r) = \begin{cases} -40r + 74 & \text{if } r \le 1.3 \\ \dfrac{130r}{3} - \dfrac{103}{3} & \text{if } r > 1.3 \end{cases}.$$

Exercises 47 and 48 are based on this model.

47. ◆ There are currently 1.1 available men per available woman in Littleville, and this ratio is increasing by 0.05 per year. What is happening to the divorce rate?

48. ◆ There are currently 1.5 available men per available woman in Largeville, and this ratio is decreasing by 0.03 per year. What is happening to the divorce rate?

COMMUNICATION AND REASONING EXERCISES

49. Why is this section titled "related rates"?

50. If you know how fast one quantity is changing and need to compute how fast a second quantity is changing, what kind of information do you need?

51. In a related rates problem, there is no limit to the number of changing quantities we can consider. Illustrate this by creating a related rates problem with four changing quantities.

---

[62] The cited study, by Scott J. South and associates, appeared in the *American Sociological Review* (February, 1995). Figures are rounded. Source: *The New York Times*, February 19, 1995, p. 40.

52. If three quantities are related by a single equation, how would you go about computing how fast one of them is changing based on a knowledge of the other two?

53. ▼ The demand and unit price for your store's checkered T-shirts are changing with time. Show that the percentage rate of change of revenue equals the sum of the percentage rates of change of price and demand. (The percentage rate of change of a quantity Q is $Q'(t)/Q(t)$.)

54. ▼ The number N of employees and the total floor space S of your company are both changing with time. Show that the percentage rate of change of square footage per employee equals the percentage rate of change of S minus the percentage rate of change of N. (The percentage rate of change of a quantity Q is $Q'(t)/Q(t)$.)

55. ▼ In solving a related rates problem, a key step is solving the derived equation for the unknown rate of change (once we have substituted the other values into the equation). Call the unknown rate of change X. The derived equation is what kind of equation in X?

56. ▼ On a recent exam, you were given a related rates problem based on an algebraic equation relating two variables x and y. Your friend told you that the correct relationship between dx/dt and dy/dt was given by

$$\left(\frac{dx}{dt}\right) = \left(\frac{dy}{dt}\right)^2.$$

Could he be correct?

57. ▼ Transform the following into a mathematical statement about derivatives: If my grades are improving at twice the speed of yours, then your grades are improving at half the speed of mine.

58. ▼ If two quantities x and y are related by a linear equation, how are their rates of change related?

5.6 Elasticity

You manufacture an extremely popular brand of sneakers and want to know what will happen if you increase the selling price. Common sense tells you that demand will drop as you raise the price. But will the drop in demand be enough to cause your revenue to fall? Or will it be small enough that your revenue will rise because of the higher selling price? For example, if you raise the price by 1%, you might suffer only a 0.5% loss in sales. In this case, the loss in sales will be more than offset by the increase in price and your revenue will rise. In such a case, we say that the demand is **inelastic**, because it is not very sensitive to the increase in price. On the other hand, if your 1% price increase results in a 2% drop in demand, then raising the price will cause a drop in revenues. We then say that the demand is **elastic** because it reacts strongly to a price change.

✱ NOTE Coming up with a good demand equation is not always easy. We saw in Chapter 1 that it is possible to find a linear demand equation if we know the sales figures at two different prices. However, such an equation is only a first approximation. To come up with a more accurate demand equation, we might need to gather data corresponding to sales at several different prices and use curve-fitting techniques like regression. Another approach would be an analytic one, based on mathematical modeling techniques that an economist might use.

We can use calculus to measure the response of demand to price changes if we have a demand equation for the item we are selling.✱ We need to know the *percentage drop in demand per percentage increase in price*. This ratio is called the **elasticity of demand**, or **price elasticity of demand**, and is usually denoted by E. Let's derive a formula for E in terms of the demand equation.

Assume that we have a demand equation

$$q = f(p)$$

where q stands for the number of items we would sell (per week, per month, or what have you) if we set the price per item at p. Now suppose we increase the price p by a very small amount, Δp. Then our percentage increase in price is $(\Delta p/p) \times 100\%$. This increase in p will presumably result in a decrease in the demand q. Let's denote this corresponding decrease in q by $-\Delta q$ (we use the minus sign because, by convention, Δq stands for the *increase* in demand). Thus, the percentage decrease in demand is $(-\Delta q/q) \times 100\%$.

Now E is the ratio

$$E = \frac{\text{Percentage decrease in demand}}{\text{Percentage increase in price}}$$

so

$$E = \frac{-\dfrac{\Delta q}{q} \times 100\%}{\dfrac{\Delta p}{p} \times 100\%}.$$

Canceling the 100%s and reorganizing, we get

$$E = -\frac{\Delta q}{\Delta p} \cdot \frac{p}{q}.$$

Q: *What small change in price will we use for Δp?*

A: It should probably be pretty small. If, say, we increased the price of sneakers to $1 million per pair, the sales would likely drop to zero. But knowing this tells us nothing about how the market would respond to a modest increase in price. In fact, we'll do the usual thing we do in calculus and let Δp approach 0.

In the expression for E, if we let Δp go to 0, then the ratio $\Delta q/\Delta p$ goes to the derivative dq/dp. This gives us our final and most useful definition of the elasticity.

Price Elasticity of Demand

The **price elasticity of demand E** is the percentage rate of decrease of demand per percentage increase in price. E is given by the formula

$$E = -\frac{dq}{dp} \cdot \frac{p}{q}.$$

We say that the demand is **elastic** if $E > 1$, is **inelastic** if $E < 1$, and has **unit elasticity** if $E = 1$.

Quick Example

Suppose that the demand equation is $q = 20{,}000 - 2p$ where p is the price in dollars. Then

$$E = -(-2)\frac{p}{20{,}000 - 2p} = \frac{p}{10{,}000 - p}.$$

If $p = \$2{,}000$, then $E = 1/4$, and demand is inelastic at this price.

If $p = \$8{,}000$, then $E = 4$, and demand is elastic at this price.

If $p = \$5{,}000$, then $E = 1$, and the demand has unit elasticity at this price.

We are generally interested in the price that maximizes revenue and, in ordinary cases, the price that maximizes revenue must give unit elasticity. One way of seeing this is as follows:* If the demand is inelastic (which ordinarily occurs at a low unit price) then raising the price by a small percentage—1% say—results in a smaller percentage drop in demand. For example, in the Quick Example above, if $p = \$2{,}000$, d then the demand would drop by only $\frac{1}{4}$% for every 1% increase in price. To see the effect on revenue, we use the fact* that, for small changes in price,

✱ **NOTE** For another—more rigorous—argument, see Exercise 27.

✱ **NOTE** See, for example, Exercise 53 in Section 5.4.

Percentage change in revenue $\approx$ Percentage change in price

$+$ Percentage change in demand

$$= 1 + \left(-\frac{1}{4}\right) = \frac{3}{4}\%.$$

Thus, the revenue will increase by about 3/4%. Put another way:

If the demand is inelastic, raising the price increases revenue.

On the other hand, if the price is elastic (which ordinarily occurs at a high unit price), then increasing the price slightly will lower the revenue, so:

If the demand is elastic, lowering the price increases revenue.

The price that results in the largest revenue must therefore be at unit elasticity.

EXAMPLE 1 Price Elasticity of Demand: Dolls

Suppose that the demand equation for Bobby Dolls is given by $q = 216 - p^2$, where p is the price per doll in dollars and q is the number of dolls sold per week.

a. Compute the price elasticity of demand when $p = \$5$ and $p = \$10$, and interpret the results.

b. Find the ranges of prices for which the demand is elastic and the range for which the demand is inelastic

c. Find the price at which the weekly revenue is maximized. What is the maximum weekly revenue?

Solution

a. The price elasticity of demand is

$$E = -\frac{dq}{dp} \cdot \frac{p}{q}.$$

Taking the derivative and substituting for q gives

$$E = 2p \cdot \frac{p}{216 - p^2} = \frac{2p^2}{216 - p^2}.$$

When $p = \$5$,

$$E = \frac{2(5)^2}{216 - 5^2} = \frac{50}{191} \approx 0.26.$$

using Technology

See the Technology Guides at the end of the chapter to find out how to automate computations like those in part (a) of Example 1 using a graphing calculator or Excel. Here is an outline for the TI-83/84 Plus:

TI-83/84 Plus
Y_1=216-X^2
Y_2=-nDeriv(Y_1,X,X)*X/Y_1
2ND TABLE Enter $x = 5$
[More details on page 448.]

Excel
Enter values of p: 4.9, 4.91, ..., 5.0, 5.01, ..., 5.1 in A5–A25.
In B5 enter 216-A5^2 and copy down to B25.
In C5 enter =(A6-A5)/A5 and paste the formula in C5–D24.
In E5 enter = -D5/C5 and copy down to E24. This column contains the values of E for the values of p in column A.
[More details on page 448.]

Thus, when the price is set at $5, the demand is dropping at a rate of 0.26% per 1% increase in the price. Because $E < 1$, the demand is inelastic at this price, so raising the price will increase revenue.

When $p = \$10$,

$$E = \frac{2(10)^2}{216 - 10^2} = \frac{200}{116} \approx 1.72.$$

Thus, when the price is set at $10, the demand is dropping at a rate of 1.72% per 1% increase in the price. Because $E > 1$, demand is elastic at this price, so raising the price will decrease revenue; lowering the price will increase revenue.

b. and **c.** We answer part (c) first. Setting $E = 1$, we get

$$\frac{2p^2}{216 - p^2} = 1$$
$$p^2 = 72.$$

Thus, we conclude that the maximum revenue occurs when $p = \sqrt{72} \approx \$8.49$. We can now answer part (b): The demand is elastic when $p > \$8.49$ (the price is too high), and the demand is inelastic when $p < \$8.49$ (the price is too low). Finally, we calculate the maximum weekly revenue, which equals the revenue corresponding to the price of $8.49:

$$R = qp = (216 - p^2)p = (216 - 72)\sqrt{72} = 144\sqrt{72} \approx \$1,222.$$

The concept of elasticity can be applied in other situations. In the following example we consider *income* elasticity of demand—the percentage increase in demand for a particular item per percentage increase in personal income.

EXAMPLE 2 Income Elasticity of Demand: Porsches

You are the sales director at Suburban Porsche and have noticed that demand for Porsches depends on income according to

$$q = 0.005e^{-0.05x^2+x}. \qquad (1 \le x \le 10)$$

Here, x is the income of a potential customer in hundreds of thousands of dollars and q is the probability that the person will actually purchase a Porsche.[*] The **income elasticity of demand** is

$$E = \frac{dq}{dx}\frac{x}{q}.$$

Compute and interpret E for $x = 2$ and 9.

✳ NOTE In other words, q is the fraction of visitors to your showroom having income x who actually purchase a Porsche.

Solution

Q: *Why is there no negative sign in the formula?*

A: Because we anticipate that the demand will increase as income increases, the ratio

$$\frac{\text{Percentage increase in demand}}{\text{Percentage increase in income}}$$

will be positive, so there is no need to introduce a negative sign.

Turning to the calculation, since $q = 0.005e^{-0.05x^2+x}$,

$$\frac{dq}{dx} = 0.005e^{-0.05x^2+x}(-0.1x + 1)$$

and so

$$E = \frac{dq}{dx}\frac{x}{q}$$

$$= 0.005e^{-0.05x^2+x}(-0.1x + 1)\frac{x}{0.005e^{-0.05x^2+x}}$$

$$= x(-0.1x + 1).$$

When $x = 2$, $E = 2[-0.1(2) + 1] = 1.6$. Thus, at an income level of $200,000, the probability that a customer will purchase a Porsche increases at a rate of 1.6% per 1% increase in income.

When $x = 9$, $E = 9[-0.1(9) + 1] = 0.9$. Thus, at an income level of $900,000, the probability that a customer will purchase a Porsche increases at a rate of 0.9% per 1% increase in income.

5.6 EXERCISES

▼ more advanced   ◆ challenging
T indicates exercises that should be solved using technology

APPLICATIONS

1. **Demand for Oranges** The weekly sales of Honolulu Red Oranges is given by $q = 1,000 - 20p$. Calculate the price elasticity of demand when the price is $30 per orange (yes, $30 per orange[63]). Interpret your answer. Also, calculate the price that gives a maximum weekly revenue, and find this maximum revenue. HINT [See Example 1.]

2. **Demand for Oranges** Repeat the preceding exercise for weekly sales of $1,000 - 10p$. HINT [See Example 1.]

3. **Tissues** The consumer demand equation for tissues is given by $q = (100 - p)^2$, where p is the price per case of tissues and q is the demand in weekly sales.

a. Determine the price elasticity of demand E when the price is set at $30, and interpret your answer.

b. At what price should tissues be sold in order to maximize the revenue?

c. Approximately how many cases of tissues would be demanded at that price?

4. **Bodybuilding** The consumer demand curve for Professor Stefan Schwarzenegger dumbbells is given by $q = (100 - 2p)^2$, where p is the price per dumbbell, and q is the demand in weekly sales. Find the price Professor Schwarzenegger should charge for his dumbbells in order to maximize revenue.

5. **T-Shirts** The Physics Club sells $E = mc^2$ T-shirts at the local flea market. Unfortunately, the club's previous administration has been losing money for years, so you decide to do an analysis of the sales. A quadratic regression based on old sales data reveals the following demand equation for the T-shirts:

$$q = -2p^2 + 33p. \quad (9 \le p \le 15)$$

---

[63] They are very hard to find, and their possession confers considerable social status.

Here, p is the price the club charges per T-shirt, and q is the number it can sell each day at the flea market.

a. Obtain a formula for the price elasticity of demand for $E = mc^2$ T-shirts.

b. Compute the elasticity of demand if the price is set at $10 per shirt. *Interpret the result.*

c. How much should the Physics Club charge for the T-shirts in order to obtain the maximum daily revenue? What will this revenue be?

6. *Comics* The demand curve for original *Iguanawoman* comics is given by

$$q = \frac{(400 - p)^2}{100} \quad (0 \le p \le 400)$$

where q is the number of copies the publisher can sell per week if it sets the price at $p.

a. Find the price elasticity of demand when the price is set at $40 per copy.

b. Find the price at which the publisher should sell the books in order to maximize weekly revenue.

c. What, to the nearest $1, is the maximum weekly revenue the publisher can realize from sales of *Iguanawoman* comics?

7. *College Tuition* A study of about 1,800 U.S. colleges and universities resulted in the demand equation $q = 9,900 - 2.2p$, where q is the enrollment at a college or university, and p is the average annual tuition (plus fees) it charges.[64]

a. The study also found that the average tuition charged by universities and colleges was $2,900. What is the corresponding price elasticity of demand? Is the price elastic or inelastic? Should colleges charge more or less on average to maximize revenue?

b. Based on the study, what would you advise a college to charge its students in order to maximize total revenue, and what would the revenue be?

8. *Demand for Fried Chicken* A fried chicken franchise finds that the demand equation for its new roast chicken product, "Roasted Rooster," is given by

$$p = \frac{40}{q^{1.5}}$$

where p is the price (in dollars) per quarter-chicken serving and q is the number of quarter-chicken servings that can be sold per hour at this price. Express q as a function of p and find the price elasticity of demand when the price is set at $4 per serving. Interpret the result.

9. *Paint-By-Number* The estimated monthly sales of *Mona Lisa* paint-by-number sets is given by the formula $q = 100e^{-3p^2 + p}$,

where q is the demand in monthly sales and p is the retail price in yen.

a. Determine the price elasticity of demand E when the retail price is set at ¥3 and interpret your answer.

b. At what price will revenue be a maximum?

c. Approximately how many paint-by-number sets will be sold per month at the price in part (b)?

10. *Paint-By-Number* Repeat the previous exercise using the demand equation $q = 100e^{p - 3p^2/2}$.

11. ▼ *Linear Demand Functions* A general linear demand function has the form $q = mp + b$ (m and b constants, $m \ne 0$).

a. Obtain a formula for the price elasticity of demand at a unit price of p.

b. Obtain a formula for the price that maximizes revenue.

12. ▼ *Exponential Demand Functions* A general exponential demand function has the form $q = Ae^{-bp}$ (A and b nonzero constants).

a. Obtain a formula for the price elasticity of demand at a unit price of p.

b. Obtain a formula for the price that maximizes revenue.

13. ▼ *Hyperbolic Demand Functions* A general hyperbolic demand function has the form $q = \dfrac{k}{p^r}$ (r and k nonzero constants).

a. Obtain a formula for the price elasticity of demand at unit price p.

b. How does E vary with p?

c. What does the answer to part (b) say about the model?

14. ▼ *Quadratic Demand Functions* A general quadratic demand function has the form $q = ap^2 + bp + c$ (a, b, and c constants with $a \ne 0$).

a. Obtain a formula for the price elasticity of demand at a unit price p.

b. Obtain a formula for the price or prices that could maximize revenue.

15. ▼ *Modeling Linear Demand* You have been hired as a marketing consultant to Johannesburg Burger Supply, Inc., and you wish to come up with a unit price for its hamburgers in order to maximize its weekly revenue. To make life as simple as possible, you assume that the demand equation for Johannesburg hamburgers has the linear form $q = mp + b$, where p is the price per hamburger, q is the demand in weekly sales, and m and b are certain constants you must determine.

a. Your market studies reveal the following sales figures: When the price is set at $2.00 per hamburger, the sales amount to 3,000 per week, but when the price is set at $4.00 per hamburger, the sales drop to zero. Use these data to calculate the demand equation.

b. Now estimate the unit price that maximizes weekly revenue and predict what the weekly revenue will be at that price.

[64] Based on a study by A.L. Ostrosky Jr. and J.V. Koch , as cited in their book, *Introduction to Mathematical Economics* (Waveland Press, Illinois, 1979) p. 133.

16. ▼ **Modeling Linear Demand** You have been hired as a marketing consultant to Big Book Publishing, Inc., and you have been approached to determine the best selling price for the hit calculus text by Whiner and Istanbul entitled *Fun with Derivatives*. You decide to make life easy and assume that the demand equation for *Fun with Derivatives* has the linear form $q = mp + b$, where p is the price per book, q is the demand in annual sales, and m and b are certain constants you'll have to figure out.

a. Your market studies reveal the following sales figures: when the price is set at $50.00 per book, the sales amount to 10,000 per year; when the price is set at $80.00 per book, the sales drop to 1000 per year. Use these data to calculate the demand equation.

b. Now estimate the unit price that maximizes annual revenue and predict what Big Book Publishing, Inc.'s annual revenue will be at that price.

17. *Income Elasticity of Demand: Live Drama* The likelihood that a child will attend a live theatrical performance can be modeled by

$$q = 0.01(-0.0078x^2 + 1.5x + 4.1) \qquad (15 \le x \le 100)$$

Here, q is the fraction of children with annual household income x thousand dollars who will attend a live dramatic performance at a theater during the year.[65] Compute the income elasticity of demand at an income level of $20,000 and interpret the result. (Round your answer to two significant digits.) HINT [See Example 2.]

18. *Income Elasticity of Demand: Live Concerts* The likelihood that a child will attend a live musical performance can be modeled by

$$q = 0.01(0.0006x^2 + 0.38x + 35). \quad (15 \le x \le 100)$$

Here, q is the fraction of children with annual household income x who will attend a live musical performance during the year.[66] Compute the income elasticity of demand at an income level of $30,000 and interpret the result. HINT [See Example 2.]

19. *Income Elasticity of Demand: Computer Usage* The demand for personal computers in the home goes up with household income. The following graph shows some data on computer usage together with the logarithmic model $q = 0.3454 \ln(x) - 3.047$, where q is the probability that a household with annual income x will have a computer.[67]

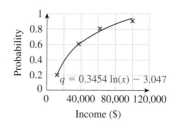

a. Compute the income elasticity of demand for computers, to two decimal places, for a household income of $60,000 and interpret the result.

b. As household income increases, how is income elasticity of demand affected?

c. How reliable is the given model of demand for incomes well above $120,000? Explain.

d. What can you say about E for incomes much larger than those shown?

20. *Income Elasticity of Demand: Internet Usage* The demand for Internet connectivity also goes up with household income. The following graph shows some data on Internet usage, together with the logarithmic model $q = 0.2802 \ln(x) - 2.505$, where q is the probability that a home with annual household income x will have an Internet connection.[68]

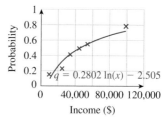

a. Compute the income elasticity of demand to two decimal places for a household income of $60,000 and interpret the result.

b. As household income increases, how is income elasticity of demand affected?

c. The logarithmic model shown above is not appropriate for incomes well above $100,000. Suggest a model that might be more appropriate.

d. In the model you propose, how does E behave for very large incomes?

21. ▼ *Income Elasticity of Demand* (based on a question on the GRE Economics Test) If $Q = aP^\alpha Y^\beta$ is the individual's demand function for a commodity, where P is the (fixed) price of the commodity, Y is the individual's income, and a, α, and β are parameters, explain why β can be interpreted as the income elasticity of demand.

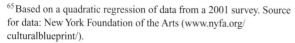

[65] Based on a quadratic regression of data from a 2001 survey. Source for data: New York Foundation of the Arts (www.nyfa.org/culturalblueprint/).

[66] Ibid.

[67] All figures are approximate. The model is a regression model, and x measures the probability that a given household will have one or more computers. Source: Income distribution computer data: Forrester Research/*The New York Times*, August 8, 1999, p. BU4.

[68] All figures are approximate, and the model is a regression model. The Internet connection figures were actually quoted as "share of consumers who use the Internet, by household income." Sources: Luxembourg Income Study/*The New York Times*, August 14, 1995, p. A9, Commerce Department, Deloitte & Touche Survey/*The New York Times*, November 24, 1999, p. C1.

22. ▼ *College Tuition* (*from the GRE Economics Test*) A time-series study of the demand for higher education, using tuition charges as a price variable, yields the following result:

$$\frac{dq}{dp} \cdot \frac{p}{q} = -0.4$$

where p is tuition and q is the quantity of higher education. Which of the following is suggested by the result?

(A) As tuition rises, students want to buy a greater quantity of education.
(B) As a determinant of the demand for higher education, income is more important than price.
(C) If colleges lowered tuition slightly, their total tuition receipts would increase.
(D) If colleges raised tuition slightly, their total tuition receipts would increase.
(E) Colleges cannot increase enrollments by offering larger scholarships.

23. ▼ *Modeling Exponential Demand* As the new owner of a supermarket, you have inherited a large inventory of unsold imported Limburger cheese, and you would like to set the price so that your revenue from selling it is as large as possible. Previous sales figures of the cheese are shown in the following table:

Price per Pound, p	$3.00	$4.00	$5.00
Monthly Sales in Pounds, q	407	287	223

a. Use the sales figures for the prices $3 and $5 per pound to construct a demand function of the form $q = Ae^{-bp}$, where A and b are constants you must determine. (Round A and b to two significant digits.)
b. Use your demand function to find the price elasticity of demand at each of the prices listed.
c. At what price should you sell the cheese in order to maximize monthly revenue?
d. If your total inventory of cheese amounts to only 200 pounds, and it will spoil one month from now, how should you price it in order to receive the greatest revenue? Is this the same answer you got in part (c)? If not, give a brief explanation.

24. ▼ *Modeling Exponential Demand* Repeat the preceding exercise, but this time use the sales figures for $4 and $5 per pound to construct the demand function.

COMMUNICATION AND REASONING EXERCISES

25. Complete the following: When demand is inelastic, revenue will decrease if _____ .

26. Complete the following: When demand has unit elasticity, revenue will decrease if _____ .

27. ▼ Given that the demand q is a differentiable function of the unit price p, show that the revenue $R = pq$ has a stationary point when

$$q + p\frac{dq}{dp} = 0.$$

Deduce that the stationary points of R are the same as the points of unit price elasticity of demand. (Ordinarily, there is only one such stationary point, corresponding to the absolute maximum of R.) HINT [Differentiate R with respect to p.]

28. ▼ Given that the demand q is a differentiable function of income x, show that the quantity $R = q/x$ has a stationary point when

$$q - x\frac{dq}{dx} = 0.$$

Deduce that stationary points of R are the same as the points of unit income elasticity of demand. HINT [Differentiate R with respect to x.]

29. ◆ Your calculus study group is discussing price elasticity of demand, and a member of the group asks the following question: "Since elasticity of demand measures the response of demand to change in unit price, what is the difference between elasticity of demand and the quantity $-dq/dp$?" How would you respond?

30. ◆ Another member of your study group claims that unit price elasticity of demand need not always correspond to maximum revenue. Is he correct? Explain your answer.

KEY CONCEPTS

Web Site www.AppliedCalc.org
Go to the student Web site at
  www.AppliedCalc.org to find a
  comprehensive and interactive
  Web-based summary of Chapter 5.

5.1 Maxima and Minima

Relative maximum, relative minimum
  p. 371

Absolute maximum, absolute
  minimum p. 371

Stationary points, singular points,
  endpoints p. 373

Finding and classifying maxima
  and minima p. 373

First derivative test for relative
  extrema p. 375

Extreme value theorem p. 379

Using technology to locate approximate
  extrema p. 380

5.2 Applications of Maxima and Minima

Minimizing average cost p. 384

Maximizing area p. 385

Steps in solving optimization
  problems p. 387

Maximizing revenue p. 387

Optimizing resources p. 388

Allocation of labor p. 390

5.3 Higher Order Derivatives: Acceleration and Concavity

The second derivative of a function f is
  the derivative of the derivative of f,
  written as f'' p. 398

The acceleration of a moving object is
  the second derivative of the position
  function p. 398

Acceleration due to gravity p. 399

Acceleration of sales p. 399

Concave up, concave down, point of
  inflection p. 400

Locating points of inflection p. 401

Application to inflation p. 401

Second derivative test for relative
  extrema p. 404

Higher order derivatives p. 405

5.4 Analyzing Graphs

Features of a graph: x- and y-intercepts,
  relative extrema, points of inflection;
  behavior near points where the

function is not defined, behavior at
  infinity p. 415

Analyzing a graph p. 416

5.5 Related Rates

If Q is a quantity changing over time t,
  then the derivative dQ/dt is the rate at
  which Q changes over time p. 423

The expanding circle p. 423

Steps in solving related rates
  problems p. 424

The falling ladder p. 424

Average cost p. 426

Allocation of labor p. 427

5.6 Elasticity

Price elasticity of demand
$$E = -\frac{dq}{dp} \cdot \frac{p}{q}; \text{ demand is elastic}$$
  if $E > 1$, inelastic if $E < 1$, has unit
  elasticity if $E = 1$ p. 433

Computing and interpreting elasticity,
  and maximizing revenue p. 433

Using technology to compute
  elasticity p. 435

Income elasticity of demand p. 435

REVIEW EXERCISES

*In Exercises 1–8, find all the relative and absolute extrema of
the given functions on the given domain (if supplied) or on the
largest possible domain (if no domain is supplied).*

1. $f(x) = 2x^3 - 6x + 1$ on $[-2, +\infty)$

2. $f(x) = x^3 - x^2 - x - 1$ on $(-\infty, \infty)$

3. $g(x) = x^4 - 4x$ on $[-1, 1]$

4. $f(x) = \dfrac{x+1}{(x-1)^2}$ on $[-2, 1) \cup (1, 2]$

5. $g(x) = (x-1)^{2/3}$ **6.** $g(x) = x^2 + \ln x$ on $(0, +\infty)$

7. $h(x) = \dfrac{1}{x} + \dfrac{1}{x^2}$ **8.** $h(x) = e^{x^2} + 1$

*In Exercises 9–12, the graph of the function f or its derivative is
given. Find the approximate x-coordinates of all relative extrema
and points of inflection of the original function f (if any).*

9. Graph of f:

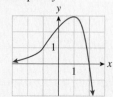

10. Graph of f:

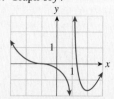

11. Graph of f':

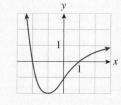

12. Graph of f':

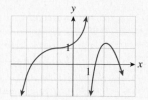

*In Exercises 13 and 14, the graph of the second derivative of a
function f is given. Find the approximate x-coordinates of all
points of inflection of the original function f (if any).*

13. Graph of f''

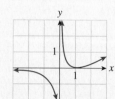

14. Graph of f''

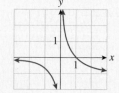

In Exercises 15 and 16, the position s of a point (in meters) is given as a function of time t (in seconds). Find (a) its acceleration as a function of t and (b) its acceleration at the specified time.

15. $s = \dfrac{2}{3t^2} - \dfrac{1}{t}; t = 1$ **16.** $s = \dfrac{4}{t^2} - \dfrac{3t}{4}; t = 2$

In Exercises 17–22, sketch the graph of the given function, indicating all relative and absolute extrema and points of inflection. Find the coordinates of these points exactly, where possible. Also indicate any horizontal and vertical asymptotes.

17. $f(x) = x^3 - 12x$ on $[-2, +\infty)$

18. $g(x) = x^4 - 4x$ on $[-1, 1]$

19. $f(x) = \dfrac{x^2 - 3}{x^3}$

20. $f(x) = (x - 1)^{2/3} + \dfrac{2x}{3}$

21. $g(x) = (x - 3)\sqrt{x}$

22. $g(x) = (x + 3)\sqrt{x}$

APPLICATIONS

23. Revenue Demand for the latest best-seller at OHaganBooks.com, *A River Burns Through It*, is given by

$$q = -p^2 + 33p + 9 \qquad (18 \le p \le 28)$$

copies sold per week when the price is p dollars. What price should the company charge to obtain the largest revenue?

24. Revenue Demand for *The Secret Loves of John O*, a romance novel by Margó Dufón that flopped after two weeks on the market, is given by

$$q = -2p^2 + 5p + 6 \qquad (0 \le p \le 3.3)$$

copies sold per week when the price is p dollars. What price should OHaganBooks charge to obtain the largest revenue?

25. Profit Taking into account storage and shipping, it costs OHaganBooks.com

$$C = 9q + 100$$

dollars to sell q copies of *A River Burns Through It* in a week (see Exercise 23).

  a. If demand is as in Exercise 23, express the weekly profit earned by OHaganBooks.com from the sale of *A River Burns Through It* as a function of unit price p.

  b. What price should the company charge to get the largest weekly profit? What is the maximum possible weekly profit?

  c. Compare your answer in part (b) with the price the company should charge to obtain the largest revenue (Exercise 23). Explain any difference.

26. Profit Taking into account storage and shipping, it costs OHaganBooks.com

$$C = 3q$$

dollars to sell q copies of Margó Dufón's *The Secret Loves of John O* in a week (see Exercise 24).

  a. If demand is as in Exercise 24, express the weekly profit earned by OHaganBooks.com from the sale of *The Secret Loves of John O* as a function of unit price p.

  b. What price should the company charge to get the largest weekly profit? What is the maximum possible weekly profit?

  c. Compare your answer in part (b) with the price the company should charge to obtain the largest revenue (Exercise 24). Explain any difference.

27. Box Design The sales department at OHaganBooks.com, which has decided to send chocolate lobsters to each of its customers, is trying to design a shipping box with a square base. It has a roll of cardboard 36 inches wide from which to make the boxes. Each box will be obtained by cutting out corners from a rectangle of cardboard as shown in the following diagram:

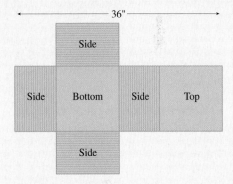

(Notice that the top and bottom of each box will be square, but the sides will not necessarily be square.) What are the dimensions of the boxes with the largest volume that can be made in this way? What is the maximum volume?

28. Box Redesign The sales department at OHaganBooks.com was not pleased with the result of the box design in the preceding exercise; the resulting box was too large for the chocolate lobsters, so, following a suggestion by a math major student intern, the department decided to redesign the boxes to meet the following specifications: As in Exercise 27, each box would be obtained by cutting out corners from a rectangle of cardboard as shown in the following diagram:

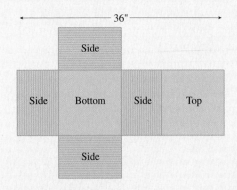

(Notice that the top and bottom of each box would be square, but not necessarily the sides.) The dimensions would be such that the total surface area of the sides plus the bottom of the box would be as large as possible. What are the dimensions of the boxes with the largest area that can be made in this way? How does this box compare with that obtained in Exercise 27?

29. **Elasticity of Demand** (Compare Exercise 23). Demand for the latest best-seller at OHaganBooks.com, *A River Burns Through It*, is given by

$$q = -p^2 + 33p + 9 \quad (18 \le p \le 28)$$

copies sold per week when the price is p dollars.

   a. Find the price elasticity of demand as a function of p.
   b. Find the elasticity of demand for this book at a price of $20 and at a price of $25. (Round your answers to two decimal places.) Interpret the answers.
   c. What price should the company charge to obtain the largest revenue?

30. **Elasticity of Demand** (Compare Exercise 24). Demand for *The Secret Loves of John O*, a romance novel by Margó Dufón that flopped after two weeks on the market, is given by

$$q = -2p^2 + 5p + 6 \quad (0 \le p \le 3.3)$$

copies sold per week when the price is p dollars.

   a. Find the price elasticity of demand as a function of p.
   b. Find the elasticity of demand for this book at a price of $1 and at a price of $3. (Round your answers to two decimal places.) Interpret the answers.
   c. What price should the company charge to obtain the largest revenue?

31. **Elasticity of Demand** Last year OHaganBooks.com experimented with an online subscriber service, Red On Line (ROL), for its electronic book service. The consumer demand for ROL was modeled by the equation

$$q = 1,000e^{-p^2+p}$$

where p was the monthly access charge and q is the number of subscribers.

   a. Obtain a formula for the price elasticity of demand, E, for ROL services.
   b. Compute the elasticity of demand if the monthly access charge is set at $2 per month. Interpret the result.
   c. How much should the company have charged in order to obtain the maximum monthly revenue? What would this revenue have been?

32. **Elasticity of Demand** JungleBooks.com (one of OHaganBooks' main competitors) responded with its own online subscriber service, Better On Line (BOL), for its electronic book service. The consumer demand for BOL was modeled by the equation

$$q = 2,000e^{-3p^2+2p}$$

where p was the monthly access charge and q is the number of subscribers.

   a. Obtain a formula for the price elasticity of demand, E, for BOL services.
   b. Compute the elasticity of demand if the monthly access charge is set at $2 per month. Interpret the result.
   c. How much should the company have charged in order to obtain the maximum monthly revenue? What would this revenue have been?

33. **Sales** OHaganBooks.com modeled its weekly sales over a period of time with the function

$$s(t) = 6,053 + \frac{4,474}{1 + e^{-0.55(t-4.8)}}$$

where t is the time in weeks. Following are the graphs of s, s', and s'':

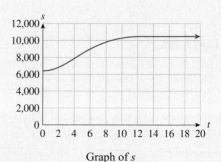

Graph of s

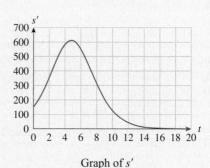

Graph of s'

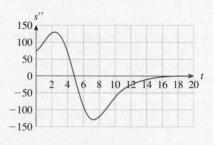

Graph of s''

a. Estimate when, to the nearest week, the weekly sales were growing fastest.

b. To what features on the graphs of s, s', and s'' does your answer to part (a) correspond?

c. The graph of s has a horizontal asymptote. What is the approximate value (s-coordinate) of this asymptote, and what is its significance in terms of weekly sales at OHaganBooks.com?

d. The graph of s' has a horizontal asymptote. What is the value (s'-coordinate) of this asymptote, and what is its significance in terms of weekly sales at OHaganBooks.com?

34. *Sales* The quarterly sales of OHagan χPods (OHaganBooks' answer to the *iPod*; a portable audio book unit with an incidental music feature) from the fourth quarter of 2009 can be roughly approximated by the function

$$N(t) = \frac{1{,}100}{1 + 9(1.8)^{-t}} \quad (t \ge 0)$$

where t is time in quarters since the fourth quarter of 2009. Following are the graphs of N, N', and N'':

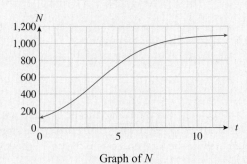

Graph of N

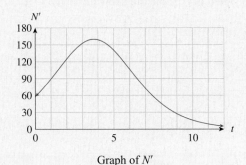

Graph of N'

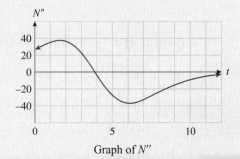

Graph of N''

a. Estimate when, to the nearest quarter, the quarterly sales were growing fastest.

b. To what features on the graphs of N, N', and N'' does your answer to part (a) correspond?

c. The graph of N has a horizontal asymptote. What is the approximate value (N-coordinate) of this asymptote, and what is its significance in terms of quarterly sales of χPods?

d. The graph of N' has a horizontal asymptote. What is the value (N'-coordinate) of this asymptote, and what is its significance in terms of quarterly sales of χPods?

35. *Chance Encounter* Marjory Duffin is walking north towards the corner entrance of OHaganBooks.com company headquarters at 5 ft/s, while John O'Hagan is walking west toward the same entrance, also at 5 ft/s. How fast is their distance apart decreasing when:

a. Each of them is 2 ft from the corner?

b. Each of them is 1 ft. from the corner?

c. Each of them is h ft. from the corner?

d. They collide on the corner?

36. *Company Logos* OHaganBooks.com's Web site has an animated graphic with its name in a rectangle whose height and width change; on either side of the rectangle are semicircles, as in the figure, whose diameters are the same as the height of the rectangle.

For reasons too complicated to explain, the designer wanted the combined area of the rectangle and semicircles to remain constant. At one point during the animation, the width of the rectangle is 1 inch, growing at a rate of 0.5 inches per second, while the height is 3 inches. How fast is the height changing?

Case Study   **Production Lot Size Management**

Your publishing company, Knockem Dead Paperbacks, Inc., is about to release its next best-seller, *Henrietta's Heaving Heart* by Celestine A. Lafleur. The company expects to sell 100,000 books each month in the next year. You have been given the job of scheduling print runs to meet the anticipated demand and minimize total costs to the company. Each print run has a setup cost of $5,000, each book costs $1 to produce, and monthly storage costs for books awaiting shipment average 1¢ per book. What will you do?

If you decide to print all 1,200,000 books (the total demand for the year, 100,000 books per month for 12 months) in a single run at the start of the year and sales run as predicted, then the number of books in stock would begin at 1,200,000 and decrease to zero by the end of the year, as shown in Figure 46.

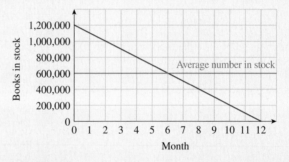

Figure 46

On average, you would be storing 600,000 books for 12 months at 1¢ per book, giving a total storage cost of $600,000 \times 12 \times .01 = \$72,000$. The setup cost for the single print run would be $5,000. When you add to these the total cost of producing 1,200,000 books at $1 per book, your total cost would be $1,277,000.

If, on the other hand, you decide to cut down on storage costs by printing the book in two runs of 600,000 each, you would get the picture shown in Figure 47.

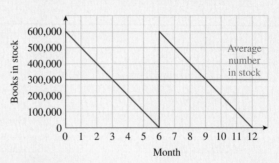

Figure 47

Now, the storage cost would be cut in half because on average there would be only 300,000 books in stock. Thus, the total storage cost would be $36,000, and the setup cost would double to $10,000 (because there would now be two runs). The production costs would be the same: 1,200,000 books @ $1 per book. The total cost would therefore be reduced to $1,246,000, a savings of $31,000 compared to your first scenario.

"Aha!" you say to yourself, after doing these calculations. "Why not drastically cut costs by setting up a run every month?" You calculate that the setup costs alone would be $12 \times \$5{,}000 = \$60{,}000$, which is already more than the setup plus storage costs for two runs, so a run every month will cost too much. Perhaps, then, you should investigate three runs, four runs, and so on, until you find the lowest cost. This strikes you as too laborious a process, especially considering that you will have to do it all over again when planning for Lafleur's sequel, *Lorenzo's Lost Love,* due to be released next year. Realizing that this is an optimization problem, you decide to use some calculus to help you come up with a *formula* that you can use for all future plans. So you get to work.

Instead of working with the number 1,200,000, you use the letter N so that you can be as flexible as possible. (What if *Lorenzo's Lost Love* sells more copies?) Thus, you have a total of N books to be produced for the year. You now calculate the total cost of using x print runs per year. Because you are to produce a total of N books in x print runs, you will have to produce N/x books in each print run. N/x is called the **lot size**. As you can see from the diagrams above, the average number of books in storage will be half that amount, $N/(2x)$.

Now you can calculate the total cost for a year. Write P for the setup cost of a single print run ($P = \$5{,}000$ in your case) and c for the *annual* cost of storing a book (to convert all of the time measurements to years; $c = \$0.12$ here). Finally, write b for the cost of producing a single book ($b = \$1$ here). The costs break down as follows.

Setup Costs: x print runs @ P dollars per run: $\qquad\qquad Px$

Storage Costs: $N/(2x)$ books stored @ c dollars per year: $\quad cN/(2x)$

Production Costs: N books @ b dollars per book: $\qquad\qquad \dfrac{Nb}{}$

Total Cost: $Px + \dfrac{cN}{2x} + Nb$

Remember that P, N, c, and b are all constants and x is the only variable. Thus, your cost function is

$$C(x) = Px + \frac{cN}{2x} + Nb$$

and you need to find the value of x that will minimize $C(x)$. But that's easy! All you need to do is find the relative extrema and select the absolute minimum (if any).

The domain of $C(x)$ is $(0, +\infty)$ because there is an x in the denominator and x can't be negative. To locate the extrema, you start by locating the critical points:

$$C'(x) = P - \frac{cN}{2x^2}.$$

The only singular point would be at $x = 0$, but 0 is not in the domain. To find stationary points, you set $C'(x) = 0$ and solve for x:

$$P - \frac{cN}{2x^2} = 0$$

$$2x^2 = \frac{cN}{P}$$

so

$$x = \sqrt{\frac{cN}{2P}}.$$

There is only one stationary point, and there are no singular points or endpoints. To graph the function you will need to put in numbers for the various constants. Substituting $N = 1,200,000$, $P = 5,000$, $c = 0.12$, and $b = 1$, you get

$$C(x) = 5,000x + \frac{72,000}{x} + 1,200,000$$

with the stationary point at

$$x = \sqrt{\frac{(0.12)(1,200,000)}{2(5000)}} \approx 3.79.$$

The total cost at the stationary point is

$$C(3.79) \approx 1,240,000.$$

You now graph $C(x)$ in a window that includes the stationary point, say, $0 \le x \le 12$ and $1,100,000 \le C \le 1,500,000$, getting Figure 48.

From the graph, you can see that the stationary point is an absolute minimum. In the graph it appears that the graph is always concave up, which also tells you that your stationary point is a minimum. You can check the concavity by computing the second derivative:

$$C''(x) = \frac{cN}{x^3} > 0.$$

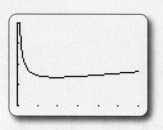

Figure 48

The second derivative is always positive because c, N, and x are all positive numbers, so indeed the graph is always concave up. Now you also know that it works regardless of the particular values of the constants.

So now you are practically done! You know that the absolute minimum cost occurs when you have $x \approx 3.79$ print runs per year. Don't be disappointed that the answer is not a whole number; whole number solutions are rarely found in real scenarios. What the answer (and the graph) do indicate is that either 3 or 4 print runs per year will cost the least money. If you take $x = 3$, you get a total cost of

$$C(3) = \$1,239,000$$

If you take $x = 4$, you get a total cost of

$$C(4) = \$1,238,000$$

So, four print runs per year will allow you to minimize your total costs.

EXERCISES

1. *Lorenzo's Lost Love* will sell 2,000,000 copies in a year. The remaining costs are the same. How many print runs should you use now?
2. In general, what happens to the number of runs that minimizes cost if both the setup cost and the total number of books are doubled?
3. In general, what happens to the number of runs that minimizes cost if the setup cost increases by a factor of 4?
4. Assuming that the total number of copies and storage costs are as originally stated, find the setup cost that would result in a single print run.
5. Assuming that the total number of copies and setup cost are as originally stated, find the storage cost that would result in a print run each month.

6. In Figure 47 we assumed that all the books in each run were manufactured in a very short time; otherwise the figure might have looked more like Figure 49, which shows the inventory, assuming a slower rate of production.

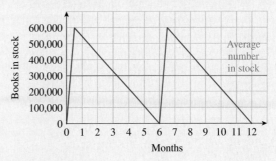

Figure 49

How would this affect the answer?

7. Referring to the general situation discussed in the text, find the cost as a function of the total number of books produced, assuming that the number of runs is chosen to minimize total cost. Also find the average cost per book.

8. Let $\bar{C}$ be the average cost function found in the preceding exercise. Calculate $\lim_{N \to +\infty} \bar{C}(N)$ and interpret the result.

TECHNOLOGY GUIDE

TI-83/84 Plus   **Technology Guide**

Section **5.6**

Example 1(a) (page 434)   Suppose that the demand equation for Bobby Dolls is given by $q = 216 - p^2$, where p is the price per doll in dollars and q is the number of dolls sold per week. Compute the price elasticity of demand when $p = \$5$ and $p = \$10$, and interpret the results.

Solution with Technology

The TI-83/84 Plus function `nDeriv` can be used to compute approximations of the elasticity E at various prices.

1. Set

$$Y_1 = 216 - X^2 \qquad \text{Demand equation}$$
$$Y_2 = -\text{nDeriv}(Y_1, X, X) * X/Y_1 \qquad \text{Formula for } E$$

2. Use the table feature to list the values of elasticity for a range of prices. For part (a) we chose values of X close to 5:

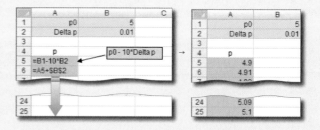

EXCEL   **Technology Guide**

Section **5.6**

Example 1(a) (page 434)   Suppose that the demand equation for Bobby Dolls is given by $q = 216 - p^2$, where p is the price per doll in dollars and q is the number of dolls sold per week. Compute the price elasticity of demand when $p = \$5$ and $p = \$10$, and interpret the results.

Solution with Technology

To approximate E in Excel, we can use the following approximation of E.

$$E \approx \frac{\text{Percentage decrease in demand}}{\text{Percentage increase in price}} \approx -\frac{\left(\dfrac{\Delta q}{q}\right)}{\left(\dfrac{\Delta p}{p}\right)}$$

The smaller Δp is, the better the approximation. Let's use $\Delta p = 1\cent$, or 0.01 (which is small compared with the typical prices we consider—around \$5 to \$10).

1. We start by setting up our worksheet to list a range of prices, in increments of Δp, on either side of a price in which we are interested, such as $p_0 = \$5$:

We start in cell A5 with the formula for $p_0 - 10\Delta p$ and then successively add Δp going down column A. You will find that the value $p_0 = 5$ appears midway down the list.

2. Next, we compute the corresponding values for the demand q in Column B.

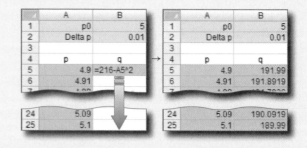

3. We add two new columns for the percentage changes in p and q. The formula shown in cell C5 is copied down columns C and D, to Row 24. (Why not Row 25?)

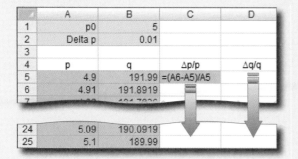

4. The elasticity can now be computed in column E as shown:

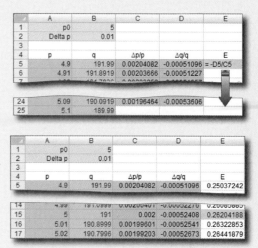

Answers to Selected Exercises

Chapter 0

Section 0.1
1. -48 **3.** $2/3$ **5.** -1 **7.** 9 **9.** 1 **11.** 33 **13.** 14
15. $5/18$ **17.** 13.31 **19.** 6 **21.** $43/16$ **23.** 0
25. `3*(2-5)`   **27.** `3/(2-5)`   **29.** `(3-1)/(8+6)`
31. `3-(4+7)/8`   **33.** `2/(3+x)-x*y^2`
35. `3.1x^3-4x^(-2)-60/(x^2-1)`   **37.** `(2/3)/5`
39. `3^(4-5)*6`   **41.** `3*(1+4/100)^(-3)`
43. `3^(2*x-1)+4^x-1`   **45.** `2^(2x^2-x+1)`
47. `4*e^(-2*x)/(2-3e^(-2*x))`   or   `4(*e^(-2*x))/`
`(2-3e^(-2*x))`   **49.** `3(1-(-1/2)^2)^2+1`

Section 0.2
1. 27 **3.** -36 **5.** $4/9$ **7.** $-1/8$ **9.** 16 **11.** 2 **13.** 32
15. 2 **17.** x^5 **19.** $-\dfrac{y}{x}$ **21.** $\dfrac{1}{x}$ **23.** $x^3 y$ **25.** $\dfrac{z^4}{y^3}$ **27.** $\dfrac{x^6}{y^6}$
29. $\dfrac{x^4 y^6}{z^4}$ **31.** $\dfrac{3}{x^4}$ **33.** $\dfrac{3}{4x^{2/3}}$ **35.** $1 - 0.3x^2 - \dfrac{6}{5x}$ **37.** 2
39. $1/2$ **41.** $4/3$ **43.** $2/5$ **45.** 7 **47.** 5 **49.** -2.668
51. $3/2$ **53.** 2 **55.** 2 **57.** ab **59.** $x+9$ **61.** $x\sqrt[3]{a^3 + b^3}$
63. $\dfrac{2y}{\sqrt{x}}$ **65.** $3^{1/2}$ **67.** $x^{3/2}$ **69.** $(xy^2)^{1/3}$ **71.** $x^{3/2}$
73. $\dfrac{3}{5}x^{-2}$ **75.** $\dfrac{3}{2}x^{-1.2} - \dfrac{1}{4}x^{-2.1}$ **77.** $\dfrac{2}{3}x - \dfrac{1}{2}x^{0.1} + \dfrac{4}{3}x^{-1.1}$
79. $\dfrac{3}{4}x^{1/2} - \dfrac{5}{3}x^{-1/2} + \dfrac{4}{3}x^{-3/2}$ **81.** $\dfrac{3}{4}x^{2/5} - \dfrac{7}{2}x^{-3/2}$
83. $(x^2 + 1)^{-3} - \dfrac{3}{4}(x^2 + 1)^{-1/3}$ **85.** $\sqrt[3]{2^2}$ **87.** $\sqrt[3]{x^4}$
89. $\sqrt[5]{\sqrt{x}\sqrt[3]{y}}$ **91.** $-\dfrac{3}{2\sqrt[4]{x}}$ **93.** $\dfrac{0.2}{\sqrt[3]{x^2}} + \dfrac{3\sqrt{x}}{7}$
95. $\dfrac{3}{4\sqrt{(1-x)^5}}$ **97.** 64 **99.** $\sqrt{3}$ **101.** $1/x$ **103.** xy
105. $\left(\dfrac{y}{x}\right)^{1/3}$ **107.** ± 4 **109.** $\pm 2/3$ **111.** $-1, -1/3$
113. -2 **115.** 16 **117.** ± 1 **119.** $33/8$

Section 0.3
1. $4x^2 + 6x$ **3.** $2xy - y^2$ **5.** $x^2 - 2x - 3$
7. $2y^2 + 13y + 15$ **9.** $4x^2 - 12x + 9$ **11.** $x^2 + 2 + 1/x^2$
13. $4x^2 - 9$ **15.** $y^2 - 1/y^2$ **17.** $2x^3 + 6x^2 + 2x - 4$
19. $x^4 - 4x^3 + 6x^2 - 4x + 1$ **21.** $y^5 + 4y^4 + 4y^3 - y$
23. $(x + 1)(2x + 5)$ **25.** $(x^2 + 1)^5(x + 3)^3(x^2 + x + 4)$
27. $-x^3(x^3 + 1)\sqrt{x + 1}$ **29.** $(x + 2)\sqrt{(x + 1)^3}$
31. a. $x(2 + 3x)$ **b.** $x = 0, -2/3$ **33. a.** $2x^2(3x - 1)$
b. $x = 0, 1/3$ **35. a.** $(x - 1)(x - 7)$ **b.** $x = 1, 7$
37. a. $(x - 3)(x + 4)$ **b.** $x = 3, -4$ **39. a.** $(2x + 1)(x - 2)$
b. $x = -1/2, 2$ **41. a.** $(2x + 3)(3x + 2)$
b. $x = -3/2, -2/3$ **43. a.** $(3x - 2)(4x + 3)$

b. $x = 2/3, -3/4$ **45. a.** $(x + 2y)^2$ **b.** $x = -2y$
47. a. $(x^2 - 1)(x^2 - 4)$ **b.** $x = \pm 1, \pm 2$

Section 0.4
1. $\dfrac{2x^2 - 7x - 4}{x^2 - 1}$ **3.** $\dfrac{3x^2 - 2x + 5}{x^2 - 1}$ **5.** $\dfrac{x^2 - x + 1}{x + 1}$
7. $\dfrac{x^2 - 1}{x}$ **9.** $\dfrac{2x - 3}{x^2 y}$ **11.** $\dfrac{(x + 1)^2}{(x + 2)^4}$ **13.** $\dfrac{-1}{\sqrt{(x^2 + 1)^3}}$
15. $\dfrac{-(2x + y)}{x^2(x + y)^2}$

Section 0.5
1. -1 **3.** 5 **5.** $13/4$ **7.** $43/7$ **9.** -1 **11.** $(c - b)/a$
13. $x = -4, 1/2$ **15.** No solutions   **17.** $\pm\sqrt{\dfrac{5}{2}}$ **19.** -1
21. $-1, 3$ **23.** $\dfrac{1 \pm \sqrt{5}}{2}$ **25.** 1 **27.** $\pm 1, \pm 3$
29. $\pm\sqrt{\dfrac{-1 \pm \sqrt{5}}{2}}$ **31.** $-1, -2, -3$ **33.** -3 **35.** 1
37. -2 **39.** $1, \pm\sqrt{5}$ **41.** $\pm 1, \pm\dfrac{1}{\sqrt{2}}$ **43.** $-2, -1, 2, 3$

Section 0.6
1. $0, 3$ **3.** $\pm\sqrt{2}$ **5.** $-1, -5/2$ **7.** -3 **9.** $0, -1, 1$
11. $x = -1$ ($x = -2$ is not a solution.)   **13.** $-2, -3/2, -1$
15. -1 **17.** $\pm\sqrt[4]{2}$ **19.** ± 1 **21.** ± 3 **23.** $2/3$ **25.** $-4, -1/4$

Section 0.7
1. $P(0, 2)$, $Q(4, -2)$, $R(-2, 3)$, $S(-3.5, -1.5)$,
$T(-2.5, 0)$, $U(2, 2.5)$.

3.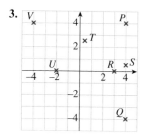

5.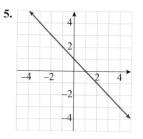

7.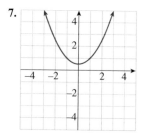

9.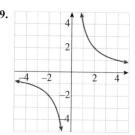

11.

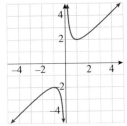

13. $\sqrt{2}$

15. $\sqrt{a^2 + b^2}$

17. $1/2$

19. Circle with center $(0, 0)$ and radius 3

Chapter 1

Section 1.1

1. a. 2 **b.** 0.5 **3. a.** -1.5 **b.** 8 **c.** -8 **5. a.** 20 **b.** 30
c. 30 **d.** 20 **e.** 0 **7. a.** -1 **b.** 1.25 **c.** 0 **d.** 1 **e.** 0
9. a. Yes; $f(4) = 63/16$ **b.** Not defined **c.** Not defined
11. a. Not defined **b.** Not defined **c.** Yes, $f(-10) = 0$
13. a. -7 **b.** -3 **c.** 1 **d.** $4y - 3$ **e.** $4(a + b) - 3$ **15. a.** 3
b. 6 **c.** 2 **d.** 6 **e.** $a^2 + 2a + 3$ **f.** $(x + h)^2 + 2(x + h) + 3$
17. a. 2 **b.** 0 **c.** 65/4 **d.** $x^2 + 1/x$ **e.** $(s + h)^2 + 1/(s + h)$
f. $(s + h)^2 + 1/(s + h) - (s^2 + 1/s)$

19.

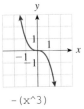

$-(x^3)$

21.

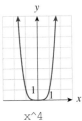

x^4

23.

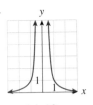

$1/x^2$

25. a. (I) **b.** (IV) **c.** (V) **d.** (VI) **e.** (III) **f.** (II)
27. $0.1*x^2-4*x+5$

x	0	1	2	3
$f(x)$	5	1.1	-2.6	-6.1
x	4	5	6	7
$f(x)$	-9.4	-12.5	-15.4	-18.1
x	8	9	10	
$f(x)$	-20.6	-22.9	-25	

29. $(x^2-1)/(x^2+1)$

x	0.5	1.5	2.5	3.5
$h(x)$	-0.6000	0.3846	0.7241	0.8491
x	4.5	5.5	6.5	7.5
$h(x)$	0.9059	0.9360	0.9538	0.9651
x	8.5	9.5	10.5	
$h(x)$	0.9727	0.9781	0.9820	

31. a. -1 **b.** 2 **c.** 2   **33. a.** 1 **b.** 0 **c.** 1

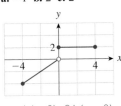

$x* (x<0) +2* (x>=0)$

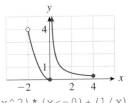

$(x^2) * (x<=0) + (1/x) *$
$(0<x)$

35. a. 0 **b.** 2 **c.** 3 **d.** 3

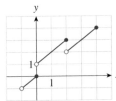

$x* (x<=0) + (x+1) *$
$(0<x) * (x<=2) + x*$
$(2<x)$

37. a. $h(2x + h)$ **b.** $2x + h$ **39. a.** $-h(2x + h)$
b. $-(2x + h)$ **41. a.** $I(3) = 1.55$. In 2003 the United States
imported 1.55 million gallons/day. $I(5) = 1.5$. In 2005 the
United States imported 1.5 million gallons/day. $I(6) = 1.5$.
In 2006 the United States imported 1.5 million gallons/day.
b. $[1, 6]$ **c.** Graph:

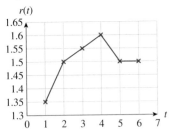

$I(4.5) \approx 1.55$. Thus the United States imported 1.55 million
gallons/day in the year ending June 30, 2005 (or the year
starting July 1, 2004). **43.** $f(4) \approx 1,600$, $f(5) \approx 1,700$,
$f(6.5) \approx 1,300$. There were 1.6 million housing starts in 2004,
1.7 million housing starts in 2005, and 1.3 million housing
starts in the year beginning July 2006. **45.** $f(7) - f(5)$
The change in the number of housing starts from 2005 to 2007
was larger in magnitude than the change from 2000 to 2005.

47. a. [0, 10]. $t \geq 0$ is not an appropriate domain because it would predict U.S. trade with China into the indefinite future with no basis. **b.** $280 billion; U.S. trade with China in 2004 was valued at approximately $280 billion.   **49. a.** [1, 6]
b. $L(2) \approx 400$; $L(5) \approx 900$, $L(6) \approx 1,100$. Sirius lost around $400 million in 2002, $900 million in 2005, and $1,100 million (or $1.1 billion) in 2006. **c.** $t \approx 4.5$; Sirius' losses were increasing fastest approximately midway through 2004.
51. a. $P(0) = 200$: At the start of 1995 the processor speed was 200 megahertz. $P(4) = 500$: At the start of 1999 the processor speed was 500 megahertz. $P(5) = 1,100$: At the start of 2000 the processor speed was 1,100 megahertz.
b. Graph:

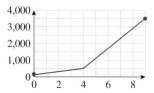

Midway through 2001 **c.**:

t	0	1	2	3	4	5	6	7	8	9
P(t)	200	275	350	425	500	1,100	1,700	2,300	2,900	3,500

53. $T(26,000) = \$3,508.75$; $T(65,000) = \$12,673.75$
55. a. 100*(1-12200/t^4.48)
b. Graph:

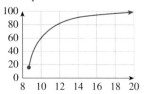

c.

t	9	10	11	12	13	14
p(t)	35.2	59.6	73.6	82.2	87.5	91.1
t	15	16	17	18	19	20
p(t)	93.4	95.1	96.3	97.1	97.7	98.2

d. 82.2% **e.** 14 months   **57.** t; m **59.** $y(x) = 4x^2 - 2$ (or $f(x) = 4x^2 - 2$)   **61.** True. We can construct a table of values from any graph by reading off a set of values.   **63.** False. In a numerically specified function, only certain values of the function are specified so we cannot know its value on every real number in [0, 10], whereas an algebraically specified function would give values for every real number in [0, 10].   **65.** False: Functions with infinitely many points in their domain (such as $f(x) = x^2$) cannot be specified numerically.   **67.** As the text reminds us: to evaluate f of a quantity (such as $x + h$) replace x everywhere by the *whole quantity* $x + h$, getting $f(x + h) = (x + h)^2 - 1$.
69. They are different portions of the graph of the associated equation $y = f(x)$.   **71.** The graph of $g(x)$ is the same as the graph of $f(x)$, but shifted 5 units to the right.

Section 1.2

1. $N(t) = 200 + 10t$ (N = number of sound files, t = time in days)   **3.** $A(x) = x^2/2$ **5.** $C(x) = 12x$

7. $C(x) = 1,500x + 1,200$ per day **a.** $5,700 **b.** $1,500
c. $1,500 **d.** Variable cost $= \$1,500x$; Fixed cost $= \$1,200$; Marginal cost $= \$1,500$ per piano
e. Graph:

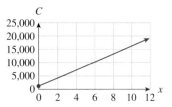

9. a. $C(x) = 0.4x + 70$, $R(x) = 0.5x$, $P(x) = 0.1x - 70$
b. $P(500) = -20$; a loss of $20 **c.** 700 copies
11. $R(x) = 100x$, $P(x) = -2,000 + 90x - 0.2x^2$; at least 24 jerseys.   **13.** $P(x) = -1.7 - 0.02x + 0.0001x^2$; approximately 264 thousand square feet
15. $P(x) = 100x - 5,132$, with domain [0, 405]. For profit, $x \geq 52$ **17.** 5,000 units   **19.** $FC/(SP - VC)$
21. $P(x) = 579.7x - 20,000$, with domain $x \geq 0$; $x = 34.50$ g per day for break even
23. a. Graph:

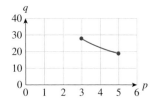

b. Ridership drops by about 3,070 rides per day.
25. a. 358,600 **b.** 361,200 **c.** $6.00   **27.** $240 per skateboard.   **29. a.** $110 per phone. **b.** Shortage of 25 million phones   **31. a.** $3.50 per ride.
Graph:

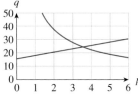

b. A surplus of around 9,170 rides.
33. a. $12,000 **b.** $N(q) = 2,000 + 100q^2 - 500q$; $N(20) = \$32,000$ **35. a. (B) b.** $36.8 billion
37. a. Models **(A)** and **(B) b.** Model **(A)**, which predicts about 3,757 tons of Freon.   **39. a. (C) b.** $20.80 per shirt if the team buys 70 shirts
Graph:

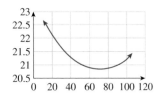

41. A quadratic model (B) is the best choice; the other models either predict perpetually increasing value of the euro or perpetually decreasing value of the euro.   **43.** $A(t) = 5,000$ $(1 + 0.0494/12)^{12t}$; $7,061   **45.** At the beginning of 2016   **47.** 31.0 grams, 9.25 grams, 2.76 grams   **49.** 20,000 years   **51. a.** 1,000 years: 65%, 2,000 years: 42%, 3,000 years: 27%   **b.** 1,600 years   **53.** 30   **55.** Curve-fitting. The model is based on fitting a curve to a given set of observed data.   **57.** The cost of downloading a movie was $4 in January and is decreasing by 20¢ per month.   **59.** Variable; marginal.   **61.** Yes, as long as the supply is going up at a faster rate, as illustrated by the following graph:

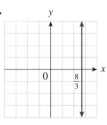

63. Extrapolate both models and choose the one that gives the most reasonable predictions.

Section 1.3

1. $m = 3$ **3.** $m = -1$ **5.** $m = 3/2$ **7.** $f(x) = -x/2 - 2$ **9.** $f(0) = -5$, $f(x) = -x - 5$ **11.** f is linear: $f(x) = 4x + 6$ **13.** g is linear: $g(x) = 2x - 1$ **15.** $-3/2$ **17.** $1/6$ **19.** Undefined   **21.** 0   **23.** $-4/3$

25.

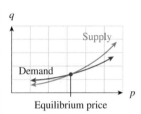

27.

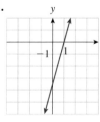

29.

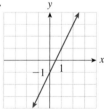

31.

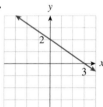

33.

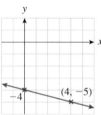

35.

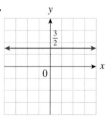

37.

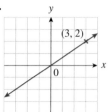

39. 2   **41.** 2   **43.** -2 **45.** Undefined   **47.** 1.5   **49.** -0.09 **51.** $1/2$ **53.** $(d - b)/(c - a)$ **55. a.** 1   **b.** 1/2   **c.** 0   **d.** 3   **e.** $-1/3$ **f.** -1 **g.** Undefined   **h.** $-1/4$ **i.** -2 **57.** $y = 3x$ **59.** $y = \frac{1}{4}x - 1$ **61.** $y = 10x - 203.5$ **63.** $y = -5x + 6$ **65.** $y = -3x + 2.25$ **67.** $y = -x + 12$ **69.** $y = 2x + 4$ **71.** $y = \frac{q}{p}x$ **73.** $y = q$ **75.** Fixed cost $= 8,000$, marginal cost $= 25$ per bicycle   **77.** $C = 145x + 75$; $145 per iPod; $14,575   **79.** $q = -40p + 2000$ **81. a.** $q = -p + 156.4$; 53.4 million phones;   **b.** $1, 1 million   **83. a.** $q = -4,500p + 41,500$ **b.** Rides/day per $1 increase in the fare; ridership decreases by 4,500 rides per day for every $1 increase in the fare.   **c.** 14,500 rides/day   **85. a.** Demand: $q = -60p + 150$; supply: $q = 80p - 60$ **b.** $1.50 each   **87. a.** $q = 40t + 290$ **b.** $q(15) = 890$ million pounds   **89. a.** $N = 1.45t - 4.05$ **b.** Million subscribers per year; the number of Sirius Satellite Radio subscribers grew at a rate of 1.45 million subscribers per year.   **c.** 4.65 million subscribers, considerably less than the actual number.   **91. a.** 2.5 ft/s   **b.** 20 feet along the track   **c.** after 6 seconds   **93. a.** 130 miles per hour   **b.** $s = 130t - 1,300$ **95.** $F = 1.8C + 32$; 86°F; 72°F; 14°F; 7°F   **97.** $I(N) = 0.05N + 50,000$; $N = 1,000,000$; marginal income is $m = 5$¢ per dollar of net profit   **99.** $T(r) = (1/4)r + 45$; $T(100) = 70$°F   **101.** Increasing by $130,000 per year.   **103. a.** $y = -30t + 200$ **b.** $y = 60t - 250$

c. $y = \begin{cases} -30t + 200 & \text{if } 0 \le t \le 5 \\ 60t - 250 & \text{if } 5 < t \le 12 \end{cases}$ **d.** 170

105. $N = \begin{cases} 0.22t + 3 & \text{if } 0 \le t \le 5 \\ -0.15t + 4.85 & \text{if } 5 < t \le 9 \end{cases}$

3.8 million jobs

107. Compute the corresponding successive changes Δx in x and Δy in y, and compute the ratios $\Delta y/\Delta x$. If the answer is always the same number, then the values in the table come from a linear function.   **109.** $f(x) = -\frac{a}{b}x + \frac{c}{b}$. If $b = 0$, then $\frac{a}{b}$ is undefined, and y cannot be specified as a function of x. (The graph of the resulting equation would be a vertical line.)   **111.** slope, 3.   **113.** If m is positive, then y will increase as x increases; if m is negative then y will decrease as x increases; if m is zero then y will not change as x changes.   **115.** The slope increases, because an increase in the y-coordinate of the second point increases Δy while leaving Δx fixed.   **117.** The units of the slope m are units of y (bootlags) per unit of x (zonars). The intercept b is on the y-axis, and is thus measured in units of y (bootlags). Thus, m is measured in bootlags per zonar and b is measured in bootlags.   **119.** It must increase by 10 units each day, including the third.   **121.** (B)   **123.** Increasing the number of items from the break even results in a profit: Because the slope of the revenue graph is larger than the slope of the cost graph, it is higher than the cost graph to the right of the point of intersection, and hence corresponds to a profit.

Section 1.4

1. 6   **3.** 86   **5. a.** 0.5 (better fit) **b.** 0.75
7. a. 27.42 **b.** 27.16 (better fit)
9.
$$y = 1.5x - 0.6667$$
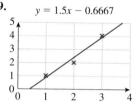
11.
$$y = 0.4118x + 0.9706$$
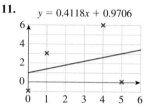

13. a. $r = 0.9959$ (best, not perfect) **b.** $r = 0.9538$
c. $r = 0.3273$ (worst)

15.

x	y	xy	x^2
3	500	1,500	9
5	600	3,000	25
7	800	5,600	49
Totals 15	1,900	10,100	83

$y = 75x + 258.33$; 858.33 million

17. $y = 3.65t + 4.62$; $26.52 billion   **19.** $y = 0.135x + 0.15$;
6.9 million jobs   **21. a.** $y = 1.62x - 23.87$.
Graph:

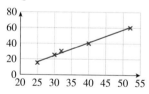

b. Each acre of cultivated land produces about 1.62 tons of soybeans.   **23. a.** Regression line: $y = 0.032x + 0.042$
Graph:

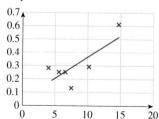

b. There are about 32 motorcycles per 1,000 automobiles.
c. $r \approx 0.7739$; not a strong correlation.

25. a. $p = 0.13t + 0.22$
Graph:

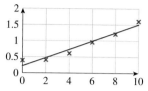

b. Yes; the first and last points lie above the regression line, while the central points lie below it, suggesting a curve.
c.

	A	B	C	D
1	t	p (Observed)	p (predicted)	Residual
2	0	0.38	0.22	0.16
3	2	0.4	0.48	-0.08
4	4	0.6	0.74	-0.14
5	6	0.95	1	-0.05
6	8	1.2	1.26	-0.06
7	10	1.6	1.52	0.08
8				

Notice that the residuals are positive at first, become negative, and then become positive, confirming the impression from the graph.   **27.** The line that passes through (a, b) and (c, d) gives a sum-of-squares error SSE $= 0$, which is the smallest value possible.   **29.** The regression line is the line passing through the given points.   **31.** 0   **33.** No. The regression line through $(-1, 1)$, $(0, 0)$, and $(1, 1)$ passes through none of these points.

Chapter 1 Review

1. a. 1 **b.** -2 **c.** 0 **d.** -1 **3. a.** 1 **b.** 0 **c.** 0 **d.** -1
5.

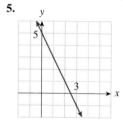

7.

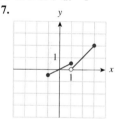

9. Absolute value   **11.** Linear   **13.** Quadratic
15. $y = -3x + 11$ **17.** $y = (1/2)x + 3/2$ **19.** The second line, $y = -x/4 + 1$, is a better fit.   **21.** $y = -0.214x + 1.14$, $r \approx -0.33$ **23. a.** Exponential.
Graph:

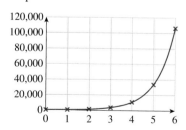

b. The ratios (rounded to 1 decimal place) are:

$V(1)/V(0)$	$V(2)/V(1)$	$V(3)/V(2)$	$V(4)/V(3)$	$V(5)/V(4)$	$V(6)/V(5)$
3	3.3	3.3	3.2	3.2	3.2

They are close to 3.2.

c. About 343,700 visits/day   **25. a.** (A) **b.** (A) Leveling off (B) Rising (C) Rising; they begin to fall after 7 months (D) Rising   **27. a.** 2,080 hits per day **b.** Probably not. This model predicts that Web site traffic will start to decrease as advertising increases beyond $8,500 per month, and then drop toward zero.   **29. a.** $q = -60p + 950$ **b.** 50 novels per month **c.** $10, for a profit of $1,200.

Chapter 2

Section 2.1

1. Vertex: $(-3/2, -1/4)$, y-intercept: 2, x-intercepts: $-2, -1$

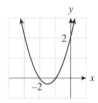

3. Vertex: $(2,0)$, y-intercept: -4, x-intercept: 2

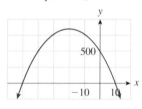

5. Vertex: $(-20, 900)$, y-intercept: 500, x-intercepts: $-50, 10$

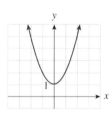

7. Vertex: $(-1/2, -5/4)$, y-intercept: -1, x-intercepts: $-1/2 \pm \sqrt{5}/2$

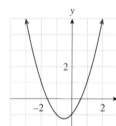

9. Vertex: $(0, 1)$, y-intercept: 1, no x-intercepts

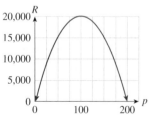

11. $R = -4p^2 + 100p$; Maximum revenue when $p = \$12.50$

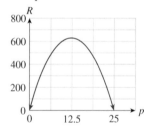

13. $R = -2p^2 + 400p$; Maximum revenue when $p = \$100$

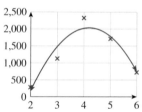

15. $y = -0.7955x^2 + 4.4591x - 1.6000$
17. $y = -1.1667x^2 - 6.1667x - 3.0000$
19. a. Positive because the data suggest a curve that is concave up. **b.** (C) **c.** 1998. Extrapolating in the positive direction leads one to predict more and more steeply rising military expenditure, which may or may not occur; extrapolating in the negative direction predicts continually more an more steeply rising military expenditure as we go back in time, contradicting history. **21.** 2003; about 1.6 million barrels/day   **23.** 5,000 pounds. The model is not trustworthy for vehicle weights larger than 5,000 pounds, as it predicts increasing fuel economy with increasing weight, and 5,000 is close to the upper limit of the domain of the function.   **25.** Maximum revenue when $p = \$140$, $R = \$9,800$ **27.** Maximum revenue with 70 houses, $R = \$9,800,000$ **29. a.** $q = -4,500p + 41,500$ **b.** $4.61 for a daily revenue of $95,680.55 **c.** No **31. a.** $q = -560x + 1,400$; $R = -560x^2 + 1,400x$ **b.** $P = -560x^2 + 1,400x - 30$; $x = \$1.25$; $P = \$845$ per month   **33.** $C = -200x + 620$; $P = -400x^2 + 1,400x - 620$; $x = \$1.75$ per log-on; $P = \$605$ per month   **35. a.** $q = -10p + 400$ **b.** $R = -10p^2 + 400p$ **c.** $C = -30p + 4,200$ **d.** $P = -10p^2 + 430p - 4,200$; $p = \$21.50$ **37.** $f(t) = 6.25t^2 - 100t + 1,200$; $1,425 billion, which is $25 billion lower than the actual value. **39. a.** $S(t) = -391t^2 + 3,278t - 4,844$; Graph:

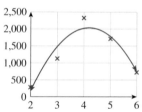

b. $-1,057$ thousand units. This makes no sense, and shows the danger of extrapolating mathematical models beyond their domains. Actual sales in the third quarter of 2008 were 6.9 million.   **41.** The graph is a straight line.   **43.** (C) **45.** Positive; the x coordinate of the vertex is negative, so $-b/(2a)$ must be negative. Because a is positive (the parabola is concave up), this means that b must also be positive to make $-b/(2a)$ negative.   **47.** The x coordinate of the vertex represents the unit price that leads to the maximum revenue, the y coordinate of the vertex gives the maximum possible revenue, the x-intercepts give the unit prices that result in zero revenue, and the y-intercept gives the revenue resulting from zero unit price (which is obviously zero).   **49.** Graph the data to see whether the points suggest a curve rather than a straight line. It the curve suggested by the graph is concave up or concave down, then a quadratic model would be a likely candidate. **51.** No; the graph of a quadratic function is a parabola. In the case of a concave-up parabola, the curve would unrealistically predict sales increasing without bound in the future. In the case of a concave-down parabola, the curve would predict "negative" sales from some point on.   **53.** If $q = mp + b$ (with $m < 0$), then the revenue is given by $R = pq = mp^2 + bp$. This is the equation of a parabola with $a = m < 0$, and so is concave down. Thus, the vertex is the highest point on the parabola, showing that there is a single highest value for R, namely, the y coordinate of the vertex. **55.** Since $R = pq$, the demand must be given by

$$q = \frac{R}{p} = \frac{-50p^2 + 60p}{p} = -50p + 60.$$

Section 2.2

1. 4^x

x	-3	-2	-1	0	1	2	3
$f(x)$	$\frac{1}{64}$	$\frac{1}{16}$	$\frac{1}{4}$	1	4	16	64

3. 3^(-x)

x	-3	-2	-1	0	1	2	3
$f(x)$	27	9	3	1	$\frac{1}{3}$	$\frac{1}{9}$	$\frac{1}{27}$

5. 2*2^x or 2*(2^x)

x	-3	-2	-1	0	1	2	3
$f(x)$	$\frac{1}{4}$	$\frac{1}{2}$	1	2	4	8	16

7. -3*2^(-x)

x	-3	-2	-1	0	1	2	3
$f(x)$	-24	-12	-6	-3	$-\frac{3}{2}$	$-\frac{3}{4}$	$-\frac{3}{8}$

9. 2^x-1

x	-3	-2	-1	0	1	2	3
$f(x)$	$-\frac{7}{8}$	$-\frac{3}{4}$	$-\frac{1}{2}$	0	1	3	7

11. 2^(x-1)

x	-3	-2	-1	0	1	2	3
$f(x)$	$\frac{1}{16}$	$\frac{1}{8}$	$\frac{1}{4}$	$\frac{1}{2}$	1	2	4

13.   **15.**   **17.**

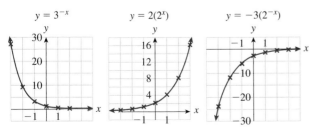

19. Both; $f(x) = 4.5(3^x)$. $g(x) = 2(1/2)^x$, or $2(2^{-x})$
21. Neither   **23.** g; $g(x) = 4(0.2)^x$
25. e^(-2*x) or EXP(-2*x)

x	-3	-2	-1	0	1	2	3
$f(x)$	403.4	54.60	7.389	1	0.1353	0.01832	0.002479

27. 1.01*2.02^(-4*x)

x	-3	-2	-1	0	1	2	3
$f(x)$	4662	280.0	16.82	1.01	0.06066	0.003643	0.0002188

29. 50*(1+1/3.2)^(2*x)

x	-3	-2	-1	0	1	2	3
$f(x)$	9.781	16.85	29.02	50	86.13	148.4	255.6

31. 2^(x-1) *not* 2^x-1   **33.** 2/(1-2^(-4*x)) *not* 2/1-2^-4*x *and not* 2/1-2^(-4*x)
35. (3+x)^(3*x)/(x+1) or ((3+x)^(3*x))/(x+1) *not* (3+x)^(3*x)/x+1 *and not* (3+x^(3*x))/(x+1)
37. 2*e^((1+x)/x) or 2*EXP((1+x)/x) *not* 2*e^1+x/x *and not* 2*e^(1+x)/x *and not* 2*EXP(1+x)/x
39.   **41.**

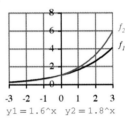

y1 = 1.6^x   y2 = 1.8^x   y1 = 300*1.1^x
                                 y2 = 300*1.1^(2*x)

43.   **45.**

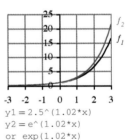

y1 = 2.5^(1.02*x)   y1 = 1000*1.045^(-3*x)
y2 = e^(1.02*x)   y2 = 1000*1.045^(3*x)
or exp(1.02*x)

47. $f(x) = 500(0.5)^x$ **49.** $f(x) = 10(3)^x$
51. $f(x) = 500(0.45)^x$ **53.** $f(x) = -100(1.1)^x$
55. $y = 4(3^x)$ **57.** $y = -1(0.2^x)$ **59.** $y = 2.1213(1.4142^x)$
61. $y = 3.6742(0.9036^x)$ **63.** $f(t) = 5,000e^{0.10t}$
65. $f(t) = 1,000e^{-0.063t}$ **67.** $y = 1.0442(1.7564)^x$
69. $y = 15.1735(1.4822)^x$ **71.** $f(t) = 300(0.5)^t$; 9.375 mg
73. a. Linear model: $F = 65t - 60$. Exponential model: $F = 97.2(1.20)^t$. The exponential model is more appropriate.
b. 418 tons, not too far off the projected figure
75. a. $P = 180(1.01091)^t$ million   **b.** 5 significant digits
c. 345 million   **77. a.** $y = 50,000(1.5^{t/2})$, $t =$ time in years since two years ago   **b.** 91,856 tags   **79.** $y = 1,000(2^{t/3})$; 65,536,000 bacteria after 2 days   **81.** $A(t) = 167(1.18)^t$; 1,695 cases   **83.** $A(t) = 5,000(1 + 0.0494/12)^{12t}$; $7,061
85. At the beginning of 2016   **87.** 491.82   **89.** $A(t) = 1.3e^{-0.3t}$; 2008: 0.53 million; 2009: 0.39 million

91. a.

Year	1950	2000	2050	2100
$C(t)$ parts per million	561	669	799	953

b. 2010 $(t = 260)$

93. a. $P(t) = 0.339(1.169)^t$.
Graph:

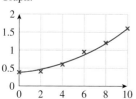

b. $1.9 million

95. a. $n = 1.127(3.544)^t$
Graph:

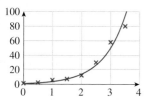

b. 3.544 **c.** 178 million **97.** (B) **99.** Exponential functions of the form $f(x) = Ab^x$ $(b > 0)$ increase rapidly for large values of x. In real-life situations, such as population growth, this model is reliable only for relatively short periods of growth. Eventually, population growth tapers off because of pressures such as limited resources and overcrowding. **101.** The article was published about a year before the "housing bubble" burst in 2006, whereupon house prices started to fall, contrary to the prediction of the graph, as documented in Exercise 90. This shows the danger of using any mathematical model to extrapolate. The blogger was, however, cautious in the choice of words, claiming only to be estimating what the future U.S. median house price "might be." **103.** Linear functions better: cost models where there is a fixed cost and a variable cost; simple interest, where interest is paid on the original amount invested. Exponential models better: compound interest, population growth. (In both of these, the rate of growth depends on the present number of items, rather than on some fixed quantity.) **105.** Take the ratios y_2/y_1 and y_3/y_2. If they are the same, the points fit on an exponential curve. **107.** This reasoning is suspect—the bank need not use its computer resources to update all the accounts every minute, but can instead use the continuous compounding formula to calculate the balance in any account at any time.

Section 2.3

1.

Logarithmic Form	$\log_{10} 10{,}000 = 4$	$\log_4 16 = 2$	$\log_3 27 = 3$	$\log_5 5 = 1$	$\log_7 1 = 0$	$\log_4 \frac{1}{16} = -2$

3.

Exponential Form	$(0.5)^2 = 0.25$	$5^0 = 1$	$10^{-1} = 0.1$	$4^3 = 64$	$2^8 = 256$	$2^{-2} = \frac{1}{4}$

5. 1.4650 **7.** −1.1460 **9.** −0.7324 **11.** 6.2657
13. 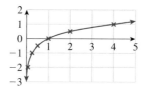 **15.**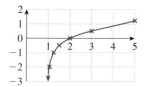

17.

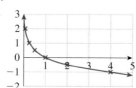

19. $Q = 1000e^{-t \ln 2}$ **21.** $Q = 1000e^{t(\ln 2)/2}$
23. Doubling time $= 2 \ln 2$ **25.** Half-life $= (\ln 2)/4$
27. $f(x) = 4(7.389)^x$ **29.** $f(t) = 2.1e^{0.000\,9995t}$
31. $f(t) = 10e^{-0.01309t}$. **33.** 3.36 years **35.** 11 years
37. 23.1% **39.** 63,000 years old **41.** 11 years
43. 207 months **45.** 12 years **47.** 17.77 years
49. 1,600 years **51. a.** $b = 3^{1/6} \approx 1.20$ **b.** 3.8 months
53. a. $Q(t) = Q_0 e^{-0.139t}$ **b.** 3 years **55.** 2,360 million years
57. 3.2 hours **59.** 3.89 days
61. a. $P(t) = 6.591 \ln(t) - 17.69$ **b.** 1 digit **c.** (A)
63. $57.51 \ln t + 30.96$
Graph:

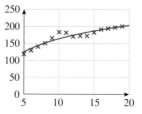

Extrapolating in the positive direction results in a prediction of ever-increasing R&D expenditures by industry. This is reasonable to a point, as expenditures cannot reasonably be expected to increase without bound. Extrapolating in the negative direction eventually leads to negative values, which does not model reality. **65. a.** About 1.259×10^{24} ergs **b.** about 2.24% **c.** $E = 10^{1.5R+11.8}$ **d.** Proof **e.** 1,000 **67. a.** 75 dB, 69 dB, 61 dB **b.** $D = 95 - 20 \log r$ **c.** 57,000 feet
69. Graph:

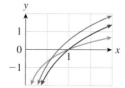

The green curve is $y = \ln x$. The blue curve is $y = 2\ln x$, and the red curve is $y = 2\ln x + 0.5$. Multiplying by A stretches the graph in the y-direction by a factor of A. Adding C moves the graph C units vertically up. **71.** The logarithm of a negative number, were it defined, would be the power to which a base must be raised to give that negative number. But raising a base to a power never results in a negative number, so there can be no such number as the logarithm of a negative number. **73.** Any logarithmic curve $y = \log_b t + C$ will eventually surpass 100%, and hence not be suitable as a long-term predictor of market share. **75.** $\log_4 y$ **77.** 8 **79.** x **81.** Time is increasing logarithmically with population; solving $P = Ab^t$ for t gives $t = \log_b(P/A) = \log_b P - \log_b A$, which is of the form $t = \log_b P + C$. **83.** (Proof)

Section 2.4

1. $N = 7$, $A = 6$, $b = 2$;
7/(1+6*2^-x)

3. $N = 10$, $A = 4$, $b = 0.3$;
10/(1+4*0.3^-x)

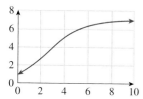

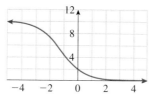

5. $N = 4$, $A = 7$, $b = 1.5$;
4/(1+7*1.5^-x)

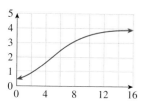

7. $f(x) = \dfrac{200}{1 + 19(2^{-x})}$ **9.** $f(x) = \dfrac{6}{1 + 2^{-x}}$

11. (B) **13.** (B) **15.** (C)

17. $y = \dfrac{7.2}{1 + 2.4(1.05)^{-x}}$ **19.** $y = \dfrac{97}{1 + 2.2(0.942)^{-x}}$

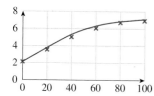

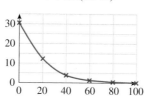

21. a. (A) **b.** 2003 **23. a.** (A) **b.** 20% per year
25. a. 91% **b.** $P(x) \approx 14.33(1.05)^x$ **c.** $38,000

27. $N(t) = \dfrac{10,000}{1 + 9(1.25)^{-t}}$; $N(7) \approx 3{,}463$ cases

29. $N(t) = \dfrac{3,000}{1 + 29(2^{1/5})^{-t}}$; $t = 16$ days

31. a. $A(t) = \dfrac{6.3}{1 + 4.8(1.2)^{-t}}$; 6,300 articles

b. 5,200 articles **33. a.** $B(t) = \dfrac{1,070}{1 + 0.391(1.10)^{-t}}$;

Leveling off value $\approx 1{,}070$

b. $t \approx -9.85$. According to the model, the number of teams was rising fastest about 9.85 years *prior* to 1990; that is, some time during 1980. **c.** The number of men's basketball teams was growing by about 10% per year around 1990.

35. $y = \dfrac{4,500}{1 + 1.1466(1.0357)^{-t}}$; 2013

37. Just as diseases are communicated via the spread of a pathogen (such as a virus), new technology is communicated via the spread of information (such as advertising and publicity). Further, just as the spread of a disease is ultimately limited by the number of susceptible individuals, so the spread of a new technology is ultimately limited by the size of the potential market. **39.** It can be used to predict where the sales of a new commodity might level off. **41.** The curve is still a logistic curve, but decreases when $b > 1$ and increases when $b < 1$. **43.** (Proof)

Chapter 2 Review

1.

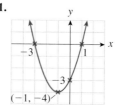

3. f: $f(x) = 5(1/2)^x$, or $5(2^{-x})$

5. **7.**

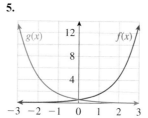

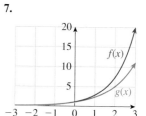

9. $3,484.85 **11.** $3,705.48 **13.** $3,485.50

15. $f(x) = 4.5(9^x)$ **17.** $f(x) = \dfrac{2}{3}3^x$ **19.** $-\dfrac{1}{2}\log_3 4$

21. $\dfrac{1}{3}\log 1.05$

23.

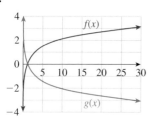

25. $Q = 5e^{-0.00693t}$ **27.** $Q = 2.5e^{0.347t}$ **29.** 10.2 years

31. 10.8 years   **33.** $f(x) = \dfrac{900}{1 + 8(1.5)^{-x}}$

35. $f(x) = \dfrac{20}{1 + 3(0.8)^{-x}}$ **37. a.** \$8,500 per month;
an average of approximately 2,100 hits per day
b. \$29,049 per month   **c.** The fact that -0.000005,
the coefficient of c^2, is negative.   **39. a.** $R = -60p^2 + 950p$;
$p = \$7.92$ per novel, Monthly revenue $= \$3,760.42$
b. $P = -60p^2 + 1,190p - 4,700$; $p = \$9.92$ per novel,
Monthly profit $= \$1,200.42$ **41. a.** 10, 34
b. About 360,000 pounds   **43.** 2008   **45.** 299,000 pounds
47. $n(t) = 10(0.66^t)$ million pounds of lobster   **49.** (C)

Chapter 3

Section 3.1
1. 0   **3.** 4   **5.** Does not exist   **7.** 1.5   **9.** 0.5   **11.** Diverges to
$+\infty$ **13.** 0   **15.** 1   **17.** 0   **19. a.** -2 **b.** -1 **21. a.** 2 **b.** 1
c. 0 **d.** $+\infty$ **23. a.** 0 **b.** 2 **c.** -1 **d.** Does not exist **e.** 2
f. $+\infty$ **25. a.** 1 **b.** 1 **c.** 2 **d.** Does not exist **e.** 1 **f.** 2
27. a. 1 **b.** $+\infty$ **c.** $+\infty$ **d.** $+\infty$ **e.** not defined **f.** -1
29. a. -1 **b.** $+\infty$ **c.** $-\infty$ **d.** Does not exist **e.** 2 **f.** 1   **31.** 210
trillion pesos per year. In the long term, the model predicts that the
value of sold goods in Mexico will approach 210 trillion pesos per
year.   **33.** 7.0; in the long term, the number of research articles in
Physical Review written by researchers in Europe approaches 7,000
per year.   **35.** 470. This suggests that students whose parents earn
an exceptionally large income score an average of 470 on the SAT
verbal test.   **37.** $\lim_{t \to +\infty} p(t) = 15$; the home price index will
approach a value 15% above the 2003 level in the long term.
39. $\lim_{t \to 1^-} C(t) = 0.06$, $\lim_{t \to 1^+} C(t) = 0.08$, so
$\lim_{t \to 1} C(t)$ does not exist.   **41.** $\lim_{t \to +\infty} I(t) = +\infty$,
$\lim_{t \to +\infty}(I(t)/E(t)) \approx 2.5$. In the long term, U.S. imports from
China will rise without bound and be 2.5 times U.S. exports to
China. In the real world, imports and exports cannot rise without
bound. Thus, the given models should not be extrapolated far into
the future.   **43.** To approximate $\lim_{x \to a} f(x)$ numerically, choose
values of x closer and closer to, and on either side of $x = a$, and
evaluate $f(x)$ for each of them. The limit (if it exists) is then the
number that these values of $f(x)$ approach. A disadvantage of this
method is that it may never give the exact value of the limit, but
only an approximation. (However, we can make this as accurate as
we like.)   **45.** Any situation in which there is a sudden change can
be modeled by a function in which $\lim_{t \to a^+} f(t)$ is not the same

as $\lim_{t \to a^-} f(t)$. One example is the value of a stock market
index before and after a crash: $\lim_{t \to a^-} f(t)$ is the value immediately before the crash at time $t = a$, while $\lim_{t \to a^+} f(t)$ is the
value immediately after the crash. Another example might be the
price of a commodity that is suddenly increased from one level to
another.   **47.** It is possible for $\lim_{x \to a} f(x)$ to exist even though
$f(a)$ is not defined. An example is $\lim_{x \to 1} \dfrac{x^2 - 3x + 2}{x - 1}$.
49. The limit may not be defined and, even if it is, may not equal
$f(a)$. See, for example, Exercises 23 and 24.   **51.** An example is
$f(x) = (x - 1)(x - 2)$.

Section 3.2
1. Continuous on its domain   **3.** Continuous on its domain
5. Discontinuous at $x = 0$ **7.** Discontinuous at $x = -1$
9. Continuous on its domain   **11.** Discontinuous at $x = -1$
and 0   **13.** (A), (B), (D), (E)   **15.** 0   **17.** -1 **19.** No
value possible   **21.** -1 **23.** Continuous on its domain
25. Continuous on its domain   **27.** Discontinuity at $x = 0$
29. Discontinuity at $x = 0$ **31.** Continuous on its domain
33. Not unless the domain of the function consists of all real
numbers. (It is impossible for a function to be continuous at
points not in its domain.) For example, $f(x) = 1/x$ is continuous on its domain—the set of nonzero real numbers—but not
at $x = 0$.   **35.** True. If the graph of a function has a break in its
graph at any point a, then it cannot be continuous at the point a.
37. Answers may vary. $f(x) = 1/[(x - 1)(x - 2)(x - 3)]$ is
such a function; it is undefined at $x = 1, 2, 3$ and so its graph consists of three distinct curves.   **39.** Answers may vary.

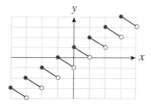

41. Answers may vary. The price of OHaganBooks.com stocks
suddenly drops by \$10 as news spreads of a government
investigation. Let $f(x) =$ Price of OHaganBooks.com stocks.

Section 3.3
1. $x = 1$ **3.** 2   **5.** Determinate; diverges to $+\infty$
7. Determinate; does not exist   **9.** Determinate; diverges to
$-\infty$ **11.** Determinate; 0   **13.** Indeterminate; $-1/3$
15. Indeterminate; 0   **17.** Determinate; 0   **19.** Determinate;
-60 **21.** 1   **23.** 2   **25.** 0   **27.** 6   **29.** 4   **31.** 2   **33.** 0   **35.** 0
37. 12   **39.** $+\infty$ **41.** Does not exist; left and right (infinite)
limits differ.   **43.** $-\infty$ **45.** Does not exist   **47.** $+\infty$ **49.** 3/2
51. 1/2   **53.** $+\infty$ **55.** 0   **57.** 3/2   **59.** 1/2   **61.** $-\infty$ **63.** 0
65. 12   **67.** 0   **69.** $+\infty$ **71.** 0   **73.** Discontinuity at $x = 0$
75. Continuous everywhere   **77.** Discontinuity at $x = 0$
79. Discontinuity at $x = 0$ **81. a.** $\lim_{t \to 5^-} N(t) = \lim_{t \to 5^+}$
$N(t) = 4.1$; shortly before and after 2000 ($t = 5$) the number
of workers employed in manufacturing jobs in Mexico was

close to 4.1 million. **b.** N is continuous at $t = 5$; no abrupt changes **83. a.** 0.49, 1.16. Shortly before 1999 annual advertising expenditures were close to $0.49 billion. Shortly after 1999 annual advertising expenditures were close to $1.16 billion. **b.** Not continuous; movie advertising expenditures jumped suddenly in 1999. **85.** 1.59; if the trend continued indefinitely, the annual spending on police would be 1.59 times the annual spending on courts in the long run. **87.** 825; in the long term, annual revenues will approach $825 million. **89.** $\lim_{t \to +\infty} I(t) = +\infty$, $\lim_{t \to +\infty} (I(t)/E(t)) = 2.5$. In the long term, U.S. imports from China will rise without bound and be 2.5 times U.S. exports to China. In the real world, imports and exports cannot rise without bound. Thus, the given models should not be extrapolated far into the future. **91.** $\lim_{t \to +\infty} p(t) = 100$. The percentage of children who learn to speak approaches 100% as their age increases. **93.** To evaluate $\lim_{x \to a} f(x)$ algebraically, first check whether $f(x)$ is a closed-form function. Then check whether $x = a$ is in its domain. If so, the limit is just $f(a)$; that is, it is obtained by substituting $x = a$. If not, then try to first simplify $f(x)$ in such a way as to transform it into a new function such that $x = a$ is in its domain, and then substitute. A disadvantage of this method is that it is sometimes extremely difficult to evaluate limits algebraically, and rather sophisticated methods are often needed. **95.** She is wrong. Closed-form functions are continuous only at points in their domains, and $x = 2$ is not in the domain of the closed-form function $f(x) = 1/(x - 2)^2$. **97.** Answers may vary. (1) See Example 2: $\lim_{x \to 2} \dfrac{x^3 - 8}{x - 2}$, which leads to the indeterminate form $0/0$ but the limit is 12. (2) $\lim_{x \to +\infty} \dfrac{60x}{2x}$, which leads to the indeterminate form ∞/∞, but where the limit exists and equals 30. **99.** The statement may not be true, for instance, if $f(x) = \begin{cases} x + 2 & \text{if } x < 0 \\ 2x - 1 & \text{if } x \geq 0 \end{cases}$, then $f(0)$ is defined and equals -1, and yet $\lim_{x \to 0} f(x)$ does not exist. The statement can be corrected by requiring that f be a closed-form function: "If f is a closed form function, and $f(a)$ is defined, then $\lim_{x \to a} f(x)$ exists and equals $f(a)$." **101.** Answers may vary, for example $f(x) = \begin{cases} 0 & \text{if } x \text{ is any number other than 1 or 2} \\ 1 & \text{if } x = 1 \text{ or } 2 \end{cases}$

103. Answers may vary.

(1) $\lim_{x \to +\infty} [(x + 5) - x] = \lim_{x \to +\infty} 5 = 5$

(2) $\lim_{x \to +\infty} [x^2 - x] = \lim_{x \to +\infty} x(x - 1) = +\infty$

(3) $\lim_{x \to +\infty} [(x - 5) - x] = \lim_{x \to +\infty} -5 = -5$

Section 3.4

1. -3 **3.** 0.3   **5.** $-\$25,000$ per month   **7.** -200 items per dollar   **9.** $1.33 per month   **11.** 0.75 percentage point increase in unemployment per 1 percentage point increase in the deficit   **13.** 4   **15.** 2   **17.** 7/3

19.

h	Ave. Rate of Change
1	2
0.1	0.2
0.01	0.02
0.001	0.002
0.0001	0.0002

21.

h	Ave. Rate of Change
1	-0.1667
0.1	-0.2381
0.01	-0.2488
0.001	-0.2499
0.0001	-0.24999

23.

h	Ave. Rate of Change
1	9
0.1	8.1
0.01	8.01
0.001	8.001
0.0001	8.0001

25. a. $25 billion per year; world military expenditure increased at an average rate of $25 billion per year during 1994–2006. **b.** $50 billion per year; world military expenditure increased at an average rate of $50 billion per year during 1998–2006. **27. a.** $-20,000$ barrels/year; during 2002–2007, daily oil production by **Pemex** was decreasing at an average rate of 20,000 barrels of oil per year. **b.** (C) **29. a.** 1.7; the percentage of mortgages classified as subprime was increasing at an average rate of around 1.7 percentage points per year between 2000 and 2006. **b.** 2004–2006 **31. a.** The second and third quarter of 2007. During the second and third quarter of 2007 iPhone sales were increasing at an average rate of 1,022,500 phones per quarter. **b.** Fourth quarter of 2007 and first quarter of 2008. During the fourth quarter of 2007 and first quarter of 2008 iPhone sales were decreasing at an average rate of 797,500 phones per quarter. **33. a.** [3, 5]; -0.25 thousand articles per year. During the period 1993–1995, the number of articles authored by U.S. researchers decreased at an average rate of 250 articles per year. **b.** Percentage rate ≈ -0.1765, Average rate $= -0.09$ thousand articles/year. Over the period 1993–2003, the number of articles authored by U.S. researchers decreased at an average rate of 90 per year, representing a 17.65% decrease over that period. **35. a.** 12 teams per year **b.** Decreased **37. a.** (C) **b.** (A) **c.** (B) **d.** Approximately -0.0063 (to two significant digits) billion dollars per year ($-\$6,300,000$ per year). This is much less than the (positive) slope of the regression line, $0.0125 \approx 0.013$ billion dollars per year ($13,000,000 per year). **39.** Answers may vary. Graph:

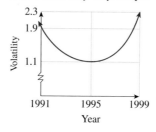

41. The index was increasing at an average rate of 300 points per day.   **43. a.** $0.15 per year **b.** No; according to the model, during that 25-year period the price of oil went down from around $93 to a low of around $25 in 1993 before climbing back up.   **45. a.** 47.3 new cases per day; the number of SARS cases was growing at an average rate of 47.3 new cases per day over the period March 17 to March 23. **b.** (A) **47. a.** 8.85 manatee deaths per 100,000 boats; 23.05 manatee deaths per 100,000 boats **b.** More boats result in more manatee deaths per additional boat.   **49. a.** $-0.88, -0.79, -0.69, -0.60, -0.51, -0.42$ **b.** For household incomes between $40,000 and $40,500, the poverty rate decreases at an average rate of 0.69 percentage points per $1,000 increase in the median household income. **c.** (B) **d.** (B)   **51.** The average rate of change of f over an interval $[a, b]$ can be determined numerically, using a table of values, graphically, by measuring the slope of the corresponding line segment through two points on the graph, or algebraically, using an algebraic formula for the function. Of these, the least precise is the graphical method, because it relies on reading coordinates of points on a graph.   **53.** No, the formula for the average rate of a function f over $[a, b]$ depends only on $f(a)$ and $f(b)$, and not on any values of f between a and b.   **55.** Answers will vary. Graph:

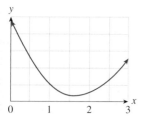

57. 6 units of quantity A per unit of quantity C   **59.** (A)
61. Yes. Here is an example:

Year	2000	2001	2002	2003
Revenue ($ billion)	$10	$20	$30	$5

63. (A)

Section 3.5
1. 6   **3.** -5.5
5.

h	1	0.1	0.01
Ave. rate	39	39.9	39.99

Instant. Rate $= \$40$ per day

7.

h	1	0.1	0.01
Ave. Rate	140	66.2	60.602

Instant. Rate $= \$60$ per day

9.

h	10	1
C_{ave}	4.799	4.7999

11.

h	10	1
C_{ave}	99.91	99.90

$C'(1,000) = \$4.8$ per item $C'(100) = \$99.9$ per item
13. 1/2   **15.** 0   **17. a.** R b. P **19. a.** P b. R **21. a.** Q b. P
23. a. Q b. R c. P **25. a.** R b. Q c. P **27. a.** $(1, 0)$
b. None **c.** $(-2, 1)$ **29. a.** $(-2, 0.3)$, $(0, 0)$, $(2, -0.3)$
b. None **c.** None   **31.** $(a, f(a))$; $f'(a)$ **33.** (B)
35. a. (A) **b.** (C) **c.** (B) **d.** (B) **e.** (C)   **37.** -2 **39.** -1.5
41. -5 **43.** 16   **45.** 0   **47.** -0.0025

49. a. 3 **b.** $y = 3x + 2$ **51. a.** $\dfrac{3}{4}$ **b.** $y = \dfrac{3}{4}x + 1$

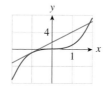 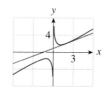

53. a. $\dfrac{1}{4}$ **b.** $y = \dfrac{1}{4}x + 1$

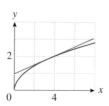

55. 1.000   **57.** 1.000   **59.** (C)   **61.** (A)   **63.** (F)
65. Increasing for $x < 0$; decreasing for $x > 0$.   **67.** Increasing for $x < -1$ and $x > 1$; decreasing for $-1 < x < 1$
69. Increasing for $x > 1$; decreasing for $x < 1$.   **71.** Increasing for $x < 0$; decreasing for $x > 0$.   **73.** $x = -1.5, x = 0$
Graph:

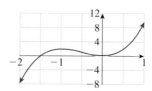

75. Note: Answers depend on the form of technology used. Excel ($h = 0.1$):

	A	B	C	D	E
1	x	f(x)	f'(x)	xmin	4
2	4	6	-4.545454545	h	0.1
3		4.1 5.545454545	-3.787878788		
4		4.2 5.166666667	-3.205128205		
5		4.3 4.846153846	-2.747252747		
6		4.4 4.571428571	-2.380952381		
7		4.5 4.333333333	-2.083333333		
8		4.6	4.125 -1.838235294		
9		4.7 3.941176471	-1.633986928		
10		4.8 3.777777778	-1.461988304		
11		4.9 3.631578947	-1.315789474		
12		5	3.5		
13					
14					

Graphs:

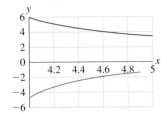

77. $q(100) = 50{,}000$, $q'(100) = -500$. A total of 50,000 pairs of sneakers can be sold at a price of $100, but the demand is decreasing at a rate of 500 pairs per $1 increase in the price. **79. a.** -0.05; daily oil imports from Mexico in 2005 were 1.6 million barrels and declining at a rate of 0.05 million barrels (or 50,000 barrels) per year. **b.** Decreasing **81. a.** (B) **b.** (B) **c.** (A) **d.** 1992 **e.** 0.05; in 1996, the total number of state prisoners was increasing at a rate of approximately 50,000 prisoners per year. **83. a.** -96 ft/s **b.** -128 ft/s **85. a.** $0.60 per year; the price per barrel of crude oil in constant 2008 dollars was growing at an average rate of about 60¢ per year over the 28-year period beginning at the start of 1980. **b.** $-$12 per year; the price per barrel of crude oil in constant 2008 dollars was dropping at an instantaneous rate of about $12 per year at the start of 1980. **c.** The price of oil was decreasing in January 1980, but eventually began to increase (making the average rate of change in part (a) positive). **87. a.** 144.7 new cases per day; the number of SARS cases was growing at a rate of about 144.7 new cases per day on March 27. **b.** (A) **89.** $S(5) \approx 109$, $\dfrac{dS}{dt}\bigg|_{t=5} \approx 9.1$. After 5 weeks, sales are 109 pairs of sneakers per week, and sales are increasing at a rate of 9.1 pairs per week each week. **91.** $A(0) = 4.5$ million; $A'(0) = 60{,}000$ subscribers/week **93. a.** 60% of children can speak at the age of 10 months. At the age of 10 months, this percentage is increasing by 18.2 percentage points per month. **b.** As t increases, p approaches 100 percentage points (all children eventually learn to speak), and dp/dt approaches zero because the percentage stops increasing. **95. a.** $A(6) \approx 12.0$; $A'(6) \approx 1.4$; at the start of 2006, about 12% of U.S. mortgages were subprime, and this percentage was increasing at a rate of about 1.4 percentage points per year **b.** Graphs:

Graph of A:

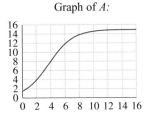

Graph of A':

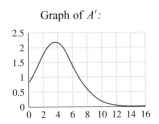

From the graphs, $A(t)$ approaches 15 as t becomes large (in terms of limits, $\lim_{x \to +\infty} A(t) = 15$) and $A'(t)$ approaches 0 as t becomes large (in terms of limits, $\lim_{x \to +\infty} A'(t) = 0$).

Interpretation: If the trend modeled by the function A had continued indefinitely, in the long term 15% of U.S. mortgages would have been subprime, and this percentage would not be changing. **97. a.** (D) **b.** 33 days after the egg was laid **c.** 50 days after the egg was laid. Graph:

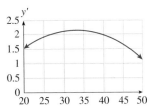

99. $L(.95) = 31.2$ meters and $L'(.95) = -304.2$ meters/warp. Thus, at a speed of warp 0.95, the spaceship has an observed length of 31.2 meters and its length is decreasing at a rate of 304.2 meters per unit warp, or 3.042 meters per increase in speed of 0.01 warp. **101.** The difference quotient is not defined when $h = 0$ because there is no such number as $0/0$. **103.** (D) **105.** The derivative is positive and decreasing toward zero. **107.** Company B. Although the company is currently losing money, the derivative is positive, showing that the profit is increasing. Company A, on the other hand, has profits that are declining. **109.** (C) is the only graph in which the instantaneous rate of change on January 1 is greater than the one-month average rate of change. **111.** The tangent to the graph is horizontal at that point, and so the graph is almost horizontal near that point. **113.** Answers may vary.

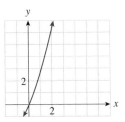

115. If $f(x) = mx + b$, then its average rate of change over any interval $[x, x + h]$ is $\dfrac{m(x + h) + b - (mx + b)}{h} = m$. Because this does not depend on h, the instantaneous rate is also equal to m. **117.** Increasing because the average rate of change appears to be rising as we get closer to 5 from the left. (See the bottom row.)

119. Answers may vary.

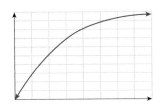

121. Answers may vary.

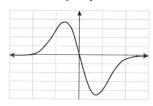

123. (B)   **125.** Answers will vary.

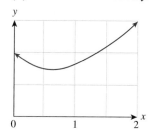

Section 3.6

1. 4   **3.** 3   **5.** 7   **7.** 4   **9.** 14   **11.** 1   **13.** m **15.** $2x$

17. 3   **19.** $6x + 1$ **21.** $2 - 2x$ **23.** $3x^2 + 2$ **25.** $1/x^2$

27. m **29.** -1.2 **31.** 30.6   **33.** -7.1 **35.** 4.25   **37.** -0.6

39. $y = 4x - 7$ **41.** $y = -2x - 4$ **43.** $y = -3x - 1$

45. $s'(t) = -32t$; $s'(4) = -128$ ft/s

47. $\dfrac{dI}{dt} = -0.030t + 0.1$, daily oil imports were decreasing at a rate of 0.11 million barrels per year.   **49.** $R'(t) = 24t + 500$; annual U.S. sales of bottled water were increasing by 620 million gallons per year in 2005.   **51.** $f'(8) = 26.6$ manatee deaths per 100,000 boats. At a level of 800,000 boats, the number of manatee deaths is increasing at a rate of 26.6 manatees per 100,000 additional boats.   **53. a.** Yes; $\lim_{t \to 8^-} C(t) = \lim_{t \to 8^+} C(t) = 1.24 = C(8)$. **b.** No; $\lim_{t \to 8^-} C'(t) = 0.08$ while $\lim_{t \to 8^+} C'(t) = 0.13$. Until 1998, the cost of a Super Bowl ad was increasing at a rate of $80,000 per year. Immediately thereafter, it was increasing at a rate of $130,000 per year.   **55.** The algebraic method because it gives the exact value of the derivative. The other two approaches give only approximate values (except in some special cases).   **57.** The error is in the second line: $f(x + h)$ is *not* equal to $f(x) + h$. For instance, if $f(x) = x^2$, then $f(x + h) = (x + h)^2$, whereas $f(x) + h = x^2 + h$.   **59.** The error is in the second line: One could only cancel the h if it were a *factor* of both the numerator and denominator; it is not a factor of the numerator.   **61.** Because the algebraic computation of $f'(a)$ is exact and not an approximation, it makes no difference whether one uses the balanced difference quotient or the ordinary difference quotient in the algebraic computation.   **63.** The computation results in a limit that cannot be evaluated.

Chapter 3 Review

1. 5   **3.** Does not exist   **5. a.** -1 **b.** 3 **c.** Does not exist

7. $-4/5$ **9.** -1 **11.** Does not exist   **13.** Does not exist

15. $+\infty$ **17.** Diverges to $-\infty$ **19.** 0   **21.** 2/5   **23.** 1

25.

h	1	0.01	0.001
Ave. Rate of Change	-0.5	-0.9901	-0.9990

Slope ≈ -1

27.

h	1	0.01	0.001
Avg. Rate of Change	6.3891	2.0201	2.0020

Slope ≈ 2

29. (i) P **(ii)** Q **(iii)** R **(iv)** S **31. (i)** Q **(ii)** None **(iii)** None **(iv)** None   **33. a.** (B) **b.** (B) **c.** (B) **d.** (A) **e.** (C)

35. $2x + 1$ **37.** $2/x^2$

39.

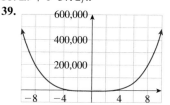

41.

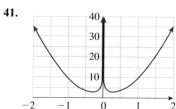

43. a. $P(3) = 25$: O'Hagan purchased the stock at $25. $\lim_{t \to 3^-} P(t) = 25$: The value of the stock had been approaching $25 up the time he bought it. $\lim_{t \to 3^+} P(t) = 10$: The value of the stock dropped to $10 immediately after he bought it. **b.** Continuous but not differentiable. Interpretation: the stock price changed continuously but suddenly reversed direction (and started to go up) the instant O'Hagan sold it.

45. a. $\lim_{t \to 3} p(t) \approx 40$; $\lim_{t \to +\infty} p(t) = +\infty$. Close to 2007 ($t = 3$), the home price index was about 40. In the long term, the home price index will rise without bound. **b.** 10 (The slope of the linear portion of the curve is 10.) In the long term, the home price index will rise about 10 points per year.

47. a. 500 books per week **b.** [3, 4], [4, 5] **c.** [3, 5]; 650 books per week   **49. a.** 3 percentage points per year **b.** 0 percentage points per year **c.** (D)   **51. a.** $72t + 250$ **b.** 322 books per week **c.** 754 books per week.

Chapter 4

Section 4.1

1. $5x^4$ **3.** $-4x^{-3}$ **5.** $-0.25x^{-0.75}$ **7.** $8x^3 + 9x^2$

9. $-1 - 1/x^2$ **11.** $\dfrac{dy}{dx} = 10(0) = 0$ (constant multiple and power rule)   **13.** $\dfrac{dy}{dx} = \dfrac{d}{dx}(x^2) + \dfrac{d}{dx}(x)$ (sum rule) $= 2x + 1$

(power rule)   **15.** $\dfrac{dy}{dx} = \dfrac{d}{dx}(4x^3) + \dfrac{d}{dx}(2x) - \dfrac{d}{dx}$ (1) (sum and difference)

17. $f'(x) = 2x - 3$ **19.** $f'(x) = 1 + 0.5x^{-0.5}$

21. $g'(x) = -2x^{-3} + 3x^{-2}$ **23.** $g'(x) = -\dfrac{1}{x^2} + \dfrac{2}{x^3}$

25. $h'(x) = -\dfrac{0.8}{x^{1.4}}$ **27.** $h'(x) = -\dfrac{2}{x^3} - \dfrac{6}{x^4}$

29. $r'(x) = -\dfrac{2}{3x^2} + \dfrac{0.1}{2x^{1.1}}$ **31.** $r'(x) = \dfrac{2}{3} - \dfrac{0.1}{2x^{0.9}} - \dfrac{4.4}{3x^{2.1}}$

33. $t'(x) = |x|/x - 1/x^2$ **35.** $s'(x) = \dfrac{1}{2\sqrt{x}} - \dfrac{1}{2x\sqrt{x}}$

37. $s'(x) = 3x^2$ **39.** $t'(x) = 1 - 4x$ **41.** $2.6x^{0.3} + 1.2x^{-2.2}$
43. $1.2(1 - |x|/x)$ **45.** $3at^2 - 4a$ **47.** $5.15x^{9.3} - 99x^{-2}$

49. $-\dfrac{2.31}{t^{2.1}} - \dfrac{0.3}{t^{0.4}}$ **51.** $4\pi r^2$ **53.** 3 **55.** -2 **57.** -5

59. $y = 3x + 2$ **61.** $y = \dfrac{3}{4}x + 1$

    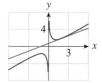

63. $y = \dfrac{1}{4}x + 1$ **65.** $x = -3/4$

67. No such values

69. $x = 1, -1$

73.

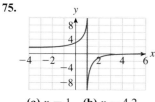

(a) $x = 3$ **(b)** None

75.

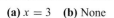

(a) $x = 1$ **(b)** $x = 4.2$

77. a. $f'(1) = 1/3$ **b.** Not differentiable at 0
79. a. Not differentiable at 1   **b.** Not differentiable at 0
81. Yes; 0   **83.** Yes; 12   **85.** No; 3   **87.** Yes; 3/2
89. Yes; diverges to $-\infty$ **91.** Yes; diverges to $-\infty$
93. $P'(t) = 0.9t - 12$; $P'(20) = 6$; the price of a barrel of crude oil was increasing at a rate of $6 per year in 2000.

95. a. $n'(t) = -1.12t + 14$ **b.** 7 teams/year   **c.** Decreases; $n'(t)$ is a linear function with negative slope, so it decreases with increasing t.   **97.** 0.55   **99. a.** $s'(t) = -32t$; 0, -32, -64, -96, -128 ft/s   **b.** 5 seconds; downward at 160 ft/s
101. a. $S'(t) = -780t + 3{,}300$; dropping at a rate of 600,000 iPhones per quarter.   **b.** (B); geometrically: The graph is rising but less steeply, over [2, 4]. Algebraically: The slope is the derivative: $-780t + 3{,}300$, which is positive but decreasing over [2, 4].   **103. a.** $f'(x) = 7.1x - 30.2$ manatees per 100,000 boats.   **b.** Increasing; the number of manatees killed per additional 100,000 boats increases as the number of boats increases.   **c.** $f'(8) = 26.6$ manatees per 100,000 additional boats. At a level of 800,000 boats, the number of manatee deaths is increasing at a rate of 26.6 manatees per 100,000 additional boats.   **105. a.** $c(t) - m(t)$ measures the combined market share of the other three providers (Comcast, Earthlink, and AOL); $c'(t) - m'(t)$ measures the rate of change of the combined market share of the other three providers.   **b.** (A)   **c.** (A)   **d.** 3.72% per year. In 1992, the combined market share of the other three providers was increasing at a rate of about 3.72 percentage points per year.   **107.** After graphing the curve $y = 3x^2$, draw the line passing through $(-1, 3)$ with slope -6.   **109.** The slope of the tangent line of g is twice the slope of the tangent line of f.   **111.** $g'(x) = -f'(x)$ **113.** The left-hand side is not equal to the right-hand side. The *derivative* of the left-hand side is equal to the right-hand side, so your friend should have written $\dfrac{d}{dx}\left(3x^4 + 11x^5\right) = 12x^3 + 55x^4$.

115. The derivative of a constant times a function is the constant times the derivative of the function, so that $f'(x) = (2)(2x) = 4x$. Your enemy mistakenly computed the *derivative* of the constant times the derivative of the function. (The derivative of a product of two functions is not the product of the derivative of the two functions. The rule for taking the derivative of a product is discussed later in the chapter.).
117. For a general function f, the derivative of f is defined to be $f'(x) = \lim\limits_{h \to 0} \dfrac{f(x + h) - f(x)}{h}$. One then finds by calculation that the derivative of the specific function x^n is nx^{n-1}. In short, nx^{n-1} is the derivative of a specific function: $f(x) = x^n$, it is not the *definition* of the derivative of a general function or even the definition of the derivative of the function $f(x) = x^n$.
119. Answers may vary.

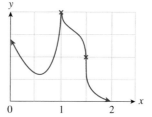

Section 4.2

1. $C'(1,000) = \$4.80$ per item   **3.** $C'(100) = \$99.90$ per item
5. $C'(x) = 4$; $R'(x) = 8 - x/500$; $P'(x) = 4 - x/500$;
$P'(x) = 0$ when $x = 2,000$. Thus, at a production level of 2,000,
the profit is stationary (neither increasing nor decreasing) with
respect to the production level. This may indicate a maximum
profit at a production level of 2,000.   **7. a.** (B) **b.** (C) **c.** (C)
9. a. $C'(x) = 2,250 - 0.04x$. The cost is going up at a rate of
$2,249,840 per television commercial. The exact cost of airing
the fifth television commercial is $C(5) - C(4) = \$2,249,820$.
b. $\overline{C}(x) = 150/x + 2,250 - 0.02x$; $\overline{C}(4) = \$2,287,420$ per
television commercial. The average cost of airing the first four
television commercials is $2,287,420.   **11. a.** $R'(x) = 0.90$,
$P'(x) = 0.80 - 0.002x$ **b.** Revenue: $450, Profit: $80, Marginal
revenue: $0.90, Marginal profit: $-\$0.20$. The total revenue from
the sale of 500 copies is $450. The profit from the production
and sale of 500 copies is $80. Approximate revenue from the
sale of the 501st copy is 90¢. Approximate loss from the sale of
the 501st copy is 20¢. **c.** $x = 400$. The profit is a maximum
when you produce and sell 400 copies.   **13.** The profit on the
sale of 1,000 DVDs is $3,000, and is decreasing at a rate of $3
per additional DVD sold.   **15.** $P \approx \$257.07$ and
$dP/dx \approx 5.07$. Your current profit is $257.07 per month, and
this would increase at a rate of $5.07 per additional magazine
in sales.   **17. a.** $2.50 per pound **b.** $R(q) = 20,000/q^{0.5}$
c. $R(400) = \$1,000$. This is the monthly revenue that will
result from setting the price at $2.50 per pound. $R'(400) =$
$-\$1.25$ per pound of tuna. Thus, at a demand level of 400
pounds per month, the revenue is decreasing at a rate of
$1.25 per pound. **d.** The fishery should raise the price
(to reduce the demand).   **19.** $P'(50) = \$350$. This means that,
at an employment level of 50 workers, the firm's daily profit will
increase at a rate of $350 per additional worker it hires.
21. a. (B) **b.** (B) **c.** (C)
23. a. $C(x) = 500,000 + 1,600,000x - 100,000\sqrt{x}$;

$$C'(x) = 1,600,000 - \frac{50,000}{\sqrt{x}};$$

$$\overline{C}(x) = \frac{500,000}{x} + 1,600,000 - \frac{100,000}{\sqrt{x}}$$

b. $C'(3) \approx \$1,570,000$ per spot, $\overline{C}(3) \approx \$1,710,000$ per spot.
The average cost will decrease as x increases.
25. a. $C'(q) = 200q$; $C'(10) = \$2,000$ per one-pound
reduction in emissions. **b.** $S'(q) = 500$. Thus $S'(q) = C'(q)$
when $500 = 200q$, or $q = 2.5$ pounds per day reduction.
c. $N(q) = C(q) - S(q) = 100q^2 - 500q + 4,000$. This is a
parabola with lowest point (vertex) given by $q = 2.5$. The net
cost at this production level is $N(2.5) = \$3,375$ per day. The

value of q is the same as that for part (b). The net cost to the
firm is minimized at the reduction level for which the cost of
controlling emissions begins to increase faster than the subsidy.
This is why we get the answer by setting these two rates of
increase equal to each other.   **27.** $M'(10) \approx 0.0002557$ mpg/mph.
This means that, at a speed of 10 mph, the fuel economy is
increasing at a rate of 0.0002557 miles per gallon per 1-mph
increase in speed. $M'(60) = 0$ mpg/mph. This means that, at a
speed of 60 mph, the fuel economy is neither increasing nor
decreasing with increasing speed. $M'(70) \approx -0.00001799$. This
means that, at 70 mph, the fuel economy is decreasing at a rate
of 0.00001799 miles per gallon per 1-mph increase in speed.
Thus 60 mph is the most fuel-efficient speed for the car.
29. (C)   **31.** (D)   **33.** (B)   **35.** Cost is often measured as a
function of the number of items x. Thus, $C(x)$ is the cost of
producing (or purchasing, as the case may be) x items.
a. The average cost function $\overline{C}(x)$ is given by $\overline{C}(x) = C(x)/x$.
The marginal cost function is the derivative, $C'(x)$, of the cost
function. **b.** The average cost $\overline{C}(r)$ is the slope of the line
through the origin and the point on the graph where $x = r$.
The marginal cost of the rth unit is the slope of the tangent
to the graph of the cost function at the point where $x = r$.
c. The average cost function $\overline{C}(x)$ gives the average cost of
producing the first x items. The marginal cost function $C'(x)$ is
the rate at which cost is changing with respect to the number of
items x, or the incremental cost per item, and approximates the
cost of producing the $(x + 1)$st item.   **37.** The marginal cost
39. Not necessarily. For example, it may be the case that the
marginal cost of the 101st item is larger than the average cost of
the first 100 items (even though the marginal cost is decreasing). Thus, adding this additional item will *raise* the average
cost.   **41.** The circumstances described suggest that the average
cost function is at a relatively low point at the current production level, and so it would be appropriate to advise the company
to maintain current production levels; raising or lowering the
production level will result in increasing average costs.

Section 4.3

1. 3   **3.** $3x^2$ **5.** $2x + 3$ **7.** $210x^{1.1}$ **9.** $-2/x^2$
11. $2x/3$ **13.** $3(4x^2 - 1) + 3x(8x) = 36x^2 - 3$
15. $3x^2(1 - x^2) + x^3(-2x) = 3x^2 - 5x^4$
17. $2(2x + 3) + (2x + 3)(2) = 8x + 12$ **19.** $3\sqrt{x}/2$
21. $(x^2 - 1) + 2x(x + 1) = (x + 1)(3x - 1)$
23. $(x^{-0.5} + 4)(x - x^{-1}) + (2x^{0.5} + 4x - 5)(1 + x^{-2})$
25. $8(2x^2 - 4x + 1)(x - 1)$
27. $(1/3.2 - 3.2/x^2)(x^2 + 1) + 2x(x/3.2 + 3.2/x)$
29. $2x(2x + 3)(7x + 2) + 2x^2(7x + 2) + 7x^2(2x + 3)$

31. $5.3(1 - x^{2.1})(x^{-2.3} - 3.4) - 2.1x^{1.1}(5.3x - 1)(x^{-2.3} - 3.4) - 2.3x - 3.3(5.3x - 1)(1 - x^{2.1})$

33. $\dfrac{1}{2\sqrt{x}}\left(\sqrt{x} + \dfrac{1}{x^2}\right) + (\sqrt{x} + 1)\left(\dfrac{1}{2\sqrt{x}} - \dfrac{2}{x^3}\right)$ **35.** $\dfrac{2(3x - 1) - 3(2x + 4)}{(3x - 1)^2} = -14/(3x - 1)^2$

37. $\dfrac{(4x + 4)(3x - 1) - 3(2x^2 + 4x + 1)}{(3x - 1)^2} = (6x^2 - 4x - 7)/(3x - 1)^2$

39. $\dfrac{(2x - 4)(x^2 + x + 1) - (x^2 - 4x + 1)(2x + 1)}{(x^2 + x + 1)^2} = (5x^2 - 5)/(x^2 + x + 1)^2$

41. $\dfrac{(0.23x^{-0.77} - 5.7)(1 - x^{-2.9}) - 2.9x^{-3.9}(x^{0.23} - 5.7x)}{(1 - x^{-2.9})^2}$ **43.** $\dfrac{\frac{1}{2}x^{-1/2}(x^{1/2} - 1) - \frac{1}{2}x^{-1/2}(x^{1/2} + 1)}{(x^{1/2} - 1)^2} = \dfrac{-1}{\sqrt{x}\left(\sqrt{x} - 1\right)^2}$

45. $-3/x^4$ **47.** $\dfrac{[(x + 1) + (x + 3)](3x - 1) - 3(x + 3)(x + 1)}{(3x - 1)^2} = (3x^2 - 2x - 13)/(3x - 1)^2$

49. $\dfrac{[(x + 1)(x + 2) + (x + 3)(x + 2) + (x + 3)(x + 1)](3x - 1) - 3(x + 3)(x + 1)(x + 2)}{(3x - 1)^2}$

51. $4x^3 - 2x$ **53.** 64   **55.** 3
57. Difference; $4x^3 - 12x^2 + 2x - 480$
59. Sum; $1 + 2/(x + 1)^2$

61. Product; $\left[\dfrac{x}{x + 1}\right] + (x + 2)\dfrac{1}{(x + 1)^2}$

63. Difference; $2x - 1 - 2/(x + 1)^2$ **65.** $y = 12x - 8$
67. $y = x/4 + 1/2$ **69.** $y = -2$ **71.** $q'(5) = 1,000$ units/
month (sales are increasing at a rate of 1,000 units per month);
$p'(5) = -\$10$/month (the price of a sound system is dropping
at a rate of \$10 per month); $R'(5) = 900,000$ (revenue is
increasing at a rate of \$900,000 per month).   **73.** \$242 million;
increasing at a rate of \$39 million per year.   **75.** Decreasing at
a rate of \$1 per day   **77.** Decreasing at a rate of approximately
\$0.10 per month

79. $M'(x) = \dfrac{3,000(3,600x^{-2} - 1)}{(x + 3,600x^{-1})^2}$; $M'(10) \approx 0.7670$ mpg/mph.

This means that, at a speed of 10 mph, the fuel economy is
increasing at a rate of 0.7670 miles per gallon per one mph
increase in speed. $M'(60) = 0$ mpg/mph. This means that, at a
speed of 60 mph, the fuel economy is neither increasing nor
decreasing with increasing speed. $M'(70) \approx -0.0540$. This
means that, at 70 mph, the fuel economy is decreasing at a rate
of 0.0540 miles per gallon per one mph increase in speed.
60 mph is the most fuel-efficient speed for the car. (In the next
chapter we shall discuss how to locate largest values in general.)
81. a. $P(t) - I(t)$ represents the daily production of oil in
Mexico that was not exported to the United States. $I(t)/P(t)$
represents U.S. imports of oil from Mexico as a fraction of the
total produced there. **b.** -0.023 per year; at the start of 2008,
the fraction of oil produced in Mexico that was imported by the
United States was decreasing at a rate of 0.023 (or 2.3 percentage points) per year.   **83.** Increasing at a rate of about
\$3,420 million per year.

85. $R'(p) = -\dfrac{5.625}{(1 + 0.125p)^2}$; $R'(4) = -2.5$ thousand

organisms per hour, per 1,000 organisms. This means that the
reproduction rate of organisms in a culture containing 4,000
organisms is declining at a rate of 2,500 organisms per hour, per
1,000 additional organisms.   **87.** Oxygen consumption is
decreasing at a rate of 1,600 milliliters per day. This is due to
the fact that the number of eggs is decreasing, because $C'(25)$ is
positive.   **89.** 20; 33   **91.** 5/4; $-17/16$ **93.** The analysis is
suspect, as it seems to be asserting that the annual increase in
revenue, which we can think of as dR/dt, is the product of the
annual increases, dp/dt in price, and dq/dt in sales. However,
because $R = pq$, the product rule implies that dR/dt is not
the product of dp/dt and dq/dt, but is instead

$$\dfrac{dR}{dt} = \dfrac{dp}{dt} \cdot q + p \cdot \dfrac{dq}{dt}.$$ **95.** Answers will vary.

$q = -p + 1,000$ is one example.   **97.** Mine; it is increasing
twice as fast as yours. The rate of change of revenue is given by
$R'(t) = p'(t)q(t)$ because $q'(t) = 0$. Thus, $R'(t)$ does not depend
on the selling price $p(t)$.   **99.** (A)

Section 4.4
1. $4(2x + 1)$ **3.** $-(x - 1)^{-2}$ **5.** $2(2 - x)^{-3}$
7. $(2x + 1)^{-0.5}$ **9.** $-4(4x - 1)^{-2}$ **11.** $-3/(3x - 1)^2$
13. $4(x^2 + 2x)^3(2x + 2)$ **15.** $-4x(2x^2 - 2)^{-2}$
17. $-5(2x - 3)(x^2 - 3x - 1)^{-6}$ **19.** $-6x/(x^2 + 1)^4$
21. $1.5(0.2x - 4.2)(0.1x^2 - 4.2x + 9.5)^{0.5}$
23. $4(2s - 0.5s^{-0.5})(s^2 - s^{0.5})^3$ **25.** $-x/\sqrt{1 - x^2}$
27. $-[(x + 1)(x^2 - 1)]^{-3/2}(3x - 1)(x + 1)$
29. $6.2(3.1x - 2) + 6.2/(3.1x - 2)^3$
31. $2[(6.4x - 1)^2 + (5.4x - 2)^3][12.8(6.4x - 1) + 16.2(5.4x - 2)^2]$ **33.** $-2(x^2 - 3x)^{-3}(2x - 3)(1 - x^2)^{0.5} - x(x^2 - 3x)^{-2}(1 - x^2)^{-0.5}$

35. $-56(x+2)/(3x-1)^3$ **37.** $3z^2(1-z^2)/(1+z^2)^4$

39. $3[(1+2x)^4 - (1-x)^2]^2[8(1+2x)^3 + 2(1-x)]$

41. $-0.43(x+1)^{-1.1}[2+(x+1)^{-0.1}]^{3.3}$

43. $-\dfrac{\left(\dfrac{1}{\sqrt{2x+1}} - 2x\right)}{\left(\sqrt{2x+1} - x^2\right)^2}$

45. $54(1+2x)^2\left(1+(1+2x)^3\right)^2\left(1+\left(1+(1+2x)^3\right)^3\right)^2$

47. $(100x^{99} - 99x^{-2})dx/dt$ **49.** $(-3r^{-4} + 0.5r^{-0.5})dr/dt$

51. $4\pi r^2 dr/dt$ **53.** $-47/4$ **55.** $1/3$ **57.** $-5/3$ **59.** $1/4$

61. $\left.\dfrac{dP}{dn}\right|_{n=10} = 146{,}454.9$. At an employment level of

10 engineers, Paramount will increase its profit at a rate of
$146,454.90 per additional engineer hired.

63. $y = 35(7+0.2t)^{-0.25}$; -0.11 percentage points per month.

65. $-$$30 per additional ruby sold. The revenue is decreasing at
a rate of $30 per additional ruby sold.

67. $\dfrac{dy}{dt} = \dfrac{dy}{dx}\dfrac{dx}{dt} = (1.5)(-2) = -3$ murders per 100,000

residents/yr each year.   **69.** $5/6 \approx 0.833$; relative to the 2003
levels, home sales were changing at a rate of 0.833 percentage
points per percentage point change in price. (Equivalently, home
sales in 2008 were dropping at a rate of 0.833 percentage points
per percentage point drop in price.)   **71.** 12π mi^2/h
73. $200,000\pi$/week $\approx$ $628,000/week   **75. a.** $q'(4) \approx 333$
units per month **b.** $dR/dq = $800/unit **c.** $dR/dt \approx$ $267,000 per
month   **77.** 3% per year   **79.** 8% per year   **81.** The glob
squared, times the derivative of the glob.   **83.** The derivative
of a quantity cubed is three times the *original quantity* squared,
times the derivative of the quantity, not three times the derivative of the quantity squared. Thus, the correct answer is
$3(3x^3 - x)^2(9x^2 - 1)$.   **85.** First, the derivative of a quantity
cubed is three times the *original quantity* squared times the
derivative of the quantity, not three times the derivative of
the quantity squared. Second, the derivative of a quotient is
not the quotient of the derivatives; the quotient rule needs

to be used in calculating the derivative of $\dfrac{3x^2 - 1}{2x - 2}$.

Thus, the correct result (before simplifying) is

$3\left(\dfrac{3x^2 - 1}{2x - 2}\right)^2\left(\dfrac{6x(2x-2) - (3x^2 - 1)(2)}{(2x-2)^2}\right)$.

87. Following the calculation thought experiment, pretend that
you were evaluating the function at a specific value of x. If the
last operation you would perform is addition or subtraction,
look at each summand separately. If the last operation is
multiplication, use the product rule first; if it is division, use
the quotient rule first; if it is any other operation (such as
raising a quantity to a power or taking a radical of a quantity)
then use the chain rule first.   **89.** An example is

$f(x) = \sqrt{x + \sqrt{x + \sqrt{x + \sqrt{x + \sqrt{x+1}}}}}$.

Section 4.5

1. $1/(x-1)$ **3.** $1/(x\ln 2)$ **5.** $2x/(x^2+3)$ **7.** e^{x+3}

9. $-e^{-x}$ **11.** $4^x \ln 4$ **13.** $2^{x^2-1}2x\ln 2$ **15.** $1 + \ln x$

17. $2x\ln x + (x^2+1)/x$ **19.** $10x(x^2+1)^4\ln x + (x^2+1)^5/x$

21. $3/(3x-1)$ **23.** $4x/(2x^2+1)$

25. $(2x - 0.63x^{-0.7})/(x^2 - 2.1x^{0.3})$

27. $-2/(-2x+1) + 1/(x+1)$ **29.** $3/(3x+1) - 4/(4x-2)$

31. $1/(x+1) + 1/(x-3) - 2/(2x+9)$ **33.** $5.2/(4x-2)$

35. $2/(x+1) - 9/(3x-4) - 1/(x-9)$

37. $\dfrac{1}{(x+1)\ln 2}$ **39.** $\dfrac{1 - 1/t^2}{(t+1/t)\ln 3}$ **41.** $\dfrac{2\ln|x|}{x}$

43. $\dfrac{2}{x} - \dfrac{2\ln(x-1)}{x-1}$ **45.** $e^x(1+x)$

47. $1/(x+1) + 3e^x(x^3 + 3x^2)$ **49.** $e^x(\ln|x| + 1/x)$

51. $2e^{2x+1}$ **53.** $(2x-1)e^{x^2-x+1}$ **55.** $2xe^{2x-1}(1+x)$

57. $4(e^{2x-1})^2$ **59.** $2 \cdot 3^{2x-4}\ln 3$ **61.** $2 \cdot 3^{2x+1}\ln 3 + 3e^{3x+1}$

63. $\dfrac{2x3^{x^2}[(x^2+1)\ln 3 - 1]}{(x^2+1)^2}$ **65.** $-4/(e^x - e^{-x})^2$

67. $5e^{5x-3}$ **69.** $-\dfrac{\ln x + 1}{(x\ln x)^2}$ **71.** $2(x-1)$ **73.** $\dfrac{1}{x\ln x}$

75. $\dfrac{1}{2x\ln x}$ **77.** $y = (e/\ln 2)(x-1) \approx 3.92(x-1)$

79. $y = x$ **81.** $y = -[1/(2e)](x-1) + e$ **83.** $163 billion
and increasing at a rate of $5.75 billion per year   **85.** $163 billion and increasing at a rate of $5.75 billion per year.
87. $-1,653$ years per gram; the age of the specimen is decreasing at a rate of about 1,653 years per additional one gram of
carbon 14 present in the sample. (Equivalently, the age of the
specimen is increasing at a rate of about 1,653 years per additional one gram less of carbon 14 in the sample.)   **89.** Average
price: $1.4 million; increasing at a rate of about $220,000 per
year.   **91. a.** $N(15) \approx 1,762 \approx 1,800$ (rounded to 2 significant
digits) wiretap orders; $N'(15) \approx 89.87 \approx 90$ wiretap orders per
year (rounded to 2 significant digits). The constants in the
model are specified to 2 significant digits, so we cannot expect
the answer to be accurate to more than 2 digits. **b.** In 2005, the
number of people whose communications were intercepted was
about 180,000 and increasing at a rate of about 9,000 people per
year. **c.** (C)   **93.** $451.00 per year   **95.** $446.02 per year
97. $A(t) = 167(1.18)^t$; 280 new cases per day   **99. a.** (A)
b. The verbal SAT increases by approximately 1 point.
c. $S'(x)$ decreases with increasing x, so that as parental income
increases, the effect on SAT scores decreases.   **101. a.** -6.25
years/child; when the fertility rate is 2 children per woman, the
average age of a population is dropping at a rate of 6.25 years
per one-child increase in the fertility rate. **b.** 0.160
103. 3,300,000 cases/week; 11,000,000 cases/week; 640,000
cases/week   **105.** 2.1 percentage points per year; the rate of
change is the slope of the tangent at $t = 3$. This is also approximately the average rate of change over [2, 4], which is about
$4/2 = 2$, in approximate agreement with the answer.
107. 2.1 percentage points per year   **109.** 277,000 people
per year   **111.** 0.000283 g/yr

113. a.

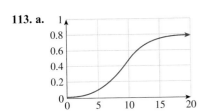

$p'(10) \approx 0.09$, so the percentage of firms using numeric control is increasing at a rate of 9 percentage points per year after 10 years. **b.** 0.80. Thus, in the long run, 80% of all firms will be using numeric control.
c. $p'(t) = 0.3816e^{4.46-0.477t}/(1 + e^{4.46-0.477t})^2$. $p'(10) = 0.0931$.
Graph:

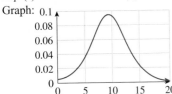

115. $R(t) = 350e^{-0.1t}(39t + 68)$ million dollars; $R(2) \approx$ $42 billion; $R'(2) \approx$ $7 billion per year   **117.** e raised to the glob, times the derivative of the glob.   **119.** 2 raised to the glob, times the derivative of the glob, times the natural logarithm of 2.   **121.** The derivative of $\ln |u|$ is not $\dfrac{1}{|u|}\dfrac{du}{dx}$; it is $\dfrac{1}{u}\dfrac{du}{dx}$.

Thus, the correct derivative is $\dfrac{3}{3x + 1}$.   **123.** The power rule does not apply when the exponent is not constant. The derivative of 3 raised to a quantity is 3 raised to the quantity, times the derivative of the quantity, times $\ln 3$. Thus, the correct answer is $3^{2x} \, 2 \ln 3$.   **125.** No. If $N(t)$ is exponential, so is its derivative.   **127.** If $f(x) = e^{kx}$, then the fractional rate of change is $\dfrac{f'(x)}{f(x)} = \dfrac{ke^{kx}}{e^{kx}} = k$, the fractional growth rate.
129. If $A(t)$ is growing exponentially, then $A(t) = A_0e^{kt}$ for constants A_0 and k. Its percentage rate of change is then
$\dfrac{A'(t)}{A(t)} = \dfrac{kA_0e^{kt}}{A_0e^{kt}} = k$, a constant.

Section 4.6
1. $-2/3$ **3.** x **5.** $(y - 2)/(3 - x)$ **7.** $-y$
9. $-\dfrac{y}{x(1 + \ln x)}$ **11.** $-x/y$ **13.** $-2xy/(x^2 - 2y)$
15. $-(6 + 9x^2y)/(9x^3 - x^2)$ **17.** $3y/x$
19. $(p + 10p^2q)/(2p - q - 10pq^2)$
21. $(ye^x - e^y)/(xe^y - e^x)$ **23.** $se^{st}/(2s - te^{st})$
25. $ye^x/(2e^x + y^3e^y)$ **27.** $(y - y^2)/(-1 + 3y - y^2)$
29. $-y/(x + 2y - xye^y - y^2e^y)$ **31. a.** 1   **b.** $y = x - 3$
33. a. -2 **b.** $y = -2x$ **35. a.** -1 **b.** $y = -x + 1$
37. a. $-2,000$ **b.** $y = -2,000x + 6,000$ **39. a.** 0
b. $y = 1$ **41. a.** -0.1898 **b.** $y = -0.1898x + 1.4721$
43. $\dfrac{2x + 1}{4x - 2}\left[\dfrac{2}{2x + 1} - \dfrac{4}{4x - 2}\right]$

45. $\dfrac{(3x + 1)^2}{4x(2x - 1)^3}\left[\dfrac{6}{3x + 1} - \dfrac{1}{x} - \dfrac{6}{2x - 1}\right]$

47. $(8x - 1)^{1/3}(x - 1)\left[\dfrac{8}{3(8x - 1)} + \dfrac{1}{x - 1}\right]$

49. $(x^3 + x)\sqrt{x^3 + 2}\left[\dfrac{3x^2 + 1}{x^3 + x} + \dfrac{1}{2}\dfrac{3x^2}{x^3 + 2}\right]$

51. $x^x(1 + \ln x)$ **53.** $-$$3,000 per worker. The monthly budget to maintain production at the fixed level P is decreasing by approximately $3,000 per additional worker at an employment level of 100 workers and a monthly operating budget of $200,000.   **55.** -125 T-shirts per dollar; when the price is set at $5, the demand is dropping by 125 T-shirts per $1 increase in price.   **57.** $\dfrac{dk}{de}\Big|_{e=15} = -0.307$ carpenters per electrician. This means that, for a $200,000 house whose construction employs 15 electricians, adding one more electrician would cost as much as approximately 0.307 additional carpenters. In other words, one electrician is worth approximately 0.307 carpenters.
59. a. 22.93 hours. (The other root is rejected because it is larger than 30.)   **b.** $\dfrac{dt}{dx} = \dfrac{4t - 20x}{0.4t - 4x}$; $\dfrac{dt}{dx}\Big|_{x=3.0} \approx -11.2$ hours per grade point. This means that, for a 3.0 student who scores 80 on the examination, 1 grade point is worth approximately 11.2 hours.
61. $\dfrac{dr}{dy} = 2\dfrac{r}{y}$, so $\dfrac{dr}{dt} = 2\dfrac{r}{y}\dfrac{dy}{dt}$ by the chain rule.
63. x, y, y, x **65.** Let $y = f(x)g(x)$.
Then $\ln y = \ln f(x) + \ln g(x)$, and
$\dfrac{1}{y}\dfrac{dy}{dx} = \dfrac{f'(x)}{f(x)} + \dfrac{g'(x)}{g(x)}$, so $\dfrac{dy}{dx} = y\left(\dfrac{f'(x)}{f(x)} + \dfrac{g'(x)}{g(x)}\right) =$
$f(x)g(x)\left(\dfrac{f'(x)}{f(x)} + \dfrac{g'(x)}{g(x)}\right) = f'(x)g(x) + f(x)g'(x)$.
67. Writing $y = f(x)$ specifies y as an explicit function of x. This can be regarded as an equation giving y as an *implicit* function of x. The procedure of finding dy/dx by implicit differentiation is then the same as finding the derivative of y as an explicit function of x: We take d/dx of both sides.
69. Differentiate both sides of the equation $y = f(x)$ with respect to y to get $1 = f'(x) \cdot \dfrac{dx}{dy}$, giving $\dfrac{dx}{dy} = \dfrac{1}{f'(x)} = \dfrac{1}{dy/dx}$.

Chapter 4 Review
1. $50x^4 + 2x^3 - 1$ **3.** $9x^2 + x^{-2/3}$ **5.** $1 - 2/x^3$
7. $-\dfrac{4}{3x^2} + \dfrac{0.2}{x^{1.1}} + \dfrac{1.1x^{0.1}}{3.2}$ **9.** $e^x(x^2 + 2x - 1)$
11. $20x(x^2 - 1)^9$ **13.** $e^x(x^2 + 1)^9(x^2 + 20x + 1)$
15. $3^x[(x - 1) \ln 3 - 1]/(x - 1)^2$ **17.** $2xe^{x^2-1}$
19. $2x/(x^2 - 1)$ **21.** $x = 7/6$ **23.** $x = \pm 2$
25. $x = (1 - \ln 2)/2$ **27.** None   **29.** $\dfrac{2x - 1}{2y}$ **31.** $-y/x$

33. $\dfrac{(2x-1)^4(3x+4)}{(x+1)(3x-1)^3}\left[\dfrac{8}{2x-1}+\dfrac{3}{3x+4}-\dfrac{1}{x+1}-\dfrac{9}{3x-1}\right]$

35. $y=-x/4+1/2$　**37.** $y=-3ex-2e$　**39.** $y=x+2$

41. a. 274 books per week　**b.** 636 books per week　**c.** The function w begins to decrease more and more rapidly after $t=14$ Graph:

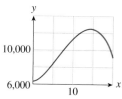

d. Because the data suggest an upward curving parabola, the long-term prediction of sales for a quadratic model would be that sales will increase without bound, in sharp contrast to (c)
43. a. \$2.88 per book　**b.** \$3.715 per book　**c.** Approximately $-\$0.000104$ per book, per additional book sold.　**d.** At a sales level of 8,000 books per week, the cost is increasing at a rate of \$2.88 per book (so that the 8,001st book costs approximately \$2.88 to sell), and it costs an average of \$3.715 per book to sell the first 8,000 books. Moreover, the average cost is decreasing at a rate of \$0.000104 per book, per additional book sold.
45. a. \$3,000 per week (rising)　**b.** 300 books per week

47. $R=pq$ gives $R'=p'q+pq'$. Thus, $R'/R=R'/(pq)=(p'q+pq')/pq=p'/p+q'/q$　**49.** \$110 per year

51. a. $s'(t)=\dfrac{2{,}475e^{-0.55(t-4.8)}}{(1+e^{-0.55(t-4.8)})^2}$; 556 books per week

b. 0; In the long term, the rate of increase of weekly sales slows to zero.　**53.** 616.8 hits per day per week.
55. a. -17.24 copies per \$1. The demand for the gift edition of *The Complete Harry Potter* is dropping at a rate of about 17.24 copies per \$1 increase in the price.　**b.** \$138 per dollar is positive, so the price should be raised.

Chapter 5

Section 5.1

1. Absolute min: $(-3,-1)$, relative max: $(-1,1)$, relative min: $(1,0)$, absolute max: $(3,2)$　**3.** Absolute min: $(3,-1)$ and $(-3,-1)$, absolute max: $(1,2)$　**5.** Absolute min: $(-3,0)$ and $(1,0)$, absolute max: $(-1,2)$ and $(3,2)$　**7.** Relative min: $(-1,1)$　**9.** Absolute min: $(-3,-1)$, relative max: $(-2,2)$, relative min: $(1,0)$, absolute max: $(3,3)$　**11.** Relative max: $(-3,0)$, absolute min: $(-2,-1)$, stationary non-extreme point: $(1,1)$　**13.** Absolute max: $(0,1)$, absolute min: $(2,-3)$, relative max: $(3,-2)$　**15.** Absolute min: $(-4,-16)$, absolute max: $(-2,16)$, absolute min: $(2,-16)$, absolute max: $(4,16)$
17. Absolute min: $(-2,-10)$, absolute max: $(2,10)$
19. Absolute min: $(-2,-4)$, relative max: $(-1,1)$, relative min: $(0,0)$　**21.** Relative max: $(-1,5)$, absolute min: $(3,-27)$
23. Absolute min: $(0,0)$　**25.** Absolute maxima at $(0,1)$ and $(2,1)$, absolute min at $(1,0)$　**27.** Relative maximum at

$(-2,-1/3)$, relative minimum at $(-1,-2/3)$, absolute maximum at $(0,1)$　**29.** Relative min: $(-2,5/3)$, relative max: $(0,-1)$, relative min: $(2,5/3)$　**31.** Relative max: $(0,0)$; absolute min: $(1/3,-2\sqrt3/9)$　**33.** Relative max: $(0,0)$, absolute min: $(1,-3)$　**35.** No relative extrema　**37.** Absolute min: $(1,1)$　**39.** Relative max: $(-1,1+1/e)$, absolute min: $(0,1)$, absolute max: $(1,e-1)$　**41.** Relative max: $(-6,-24)$, relative min: $(-2,-8)$　**43.** Absolute max $(1/\sqrt2,\sqrt{e/2})$, absolute min: $(-1/\sqrt2,-\sqrt{e/2})$　**45.** Relative min at $(0.15,-0.52)$ and $(2.45,8.22)$, relative max at $(1.40,0.29)$
47. Absolute max at $(-5,700)$, relative max at $(3.10,28.19)$ and $(6,40)$, absolute min at $(-2.10,-392.69)$ and relative min at $(5,0)$.　**49.** Stationary minimum at $x=-1$　**51.** Stationary minima at $x=-2$ and $x=2$, stationary maximum at $x=0$
53. Singular minimum at $x=0$, stationary non-extreme point at $x=1$　**55.** Stationary minimum at $x=-2$, singular non-extreme points at $x=-1$ and $x=1$, stationary maximum at $x=2$
57. Answers will vary.　　**59.** Answers will vary.

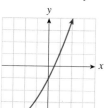　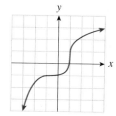

61. Not necessarily; it could be neither a relative maximum nor a relative minimum, as in the graph of $y=x^3$ at the origin.
63. Answers will vary.

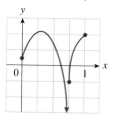

65. The graph oscillates faster and faster above and below zero as it approaches the end-point at 0, so 0 cannot be either a relative minimum or maximum.

Section 5.2

1. $x=y=5$; $P=25$　**3.** $x=y=3$; $S=6$　**5.** $x=2$, $y=4$; $F=20$　**7.** $x=20$, $y=10$, $z=20$; $P=4,000$
9. 5×5　**11.** 1,500 per day for an average cost of \$130 per iPod　**13.** $\sqrt{40}\approx6.32$ pounds of pollutant per day, for an average cost of about \$1,265 per pound　**15.** 2.5 lb
17. 5×10　**19.** 50×10 for an area of 250 sq. ft.
21. 11×22　**23.** \$10　**25.** \$78 for a quarterly revenue of \$6,084 million, or \$6.084 billion　**27.** \$4.61 for a daily revenue of \$95,680.55　**29. a.** \$1.41 per pound　**b.** 5,000 pounds
c. \$7,071.07 per month　**31.** 34.5¢ per pound, for an annual (per capita) revenue of \$5.95　**33.** \$98 for an annual profit of \$3,364 million, or \$3.364 billion　**35. a.** 656 headsets, for a